Applied Mathematics for Business and the Social and Natural Sciences
Volume One

Chester Piascik
Bryant College

Brooks/Cole Publishing Company

I(T)P An International Thomson Publishing Company

Boston * Albany * Bonn * Cincinnati * Detroit * London * Madrid * Melbourne * Mexico City
New York * Paris * San Francisco * Singapore * Tokyo * Toronto * Washington

For more information, contact Brooks/Cole Publishing Company, 511 Forest Lodge Road, Pacific Grove,
CA 93950, or electronically at http://www.thomson.com/brookscole.html

International Thomson Publishing Europe
Berkshire House 168-173
High Holborn
London, WC1V 7AA, England

International Thomson Editores
Campos Eliseos 385, Piso 7
Col. Polanco
11560 México D.F. México

Thomas Nelson Australia
102 Dodds Street
South Melbourne 3205
Victoria, Australia

International Thomson Publishing Asia
221 Henderson Road
#05-10 Henderson Building
Singapore 0315

Nelson Canada
1120 Birchmount Road
Scarborough, Ontario
Canada M1K 5G4

International Thomson Publishing Japan
Hirakawacho Kyowa Building, 3F
2-2-1 Hirakawacho
Chiyoda-ku, Tokyo 102, Japan

International Thomson Publishing GmbH
Königswinterer Strasse 418
53227 Bonn, Germany

International Thomson Publishing Southern Africa
Building 18, Constantia Park
240 Old Pretoria Road
Halfway House, 1685 South Africa

ISBN 0-324-03033-9

The Adaptable Courseware Program consists of products and additions to existing Brooks/Cole Publishing
Company products that are produced from camera-ready copy. Peer review, class testing, and accuracy are
primarily the responsibility of the author(s).

Custom Contents

R

ALGEBRA
REVIEW

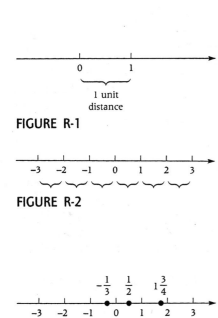

FIGURE R-1

FIGURE R-2

FIGURE R-3

R-1

• THE REAL NUMBERS AND INTERVAL NOTATION

All the numbers we will use in this text can be represented as points on a straight line. Such a representation can be constructed as follows. Begin with a straight line. Choose an arbitrary point, called the **origin,** on the line and label it 0. Then choose another point to the right of 0 and label it 1. Let the distance between 0 and 1 represent 1 unit of measure (see Figure R-1). The point on the straight line 1 unit to the right of 1 is labeled 2, the point 1 unit to the right of 2 is labeled 3, etc. (see Figure R-2). Also, the point on the straight line 1 unit to the left of 0 is labeled −1, the point 1 unit to the left of −1 is labeled −2, the point 1 unit to the left of −2 is labeled −3, etc. (see Figure R-2). The straight line in Figure R-2 is called the **real number line.** There is a one-to-one correspondence between the points on the real number line and the set of real numbers. In other words, each real number is associated with a particular point on this number line. Also, each point on this number line is associated with a particular real number. For example, the fraction 1/2 is associated with the point midway between 0 and 1, the number 1 3/4 is associated with the point three-quarters of the distance between 1 and 2, and the number −1/3 is associated with the point one-third of the distance between 0 and −1 (see Figure R-3).

There are several types of real numbers:

1. *Counting numbers.* These numbers are also called **natural numbers.**

$$1, 2, 3, 4, 5, \ldots*$$

2. *Whole numbers.*

$$0, 1, 2, 3, 4, \ldots$$

3. *Integers.*

$$\ldots, -4, -3, -2, -1, 0, 1, 2, 3, 4, \ldots$$

4. *Rational numbers.* All numbers that can be expressed as a quotient of two integers, where the denominator is not equal to 0. Examples are numbers such as 1/2, 3/4, 4/1, 3, and 1.23. Some rational numbers have decimal expansions that repeat but do not terminate. Some examples are

$$\frac{1}{3} = 0.333\ldots \text{ which is written as } 0.\overline{3}$$

$$\frac{83}{99} = 0.838383\ldots \text{ which is written as } 0.\overline{83}$$

5. *Irrational numbers.* These are all real numbers that are not rational. Ir-

---

*Here, the three dots indicate that the numbers continue indefinitely in the same manner.

rational numbers have decimal representations that are nonterminating and nonrepeating. Some examples are

$$\sqrt{2} = 1.4142135.\ .\ .^*$$
$$\pi = 3.1415926.\ .\ .$$
$$e = 2.718281.\ .\ .$$
$$-\sqrt{5} = -2.2360679.\ .\ .$$

Thus, a real number is either rational or irrational but cannot be both. The rational numbers include the integers, the integers include the whole numbers, and the whole numbers include the counting or natural numbers.

Inequality

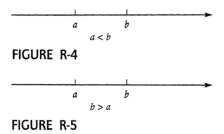

FIGURE R-4

FIGURE R-5

If a number a lies to the left of a number b on the real number line, then "a is less than b." This is written $a < b$ (see Figure R-4). Also, if a number b lies to the right of a number a on the real number line, then "b is greater than a." This is written $b > a$ (see Figure R-5). Thus, the statement "5 is less than 6" is written $5 < 6$, and the statement "8 is greater than 3" is written $8 > 3$.

The complete set of inequality phrases and their respective symbols are summarized as follows.

■ SUMMARY

Inequality Phrases and Symbols

"Is less than"	$<$
"Is greater than"	$>$
"Is less than or equal to"	$\leq$
"Is greater than or equal to"	$\geq$
"Is not equal to"	$\neq$

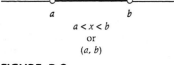

FIGURE R-6

Intervals

Sometimes it is necessary to refer to all real numbers located between two numbers a and b on the real number line (see Figure R-6). Such a set of numbers is called an **interval** and is expressed as all real numbers x such that

$$a < x < b$$

This interval is also denoted as (a, b). This way of expressing an interval is called **interval notation.** Observe that the endpoints, a and b, are not included in this interval. This situation is graphically expressed by using an open circle at each endpoint (see Figure R-6). An interval that does not

---

*These dots indicate that the decimal representations are nonterminating.

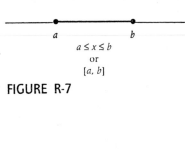

$a \leq x \leq b$
or
$[a, b]$

FIGURE R-7

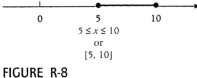

$5 \leq x \leq 10$
or
$[5, 10]$

FIGURE R-8

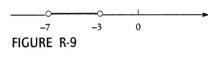

FIGURE R-9

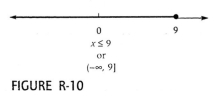

$x \leq 9$
or
$(-\infty, 9]$

FIGURE R-10

contain its endpoints is called an *open interval*. If the endpoints are to be included, then the set must be written as

$$a \leq x \leq b$$

or, in terms of interval notation, $[a, b]$. This interval is graphically expressed by using a solid circle at each endpoint (see Figure R-7). An interval that contains its endpoints is called a *closed interval*.

● **EXAMPLE R-1** _____

Graph all real numbers x such that $5 \leq x \leq 10$.

Solution

This interval includes all real numbers between 5 and 10. The endpoints are included. The graph appears in Figure R-8.

● **EXAMPLE R-2** _____

Express the interval in Figure R-9 by using the variable x and also by using interval notation.

Solution

This interval includes all real numbers between -7 and -3. The endpoints are not included. Hence, the interval is written as all real numbers x such that $-7 < x < -3$. Using interval notation, this interval is also denoted as $(-7, -3)$.

● **EXAMPLE R-3** _____

Graph all real numbers x such that $x \leq 9$.

Solution

This interval includes all real numbers less than or equal to 9. The endpoint, 9, is included. The graph appears in Figure R-10. This interval is also denoted as $(-\infty, 9]$.

_____ ●

The symbol $-\infty$ means minus infinity; the symbol ∞ means infinity. We note that ∞ is not a number; it enables us to indicate an interval that is unbounded to the right. $-\infty$ enables us to indicate an interval that is unbounded to the left. Also note that we always use open interval symbols with ∞ or $-\infty$ to indicate that ∞ and $-\infty$ are not actually real numbers that can be achieved by our intervals.

We now give further examples of interval notation.

Interval	Interval notation	Graph
$3 < x \leq 6$	$(3, 6]$	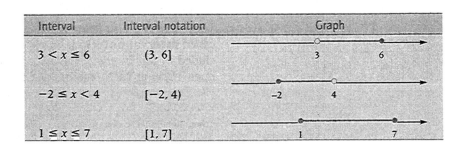
$-2 \leq x < 4$	$[-2, 4)$	
$1 \leq x \leq 7$	$[1, 7]$	

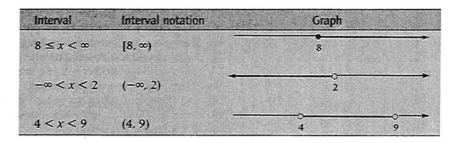

Interval	Interval notation	Graph
$8 \leq x < \infty$	$[8, \infty)$	
$-\infty < x < 2$	$(-\infty, 2)$	
$4 < x < 9$	$(4, 9)$	

Absolute Value

The absolute value of a number x, written $|x|$, is defined by

$$|x| = \begin{cases} x & \text{if } x \text{ is positive or zero} \\ -x & \text{if } x \text{ is negative} \end{cases}$$

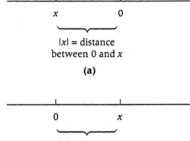

$|x|$ = distance between 0 and x

(a)

$|x|$ = distance between 0 and x

(b)

FIGURE R-11

• EXAMPLE R-4

Evaluate $|-7|$.

Solution

Since -7 is negative, then by the definition of absolute value, $|-7| = -(-7) = 7$.

• EXAMPLE R-5

Evaluate $|8|$.

Solution

Since 8 is positive, then by the definition of absolute value, $|8| = 8$.

• EXAMPLE R-6

Evaluate $|9 - 14|$.

Solution

Since $9 - 14 = -5$, a negative number, then by the definition of absolute value, $|9 - 14| = -(-5) = 5$.

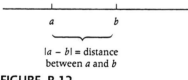

$|a - b|$ = distance between a and b

FIGURE R-12

The absolute value of a number is always non-negative. In addition, $|x|$ gives the distance on the real number line between 0 and x, as indicated in Figures R-11 (a) and (b). This is why a number and its negative both have the same absolute value.

The distance between points a and b on the real number line in Figure R-12 is given by either $|a - b|$ or $|b - a|$. Thus, the distance between 7 and 10 on the real number line in Figure R-13 is given by $|7 - 10| = |-3| = 3$. This distance is also given by $|10 - 7| = |3| = 3$.

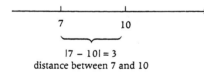

$|7 - 10| = 3$
distance between 7 and 10

FIGURE R-13

Exercises R-1

State whether each of the following is true or false.

1. $3 < 7$	**2.** $-3 < -7$	**3.** $-2 < -5$
4. $2 < 5$	**5.** $-6 < -2$	**6.** $-3 > -7$
7. $-2 > -5$	**8.** $0 < 5$	**9.** $0 > -3$
10. $9 > 6$	**11.** $8 > 10$	**12.** $-6 < -1$

13. Every counting number is a whole number.
14. Every whole number is an integer.
15. Every counting number is an integer.
16. Every integer is a rational number.
17. Every rational number is a real number.
18. Every integer is a whole number.
19. Every whole number is a counting number.
20. Every irrational number is a real number.
21. 7 is a rational number.
22. 3/5 is a rational number.
23. −2/3 is a rational number.
24. $\sqrt{11}$ is a rational number.
25. $\sqrt{11}$ is an irrational number.
26. 3.56345. . . is an irrational number.
27. 4.7065 is an irrational number.
28. 2.767676. . . is a rational number.

Graph each of the following on the real number line.

29. $-5 \leq x \leq -1$
30. $7 \leq x \leq 11$
31. $-4 < x < -2$
32. $9 < x < 15$
33. $-3 < x \leq 2$
34. $2 \leq x < 9$
35. $5 \leq x$
36. $x \geq 5$
37. $x \leq -3$
38. $x < 10$
39. $x > -2$
40. $x > 4$
41. $2 < x$
42. $x \geq -1$
43. $x \neq 2$
44. $x \neq -3, x \neq 5$

State whether each of the following is an open interval or a closed interval.

45. $3 \leq x \leq 8$
46. $3 < x < 8$
47. $-4 < x < -1$
48. $-6 \leq x \leq -2$
49. $8 \leq x \leq 10$
50. $6 < x \leq 9$

Graph each of the following on the real number line:

51. $[3, 9]$
52. $(-1, 5)$
53. $(-\infty, -4]$
54. $[6, \infty)$
55. $(-\infty, 6)$
56. $(9, \infty)$
57. $(4, 9]$
58. $[2, 9)$

Evaluate each of the following:

59. $|0|$
60. $|-1|$
61. $|1|$
62. $|-21|$
63. $|-2|$
64. $|15|$
65. $|-15|$
66. $|-20|$
67. $|20|$
68. $|5 - 9|$
69. $|9 - 5|$
70. $|16 - 7|$
71. $|7 - 16|$
72. $|14 - 8|$
73. $|9 - 15|$
74. $|-5 - 3|$
75. $|-4 - 9|$
76. $|-6 - 4|$

77. Find the distance between 5 and 11 on the real number line.
78. Find the distance between −3 and 10 on the real number line.
79. Find the distance between −9 and −4 on the real number line.

R-2 • LINEAR EQUATIONS AND INEQUALITIES

Linear Equations in One Variable

A statement such as

$$3x + 5 = 17$$

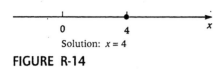

Solution: $x = 4$

FIGURE R-14

is a linear equation (equality) in one variable. To find its solution, we first subtract 5 from both sides to obtain

$$3x = 12$$

Then we divide both sides by 3 to obtain the solution

$$x = 4$$

The solution is sketched on the real number line in Figure R-14.

When solving linear equations such as $3x + 5 = 17$, we use the following rules of equalities.

■ **SUMMARY**

Rules of Equalities

Rule 1 If the same number is either added to or subtracted from both sides of an equality, the resulting equality remains true.

Rule 2 If both sides of an equality are either multiplied by or divided by the same nonzero number, the resulting equality remains true.

Linear Inequalities

We now consider linear inequalities. In general, if the equal sign (=) of a linear equality such as

$$3x + 5 = 7$$

is replaced by an inequality sign ($<$, $>$, $\leq$, $\geq$), the resulting statement is a linear inequality. Thus, the statements

$$3x + 5 < 7$$
$$3x + 5 > 7$$
$$3x + 5 \leq 7$$
$$3x + 5 \geq 7$$

are examples of linear inequalities. To solve linear inequalities, we may use the following rules of inequalities.

■ **SUMMARY**

Rules of Inequalities

Rule 1 If the same number is either added to or subtracted from both sides of an inequality, the resulting inequality remains true.

Rule 2
a) If both sides of an inequality are either multiplied by or divided by the same *positive* number, the resulting inequality remains true.
b) If both sides of an inequality are either multiplied by or divided by the same *negative* number, the original inequality sign must be *reversed* in order for the resulting inequality to remain true.

Note that the rules of equalities also hold for inequalities with the exception involving either multiplication by or division by a negative number. Thus, if

$$2 < 5$$

then

$$-4(2) > -4(5)$$
$$-8 > -20$$

• EXAMPLE R-7

Solve the inequality $-5x + 3 \leq 13$ for x, sketch the solution on a real number line, and give the answer in interval notation.

Solution

We first subtract 3 from both sides (rule 1) to obtain

$$-5x \leq 10$$

Then we divide both sides by -5 [rule 2(b)] to get

$$x \geq -2$$

The solution is sketched in Figure R-15.

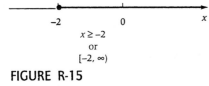

$x \geq -2$
or
$[-2, \infty)$

FIGURE R-15

• EXAMPLE R-8

Solve the inequality $3x + 5 < 17$ for x, sketch the solution on a real number line, and give the answer in interval notation.

Solution

Subtracting 5 from both sides (rule 1), we obtain

$$3x < 12$$

Dividing both sides by 3 [rule 2(a)] yields

$$x < 4$$

The solution is sketched in Figure R-16.

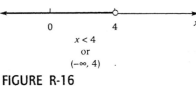

$x < 4$
or
$(-\infty, 4)$

FIGURE R-16

• EXAMPLE R-9

Solve the inequality $(-1/2)x + 3 \geq -1$ for x, sketch the solution on a real number line, and give the answer in interval notation.

Solution

Subtracting 3 from both sides (rule 1) gives us

$$-\frac{1}{2}x \geq -4$$

Multiplying both sides by -2 [rule 2(b)] yields

$$x \leq 8$$

The solution is sketched in Figure R-17.

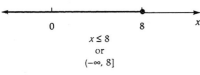

$x \leq 8$
or
$(-\infty, 8]$

FIGURE R-17

Exercises R-2

Solve each of the following.

1. $4x + 8 = 32$
2. $5x + 30 = 80$
3. $-2x + 6 = -12$
4. $-5x + 8 = -52$

5. $4x - 3 = 21 + 2x$ 6. $6x - 7 = 47 - 3x$
7. $(1/2)x + 6 = 10$ 8. $(3/4)x - 2 = 10$
9. $5y + 2 = 7y - 18$ 10. $6z + 4 = 10z - 28$

Solve each of the following inequalities, graph its solution on a real number line, and give the answer in interval notation.

11. $2x + 4 \leq 15$ 12. $-3x + 5 \leq 32$
13. $4x - 5 < 25$ 14. $5x + 3 > 17$
15. $-3x + 17 \geq -14$ 16. $-6x + 5 > 23$
17. $-6x - 5 \geq -23$ 18. $-3x - 2 \leq -14$
19. $3(x - 5) \geq 18$ 20. $-4(x + 7) < 32$

R-3   • EXPONENTS AND RADICALS

Exponents

If x is a number, the product of n x's is denoted by x^n. That is,

$$x^n = \underbrace{x \cdot x \cdot \ldots \cdot x}_{n \; x\text{'s}}$$

The positive integer n, which indicates the number of times x appears as a factor, is an **exponent.** The number x is called the **base.**

We define a negative exponent as follows:

$$x^{-n} = \frac{1}{x^n} = \frac{1}{\underbrace{x \cdot x \cdot \ldots \cdot x}_{n \; x\text{'s}}} \qquad (x \neq 0)$$

We define

$$x^0 = 1 \qquad (x \neq 0)$$

Note that 0^0 is undefined.

Laws of Exponents

In this section, we will discuss exponents and the laws governing their algebraic manipulation.

> **First Law of Exponents**
>
> If x is any nonzero real number, then
>
> $$x^m \cdot x^n = x^{m+n}$$
>
> for any non-negative integers m and n.

To verify this law, we observe that

$$x^m \cdot x^n = \underbrace{(x \cdot x \cdot \ldots \cdot x)}_{m \text{ } x's} \underbrace{(x \cdot x \cdot \ldots \cdot x)}_{n \text{ } x's}$$

$$= \underbrace{x \cdot x \cdot \ldots \cdot x}_{(m+n) \text{ } x's}$$

$$= x^{m+n}$$

For example,

$$2^3 \cdot 2^4 = 2^{3+4} = 2^7$$
$$5^3 \cdot 5^6 = 5^{3+6} = 5^9$$

Second Law of Exponents

If x is any nonzero real number, then

$$\frac{x^m}{x^n} = x^{m-n}$$

for any non-negative integers m and n.

To verify this law, we note that if $m = 5$ and $n = 2$, then

$$\frac{x^m}{x^n} = \frac{x^5}{x^2} = \frac{\not{x} \cdot \not{x} \cdot x \cdot x \cdot x}{\not{x} \cdot \not{x}}$$

$$= x^{5-2} = x^3$$

And, similarly, we have

$$\frac{5^7}{5^3} = 5^{7-3} = 5^4 = 625$$

$$\frac{4^3}{4^5} = 4^{3-5} = 4^{-2} = \frac{1}{4^2} = \frac{1}{16}$$

It should be noted that the first two laws of exponents also hold true for negative integers m and n.

Third Law of Exponents

If x is any real number, then

$$(x^m)^n = x^{m \cdot n}$$

for all integers m and n.

To verify this law, we see that

$$(x^m)^n = \underbrace{x^m \cdot x^m \cdot \ldots \cdot x^m}_{n\ x^m\text{'s}}$$

$$= x^{\overbrace{m+m+\ldots+m}^{n\ m\text{'s}}}$$

$$= x^{m\cdot n}$$

As examples, we have

$$(x^3)^2 = x^{3\cdot2} = x^6$$
$$(7^4)^5 = 7^{4\cdot5} = 7^{20}$$

Roots and Radicals

We now give meaning to the symbol $\sqrt[n]{x}$, where n is a positive integer. The symbol $\sqrt[n]{x}$ is called a **radical** and is read "the nth root of x." The nth root of x, $\sqrt[n]{x}$, represents a number that when multiplied by itself n times (i.e., raised to the nth power) yields x. Thus, if y is an nth root of x, then

$$y^n = x$$

If $n = 2$, then $\sqrt[2]{x}$ is called the **square root** of x and is usually written $\sqrt{x}$. Thus, $\sqrt{16} = 4$ since $4^2 = 16$. However, the equation $y^2 = 16$ has another solution, -4, since $(-4)^2 = 16$. In such a case, we take the **positive square root,** often called the **principal square root.** Thus, 4 is the principal square root of 16, and we write $\sqrt{16} = 4$. If we want to refer to the **negative square root** of 16, we indicate it by writing $-\sqrt{16} = -4$. Note that $\sqrt{-16}$ is undefined since there is no real number with a square of -16.

If $n = 3$, then $\sqrt[3]{x}$ is called the **cube root** of x. Note that $\sqrt[3]{8} = 2$ since $2^3 = 8$, and that $\sqrt[3]{-8} = -2$ since $(-2)^3 = -8$. Because $n = 3$ and 3 is an odd number, there is no need to define a principal cube root since the cube of a negative number is a negative number and the cube of a positive number is a positive number.

Observe that $\sqrt[4]{16} = 2$ since $2^4 = 16$. However, since $(-2)^4 = 16$, then $-\sqrt[4]{16} = -2$. Again, for even values of n, we call the positive nth root the **principal nth root.**

The preceding comments about $\sqrt[n]{x}$ are summarized as follows:

1. If $x > 0$ and n is even, then there are two solutions to the equation $y^n = x$. One is positive and the other is negative. To avoid ambiguity, we take the positive nth root, often called the principal nth root.
2. If $x < 0$ and n is even, then there are no real nth roots of x.
3. If n is odd, then there is one real nth root of x. Its sign is the same as that of x.
4. If $x = 0$, then the nth root of x is 0.

Rational Exponents

Up to this point, we have discussed only integer exponents. Thus, the first three laws of exponents were restricted to integral exponents. We now take a look at rational exponents. Consider the expression

$$x^{1/n}$$

where n is a nonzero integer. Hence, $1/n$ is a rational exponent. If $x^{1/n}$ is to be well defined, it must obey the laws of exponents. Specifically, the third law of exponents states that

$$(x^m)^n = x^{m \cdot n}$$

If this law is to hold true for $x^{1/n}$, then

$$(x^{1/n})^n = x^{(1/n)n} = x$$

This implies that the product of $x^{1/n}$ multiplied by itself n times equals x. **Hence, $x^{1/n}$ must equal the nth root of x, or**

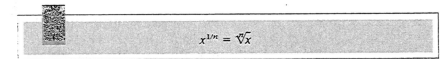

$$x^{1/n} = \sqrt[n]{x}$$

Thus, $x^{1/n}$ is now defined. Specifically,

$$x^{1/2} = \sqrt{x}$$
$$x^{1/3} = \sqrt[3]{x}$$
$$4^{1/2} = \sqrt{4} = 2$$

Note that $(-4)^{1/2} = \sqrt{-4}$, which is undefined.

Since we have defined the expression $x^{1/n}$ for integral values of n, we now discuss expressions of the form

$$x^{m/n}$$

for integral values of m and n. If the expression $x^{m/n}$ is to be well defined, it must obey the laws of exponents. Specifically, if the third law of exponents is to hold true, then

$$(x^{1/n})^m = x^{(1/n)m} = x^{m/n}$$

Thus, $x^{m/n}$ may be defined as the **mth power of the nth root of x, or**

$$x^{m/n} = (\sqrt[n]{x})^m$$

As examples, we have

$$x^{5/2} = (\sqrt{x})^5$$
$$5^{2/3} = (\sqrt[3]{5})^2$$

Since the third law of exponents also indicates that

$$x^{m/n} = (x^m)^{1/n}$$

then $x^{m/n}$ may also be defined as the **nth root of x^m, or**

$$x^{m/n} = \sqrt[n]{x^m}$$

In summary, if m/n is reduced to lowest terms, we have

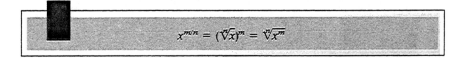

$$x^{m/n} = (\sqrt[n]{x})^m = \sqrt[n]{x^m}$$

Thus,

$$x^{5/2} = (\sqrt{x})^5 = \sqrt{x^5}$$
$$5^{2/3} = (\sqrt[3]{5})^2 = \sqrt[3]{5^2}$$

Since we have now defined rational exponents, it is appropriate to state that the first three laws of exponents hold true for all rational exponents m and n for which x^m and x^n are defined.

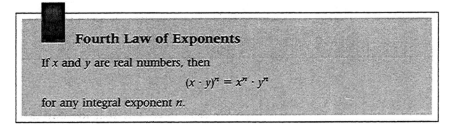

Fourth Law of Exponents

If x and y are real numbers, then

$$(x \cdot y)^n = x^n \cdot y^n$$

for any integral exponent n.

To verify this law, observe that

$$(xy)^n = \underbrace{xy \cdot xy \cdot \ldots \cdot xy}_{n \ xy\text{'s}}$$

$$= \underbrace{(x \cdot x \cdot \ldots \cdot x)}_{n \ x\text{'s}} \underbrace{(y \cdot y \cdot \ldots \cdot y)}_{n \ y\text{'s}}$$

$$= x^n \cdot y^n$$

And, specifically,

$$(4 \cdot 3)^5 = 4^5 \cdot 3^5$$
$$(5x)^3 = 5^3 \cdot x^3 = 125x^3$$
$$(-2xy)^5 = (-2)^5 x^5 y^5 = -32x^5 y^5$$

It should be noted that the fourth law of exponents also holds true for any rational exponent n for which x^n and y^n are defined.

Fifth Law of Exponents

If x and y are real numbers, with $y \neq 0$, then

$$\left(\frac{x}{y}\right)^n = \frac{x^n}{y^n}$$

for any integral exponent n.

To verify this law, note that

$$\left(\frac{x}{y}\right)^n = \underbrace{\frac{x}{y} \cdot \frac{x}{y} \cdot \ldots \cdot \frac{x}{y}}_{n\frac{x}{y}\text{'s}}$$

$$= \frac{\overbrace{x \cdot x \cdot \ldots \cdot x}^{n\,x\text{'s}}}{\underbrace{y \cdot y \cdot \ldots \cdot y}_{n\,y\text{'s}}}$$

$$= \frac{x^n}{y^n}$$

Thus,

$$\left(\frac{5}{2}\right)^3 = \frac{5^3}{2^3}$$

$$\left(\frac{-3}{y}\right)^4 = \frac{(-3)^4}{y^4} = \frac{81}{y^4}$$

Again, we note that the fifth law of exponents also holds true for any rational exponent n for which x^n and y^n are defined.

Scientific Notation

Any positive number can be expressed in the form

$$c \times 10^n$$

where $1 \le c < 10$ and n is an integral exponent. When a number is expressed in this form, it is said to be in **scientific notation.** Specifically,

$$543 = 5.43 \times 10^2$$
$$84{,}000{,}000 = 8.4 \times 10^7$$
$$0.0003 = 3.0 \times 10^{-4}$$

Exercises R-3

Simplify each of the following. No exponents should appear in the final answer.

1. 3^2
2. $\left(\frac{2}{3}\right)^4$
3. $(-5)^2$
4. $(-5)^3$
5. $(4^2)^3$
6. 5^{-3}
7. 2^{-4}
8. $(-3)^{-2}$
9. $\frac{2^7}{2}$
10. $\frac{(-3)^9}{(-3)^7}$
11. $5^3 \cdot 5^4$
12. $4^2 \cdot 4^3$
13. $\left(\frac{3}{5}\right)^2$
14. $\left(\frac{4}{3}\right)^0$
15. $(2^{-3})^2$
16. $64^{1/2}$
17. $64^{-1/2}$
18. $216^{1/3}$

19. $16^{1/2}$	**20.** $16^{-1/2}$	**21.** $49^{1/2}$
22. $49^{-1/2}$	**23.** $64^{5/2}$	**24.** $64^{-5/2}$
25. $49^{3/2}$	**26.** $49^{-3/2}$	**27.** $216^{2/3}$
28. $216^{-2/3}$	**29.** 867^0	**30.** $(-3)^0$
31. $49^{5/2}$		

Rewrite each of the following using negative exponents.

32. $\dfrac{1}{3^2}$	**33.** $\dfrac{1}{5^6}$	**34.** $\dfrac{1}{x^7}$
35. $\dfrac{1}{(-5)^3}$	**36.** $\dfrac{1}{x^n}$	**37.** $\dfrac{1}{x^8}$

Rewrite each of the following using rational exponents.

38. $\sqrt[3]{5}$	**39.** $(\sqrt{4})^9$	**40.** $\sqrt[3]{x^5}$
41. $\sqrt[5]{2}$	**42.** $\sqrt{8^7}$	**43.** $\sqrt[3]{9^4}$
44. $(\sqrt{5})^3$	**45.** $(\sqrt[3]{5})^7$	**46.** $\sqrt[4]{x}$
47. $\dfrac{1}{\sqrt{5^3}}$	**48.** $\dfrac{1}{(\sqrt[3]{5})^8}$	**49.** $\dfrac{1}{\sqrt{x^5}}$
50. $\dfrac{1}{\sqrt{x^3}}$	**51.** $\dfrac{1}{\sqrt[3]{x^2}}$	**52.** $\dfrac{1}{(\sqrt[3]{x})^7}$

Using the fourth law of exponents, $(x \cdot y)^n = x^n \cdot y^n$, simplify each of the following.

53. $(-3x)^2$	**54.** $(2y)^4$	**55.** $(5xy)^3$
56. $(xyz)^9$	**57.** $(4 \cdot 81)^{1/2}$	**58.** $\sqrt{9 \cdot 64}$

Using the fifth law of exponents, $(x/y)^n = x^n/y^n$, simplify each of the following.

59. $\left(\dfrac{5}{6}\right)^3$	**60.** $\left(\dfrac{x}{y}\right)^4$	**61.** $\left(\dfrac{x}{3}\right)^5$	**62.** $\sqrt[3]{\dfrac{8}{27}}$
63. $\left(\dfrac{x}{5}\right)^2$	**64.** $\left(\dfrac{4}{x}\right)^3$	**65.** $\left(\dfrac{-2}{x}\right)^3$	**66.** $\sqrt{\dfrac{16}{25}}$

Simplify each of the following.

67. $\left(\dfrac{2^{-3} \cdot 2^5}{2^{-2}}\right)^3$ **68.** $3^{1/2} \cdot 3^{5/2}$

69. $\dfrac{3^{-7/2} \cdot 3^{3/2}}{3^{1/2} \cdot 3^{-3/2}}$ **70.** $\left(\dfrac{27^{5/3} \cdot 27^{-1/3}}{27^{1/3}}\right)^2$

Express each of the following in scientific notation.

71. 496	**72.** 5,870,000	**73.** 8,000,000,000
74. 0.00045	**75.** 0.0000008	**76.** 59.5
77. 0.56	**78.** 8730	**79.** 0.00357

R-4 • THE DISTRIBUTIVE LAW AND FACTORING

The Distributive Law

Consider the product of 3 times the sum of 2 + 8 or

$$3(2 + 8)$$

Such a product can be determined by either of the following two methods:

1. Calculate the sum

$$2 + 8 = 10$$

and multiply the result by 3 to obtain

$$3(2 + 8) = 3(10)$$
$$= 30$$

2. Multiply both 2 and 8 by 3, and add the products to obtain

$$3(2 + 8) = (3 \cdot 2) + (3 \cdot 8)$$
$$= 6 + 24$$
$$= 30$$

Observe that, in the second method, the 3 is *distributed* throughout the sum of 2 + 8. This is a specific illustration of the *distributive law of multiplication over addition.*

Distributive Law

If *a*, *b*, and *c* are numbers, then

$$a(b + c) = ab + ac$$

• **EXAMPLE R-10** _____

Using the distributive law, multiply $4(x + 2)$.

Solution

Distributing the 4 throughout the sum of $x + 2$, we have

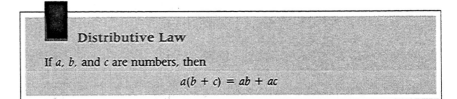

$$\boxed{4}\,(x + 2) = \boxed{4}\,x + \boxed{4} \cdot 2$$
$$= 4x + 8$$

• **EXAMPLE R-11** _____

Using the distributive law, multiply $3[x + (-5)]$.

Solution

$$\boxed{3}\,(x + (-5)) = \boxed{3}\,x + \boxed{3}\,(-5)$$
$$= 3x - 15$$

Since the sum of $x + (-5)$ is equivalent to the *difference* of $x - 5$, we should realize that the distributive law also holds true for *multiplication over subtraction.* Hence,

$$\boxed{3}\,(x - 5) = \boxed{3}\,x - \boxed{3} \cdot 5$$
$$= 3x - 15$$

• **EXAMPLE R-12** _____

Using the distributive law, multiply $6(2x - 5)$.

Solution

$$\boxed{6}\,(2x - 5) = \boxed{6} \cdot 2x - \boxed{6} \cdot 5$$
$$= 12x - 30$$

The distributive law may be applied to products involving a sum or difference of more than two numbers, as illustrated in Example R-13.

• **EXAMPLE R-13** _____

Using the distributive law, multiply $-5(x^2 + 3x - 7)$.

Solution

$$-5 (x^2 + 3x - 7) = -5 \cdot x^2 + -5 \cdot 3x - (-5)(7)$$
$$= -5x^2 - 15x + 35$$

• **EXAMPLE R-14** _____

Using the distributive law, multiply $-5xy^2(x^3 - 4x^2y)$.

Solution

$$-5xy^2 (x^3 - 4x^2y) = -5xy^2 \cdot x^3 - (-5xy^2) \cdot 4x^2y$$
$$= -5x^4y^2 + 20x^3y^3$$

Factoring

Many times the distributive law is used in *reverse*. This process is called **factoring.** Specifically, if we start with the expression

$$ab + ac$$

and rewrite it as the product

$$a(b + c)$$

then we have factored a from $ab + ac$.

• **EXAMPLE R-15** _____

Factor $3x + 6$.

Solution

$$3x + 6 = 3 \cdot x + 3 \cdot 2$$
$$= 3 (x + 2)$$

• **EXAMPLE R-16** _____

Factor $5x - 10y + 20$.

Solution

$$5x - 10y + 20 = 5 \cdot x - 5 \cdot 2y + 5 \cdot 4$$
$$= 5 (x - 2y + 4)$$

• **EXAMPLE R-17** _____

Factor $3x^5y^3 - 6x^2y^9$.

Solution

$$3x^5y^3 - 6x^2y^9 = 3x^2y^3 \cdot x^3 - 3x^2y^3 \cdot 2y^6$$
$$= 3x^2y^3 (x^3 - 2y^6)$$

R-18

FIGURE R-18

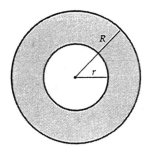

FIGURE R-19

• **EXAMPLE R-18** ──────────────────────

Given that the area of a circle of radius r (see Figure R-18) is πr^2 where $\pi \approx$ 3.1415927 to seven decimal places, show that the area of the ring of Figure R-19 is $\pi(R^2 - r^2)$.

Solution

$$\text{area of ring} = \text{area of outer circle} - \text{area of inner circle}$$
$$= \pi R^2 - \pi r^2$$
$$= \pi(R^2 - r^2)$$

• **EXAMPLE R-19** ──────────────────────

Using the distributive law, show that $P(1 + i) + P(1 + i)i = P(1 + i)^2$.

Solution

$$P(1 + i) + P(1 + i)i = \boxed{P(1 + i)} \cdot 1 + \boxed{P(1 + i)} \cdot i$$
$$= \boxed{P(1 + i)} (1 + i)$$
$$= P(1 + i)^2$$

• **EXAMPLE R-20** ──────────────────────

Factor $7x(x - 5) + 3x(x - 5)$.

Solution

$$7x \boxed{(x - 5)} + 3x \boxed{(x - 5)} = \boxed{(x - 5)} (7x + 3x)$$
$$= (x - 5)10x$$
$$= 10x(x - 5)$$

Exercises R-4

Use the distributive law to multiply each of the following.

1. $3(x + 4)$ **2.** $5(x - 3)$ **3.** $-2(x + 6)$
4. $-5(x - 8)$ **5.** $9(x + 3)$ **6.** $9(2x + 3)$
7. $-4(x^2 - 3x + 7)$ **8.** $6x(x^2 + 2x - 5)$
9. $5x(x^3 - 4x^2 + 4x + 5)$ **10.** $-2x(x^2 + 6x + 7)$
11. $3x^2y^3(x^4 - 5y^2 + 6xy)$ **12.** $-2x^4y^3(x^3 - 6y^2 + 7xy)$

Factor each of the following.

13. $5x + 20$ **14.** $-2x - 8$ **15.** $3x - 27$
16. $8x - 16$ **17.** $6x - 30$ **18.** $4x + 32$
19. $3x^2 - 27x$ **20.** $5x^2 + 60x$ **21.** $-6x^2 + 48x$
22. $-4x^2 - 36x$ **23.** $7x^2 + 28x$ **24.** $9x^2 - 18x$
25. $3x^2y^4 + 6xy^2$ **26.** $4x^3y^5 - 8x^2y^6$
27. $-5x^4y^6 + 20x^3y^7$ **28.** $-2x^5y^3 + 6x^4y^3$
29. $3x^2y^6 + 9x^5y^3 + 6x^3y^4$ **30.** $5x^4y^6 - 10x^3y^7 + 30x^2y^3$
31. $P + Prt$ **32.** $S - Sdt$
33. $P + Pi$ **34.** $ax^2 + bx$

35. $ax^2 - bx$ **36.** $ax^3 + bx^2 + cx$
37. $P(1 + i)^2 + P(1 + i)^2 i$ **38.** $P(1 + i)^3 + P(1 + i)^3 i$
39. $3x(x - 7) + 3x(x + 4)$ **40.** $5x(x + 2) - 2x(x + 2)$
41. $2x(x + 3) - y(x + 3)$ **42.** $3xy(x + 2) - 6x^2(x + 2)$
43. $5xy(x - 2) + 8x^2(x - 2)$ **44.** $4xy^2(x - 1) + 5x^2y(x - 1)$

R-5

• MULTIPLYING BINOMIALS

An algebraic expression containing exactly two terms is called a **binomial.** For example, the expression

$$x + 7$$

is a binomial because it contains two terms, x and 7. The expression

$$4x - 5$$

is a binomial because it contains two terms, $4x$ and -5. The expression

$$x^2 + 6$$

is a binomial because it contains two terms, x^2 and 6. The product of two binomials can be determined by using the distributive law

$$a(b + c) = ab + ac$$

Specifically, the product

$$(x - 3)(x + 5)$$

can be determined by treating the binomial $x - 3$ as a and employing the distributive law as follows:

$$a(b + c) = ab + ac$$
$$(x - 3)(x + 5) = (x - 3)x + (x - 3) \cdot 5$$
$$= x^2 - 3x + 5x - 15$$
$$= x^2 + 2x - 15$$

Observe that the above product can also be determined by the following mechanical procedure, called the **FOIL** method:

Step 1 Multiply the first terms of the binomial factors   F
Step 2 Multiply the outer terms of the binomial factors   0
Step 3 Multiply the inner terms of the binomial factors   I
Step 4 Multiply the last terms of the binomial factors   L
Step 5 Add the above products and simplify if possible.

Using the FOIL method, we again determine the product

$$(x - 3)(x + 5)$$

as follows:

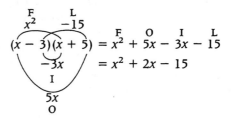

$$= x^2 + 2x - 15$$

• **EXAMPLE R-21** _____

Determine the product $(3x - 5)(x + 2)$.

Solution

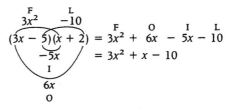

$$= 3x^2 + x - 10$$

• **EXAMPLE R-22** _____

Multiply $(4x + 3)(x - 7)$.

Solution

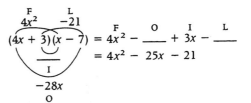

$$= 4x^2 - 25x - 21$$

Answer

$$4x^2 - \underline{28x} + 3x - \underline{21} = 4x^2 - 25x - 21$$

• **EXAMPLE R-23** _____

Multiply $(x - 5)(x + 5)$.

Solution

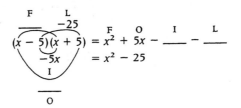

$$= x^2 - 25$$

Answer

$$x^2 + 5x - \underline{5x} - \underline{25} = x^2 - 25$$

Notice that the product, $x^2 - 25$, does not contain an x term. That is because the sum of $+5x$ and $-5x$ is 0.

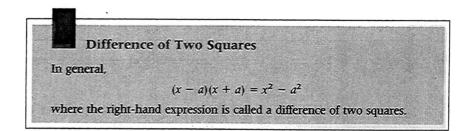

Difference of Two Squares

In general,

$$(x - a)(x + a) = x^2 - a^2$$

where the right-hand expression is called a difference of two squares.

• **EXAMPLE R-24** _____

Determine $(x + 3)^2$.

Solution

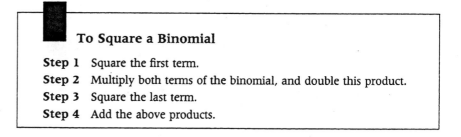

$$(x + 3)^2 = (x + 3)(x + 3) = x^2 + \underline{\quad} + 3x + 9$$
$$= x^2 + 6x + 9$$

Answer

$$x^2 + \underline{3x} + 3x + 9 = x^2 + 6x + 9$$

Since the product $x^2 + 6x + 9$ in Example R-24 is equivalent to the square of a binomial, namely $x + 3$, then $x^2 + 6x + 9$ is called a **perfect square.** Notice that when determining the square of a binomial, the products of the inner terms and outer terms are equal. In Example R-24, each is $3x$. Thus, to square a binomial, we can use the following modified procedure.

To Square a Binomial

Step 1 Square the first term.
Step 2 Multiply both terms of the binomial, and double this product.
Step 3 Square the last term.
Step 4 Add the above products.

For example,

$$(x + 5)^2 = x^2 + 2(5x) + 5^2$$
$$= x^2 + 10x + 25$$
$$(x - 7)^2 = x^2 + 2(-7x) + (-7)^2$$
$$= x^2 - 14x + 49$$
$$(2x - 5)^2 = (2x)^2 + 2[(2x)(-5)] + (-5)^2$$
$$= 4x^2 - 20x + 25$$

Exercises R-5

Determine each of the following products by using the FOIL method.

1. $(x - 2)(x + 3)$	**2.** $(x - 8)(x + 7)$
3. $(x + 1)(x + 5)$	**4.** $(x - 2)(x - 3)$
5. $(x - 8)(x - 7)$	**6.** $(x - 6)(x + 10)$
7. $(3x + 5)(x - 1)$	**8.** $(2x + 1)(3x + 4)$
9. $(4x - 7)(2x + 3)$	**10.** $(5x + 3)(x - 2)$
11. $(7x - 2)(3x + 1)$	**12.** $(9x + 1)(3x - 5)$

Determine each of the following products by using the difference of two squares formula.

13. $(x - 3)(x + 3)$	**14.** $(x - 7)(x + 7)$
15. $(x - 9)(x + 9)$	**16.** $(2x - 1)(2x + 1)$
17. $(3x - 2)(3x + 2)$	**18.** $(4x - 7)(4x + 7)$

Determine each of the following.

19. $(x - 2)^2$	**20.** $(x + 2)^2$
21. $(x + 5)^2$	**22.** $(x - 5)^2$
23. $(2x - 3)^2$	**24.** $(2x + 3)^2$

R-6

• FACTORING

In the previous section, we learned to multiply binomials. For example, we learned that the product $(x - 2)(x + 7)$ can be determined by the FOIL method as follows:

$$(x - 2)(x + 7) = x^2 + 7x - 2x - 14 = x^2 + 5x - 14$$

If we begin with $x^2 + 5x - 14$ and express it as the product $(x - 2)(x + 7)$, then we have *factored* $x^2 + 5x - 14$. The binomials $x - 2$ and $x + 7$ are called **factors**. Thus, factoring is the reverse of multiplication.

We will demonstrate the factoring process by factoring expressions of the form

$$ax^2 + bx + c$$

where a, b, and c are constants and $a \neq 0$. Also, we will begin with the special case where $a = 1$. Thus, for this special case, the above expression is written as

$$x^2 + bx + c$$

If factored, such an expression is written as the product of two binomials

$$(x + A)(x + B)$$

where A and B are constants. Thus, when we factor the expression $x^2 + bx + c$, we seek two constants, A and B, such that

$$(x + A)(x + B) = x^2 + bx + c \qquad (1)$$

If we apply the FOIL method to the left-hand side of equation (1), we obtain

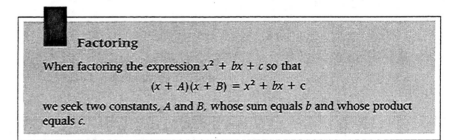

Comparing the right-hand sides of equations (1) and (2), note that

$$B + A = b \text{ and } AB = c$$

This result is expressed as follows.

> **Factoring**
>
> When factoring the expression $x^2 + bx + c$ so that
> $$(x + A)(x + B) = x^2 + bx + c$$
> we seek two constants, A and B, whose sum equals b and whose product equals c.

As an example, let us factor $x^2 + 6x - 27$. This means that we wish to write $x^2 + 6x - 27$ as a product of two factors:

$$(x + A)(x + B)$$

Thus, we seek two numbers, A and B, whose sum is 6 and whose product is -27. The numbers of the pair -3, 9 satisfy the above requirements since $-3 + 9 = 6$ and $-3 \cdot 9 = -27$. Hence,

$$(x - 3)(x + 9) = x^2 + 6x - 27$$

and our two factors are $x - 3$ and $x + 9$.

• **EXAMPLE R-25** _____

Factor $x^2 + 7x - 30$.

Solution

We wish to determine two factors such that

$$(x + \underline{\quad})(x + \underline{\quad}) = x^2 + 7x - 30$$

Thus, we seek two numbers whose sum is 7 and whose product is -30. The following are possible pairs of numbers whose product is -30:

$$-5, 6 \qquad 5, -6 \qquad -3, 10 \qquad 3, -10$$
$$-30, 1 \qquad 30, -1 \qquad 15, -2 \qquad -15, 2$$

Since the numbers of the pair -3, 10 have a sum of 7, then the factors are $x - 3$ and $x + 10$. Hence,

$$(x - 3)(x + 10) = x^2 + 7x - 30$$

Of course, we can always check our factoring by multiplying the factors to determine if their product is the original expression that was factored.

• EXAMPLE R-26

Factor $x^2 + 8x + 15$.

Solution

We wish to determine two factors such that

$$(x + \underline{\quad})(x + \underline{\quad}) = x^2 + 8x + 15$$

Thus, we seek two numbers whose sum is 8 and whose product is 15. The following are possible pairs of numbers whose product is 15:

$$3, 5 \qquad -3, -5 \qquad 1, 15 \qquad -1, -15$$

Since the numbers of the pair 3, 5 have a sum of 8, then the factors are $x + 3$ and $x + 5$. Hence,

$$(x + 3)(x + 5) = x^2 + 8x + 15$$

Of course, we can always check our factoring by multiplying the factors to determine if their product is the original expression that was factored.

• EXAMPLE R-27

Factor $x^2 - 36$.

Solution

Since $x^2 - 36$ does not contain an x term, we seek two numbers whose sum is 0 and whose product is -36. The numbers are -6 and $+6$. Hence,

$$(x - 6)(x + 6) = x^2 - 36$$

As discussed in the previous section, the expression $x^2 - 36$ in Example R-27 is called a **difference of two squares.** In general, a difference of two squares

$$x^2 - h^2$$

is factored as follows:

$$x^2 - h^2 = (x - h)(x + h)$$

• EXAMPLE R-28

Factor $x^2 + 12x + 36$.

Solution

We seek two numbers whose product is 36 and whose sum is 12. The numbers are 6 and 6, and the factors are $x + 6$ and $x + 6$. Hence,

$$(x + 6)(x + 6) = x^2 + 12x + 36$$

or

$$(x + 6)^2 = x^2 + 12x + 36$$

Since the expression $x^2 + 12x + 36$ (in Example R-28), when factored, is written as $(x + 6)^2$, the square of a binomial, then the expression $x^2 + 12x + 36$ is called a **perfect square.** In general, an expression of the form $x^2 + bx + c$ is a perfect square if, when factored, it is written as

$$(x + A)^2 = x^2 + bx + c \qquad (3)$$

where A is a constant.

We now discuss how to recognize a perfect square. Applying the FOIL method to the left-hand side of equation (3), we obtain

$$
\begin{array}{c}
\overset{F}{x^2} \qquad \overset{L}{A^2} \\
(x + A)(x + A) = x^2 + \overset{F}{Ax} + \overset{O}{Ax} + \overset{I}{A^2} \qquad \overset{L}{} \\
\overset{Ax}{I} \qquad = x^2 + 2Ax + A^2 \qquad (4) \\
\overset{Ax}{O}
\end{array}
$$

Comparing the right-hand sides of equations (3) and (4), note that *the coefficient of x is twice the square root of the constant c.* Thus, we state the following.

Perfect Square

An expression of the form

$$x^2 + bx + c$$

with $c \geq 0$ is a perfect square if

$$b = \pm 2\sqrt{c}$$

1. If $b = +2\sqrt{c}$, then the expression is written in factored form as

$$(x + \sqrt{c})^2$$

2. If $b = -2\sqrt{c}$, then the expression is written in factored form as

$$(x - \sqrt{c})^2$$

As another example, note that $x^2 - 12x + 36$ is a perfect square since $-12 = -2\sqrt{36}$. Hence,

$$x^2 - 12x + 36 = (x - 6)^2$$

We summarize the following.

$$x^2 - h^2 = (x - h)(x + h) \qquad \text{Difference of two squares}$$
$$x^2 + 2Ax + A^2 = (x + A)^2 \qquad \text{Perfect square}$$
$$x^2 - 2Ax + A^2 = (x - A)^2 \qquad \text{Perfect square}$$

Exercises R-6

Factor each of the following:

1. $x^2 + 7x - 18$
2. $x^2 - 7x - 18$
3. $x^2 + 2x - 15$
4. $x^2 + 10x + 21$
5. $x^2 - 3x + 2$
6. $x^2 + 13x + 40$
7. $x^2 - 13x + 40$
8. $x^2 - x + 42$
9. $x^2 - 81$
10. $x^2 - 64$
11. $x^2 - 49$
12. $x^2 - 25$
13. $x^2 + 6x + 9$
14. $x^2 - 6x + 9$
15. $x^2 - 10x + 25$
16. $x^2 + 10x + 25$
17. $x^2 + 18x + 81$
18. $x^2 - 18x + 81$
19. $x^2 - 6x - 27$
20. $x^2 - 100$
21. $x^2 - 4x - 45$
22. $x^2 - 20x + 100$
23. $x^2 + 7x + 6$
24. $x^2 + 2x + 1$

R-7   • MORE FACTORING

In the previous section, we demonstrated the factoring process by factoring expressions of the form

$$ax^2 + bx + c$$

where a, b, and c are constants and $a = 1$. In this section, we remove the restriction that $a = 1$. In other words, we will now discuss the factoring of expressions of the form

$$ax^2 + bx + c \qquad \cdot$$

where a, b, and c are constants, $a \neq 0$, and $a \neq 1$. As an example, we will factor

$$5x^2 + 33x - 14$$

Since the coefficient of x^2 is 5, then by the FOIL method, the product of the x terms of both factors must be $5x^2$. Hence, the x terms of the factors are $5x$ and x, and

$$(5x + \underline{\quad})(x + \underline{\quad}) = 5x^2 + 33x - 14$$

We now seek two numbers whose product is -14. We shall discover that the sum of these two numbers will not be 33, as would be the case if the coefficient of the x^2 term were 1 (i.e., if $a = 1$). The following are pairs of numbers whose product is -14:

$$7, -2 \qquad -7, 2 \qquad -1, 14 \qquad 1, -14$$

Now we must use a trial-and-error approach to determine which pair yields the correct middle term when the factors are multiplied by the FOIL method. We will begin with the pair 7, -2. Hence,

$$(5x + 7)(x - 2) \stackrel{?}{=} 5x^2 + 33x - 14 \tag{1}$$

$$= 5x^2 - 10x + 7x - 14 \tag{2}$$

$$= 5x^2 - 3x - 14 \tag{3}$$

Note that we have placed a question mark above the equal sign of equation (1). Equations (2) and (3) give the results of multiplying the two factors. Note that since the x term of the product is $-3x$ and not $33x$, then the above factorization is not correct, and we must try another combination of numbers. However, before trying a different pair of numbers, we might interchange the positions of $+7$ and -2. Hence,

$$(5x - 2)(x + 7) \stackrel{?}{=} 5x^2 + 33x - 14 \tag{4}$$

$$= 5x^2 + 35x - 2x - 14 \tag{5}$$

$$= 5x^2 + 33x - 14 \tag{6}$$

Notice that multiplication by the FOIL method in equations (5) and (6) has resulted in the correct middle term, $33x$. Thus, the above factorization in equation (4) is correct, and

$$5x^2 + 33x - 14 = (5x - 2)(x + 7)$$

• EXAMPLE R-29

Factor $6x^2 - 11x - 35$.

Solution

We wish to determine two factors such that

$$(\underline{\hspace{0.5cm}}x + \underline{\hspace{0.5cm}})(\underline{\hspace{0.5cm}}x + \underline{\hspace{0.5cm}}) = 6x^2 - 11x - 35$$

Since the coefficient of x^2 is 6, we first seek two numbers whose product is 6. From a number of possibilities, we choose 3 and 2. Hence,

$$(3x + \underline{\hspace{0.5cm}})(2x + \underline{\hspace{0.5cm}}) \stackrel{?}{=} 6x^2 - 11x - 35$$

We hasten to mention that this may not be the correct choice of numbers. This is why we have placed a question mark above the equal sign. However, we have no way of determining this until we choose the numbers for the remaining blanks in our factors and multiply by the FOIL method to determine whether the product equals $6x^2 - 11x - 35$.

Thus, we seek two numbers whose product is -35. From a number of possibilities, we choose 5 and -7. Hence,

$$(3x + 5)(2x - 7) \stackrel{?}{=} 6x^2 - 11x - 35 \tag{7}$$

$$= 6x^2 - 21x + 10x - 35 \tag{8}$$

$$= 6x^2 - 11x - 35 \tag{9}$$

Note that multiplication by the FOIL method in equations (8) and (9) has resulted in the correct middle term, $-11x$. Thus, the factorization in equation (7) is correct, and

$$6x^2 - 11x - 35 = (3x + 5)(2x - 7)$$

Exercises R-7

Factor each of the following.

1. $2x^2 - x - 28$
2. $6x^2 - 7x - 5$
3. $5x^2 + 18x - 8$
4. $21x^2 - 2x - 8$
5. $6x^2 - 13x - 5$
6. $4x^2 - 13x - 35$
7. $9x^2 - 36$
8. $64x^2 - 49$
9. $4x^2 + 20x + 25$
10. $9x^2 - 12x + 4$
11. $25x^2 - 70x + 49$
12. $81x^2 + 18x + 1$

R-8 • RATIONAL EXPRESSIONS

Expressions involving quotients such as

$$\frac{3x + 15}{2x} \qquad \frac{x^2 - 4x}{x - 7} \qquad \frac{x^2 - 36}{x + 9}$$

are called **rational expressions.** Sometimes we have to simplify or reduce such expressions to their lowest terms. Such simplifications are performed by using the following rules.

Rules Involving Rational Expressions

Assume that N, D, R, and S are expressions such that D and $S \neq 0$.

$$\frac{N \cdot S}{D \cdot S} = \frac{N}{D} \qquad \text{Fundamental rule}$$

$$\frac{N}{D} \cdot \frac{R}{S} = \frac{N \cdot R}{D \cdot S} \qquad \text{Multiplication rule}$$

$$\frac{N}{D} \div \frac{R}{S} = \frac{N}{D} \cdot \frac{S}{R} \quad (R \neq 0) \qquad \text{Division rule}$$

$$\frac{N}{D} + \frac{R}{D} = \frac{N + R}{D} \qquad \text{Addition rule}$$

$$\frac{N}{D} - \frac{R}{D} = \frac{N - R}{D} \qquad \text{Subtraction rule}$$

The following examples illustrate applications of these rules.

• EXAMPLE R-30

Simplify each of the following.

a) $\dfrac{3x + 15}{3} = \dfrac{3(x + 5)}{3} = x + 5$ Factoring, fundamental rule

b) $\dfrac{x^2 + x - 20}{x^2 - 16} = \dfrac{(x - 4)(x + 5)}{(x - 4)(x + 4)} = \dfrac{x + 5}{x + 4}$ Factoring, fundamental rule

• EXAMPLE R-31

Perform the indicated operation.

a) $\dfrac{x^2 - 25}{x + 3} \cdot \dfrac{x^2 - 2x - 15}{x^2 - 10x + 25} = \dfrac{(x - 5)(x + 5)}{(x + 3)} \cdot \dfrac{(x - 5)(x + 3)}{(x - 5)(x - 5)}$

$= x + 5$ Factoring, mulitplication rule, fundamental rule

b) $\dfrac{x^2 + 2x - 8}{x + 6} \div \dfrac{x^2 + 3x - 4}{2x + 12} = \dfrac{x^2 + 2x - 8}{x + 6} \cdot \dfrac{2x + 12}{x^2 + 3x - 8}$ Division rule

$= \dfrac{(x - 2)(x + 4)}{x + 6} \cdot \dfrac{2(x + 6)}{(x + 4)(x - 1)}$ Factoring; fundamental rule

$= \dfrac{2(x - 2)}{x - 1}$ or $\dfrac{2x - 4}{x - 1}$ Division rule, factoring, fundamental rule

c) $\dfrac{6}{7x} + \dfrac{8}{7x} = \dfrac{6 + 8}{7x} = \dfrac{14}{7x} = \dfrac{7 \cdot 2}{7x} = \dfrac{2}{x}$ Addition rule, fundamental rule

d) $\dfrac{8}{x} - \dfrac{5}{2x} + \dfrac{4}{3x} = \dfrac{6 \cdot 8}{6 \cdot x} - \dfrac{3 \cdot 5}{3 \cdot 2x} + \dfrac{2 \cdot 4}{2 \cdot 3x} = \dfrac{48}{6x} - \dfrac{15}{6x} + \dfrac{8}{6x}$

$= \dfrac{48 - 15 + 8}{6x} = \dfrac{41}{6x}$ Addition and subtraction rules; fundamental rule

• **EXAMPLE R-32** _____

Divide by x.

$$\frac{3x + 5}{x} = \frac{3\cancel{x}}{\cancel{x}} + \frac{5}{x} = 3 + \frac{5}{x} \qquad \text{Addition rule; fundamental rule}$$

• **EXAMPLE R-33** _____

Divide.

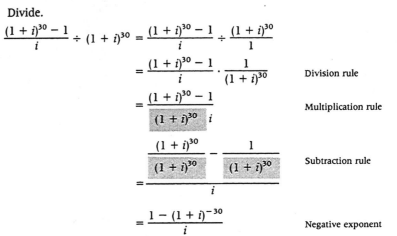

$$\frac{(1 + i)^{30} - 1}{i} \div (1 + i)^{30} = \frac{(1 + i)^{30} - 1}{i} \div \frac{(1 + i)^{30}}{1}$$

$$= \frac{(1 + i)^{30} - 1}{i} \cdot \frac{1}{(1 + i)^{30}} \qquad \text{Division rule}$$

$$= \frac{(1 + i)^{30} - 1}{(1 + i)^{30}\, i} \qquad \text{Multiplication rule}$$

$$= \frac{\dfrac{(1 + i)^{30}}{(1 + i)^{30}} - \dfrac{1}{(1 + i)^{30}}}{i} \qquad \text{Subtraction rule}$$

$$= \frac{1 - (1 + i)^{-30}}{i} \qquad \text{Negative exponent}$$

• **EXAMPLE R-34** _____

Multiply.

$$5x^3\left(1 + \frac{2}{x} - \frac{3}{x^2} + \frac{6}{x^3}\right) = 1 \cdot 5x^3 + \frac{2 \cdot 5x^3}{x} - \frac{3 \cdot 5x^3}{x^2} + \frac{6 \cdot 5x^3}{x^3}$$

$$= 5x^3 + 10x^2 - 15x + 30$$

• **EXAMPLE R-35** _____

Factor out the highest-powered term: $2x^3 + 4x^2 - 2x + 8$.

Solution

$$\frac{2x^3}{2x^3}(2x^3 + 4x^2 - 2x + 8) = 2x^3\left(\frac{2x^3 + 4x^2 - 2x + 8}{2x^3}\right)$$

$$= 2x^3\left(\frac{2x^3}{2x^3} + \frac{4x^2}{2x^3} - \frac{2x}{2x^3} + \frac{8}{2x^3}\right)$$

$$= 2x^3\left(1 + \frac{2}{x} - \frac{1}{x^2} + \frac{4}{x^3}\right)$$

Exercises R-8

Simplify each of the following.

1. $\dfrac{4x - 28}{2}$ 2. $\dfrac{-3x + 18}{3}$ 3. $\dfrac{-(2x + 14)}{2}$ 4. $\dfrac{5x - 30}{5}$

5. $\dfrac{x^2 - 6x}{x - 6}$ 6. $\dfrac{4x^2 - 32x}{x - 8}$ 7. $\dfrac{x^2 + 2x - 15}{x^2 - 25}$ 8. $\dfrac{x + 8}{x^2 - 64}$

9. $\dfrac{x^2 + 3x - 4}{x^2 - 1}$ 10. $\dfrac{x^2 + 2x - 8}{x^2 + 5x + 4}$ 11. $\dfrac{x^2 + 8x + 15}{x^2 + 7x + 10}$

Perform the indicated operations.

12. $\dfrac{x^2 - 49}{x + 2} \cdot \dfrac{x^2 + 3x + 2}{x^2 - 6x - 7}$ 13. $\dfrac{9}{6x^2} \cdot \dfrac{2x}{3}$

14. $\dfrac{20x^3}{7x} \div \dfrac{10}{21x}$ 15. $\dfrac{x^2 - 4x - 5}{x^2 + 3x + 2} \cdot \dfrac{x^2 + 5x + 6}{x^2 - 7x + 10}$

16. $\dfrac{x^2 - x - 30}{x^2 - 36} \cdot \dfrac{x^2 + 7x + 6}{x^2 + 7x + 10}$ 17. $\dfrac{x^2 - 81}{x^2 + 10x + 9} \div \dfrac{x^2 - 7x - 18}{x^2 + 4x + 3}$

18. $\dfrac{x^2 + 2x - 8}{x^2 + x - 2} \div \dfrac{x^2 + x - 12}{x^2 - 1}$

19. $\dfrac{x + 5}{4} + \dfrac{x + 7}{4}$ 20. $\dfrac{2x + 3}{5} - \dfrac{5x - 7}{10}$ 21. $\dfrac{5}{x} + \dfrac{8}{2x}$

22. $\dfrac{x}{x - 2} + \dfrac{3}{x + 2}$ 23. $\dfrac{5}{x + 6} - \dfrac{8}{x}$ 24. $\dfrac{8}{x - 5} + \dfrac{4}{x + 5}$

25. $\dfrac{5}{x^2 - 36} + \dfrac{9}{x + 6}$ 26. $\dfrac{4}{x + 8} + \dfrac{3}{x^2 - 64}$ 27. $\dfrac{7}{x - 9} - \dfrac{5}{x(x - 9)}$

Divide by x.

28. $\dfrac{4x - 9}{x}$ 29. $\dfrac{2x + 7}{x}$ 30. $\dfrac{8x - 9}{x}$ 31. $\dfrac{3x^2 - 36x}{x}$

32. $\dfrac{5x^2 + 30x}{x}$ 33. $\dfrac{4x^3 - 8x^2 + 6x}{x}$ 34. $\dfrac{5x^2 - 6x + 8}{x}$

Multiply.

35. $4x^2\left(1 + \dfrac{2}{x} - \dfrac{3}{x^2}\right)$ 36. $6x^3\left(1 + \dfrac{1}{x} + \dfrac{2}{x^2} - \dfrac{4}{x^3}\right)$

37. $5x^3\left(1 - \dfrac{1}{x} + \dfrac{6}{x^2} - \dfrac{2}{x^3}\right)$ 38. $x^3\left(2 + \dfrac{3}{x} + \dfrac{8}{x^2} - \dfrac{4}{x^3}\right)$

Factor out the highest-powered term.

39. $x^3 - 4x^2 + 7x + 5$ 40. $x^4 - 6x^3 + x^2 - x + 9$

41. $x^2 + 7x + 9$ 42. $x^3 + 6x^2 + 8x + 4$

Divide.

43. $\dfrac{(1 + i)^{20} - 1}{i} \div (1 + i)^{20}$ 44. $\dfrac{(1 + i)^{36} - 1}{i} \div (1 + i)^{26}$

45. $\dfrac{(1 + i)^{39} - (1 + i)}{i} \div (1 + i)^{38}$ 46. $\dfrac{(1 + i)^{50} - 1}{i} \div (1 + i)$

EXTRA DIVIDENDS

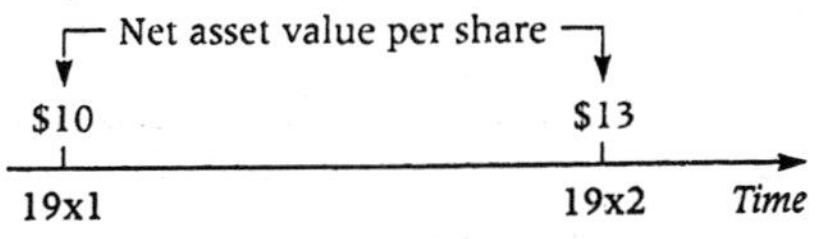

FIGURE R-20

• Percent Change

In the business world, assets usually change in value over periods of time. The amount of change is often put into perspective by expressing it as a percentage. For example, if the net asset value per share of mutual fund changes from $10 to $13 during a 1-year time period (see Figure R-20), this constitutes a change (in this case, an increase) of $13 − $10 = $3 per share during the indicated 1-year time period. If we divide the amount of change by the original value (i.e., the net asset value per share at the beginning of the year), the result

$$3/10 = 0.30$$
$$= 30\%$$

gives us the *percent change* (in this case, percent increase) in the net asset value per share of the fund during the indicated time period. We generalize as follows:

• *Percent Change*

If some quantity changes in value during a time interval, as indicated in Figure R-21, then the percent change is given by the following formula:

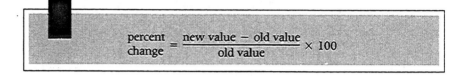

$$\text{percent change} = \frac{\text{new value} - \text{old value}}{\text{old value}} \times 100$$

If new value > old value, then the percent change is positive and thus is a percent increase. If new value < old value, then the percent change is negative and thus is a percent decrease.

Thus, if a stock's price changes from $40 to $10 during a 3-month time period, the percent change is determined as follows:

$$\text{percent change} = \frac{\text{new value} - \text{old value}}{\text{old value}} \times 100$$
$$= \frac{10 - 40}{40} \times 100$$
$$= \frac{-30}{40} \times 100$$
$$= -0.75 \times 100$$
$$= -75\%$$

Thus, the stock's price has decreased by 75%.

A percent change indicates a relationship between the new value and the old value of an asset. The equation expressing this relationship is determined by beginning with the formula for percent change and solving for the new value. Thus, if p denotes the percent change in decimal form (i.e., before we multiply by 100), OV denotes the old value, and NV denotes the new value, then

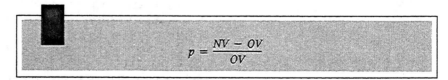

$$p = \frac{NV - OV}{OV}$$

Multiplying both sides of this equation by OV, we have

$$OV \cdot p = NV - OV$$

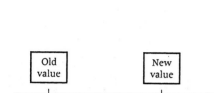

Old value   New value

Time

FIGURE R-21

Solving for NV, we have

$$OV + (OV \cdot p) = NV$$

or

$$NV = OV + (OV \cdot p)$$

Applying the distributive law to the right-hand side, we have

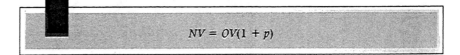

$$NV = OV(1 + p)$$

The boxed equation gives the relationship between the new value and the old value of some asset.

Thus, if an assset's value increases by 40% from $80 during a 6-month time interval, then its new value is given by the formula

$$NV = OV(1 + p)$$

where $p = 0.40$ and $OV = 80$. Hence,

$$NV = 80(1 + 0.40)$$
$$= 80(1.40)$$
$$= 112$$

Thus, the asset's new value at the end of the indicated 6-month time interval is $112.

Also, if an asset's value decreases by 30% from $80 during a specified time interval, then its new value is determined by the formula

$$NV = OV(1 + p)$$

where $p = -0.30$ and $OV = 80$. Hence,

$$NV = 80(1 - 0.30)$$
$$= 80(0.70)$$
$$= 56$$

Thus, the asset's new value at the end of the time period is $56.

Exercises

1. A mutual fund's net asset value per share changes from $40 to $50 during a 1-year time period. Find its percent change.
2. A stock's price changes from $60 to $20 during a 9-month time period. Find its percent change.
3. A stock's price increases by 20% from $60 during a 3-month time period. Find its new price.
4. A stock's price decreases by 30% from $80 during a given month. Find its new price.
5. The price of 1 ounce of gold increased by 40% to $600 during a given month. Find its old price at the beginning of the month.

R-34

TABLE R-1

Twentieth Century Growth	43.9%
Fidelity Magellan	48.0
Vanguard Windsor	56.1
Mutual Shares	60.5
Fidelity Puritan	41.9

Investment

Table R-1 gives percent changes of various mutual funds during a selected 3-year time period. If $10,000 were invested at the beginning the selected 3-year period, determine its value at the end of the 3-year period (assuming no withdrawals of either principal or income) for

6. Twentieth Century Growth   7. Fidelity Magellan
8. Vanguard Windsor   9. Mutual Shares
10. Fidelity Puritan

International: Trade

Table R-2 gives total trade (imports and exports in millions of U.S. dollars) in competitive world markets for three countries during various years. Determine the percent change from 1975 to 1980 for

11. United States   12. Soviet Union   13. Japan

Determine the percent change from 1980 to 1985 for

14. United States   15. Soviet Union   16. Japan

TABLE R-2

	1975	1980	1985
United States	$213,992	$477,771	$574,771
Soviet Union	30,791	67,059	65,967
Japan	113,569	271,737	307,652

Stocks

Table R-3 gives the total return (change in value plus income) for the selected stocks during the decade of the 1980s. If, at the end of the decade, an investor had shares worth $100,000, what was the value of such shares at the beginning of the decade, assuming the shares were purchased at the beginning of the decade and no withdrawals of either principal or income were made? Answer this question if the shares purchased were

TABLE R-3

General Electric	451%
Exxon	365
AT&T	348
General Motors	182

17. General Electric   18. Exxon
19. AT&T   20. General Motors

EXTRA DIVIDENDS

TABLE R-4 Price per quart of milk

1990	79¢
1980	56¢

• *Using Index Numbers to Measure Change*

An **index number** measures the change in some quantity (i.e., price, productivity, inventory, etc.) from one time period to another. The time periods are usually years, although this does not necessarily have to be the case. The time period used as the basis of comparison is called the **base period.** As an example, we consider the price of milk for the years 1990 and 1980, as given in Table R-4.

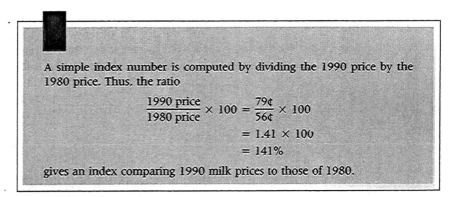

A simple index number is computed by dividing the 1990 price by the 1980 price. Thus, the ratio

$$\frac{1990 \text{ price}}{1980 \text{ price}} \times 100 = \frac{79¢}{56¢} \times 100$$
$$= 1.41 \times 100$$
$$= 141\%$$

gives an index comparing 1990 milk prices to those of 1980.

Since 1980 prices are the basis of the comparison, then 1980 is the *base year* of this index. Note that we multiply by 100 to express the index as a percentage. We will use the symbol

$$I_{80,90}$$

to denote an index number comparing the 1990 price with that of base year 1980. We summarize as follows.

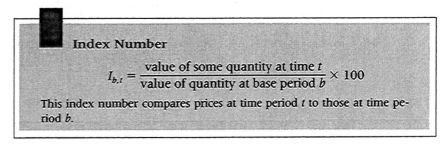

Index Number

$$I_{b,t} = \frac{\text{value of some quantity at time } t}{\text{value of quantity at base period } b} \times 100$$

This index number compares prices at time period t to those at time period b.

Usually, the base period is the earlier time period, although this is not always the case. Thus, for our example comparing milk prices, the index

$$I_{80,90} = 141\%$$

indicates that 1990 milk prices are 141% of those of the base year 1980.

Since the above index compared prices for only one commodity, it is called a **simple index.** Index numbers are usually computed to include prices of a group of commodities. Such index numbers are called **composite index numbers.** The computation of composite index numbers is beyond the scope of this discussion. Here we will stress the use and interpretation of index numbers.

The Bureau of Labor Statistics computes a very important index called the **consumer price index,** abbreviated **CPI.** The CPI is a composite index that measures the change in cost of a fixed market basket of goods and services purchased by a specified group of consumers.

• Using Index Numbers to Deflate

Index numbers are often used as price deflators. For example, suppose that in 1988 a construction worker earns $800 per week. A union negotiator wishes to determine the purchasing power of this weekly wage in 1967 dollars. In other words, the union negotiator wants to deflate the 1988 weekly wage to 1967 dollars. To deflate a 1988 price to 1967 dollars, we need an index number (often, the CPI), $I_{67,88}$, that measures the change between 1967 and 1988 prices. Since, from a simplified perspective, the index $I_{67,88}$ is interpreted as a ratio of 1988 prices to 1967 prices, this relationship can be expressed in equation form as

$$I_{67,88} = \frac{1988 \text{ prices}}{1967 \text{ prices}} \times 100$$

Multiplying both sides by the right-hand denominator gives

$$1967 \text{ price} \times I_{67,88} = 1988 \text{ prices} \times 100$$

Solving for 1967 prices, we have

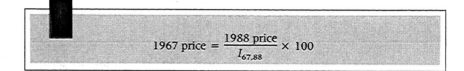

$$1967 \text{ price} = \frac{1988 \text{ price}}{I_{67,88}} \times 100$$

The above boxed formula indicates that a 1988 price is deflated to 1967 dollars by dividing the 1988 price by $I_{67,88}$ and then multiplying by 100. If $I_{67,88} = 250$, then

$$1967 \text{ price} = \frac{1988 \text{ price}}{I_{67,88}} \times 100$$
$$= \frac{800}{250} \times 100$$
$$= 320$$

Thus, the 1988 wage of $800 is the equivalent of $320 in 1967 dollars. Figure R-22 illustrates this relationship from a time diagram point of view.

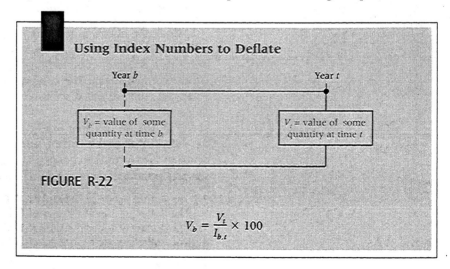

FIGURE R-22

To further illustrate the usefulness of deflating prices, we consider the following example. Suppose the construction worker of the previous example earned $300 per week in 1967. During the time period between 1967 and 1988, his percent increase in weekly wages is given by

$$\frac{800 - 300}{300} \times 100 = \frac{500}{300} \times 100$$
$$= 1.667 \times 100$$
$$= 166.7\%$$

This result is termed a 166.7% increase in nominal wages. However, if we deflate his 1988 wage of $800 to its equivalent in 1967 dollars, $320, then the percent increase in real wages (i.e., wages in 1967 dollars) is given by

$$\frac{320 - 300}{300} \times 100 = \frac{20}{300} \times 100$$
$$= .0667 \times 100$$
$$= 6.67\%$$

Thus, the construction worker's real wages have increased by only 6.67% during the 21-year period. The union negotiator, mentioned earlier, would certainly use this result as an argument for higher future wages.

Exercises

1. In 1970, a commodity sold for $80. Its 1988 price is $140. Compute $I_{70,88}$.
2. In 1980, a 94-pound bag of concrete cost $4.80. Its 1988 price is $6.90. Compute $I_{80,88}$.
3. B-MART's 1988 sales are $23,000,000. If $I_{70,88} = 280$, then deflate the 1988 sales to 1970 dollars.
4. A worker earns $600 per week during 1988. If $I_{79,88} = 240$, then deflate the 1988 wages to 1979 dollars.
5. A wage earner's 1975 income was $15,000, while her 1988 income is $30,000. If $I_{75,88} = 170$, then
   a) Compute the percent increase in nominal income.
   b) Compute the percent increase in real income.
6. A-TECH's 1980 sales were $15,000,000, while its 1988 sales are $40,000,000. If the industry's index is $I_{80,88} = 190$, then
   a) Compute the percent increase in nominal sales.
   b) Compute the percent increase in real sales.

Trade: Value of the Dollar

Figure R-23 gives a graph of index numbers indicating the dollar's value relative to base year 1980 against currencies of its major trading partners.

7. The dollar's value at the end of 1982 was what multiple of its 1980 value?
8. The dollar's value at the end of 1984 was what multiple of its 1980 value?
9. The dollar's value at the end of 1985 was what multiple of its 1980 value?
10. The dollar's value at the end of 1988 was what multiple of its 1980 value?

A weaker greenback

The dollar's value against the currencies of its major trading partners

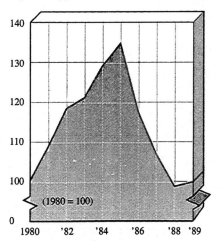

(1980 = 100)

Note: Figure for 1989 reflects the average through November.
USN&WR—Basic data: Atlanta Federal Reserve Board

Copyright ©, Dec. 25, 1989—Jan. 1, 1990,
U.S. News & World Report. Reprinted by permission.

FIGURE R-23

Despite productivity gains...

U.S. manufacturing productivity compared with major industial competitors

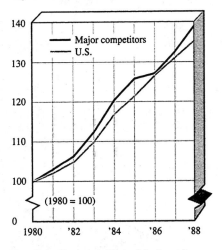

(1980 = 100)

Note: Competitors include 11 industrialized countries. Productivity is worker output per hour.
USN&WR—Basic data: U.S. Dept. of Labor

Copyright ©, Dec. 25, 1989—Jan. 1, 1990, *U.S. News & World Report.* Reprinted by permission.

FIGURE R-24

TABLE R-5 **Consumer Price Index (1967 = 100)**

	1980	1982	1984
CPI	246.8	289.1	311.1

Productivity

Figure R-24 gives a graph of index numbers indicating productivity relative to base year 1980.

11. U.S. productivity for 1983 was what multiple of its 1980 value?
12. U.S. productivity for 1986 was what multiple of its 1980 value?
13. U.S. productivity for 1987 was what multiple of its 1980 value?
14. U.S. productivity for 1988 was what multiple of its 1980 value?

Consumer Price Index (CPI)

The Table R-5 gives the CPI for various years relative to base year 1967.
Give the value in 1967 dollars of goods worth $1000 in

15. 1984 dollars   **16.** 1982 dollars   **17.** 1980 dollars

1

FUNCTIONS AND
LINEAR MODELS

Introductory Application

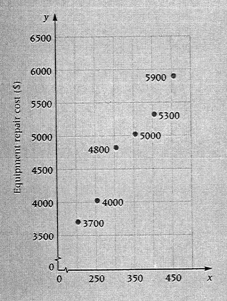

FIGURE 1-A

Cost Accounting: Cost Segregation

Businesses usually collect data giving total costs associated with various levels of a given quantity. Such data are often used to segregate the fixed and the variable portions of a total cost value. Table 1-A gives equipment repair costs for various hours of operation of a particular machine used to make precision tools. The data span a time interval of 6 months. Note that we have indicated the highest and lowest monthly repair costs.

The data are plotted to give a graph of cost versus hours of operation, as illustrated in Figure 1-A. Observe that the data points are not collinear. In other words, they do not lie in the path of a straight line.

The firm's cost accountant is faced with the following problem.

PROBLEM

Determine the fixed monthly repair cost and the variable equipment repair cost per hour of operation.

SOLUTION

Although the data points are not collinear, they seem to have a linear trend. The solution to this problem involves fitting a straight line (in other words, a linear model) to the set of data points, as illustrated in Figure 1-B. In this chapter, we will discuss linear models and how to fit such models to this type of problem.

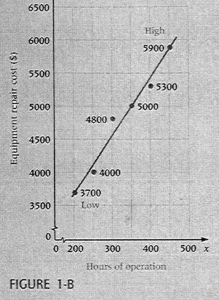

FIGURE 1-B

TABLE 1-A

	Hours of operation	Equipment repair cost ($)	
January	250	4000	
February	300	4800	
March	200	3700	Low
April	400	5300	
May	350	5000	
June	450	5900	High

1-1

• FUNCTIONS

A **function** is a rule that associates a unique **output value** with each element in a set of possible **input values.** Consider, for example, the conversion of temperature from degees Fahrenheit to degrees Celsius. Given a temperature in degrees Fahrenheit (input value), we can find the corresponding value in degrees Celsius (output value) by the following rule:

$$\underbrace{\text{Celsius temperature}}_{\substack{\text{output} \\ \text{value}}} = \frac{5}{9} \underbrace{(\text{Fahrenheit temperature}}_{\substack{\text{input} \\ \text{value}}} - 32)$$

If C is temperature in degrees Celsius and F is temperature in degrees Fahrenheit, then this rule may be expressed by the equation

$$C = \frac{5}{9}(F - 32)$$

To determine the Celsius temperature (output value) associated with 50 degrees Fahrenheit, we substitute $F = 50$ (input value) into the equation and obtain

$$C = \frac{5}{9}(50 - 32)$$

$$= \frac{5}{9}(18)$$

$$= 10 \text{ degrees Celsius}$$

Thus, 10 degrees Celsius is associated with 50 degrees Fahrenheit. Since only one value of C is associated with a value of F, then this equation defines C as a function of F.

Observing the equation

$$C = \frac{5}{9}(F - 32)$$

$$\underset{\substack{\text{output} \\ \text{value}}}{\uparrow} \qquad \underset{\substack{\text{input} \\ \text{value}}}{\uparrow}$$

note that the output value, C, is dependent on the input value, F. Thus, C is called the **dependent variable,** and F is called the **independent variable.** This relationship is usually indicated by saying that C is a *function* of F.

Functional Notation

Often a letter is used to represent a function. Specifically, if the letter f is used to name the function defined by the equation

$$y = 5x^2 + 2x + 7$$

then the dependent variable, y, is represented by the symbol $f(x)$, read "f of x." Thus, the preceding equation is written

$$f(x) = 5x^2 + 2x + 7$$

To find the output value associated with $x = 3$, we replace x with 3 to obtain

$$f(3) = 5(3)^2 + 2(3) + 7$$
$$= 45 + 6 + 7$$
$$= 58$$

Rectangular Coordinate System

It is often useful to graph functions on a plane called the **rectangular coordinate system.** Such a system consists of two perpendicular real number lines in the plane, as shown in Figure 1-1. The horizontal number line is called the **x-axis,** and the vertical number line is called the **y-axis.** The point where the lines intersect is the zero point of both lines and is called the **origin.**

The plane consists of infinitely many **points.** Each point is assigned an **ordered pair** of numbers which locates its position relative to both axes. For example, looking at Figure 1-1, the ordered pair (3, 2) is associated with the point that may be plotted by starting at the origin and moving 3 units to the right horizontally and then 2 units upward vertically. The numbers 3 and 2 of the ordered pair (3, 2) are called the **x-coordinate** and **y-coordinate,** respectively.

Similarly, the ordered pair $(-3, 2)$ in Figure 1-1 is associated with the point that may be plotted by starting at the origin and moving 3 units to the left horizontally and then 2 units upward vertically. The ordered pair $(-3, -2)$ is associated with the point that may be plotted by starting at the origin and moving 3 units to the left horizontally and then 2 units downward and vertically. The ordered pair $(3, -2)$ is associated with the point that may be plotted by starting at the origin and moving 3 units to the right horizontally and then 2 units downward vertically. The ordered pair (0, 0) is associated with the origin.

Further studying Figure 1-1, we note the following:

1. The x- and y-axes partition the plane into four quadrants, as numbered in the figure.
2. For any point in Quadrant I, the x- and y-coordinates are both positive, i.e., $(+, +)$.
3. For any point in Quadrant II, the x-coordinate is negative and the y-coordinate is positive, i.e., $(-, +)$.
4. For any point in Quadrant III, the x- and y-coordinates are both negative, i.e., $(-, -)$.
5. For any point in Quadrant IV, the x-coordinate is positive and the y-coordinate is negative, i.e., $(+, -)$.
6. Points on the axes belong to no quadrant. Points on the x-axis have y-coordinates of 0, and points on the y-axis have x-coordinates of 0.

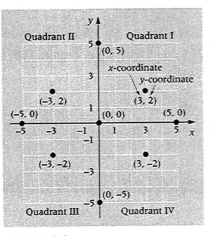

FIGURE 1-1

Functions As Sets of Ordered Pairs

A function can be expressed as a set of ordered pairs (x, y) such that each value of y is the number associated with its corresponding value of x in ac-

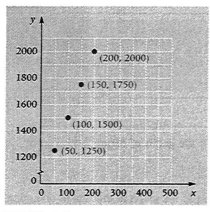
FIGURE 1-2

cordance with the rule defined by the equation. For example, consider the situation of a young entrepreneur manufacturing sneakers. She initially invests $1000 to pay for overhead items such as heat, electricity, etc. Additionally, each pair of sneakers costs $5 to manufacture. Thus, the total cost of producing x pairs of sneakers is given by the equation.

$$y = C(x) = 5x + 1000$$

During the first week of operation, the entrepreneur plans to manufacture either 50, 100, 150, or 200 pairs of sneakers. Table 1-1 shows the output value associated with each input value. The set of input values is called the **domain** of the function, and the set of output values is called the **range** of the function. Observing Table 1-1, note that the domain consists of the set of x-values (in the left column) and that the range consists of the set of y- or $C(x)$-values (in the right column). The function C consists of the set of ordered pairs (x, y) graphed in Figure 1-2.

TABLE 1-1

x	y	$y = C(x) = 5x + 1000$
50	1250	$C(50) = 5(50) + 1000 = 1250$
100	1500	$C(100) = 5(100) + 1000 = 1500$
150	1750	$C(150) = 5(150) + 1000 = 1750$
200	2000	$C(200) = 5(200) + 1000 = 2000$

We are now ready for a more formal definition of a function.

Function

A **function** is a set of ordered pairs (x, y) such that no two ordered pairs have the same first element, x, and different second elements, y. The set of first elements, x, is the **domain** of the function, and the set of second elements, y, is the **range** of the function.

Consider the equation

$$y^2 = x$$

The ordered pairs defined by this equation include $(4, 2)$, $(4, -2)$, $(9, 3)$, and $(9, -3)$. Note that the two numbers $+2$ and -2 are associated with $x = 4$. Since this equation associates more than one y-value for at least one x-value, it is not a function.

To graph the equation $y^2 = x$, we plot the points corresponding to its ordered pairs, some of which are $(4, 2)$, $(4, -2)$, $(9, 3)$, and $(9, -3)$. Figure 1-3 illustrates the graph of this equation. Referring to this illustration, note that since two y-values, $+2$ and -2, are associated with $x = 4$, a vertical line intersects the graph at two points. Generalizing, we have the following **vertical line test** for a function.

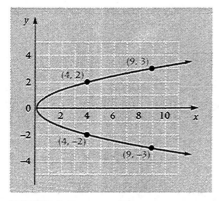
FIGURE 1-3

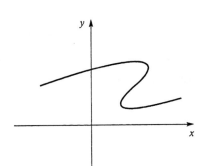

FIGURE 1-4

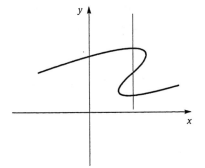

FIGURE 1-5

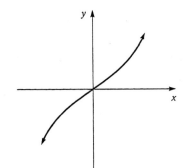

FIGURE 1-6

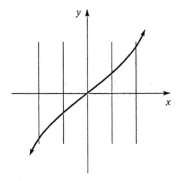

FIGURE 1-7

Vertical Line Test

If a vertical line intersects a graph at more than one point, then that graph does not represent a function.

• EXAMPLE 1-1

Use the vertical line test to determine if the graph of Figure 1-4 represents a function.

Solution

Since a vertical line can be drawn that intersects the graph at more than one point (see Figure 1-5), the graph does not represent a function.

• EXAMPLE 1-2

Use the vertical line test to determine if the graph of Figure 1-6 represents a function.

Solution

Since it is not possible to draw a vertical line that intersects the graph at more than one point (see Figure 1-7), the graph does represent a function.

Often the domain of a function is not specified. If this is the case, it is assumed that the domain is the set of all real numbers for which the function is defined. Consider the function defined by the equation

$$g(x) = \frac{1}{x - 2}$$

Since the domain of g is not specified, it is the set of all real numbers x for which $g(x)$ is defined. Note that $g(x)$ is defined for all real numbers x except $x = 2$, since

$$g(2) = \frac{1}{2 - 2} = \frac{1}{0} \quad \text{which is undefined.}$$

Thus, the domain of g is all real numbers x such that $x \neq 2$.

• EXAMPLE 1-3

Specify the domain of h where

$$h(x) = \frac{1}{(x - 3)(x + 5)}$$

Solution

Since the domain of h is not specified, it is the set of all real numbers x for which $h(x)$ is defined. Note that $h(x)$ is defined for all real numbers x except $x = 3$ and $x = -5$, since

$$h(3) = \frac{1}{(3 - 3)(3 + 5)} = \frac{1}{0} \quad \text{which is undefined,}$$

$$h(-5) = \frac{1}{(-5 - 3)(-5 + 5)} = \frac{1}{0} \quad \text{which is undefined.}$$

Thus, the domain of h is all real numbers x such that $x \neq 3$ and $x \neq -5$.

• EXAMPLE 1-4 _____

If $f(x) = \sqrt{x - 7}$, specify the domain of f.

Solution

Since $\sqrt{x - 7}$ is defined as long as $x - 7 \geq 0$ or, equivalently, $x \geq 7$, then the domain of f is all real numbers x such that $x \geq 7$.

We now give an example showing further calculations with functional notation.

• EXAMPLE 1-5 _____

Given that $f(x) = 3x^2 - 2x + 5$, calculate each of the following:

a) $f(4)$

b) $f(x + h)$

c) $f(x + h) - f(x)$

d) $\dfrac{f(x + h) - f(x)}{h}$

Solutions

a) Since $f(x) = 3x^2 - 2x + 5$, then $f(4)$ is calculated by replacing x with 4. This gives us

$$f(4) = 3(4)^2 - 2(4) + 5$$
$$= 45$$

b) Since $f(x) = 3x^2 - 2x + 5$, then $f(x + h)$ is calculated by replacing x with $x + h$. Therefore, we have

$$f(x + h) = 3(x + h)^2 - 2(x + h) + 5$$
$$= 3(x^2 + 2hx + h^2) - 2x - 2h + 5$$
$$= 3x^2 + 6hx + 3h^2 - 2x - 2h + 5$$

c) Subtracting $f(x) = 3x^2 - 2x + 5$ from the result of part b yields

$$f(x + h) - f(x) = 3x^2 + 6hx + 3h^2 - 2x - 2h + 5 - (3x^2 - 2x + 5)$$
$$= 6hx + 3h^2 - 2h$$

d) Dividing the result of part c by h, we obtain

$$\frac{f(x + h) - f(x)}{h} = \frac{6hx + 3h^2 - 2h}{h}$$
$$= 6x + 3h - 2$$

This result is called a **difference quotient** and will be discussed further in Chapter 9.

We now illustrate more functions and their graphs.

• EXAMPLE 1-6   Parcel Cost. _____

A private parcel service charges the following rates for delivering small packages:

- $1.00 for a package weighing less than 4 ounces   1.00 if weight = 0 or <4
- $1.50 for a package weighing at least 4 ounces but less than 20 ounces
- $2.00 for a package weighing at least 20 ounces but less than 32 ounces

The service does not deliver packages weighing 32 ounces or more. Express delivery cost as a function of weight and graph the function.

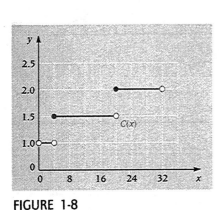

FIGURE 1-8

Solution

If x is the weight of a package, its delivery cost, $C(x)$, is given by

$$C(x) = \begin{cases} 1.00 & \text{if } 0 < x < 4 \\ 1.50 & \text{if } 4 \le x < 20 \\ 2.00 & \text{if } 20 \le x < 32 \end{cases}$$

Note that the domain of $C(x)$ is the interval $0 < x < 32$. The graph of $C(x)$ appears in Figure 1-8.

• EXAMPLE 1-7   Call Options.

A stock investor, believing that the price of a share of stock of Amtech, Inc., will rise to approximately $80 per share during the next 6 months, buys a contract entitling her to buy a specified number of shares of Amtech for $50 per share during the next 6-month time interval. The investor paid $10 per share for this contract. Determine the investor's profit function per share of stock.

Solution

This type of contract, which entitles an investor to buy a specified number of shares of a given stock at a given price (called the **striking price**) during a given time interval, is termed a **call option**. The investor's profit is dependent on the stock's market price per share. Thus, we let $P(x)$ denote the investor's profit per share at the stock's market price of x dollars per share. If the stock's market price per share is less than or equal to the striking price ($50), then the option is worthless to the investor, and, thus, the investor suffers a loss (i.e., a negative profit) of $10 per ʰare, the price paid for the option. This is written as

$$P(x) = -10 \quad \text{if} \quad 0 \le x \le 50$$

If the stock's market price per share exceeds the striking price of $50 during the given 6-month time interval, then the investor could exercise the option and buy the stock for $50 per share and obtain a profit per share of

$$\underset{\text{stock's market price} \quad \underset{\text{striking price}}{\uparrow} \quad \underset{\text{price of the call option}}{\uparrow}}{x - 50 - 10}$$

This assumes that the investor sells the stock for x dollars per share and is written as

$$P(x) = x - 50 - 10 \quad \text{if } x > 50$$

Thus, the profit function is defined as

$$P(x) = \begin{cases} -10 & \text{if } 0 \le x \le 50 \\ x - 60 & \text{if } x > 50 \end{cases}$$

and its graph appears in Figure 1-9.

If a stock's market price rises rapidly during a given time interval, a call option allows an investor to enjoy a substantial percentage gain with a small investment. For example, if Amtech's market price per share were to reach $80 within the given 6-month time interval, the investor would earn a profit of $80 - 50 - 10 = $20 per share on an investment of $10 per share, the price paid for the call option. This constitutes a 200% (i.e., $\frac{20}{10} \times 100$) rate of return during the 6-month time interval. One can understand why investors buy call options.

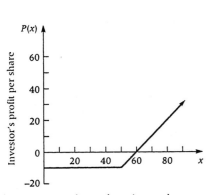

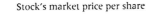

Stock's market price per share

FIGURE 1-9

Note that each function in Examples 1-6 and 1-7 is defined by more than one formula. Functions that are defined by more than one formula are said to be **piecewise defined.** We now discuss another piecewise-defined function.

Absolute Value Function

In Section R-1, we defined the absolute value of a number x. We now define the **absolute value function,** $a(x)$, as

$$a(x) = |x| = \begin{cases} x & \text{if } x \text{ is positive or zero} \\ -x & \text{if } x \text{ is negative} \end{cases}$$

Note that this function associates a non-negative number with itself. Associated with each negative number is its additive inverse. Thus, $(-3, 3)$, $(-1, 1)$, $(-1/2, 1/2)$, $(0, 0)$, $(1, 1)$, $(2, 2)$, and $(5/2, 5/2)$ are some of the ordered pairs belonging to the absolute value function. The graph of $a(x)$ appears in Figure 1-10.

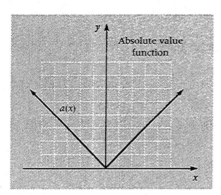

FIGURE 1-10

Exercises 1-1

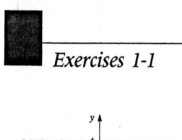

FIGURE 1-11

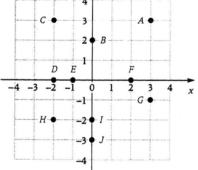

TABLE 1-2

x	$f(x)$
0	
1	
2	
3	

1. A function is defined by the equation

   $$y = 3x - 2$$

   a) Which number does this equation associate with $x = 0$?
   b) Which number does this equation associate with $x = 4$?

2. A function is defined by the equation

   $$y = 3x^2 - 4x + 5$$

   a) Which number does this equation associate with $x = 0$?
   b) Which number does this equation associate with $x = 2$?

3. If $f(x) = -2x + 7$, calculate each of the following:
   a) $f(0)$ b) $f(1)$
   c) $f(5)$ d) $f(-3)$

4. If $w(r) = r^3 - 7r^2 + 8r - 5$, calculate each of the following:
   a) $w(0)$ b) $w(2)$
   c) $w(-2)$ d) $w(4)$

5. If $z(t) = \dfrac{5}{t + 7}$, calculate each of the following:
   a) $z(0)$ b) $z(1)$
   c) $z(-6)$ d) $z(8)$

6. For each of the points A through J of Figure 1-11, find the associated ordered pair.

7. Plot each of the following points on the rectangular coordinate system: $(0, 0)$, $(2, 0)$, $(-5, 0)$, $(0, 2)$, $(0, 5)$, $(3, 1)$, $(5, 2)$, $(-7, 3)$, $(-8, -2)$, $(9, -3)$.

8. Plot the following points on the rectangular coordinate system, and state the quadrant in which each is located: $(4, 2)$, $(5, 8)$, $(-9, 3)$, $(-2, 1)$, $(-3, -5)$, $(-2, -7)$, $(8, -3)$, $(9, 2)$.

9. Graph the function defined by

   $$f(x) = 3x + 2$$

   with domain equal to the set of x-values in Table 1-2.

TABLE 1-3

x	S(x)
1/4	
1/2	
1	
2	

10. Graph the function defined by

$$S(x) = \frac{1}{x}$$

with domain equal to the set of x-values in Table 1-3.

11. If $f(x) = \dfrac{5}{(x - 2)(x + 7)}$, specify the domain of f.

12. If $g(x) = \dfrac{8}{(x - 5)}$, specify the domain of g.

13. If $f(x) = \sqrt{x - 2}$, specify the domain of f.

14. If $g(x) = \sqrt{2x + 5}$, specify the domain of g.

15. If $h(x) = \dfrac{8}{(x - 3)^2}$, specify the domain of h.

16. If $f(x) = \dfrac{6}{x^2 + x}$, specify the domain of f.

17. Which of the graphs in Figure 1-12 are graphs of functions?
18. Which of the graphs in Figure 1-13 are graphs of functions?
19. Does the equation $y^2 = x + 5$ define a function? Why or why not?
20. Does the equation $y^2 = 4x + 1$ define a function? Why or why not?
21. Given that $f(x) = x^2 - 4x + 5$, calculate each of the following:

 a) $f(x + h)$

 b) $f(x + h) - f(x)$

 c) $\dfrac{f(x + h) - f(x)}{h}$

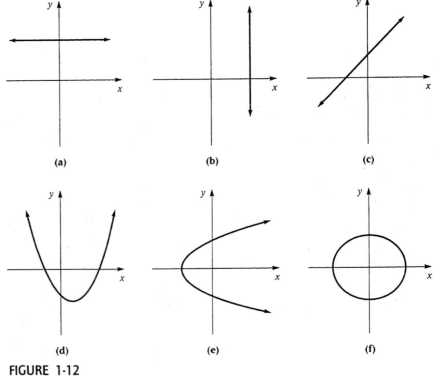

(a)   (b)   (c)

(d)   (e)   (f)

FIGURE 1-12

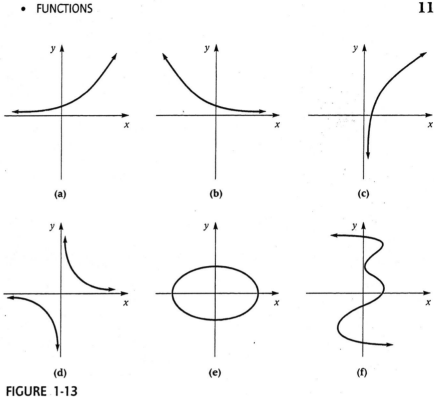

FIGURE 1-13

22. Given that $f(x) = -3x^2 + 5x - 2$, calculate each of the following:
    a) $f(x + h)$
    b) $f(x + h) - f(x)$
    c) $\dfrac{f(x + h) - f(x)}{h}$

23. Given that $f(x) = 5x^2 - 2x + 4$, calculate the difference quotient
$$\frac{f(x + h) - f(x)}{h}$$

24. Given that $f(x) = -2x^2 + 3x - 9$, calculate the difference quotient
$$\frac{f(x + h) - f(x)}{h}$$

25. Given that $g(x) = x^3 - 4x^2 + 5x - 9$, calculate the difference quotient
$$\frac{g(x + h) - g(x)}{h}$$

26. Given that $g(x) = 2x^3 - 3x + 5$, calculate the difference quotient
$$\frac{g(x + h) - g(x)}{h}$$

27. Graph the function defined by
$$h(x) = \begin{cases} 2 & \text{if } x < 1 \\ 4 & \text{if } 1 \le x < 6 \\ x & \text{if } x \ge 6 \end{cases}$$

28. Graph the function defined by

$$k(x) = \begin{cases} 3 & \text{if } x \le 4 \\ x & \text{if } 4 < x \le 9 \\ 9 & \text{if } x > 9 \end{cases}$$

29. A parcel service charges the following rates for delivering small packages:
  - $1.25 for a package weighing less than 8 ounces
  - $2.00 for a package weighing at least 8 ounces and at most 16 ounces
  - $5.00 for a package weighing more than 16 ounces and at most 40 ounces

The service delivers no packages weighing more than 40 ounces.
  a) Express delivery cost as a function of weight.
  b) Graph the function of part a.

30. *Call options*. An investor bought a call option entitling him to buy a specified number of shares of Biotech, Inc., for $30 per share during the next 3-month time interval. The investor paid $5 per share for the call option. Determine the investor's profit function per share of stock. Also, graph the profit function.

31. *Put options*. An investor, believing that the price of a share of stock of Amex, Inc., will drop to approximately $10 per share during the next 6 months, buys a contract entitling him to sell a specified number of shares of Amex for $35 per share during the next 6-month time interval. The investor is actually selling shares of stock that he does not own. However, the investor will replace these sold shares by buying the same number of shares at a lower market price. The investor paid $7 per share for this contract. This type of contract, which entitles an investor to sell a specified number of shares of a given stock at a given price (called the **striking price**) during a given time interval, is called a *put option*. Determine the investor's profit function per share of stock for this put option. Also, graph the profit function. Remember that the investor's profit is dependent on the stock's market price per share.

32. *Wind power*. In designing a windmill, an engineer must use the fact that power y available in wind varies with the cube of wind speed. Thus, if x represents wind speed (in miles per hour), we have

$$y = kx^3$$

where k is a constant real number.
  a) If a 25-mile-an-hour wind produces 5000 watts, find k.
  b) How many watts of power will a 35-mile-per-hour wind produce?

1-2

• SLOPE AND EQUATIONS OF STRAIGHT LINES

Consider the straight line drawn through the two points $(2, 8)$ and $(4, 11)$ in Figure 1-14). Suppose we place the point of a pencil at $(2, 8)$ and move along the line toward $(4, 11)$. As the pencil moves along the line, its x- and y-coordinates change. When the pencil reaches $(4, 11)$, its total vertical change (i.e., change in y) is $11 - 8 = 3$ units, and its total horizontal change (i.e., change in x) is $4 - 2 = 2$ (see Figure 1-15). The ratio 3/2 rep-

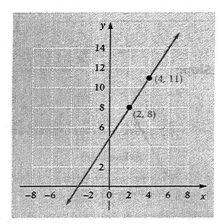

FIGURE 1-14

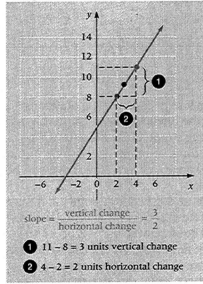

$$\text{slope} = \frac{\text{vertical change}}{\text{horizontal change}} = \frac{3}{2}$$

 $11 - 8 = 3$ units vertical change

 $4 - 2 = 2$ units horizontal change

FIGURE 1-15

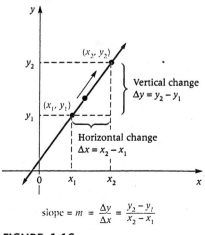

$$\text{slope} = m = \frac{\Delta y}{\Delta x} = \frac{y_2 - y_1}{x_2 - x_1}$$

FIGURE 1-16

resents the rate of change of vertical position (y) with respect to horizontal position (x) and is called the **slope** of the straight line. The slope $3/2$ implies that as the pencil moves along the straight line, for every 2 units of horizontal change to the right the pencil experiences 3 units of vertical change upward.

In general, if (x_1, y_1) and (x_2, y_2) represent two points through which a straight line passes (see Figure 1-16) and we move along the straight line from (x_1, y_1) to (x_2, y_2) then the vertical change is denoted by Δy (read "delta y"), and our horizontal change is denoted by Δx (read "delta x"). Furthermore, $\Delta y = y_2 - y_1$ and $\Delta x = x_2 - x_1$ and the slope m of the straight line is determined by the following formula.

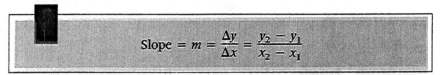

$$\text{Slope} = m = \frac{\Delta y}{\Delta x} = \frac{y_2 - y_1}{x_2 - x_1}$$

A property of a straight line is that its slope is the same no matter where it is measured. In other words, we can find the slope of a line by calculating the ratio $\Delta y/\Delta x$ from any two points on the line.

• **EXAMPLE 1-8** _____

A particle moves along the straight line from $(3, 11)$ to $(5, 7)$.

a) Find its vertical change, Δy.
b) Find its horizontal change, Δx.
c) Find the slope of the straight line.
d) Interpret the result of part c.

Solutions

a) We let $(x_1, y_1) = (3, 11)$, the point at which the particle starts, and $(x_2, y_2) = (5, 7)$. Then the vertical change is $\Delta y = y_2 - y_1 = 7 - 11 = -4$ (see Figure 1-17).

b) The horizontal change is $\Delta x = x_2 - x_1 = 5 - 3 = 2$ (see Figure 1-17).

c) The slope is given by

$$m = \frac{\Delta y}{\Delta x} = \frac{-4}{2} = -2$$

d) Referring to Figure 1-17, as the particle moves along the straight line from $(3, 11)$ to $(5, 7)$, the fact that the slope $\Delta y/\Delta x = -4/2 = -2/1$ means that for each unit of horizontal change to the right, the particle experiences 2 units of vertical change downward. If the particle were moving along the straight line from $(5, 7)$ to $(3, 11)$, as shown in Figure 1-18, then $\Delta y = 11 - 7 = 4$ and $\Delta x = 3 - 5 = -2$ so that $\Delta y/\Delta x = 4/(-2) = 2/(-1)$. Here, as the particle moves from $(5, 7)$ to $(3, 11)$, for each unit of horizontal change to the left, it experiences 2 units of vertical change upward.

Compare the straight line of Figure 1-15 with those of Figures 1-17 and 1-18. Note that a straight line with *positive slope* slants *upward to the right* whereas a straight line with *negative slope* slants *downward to the right*. This is illustrated in the following box.

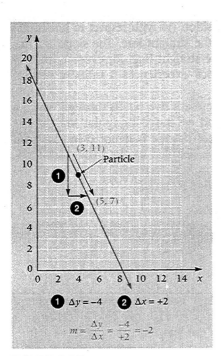

FIGURE 1-17

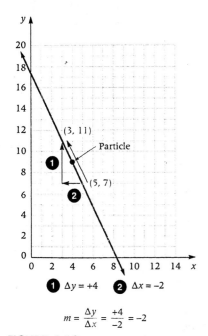

FIGURE 1-18

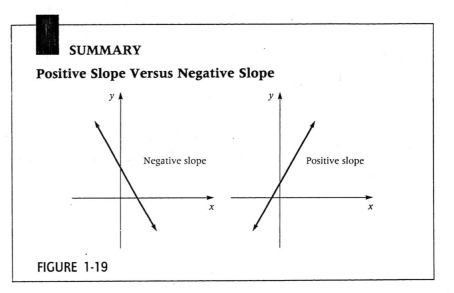

SUMMARY

Positive Slope Versus Negative Slope

FIGURE 1-19

Constant Rate of Change

Figure 1-20 again illustrates the straight line in Figure 1-14. Referring to Figure 1-20, suppose we move up along the line away from (4, 11) so that we experience 2 units of horizontal change to the right. Since the slope of the straight line is 3/2, then for each 2 units of horizontal change to the right, we experience 3 units of vertical change upward. Hence, we will be located at point (4 + 2, 11 + 3) = (6, 14).

Again referring to Figure 1-20, suppose we begin at point (2, 8) and move down along the straight line until we experience 2 units of horizontal change to the left. Since the slope of the straight line is 3/2 or $-3/(-2)$, then for each 2 units of horizontal change to the left, we experience 3 units of vertical change downward. Hence, we will now be located at point (2 − 2, 8 − 3) = (0, 5). Note that movement along this straight line results in the constant rate of change 3/2 of vertical position with respect to horizontal position.

Again refer to Figure 1-20. Note that the straight line crosses the y-axis at (0, 5). This point is called the **y-intercept** of the straight line. The point where the straight line crosses the x-axis is called the **x-intercept** of the straight line. We will learn a more formal method for determining the x- and y-intercepts of a straight line in Section 1-3.

Slope and Equations of Straight Lines

Study the straight line of Figure 1-20. Recall that this straight line was illustrated at the beginning of this section with the two points (2, 8) and (4, 11). After determining the slope to be 3/2, the rate of change concept was used to find other points on the line, specifically (6, 14) and (0, 5). The concept of slope can be used to determine other points on the line.

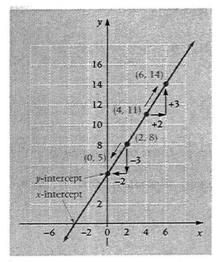

FIGURE 1-20

However, there is a better way. We must realize that the *x*- and *y*-coordinates of any point (*x*, *y*) on a straight line are related by an equation. Such an equation is called an **equation of the straight line.** An equation of a straight line exhibits the relationship between the *x*- and *y*-coordinates of any point (*x*, *y*) on the line.

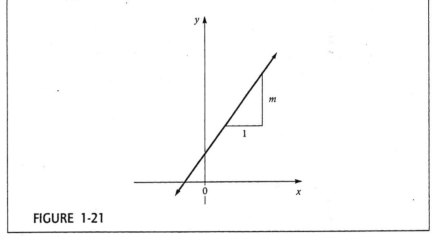

SUMMARY

Slope and Rate of Change

In general, movement along a straight line of slope *m* results in *m* vertical units gained for each horizontal unit gained. Thus, the slope, *m*, is the rate of change of vertical position (*y*) with respect to horizontal position (*x*), as is illustrated below.

FIGURE 1-21

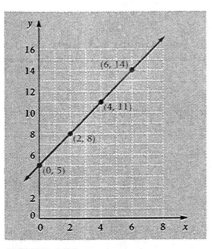

FIGURE 1-22

We will now determine the equation of the straight line of Figure 1-22. Choose one of the known points on the line, say, (2, 8). Let (*x*, y) represent any point on the line. Since the slope of the straight line is 3/2, the slope between (*x*, y) and (2, 8) must equal 3/2. Hence,

$$\frac{y - 8}{x - 2} = \frac{3}{2}$$

Multiplying both sides by *x* − 2, we obtain

$$y - 8 = \frac{3}{2}(x - 2)$$

This equation is called the **point-slope form** of the equation of the straight line. Observe that the coordinates of the point, (2, 8), and the slope, 3/2, appear conspicuously in the equation—hence, the term *point-slope form.*

Solving the point-slope form for y, we obtain

$$y = \frac{3}{2}(x - 2) + 8$$

or

$$y = \frac{3}{2}x + 5$$

This equation is called the **slope-intercept form** of the equation of the straight line. Note that the slope, 3/2, and the y-intercept, 5, appear conspicuously in the equation—hence, the term *slope-interept form*.

Thus, the equation

$$y = \frac{3}{2}x + 5$$

exhibits the relationship between the x and y coordinates of any point (x, y) on the straight line. Observe that the points of the straight line satisfy its equation.

$$(0, 5) \qquad 5 = \frac{3}{2}(0) + 5$$

$$(2, 8) \qquad 8 = \frac{3}{2}(2) + 5$$

$$(4, 11) \qquad 11 = \frac{3}{2}(4) + 5$$

$$(6, 14) \qquad 14 = \frac{3}{2}(6) + 5$$

As previously mentioned, an equation of a straight line may be used to find other points on the line. Specifically, if $x = -4$, then

$$y = \frac{3}{2}(-4) + 5 = -1$$

Thus, $(-4, -1)$ is a point on this straight line. And if $x = 8$, then

$$y = \frac{3}{2}(8) + 5 = 17$$

Therefore, $(8, 17)$ is also a point on the line.

We now state the following generalizations

Equation

An equation of a straight line reveals the relationship between the x- and y-coordinates of any point (x, y) on the line.

Point-Slope Form

Given a point (x_1, y_1) on a straight line of slope m (see Figure 1-23), the **point-slope form** of the equation of that straight line is

$$y - y_1 = m(x - x_1)$$

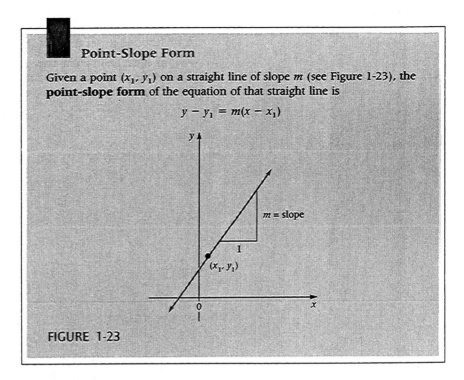

FIGURE 1-23

Slope-Intercept Form

If the point-slope form is solved for y (see Figure 1-24), the resulting equation is the **slope-intercept form**

$$y = mx + b$$

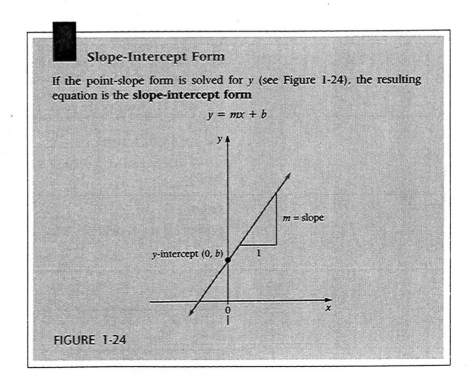

FIGURE 1-24

• EXAMPLE 1-9

A straight line passes through (4, 7) and (9, 17).

a) Find its equation in point-slope form.
b) Convert the point-slope form into the slope-intercept form.
c) Find the point on this straight line corresponding to $x = 5$.
d) Sketch this straight line.

Solutions

a) If $(x_1, y_1) = (4, 7)$ and $(x_2, y_2) = (9, 17)$,* then

$$m = \frac{y_2 - y_1}{x_2 - x_1} = \frac{17 - 7}{9 - 4} = \frac{10}{5} = 2$$

Substituting $(x_1, y_1) = (4, 7)$ and $m = 2$ into the point-slope form

$$y - y_1 = m(x - x_1)$$

we obtain

$$y - 7 = 2(x - 4)$$

b) Solving for y gives us

$$y = 2(x - 4) + 7$$

or

$$y = 2x \underbrace{- 1}$$
$$\uparrow \quad \uparrow$$
$$\text{slope} \quad y\text{-intercept}$$

c) If $x = 5$, then $y = 2(5) - 1 = 9$. Thus, (5, 9) is a point on this line.
d) Observing the slope-intercept form, note that $(0, -1)$ is the y-intercept of this straight line. Using a straightedge, we connect the y-intercept with another point on the straight line, say, (5, 9). The resulting graph is illustrated in Figure 1-25. Note that the points (4, 7) and (9, 17) also appear on the line.

• EXAMPLE 1-10

A straight line has a slope of 6 and a y-intercept of -3. Find the equation of this line.

Solution

Substituting $m = 6$ and $b = -3$ into the slope-intercept form

$$y = mx + b$$

yields

$$y = 6x - 3$$

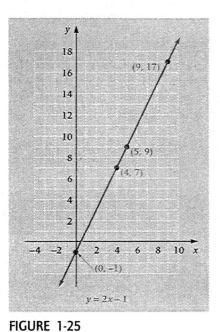

FIGURE 1-25

*Either point may be chosen as (x_1, y_1) or (x_2, y_2).

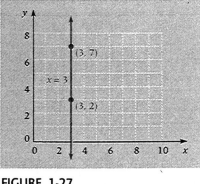

FIGURE 1-26

Horizontal Lines

Consider the straight line passing through the points (2, 5) and (8, 5). Since the y-coordinates are equal, the line passing through these points is horizontal (see Figure 1-26), and its slope is 0, as is determined below.

$$ m = \frac{\Delta y}{\Delta x} = \frac{5 - 5}{8 - 2} = \frac{0}{6} = 0 $$

Observing Figure 1-26, note that the y-intercept is 5. Substituting $m = 0$ and $b = 5$ into the slope-intercept form

$$ y = mx + b $$

we obtain

$$ y = 0x + 5 $$

or

$$ y = 5 $$

The equation $y = 5$ expresses the fact that the y-coordinate of any point on this horizontal straight line is 5.

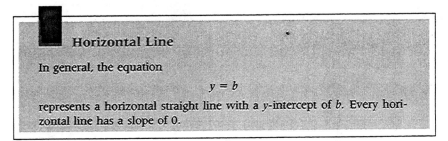

Horizontal Line

In general, the equation

$$ y = b $$

represents a horizontal straight line with a y-intercept of b. Every horizontal line has a slope of 0.

Vertical Lines

Consider the straight line passing through the points (3, 2) and (3, 7). Since the x-coordinates are equal, the straight line is vertical (see Figure 1-27). Its x-intercept is 3. Because any point on this vertical line has an x-coordinate of 3, the equation of the line is appropriately $x = 3$.

The slope of this vertical line is

$$ m = \frac{\Delta y}{\Delta x} = \frac{7 - 2}{3 - 3} = \frac{5}{0} \quad \text{which is undefined.} $$

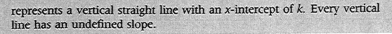

Vertical Line

In general, the equation

$$ x = k $$

represents a vertical straight line with an x-intercept of k. Every vertical line has an undefined slope.

FIGURE 1-27

Linear Equations

Up to this point, we have encountered equations of straight lines in either the *point-slope form*

$$y - y_1 = m(x - x_1)$$

or the *slope-intercept form*

$$y = mx + b$$

These equations, which represent straight lines, are called **linear equations.** Linear equations occur in forms other than the preceding. For example,

$$3x + 5y = 16$$

is a linear equation. This is verified by converting it into slope-intercept form. Solving for y yields

$$5y = -3x + 16$$

$$y = -\frac{3}{5}x + \frac{16}{5}$$

General Form

In general, equations of the form

$$ax + by = c$$

where a, b, and c are constant real numbers, with a and b not both 0, are linear equations. This form is called the **general form** of a linear equation.

• EXAMPLE 1-11

Convert $4x - 7y = 18$ into slope-intercept form.

Solution

Solving for y yields

$$-7y = -4x + 18$$

$$y = \frac{-4}{-7}x + \frac{18}{-7}$$

or

$$y = \underset{\text{slope}}{\frac{4}{7}x} - \underset{y\text{-intercept}}{\frac{18}{7}}$$

Parallel Lines

Slope, the ratio of vertical change to horizontal change resulting from movement along a straight line, is an indication of the steepness of a straight line. Straight lines that are equally steep are said to be parallel, and therefore, have the same slope.

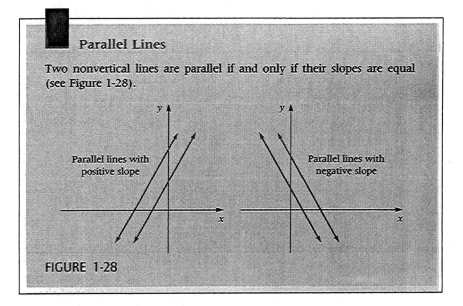

Parallel Lines

Two nonvertical lines are parallel if and only if their slopes are equal (see Figure 1-28).

Parallel lines with positive slope

Parallel lines with negative slope

FIGURE 1-28

• **EXAMPLE 1-12** _____

A straight line is parallel to the line $2x + 3y = 12$ and passes through the point (3, 9).

a) Find its equation   **b)** Graph both lines

Solutions

a) We first find the slope of the line $2x + 3y = 12$ by converting it into slope intercept form $y = mx + b$. Hence,

$$2x + 3y = 12 \quad \text{Given line}$$
$$3y = -2x + 12$$
$$y = -\frac{2}{3}x + 4 \quad \text{Slope-intercept form}$$
$$\underbrace{\qquad}_{\text{slope}}$$

From the slope-intercept form, the slope of the given line is $-2/3$, and, of course, the slope of the parallel line is also $-2/3$. Using the point-slope form, we find the equation of the parallel line.

$$y - y_1 = m(x - x_1) \quad \text{Point-slope form}$$

Letting $(x_1, y_1) = (3, 9)$ and $m = -2/3$ gives

$$y - 9 = -\frac{2}{3}(x - 3)$$
$$y - 9 = -\frac{2}{3}x + 2$$
$$y = -\frac{2}{3}x + 11 \quad \text{Equation of parallel line}$$

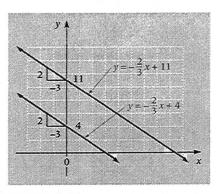

FIGURE 1-29

b) Each line is graphed by placing our straightedge at its y-intercept and setting its pitch so that there are 2 units of vertical change for every -3 units of horizontal change. This is illustrated in Figure 1-29.

Application

Tax Function

The tax rate schedule Table 1-4 gives the amount of 1989 federal income tax due for people filing singly with an income of at most $93,130.

PROBLEM

Write the equations for the amount of federal income tax due at the various income levels, and graph the result.

SOLUTION

Let x denote the amount of taxable income and $T(x)$ the respective federal income tax.

From the *first line* of the schedule, if $0 < x \le 18{,}550$, $T(x) = 0.15x$.

From the *second line* of the schedule, if $18{,}550 < x \le 44{,}900$, $T(x) = 2782.50 + 0.28(x - 18{,}550)$.

From the *third line of the schedule,* if $44{,}900 < x \le 93{,}130$, $T(x) = 10{,}160.50 + 0.33(x - 44{,}900)$.

This is written as

$$T(x) = \begin{cases} 0.15x & \text{if} \quad 0 < x \le 18{,}550 \\ 2782.50 + 0.28(x - 18{,}550) & \text{if } 18{,}550 < x \le 44{,}900 \\ 10{,}160.50 + 0.33(x - 44{,}900) & \text{if } 44{,}900 < x \le 93{,}130 \end{cases}$$

The graph of $T(x)$ is given in Figure 1-30. Notice that the different slopes indicate the tax rates.

Specifically, for a person filing singly with taxable income of $60,000, the first $18,550 of taxable income is taxed at a rate of 15%; taxable income over $18,550, but not over $44,900, is taxed at a rate of 28%; taxable income over $44,900, but not over $93,130, is taxed at a rate of 33%. Thus, the federal income tax due on taxable income of $60,000 is given by

$$T(60{,}000) = 10{,}160.50 + 0.33(60{,}000 - 44{,}900)$$

$$= \$15{,}143.50 \qquad \text{Federal income tax due on taxable income of \$60,000}$$

TABLE 1-4 Tax rate schedule

Taxable income		Federal income tax	
over	but not over		of the amount over
$ 0	$18,550	15%	$ 0
$18,550	44,900	$2782.50 + 28%	18,550
$44,900	93,130	$10,160.50 + 33%	44,900

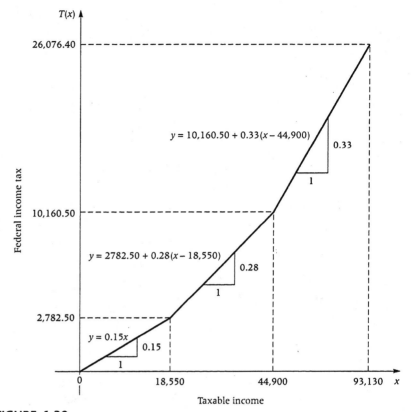

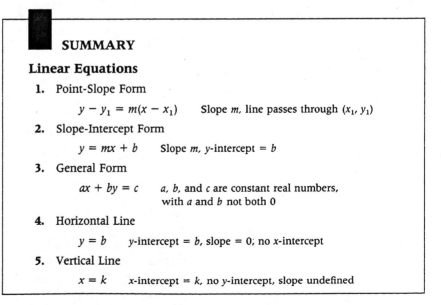

FIGURE 1-30

We close this section by providing a summary of the most common forms of linear equations.

SUMMARY

Linear Equations

1. Point-Slope Form

    $y - y_1 = m(x - x_1)$ Slope m, line passes through (x_1, y_1)

2. Slope-Intercept Form

    $y = mx + b$ Slope m, y-intercept $= b$

3. General Form

    $ax + by = c$ a, b, and c are constant real numbers, with a and b not both 0

4. Horizontal Line

    $y = b$ y-intercept $= b$, slope $= 0$; no x-intercept

5. Vertical Line

    $x = k$ x-intercept $= k$, no y-intercept, slope undefined

Note that a linear equation does not contain a variable with a nonzero exponent other than 1.

Exercises 1-2

1. A particle traveled along the straight line from (2, 5) to (6, 8).
   a) Find Δy, the change in y. b) Find Δx, the change in x.
   c) Find the slope. d) Interpret the slope.

2. A particle traveled along the straight line from (4, 12) to (7, 16).
   a) Find Δy, the change in y. b) Find Δx, the change in x.
   c) Find the slope. d) Interpret the slope.

Find the slope of the straight line passing through each of the following pairs of points.

3. (4, 5), (7, 16)   4. (1, 4), (6, 13)
5. (−1, 3), (7, 5)   6. (0, 6), (9, 4)
7. (−4, 3), (−5, −7)   8. (5, 9), (8, 7)
9. (−8, −2), (−3, −9)   10. (2, 11), (5, −3)

11. Graphically interpret each of the slopes found in Exercises 3, 8, and 10.

For each of the following, graph the straight line, given slope m through the indicated point:

12. $m = 1/3$, (0, 0)   13. $m = -1/3$, (0, 0)
14. $m = 5$, (1, 8)   15. $m = -2$, (2, 1)
16. $m = 6/5$, (0, 1)   17. $m = -3/4$, (4, −5)
18. $m = 6/5$, (10, 13)   19. $m = -5/3$, (0, 2)

Find the slope of the straight line passing through each of the following pairs of points, and graph the line.

20. (4, 6), (−7, 6)   21. (−9, −3), (−8, −3)
22. (8, 1), (11, 1)   23. (4, −2), (−6, −2)
24. (5, 3), (5, −1)   25. (6, 4), (6, −4)
26. (−2, 16), (−2, 4)   27. (4, −6), (4, 9)

For each of the following, find the equation, in point-slope form, of the straight line passing through the given pair of points. Then convert the equation into slope-intercept form, and sketch the straight line.

28. (1, 4), (3, 8)   29. (4, −1), (9, −8)
30. (5, −10), (7, −14)   31. (3, 2), (7, 10)
32. (−2, −3), (−5, 9)   33. (5, 5), (7, 7)
34. (4, 12), (6, 18)   35. (5, −3), (4, 2)

For each of the following, find the equation, in point-slope form, of the straight line passing through the given point and having slope m. Then convert the equation into slope-intercept form, and sketch the straight line.

36. (4, 3), $m = 2$ 37. (5, −1), $m = -3$
38. (0, −2), $m = -4$ 39. (−4, −9), $m = 6$
40. (−7, 2), $m = -1/2$ 41. (0, 6), $m = 5$
42. (3, 1), $m = -1/4$ 43. (−4, 7), $m = 1$

For each of the following linear equations, determine which of the given points lie on its corresponding straight line:

44. $3x - 5y = 30$; (0, −6), (5, 2), (10, 0), (15, 3)
45. $2x + 7y = 21$; (7, 1), (3, 0), (4, −3), (14, −1)
46. $8x + 6y = 0$; (0, 0), (1, 5), (−2, 8/3), (7, 13/7)
47. $y = 6x + 3$; (0, 6), (1, 9), (−1/2, 0), (−1, −3)

48. $f(x) = 2x + 4$; $(0, 4)$, $(1, 5)$, $(-1, 2)$, $(-2, 0)$
49. $g(x) = -3x$; $(0, 0)$, $(1, -3)$, $(2, -6)$, $(5, 14)$

For each of the following, find the equation of the straight line passing through the given pair of points. Also, sketch the straight line.

50. $(4, 2)$, $(4, 7)$ **51.** $(-3, 1)$, $(-3, 9)$
52. $(5, -9)$, $(8, -9)$ **53.** $(4, 1)$, $(6, 1)$

For each of the following, find the equation of the straight line passing through the given point and having slope m. Also, sketch the straight line.

54. $(4, 3)$, $m = 0$ **55.** $(-8, 1)$, $m = 0$
56. $(9, -1)$, m is undefined   **57.** $(7, 2)$, m is undefined

58. Find the equation of the straight line passing through $(9, -5)$ and parallel to $6x + 2y = 18$. Sketch both lines.

59. Straight lines intersecting each other at right angles (90°) are said to be perpendicular Figure 1-31 illustrates two perpendicular straight lines. Slopes of perpendicular straight lines are negative reciprocals of each other. In other words, if a straight line has slope m, then a straight line perpendicular to it has slope $-1/m$. This relationship between slopes of perpendicular lines does not hold for vertical or horizontal lines

Find the equation of the straight line passing through $(5, 6)$ and perpendicular to $y = 3x - 2$. Sketch both lines.

60. Find the equation of the straight line passing through $(8, -2)$ and perpendicular to $4x - 3y = 24$. Sketch both lines.

Which of the following pairs of straight lines are parallel?

61. $y = 6x - 14$, $y = 6x + 13$ **62.** $3x - 2y = 15$, $6x - 4y = 60$
63. $y = -4x + 8$, $y = 4x + 16$ **64.** $5x - 8y = 11$, $6x + y = 13$

Which of the following pairs of straight lines are perpendicular?

65. $y = 3x + 5$, $y = -(1/3)x + 16$ **66.** $y = 6x + 5$, $y = -6x + 5$
67. $y = 2x - 3$, $2y + x = 10$ **68.** $3x + 6y = 11$, $5x + 2y = 13$

Convert each of the following linear equations into slope-intercept form.

69. $3x - 5y = 11$ **70.** $x = -2y + 15$
71. $3x - 2y = 0$ **72.** $2x + 5y + 16 = 0$

Which of the following equations are linear?

73. $y = 6x - 54$ **74.** $y = x^2 - 4x$
75. $y = 3x^2 - 4$ **76.** $y^2 = 5x + 7$
77. $3x - 4y = 5$ **78.** $y = xy + 7$
79. $y = x^3 - 5$ **80.** $y^3 = x + 4$

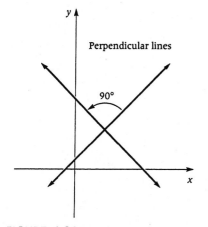

FIGURE 1-31

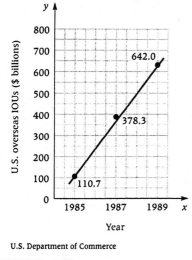

U.S. Department of Commerce

FIGURE 1-32

Applications

81. *U.S. overseas IOUs.* U.S. net foreign debt (overseas IOUs) for each of the three years is given in Figure 1-32.
   a) Find the slope of the straight line of the figure.
   b) Interpret the slope.
   c) Find the equation of the straight line. Express the final result in slope-intercept form.
   d) If U.S. net foreign debt follows the trend of this straight line, predict U.S. net foreign debt for the year 1992.

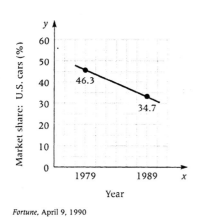

Fortune, April 9, 1990

FIGURE 1-33

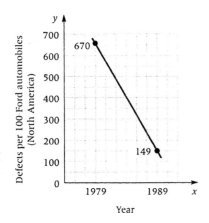

Fortune, April 9, 1990

FIGURE 1-34

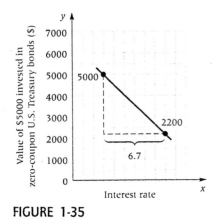

FIGURE 1-35

82. *Market share: U.S. automobiles.* General Motors' share of the U.S. automobile market slipped from 46.3% to 34.7% during the years from 1979 to 1989 as indicated in Figure 1-33.
a) Find the slope of the straight line of the figure.
b) Interpret the slope.
c) Find the equation of the straight line. Express the final result in slope-intercept form.
d) If General Motors' market share continues to decline at the same rate, predict its market share for the year 1993.

83. *Defects: U.S. automobiles.* The number of defects per 100 vehicles for Ford's North American operations declined from 670 to 149 during the years from 1979 to 1989, as indicated in Figure 1-34
a) Find the slope of the straight line of the figure.
b) Interpret the slope.
c) Find the equation of the straight line. Express the final answer in slope-intercept form.
d) If Ford's defects continue to decline at the same rate, predict its defects per 100 vehicles (North America) for the year 1991.

84. *Investment.* A money manager noted that $5000 invested in zero-coupon U.S. Treasury bonds would have declined in value to $2200 over a 4-year time interval beginning January 1, 1977, during which time interest rates rose 6.7 percentage points. This is illustrated in Figure 1-35.
a) Find the slope of the straight line of the figure.
b) Interpret the slope.

85. *Investment.* A $5000 investment in gold would have increased in value to $22,000 over a 4-year time interval beginning January 1, 1977, during which time inflation rose from 6.5% to 13.3%. This is illustrated in Figure 1-36.
a) Find the slope of the straight line of the figure.
b) Interpret the slope.

86. *Tax function.* The tax rate schedule in Table 1-5 gives the amount of 1989 federal income tax due for married people filing jointly with an income of at most $155,320.
a) Write the equations for the amount of federal income tax due at the various income levels.
b) Graph the result of part a.

87. *Tax function.* The tax rate schedule in Table 1-6 gives the amount of 1989 federal income tax due for married people filing separately with an income of at most $117,895.
a) Write the equations for the amount of federal income tax due at the various income levels.
b) Graph the result of part a.

TABLE 1-5 Tax rate schedule

Taxable income		Federal income tax	
over	but not over		of the amount over
$ 0	$ 30,950	15%	$ 0
30,950	74,850	$4642.50 + 28%	30,950
74,850	155,320	$16,934.50 + 33%	74,850

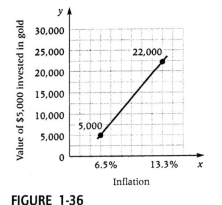

FIGURE 1-36

TABLE 1-6   **Tax rate schedule**

Taxable income		Federal income tax	
over	but not over		of the amount over
$ 0	$ 15,475	15%	$ 0
15,475	37,425	$2321.25 + 28%	15,475
37,425	117,895	$8467.25 + 33%	37,425

1-3 • GRAPHING LINEAR EQUATIONS

Since all straight lines, except vertical straight lines, are graphs of functions, their equations define **linear functions.** In this section, we will discuss the graphing of linear functions given their equations. In Section 1-2, we graphed a linear function by determining two points on the straight line and connecting them with a straightedge. In this section, instead of determining any two points on the straight line, we will determine the x-intercept and the y-intercept. Recall from Section 1-2 that the y-intercept is the point at which the straight line crosses the y-axis. Thus, the x-intercept is the point at which the straight line crosses the x-axis.

We now graph the linear function defined by

$$2x - 3y = 12$$

by finding its x-intercept and y-intercept.

x-Intercept

As previously mentioned, the x-intercept of a straight line is the point where the straight line crosses the x-axis. Thus, the x-intercept is located on the x-axis, and, therefore, its y-coordinate is 0. Since the x-intercept is also located on the straight line, its coordinates must satisfy the equation of the straight line. Thus, to determine the x-intercept of a straight line, we set $y = 0$ in its equation and solve for x. Using the straight line

$$2x - 3y = 12$$

as an example, we set $y = 0$ and solve for x to determine its x-intercept. Hence,

$$2x - 3(0) = 12$$
$$2x = 12$$
$$x = 6$$

The x-intercept (6, 0) is illustrated in Figure 1-37.

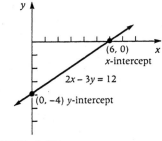

FIGURE 1-37

y-Intercept

As mentioned earlier, the *y*-intercept of a straight line is the point where the straight line crosses the *y*-axis. Thus, the *y*-intercept is located on the *y*-axis, and, therefore, its *x*-coordinate is 0. Since the *y*-intercept is also located on the straight line, its coordinates must satisfy the equation of the straight line. Thus, to determine the *y*-intercept of a straight line, we set $x = 0$ in its equation and solve for *y*. Hence, for the straight line

$$2x - 3y = 12$$

we obtain

$$2(0) - 3y = 12$$
$$-3y = 12$$
$$y = -4$$

The *y*-intercept $(0, -4)$ is illustrated in Figure 1-37.

The straight line defined by $2x - 3y = 12$ is graphed in Figure 1-37.

• **EXAMPLE 1-13** _____

Graph $-7x + 2y = 28$.

Solution

First, we find the *x*-intercept. We set $y = 0$ and solve for *x*. Hence,

$$-7x + 2(0) = 28$$
$$-7x = 28$$
$$x = -4$$

Thus, the *x*-intercept is $(-4, 0)$. Next, we determine the *y*-intercept. We set $x = 0$ and solve for *y*. Hence,

$$-7(0) + 2y = 28$$
$$2y = 28$$
$$y = 14$$

Therefore, the *y*-intercept is $(0, 14)$. The straight line is graphed in Figure 1-38.

• **EXAMPLE 1-14** _____

Sketch the graph of $y = f(x) = -3x - 2$.

Solution

First, find the *x*-intercept. Set $y = 0$ and solve for *x*. Therefore,

$$0 = -3x - 2$$
$$3x = -2$$
$$x = -\frac{2}{3}$$

Thus, the *x*-intercept is $(-2/3, 0)$. Then find the *y*-intercept. Since the equation $y = -3x - 2$ is in the slope-intercept form, by inspection we determine the *y*-intercept to be $(0, -2)$. The straight line is graphed in Figure 1-39.

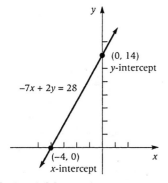

FIGURE 1-38

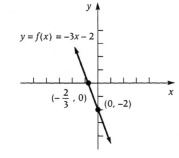

FIGURE 1-39

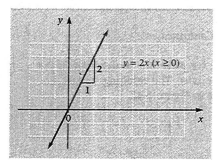

FIGURE 1-40

• EXAMPLE 1-15 _____

Graph $y = 2x$, $x \geq 0$.

Solution

The equation $y = 2x$ is in the slope-intercept form $y = mx + b$, with $m = 2$ and $b = 0$. Thus, the y-intercept is the origin, $(0, 0)$. Since the origin is also the x-intercept, we do not have two distinct intercepts to connect with a straightedge. However, if we place our straightedge at the origin and set it so that the slope is 2, we have the straight line of Figure 1-40. The restriction $x \geq 0$ implies that we are to consider only that portion of the line above the interval $x \geq 0$. Accordingly, we have sketched this portion of the line in color.

Before proceeding to the next example, we should study the graphing summary following Example 1-16.

• EXAMPLE 1-16 _____

Graph $2x + 5y = 0$.

Solution

Setting $x = 0$ to find the y-intercept yields $y = 0$, and setting $y = 0$ to find the x-intercept yields $x = 0$. Thus, both intercepts are at the origin, $(0, 0)$. This is so because the equation $2x + 5y = 0$, when solved for y, becomes $y = (-2/5)x$. Since $y = (-2/5)x$ is of the form $y = mx$, with $m \neq 0$, then, as is discussed in the graphing summary following this example, its graph goes through the origin and has a negative slope. The graph appears in Figure 1-41.

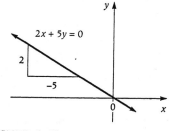

FIGURE 1-41

To Graph a Linear Equation

To graph a linear equation of the form $ax + by = c$,

1. Find the y-intercept. Set $x = 0$ and solve for y. Mark the y-intercept on the y-axis.
2. Find the x-intercept. Set $y = 0$ and solve for x. Mark the x-intercept on the x-axis.
3. Connect the intercepts with a straightedge.

To graph a linear equation in slope-intercept form, $y = mx + b$,

1. Find the y-intercept. The y-intercept is given by b. Mark the y-intercept on the y-axis.
2. Find the x-intercept. Set $y = 0$ and solve for x. Mark the x-intercept on the x-axis.
3. Connect the intercepts with a straightedge.

To graph a linear equation of the form $y = mx$, with $m \neq 0$, note the following:

1. Such an equation is in slope-intercept form, with $b = 0$. Thus, its y-intercept is the origin, $(0, 0)$.
2. Since the origin is also the x-intercept of the straight line, we do not have two distinct intercepts to connect with a straightedge.

continues

To Graph a Linear Equation—*Continued*

3. To graph such a linear equation, we place our straightedge at the origin and set it so that the slope is *m*. The resulting straight line will resemble one of those shown in Figure 1-42.

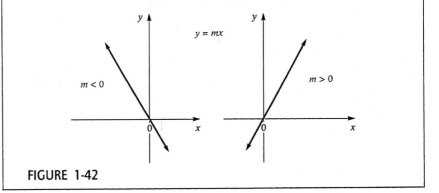

FIGURE 1-42

Exercises 1-3

Graph each of the following linear equations by finding the *x* and *y* intercepts:

1. $4x - 6y = 24$
2. $5x + 3y = 45$
3. $-3x + 2y = 8$
4. $5x - 6y = 10$
5. $2x + 7y = 11$
6. $-3x - 5y = 9$
7. $y = -4x + 13$
8. $f(x) = -2x + 15$
9. $f(x) = 6x + 4$
10. $g(x) = (5/2)x + 13$

Graph each of the following linear equations:

11. $y = 2x$
12. $f(x) = -3x$
13. $3x + 2y = 0$
14. $2x - 5y = 0$
15. $g(x) = 7x$
16. $f(x) = (-1/2)x$
17. $f(x) = x$
18. $y = -x$

Graph each of the following:

19. $f(x) = 3x + 5, x \geq 0$
20. $g(x) = 4x, x \geq 0$
21. $f(x) = 2x + 3, x \geq 1$
22. $h(x) = 3x - 15, x \geq 5$

1-4 • LINEAR MODELS

In this section, we present some applications of linear functions. The functions presented will serve as models for later applications in this text.

Cost Function

A manufacturer of chairs can produce 10 chairs at a total cost of $1100, while 50 such chairs cost $3500. The **total cost** in each case consists of two components:

1. **Fixed costs,** which include costs that must be paid no matter how few or how many units of product are produced (fixed costs usually include rent, insurance, taxes, etc.).
2. **Variable costs,** which include costs that vary in direct proportion to the number of units of product produced (variable costs usually include material costs, labor costs, and other costs directly attributed to the cost of the product).

Thus,

$$\text{total cost} = \text{variable cost} + \text{fixed cost}$$

If x = number of chairs produced and y = total cost, then we will determine

a) The variable cost per chair.
b) The equation relating x and y.

a) Since 10 chairs cost $1100 and 50 chairs cost $3500, we let (x_1, y_1) = (10, 1100) and (x_2, y_2) = (50, 3500). The variable cost per chair is given by the slope of the straight line passing through the two points. Hence,

$$m = \frac{\Delta y}{\Delta x} = \frac{y_2 - y_1}{x_2 - x_1} = \frac{3500 - 1100}{50 - 10} = \frac{2400}{40} = 60$$

Note that the production of 40 additional chairs costs an additional $2400. Thus, the variable cost per chair is the slope, i.e., $60 (see Figure 1-43.)

b) We assume that x and y are linearly related and, therefore, use the point-slope form to find the equation of the straight line passing through the two points, (10, 1100) and (50, 3500). Substituting (x_1, y_1) = (10, 1100) and m = 60 into the point-slope form

$$y - y_1 = m(x - x_1)$$

we obtain

$$y - 1100 = 60(x - 10)$$

Solving for y, we have

$$y = 60(x - 10) + 1100$$

or

$$y = \underbrace{60x}_{\text{variable cost}} + \overset{\text{fixed cost}}{500}$$

Since the equation $y = 60x + 500$ relates total cost to number of units produced, it is called a **cost equation.** The function that it defines is called a

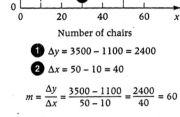

① $\Delta y = 3500 - 1100 = 2400$

② $\Delta x = 50 - 10 = 40$

$$m = \frac{\Delta y}{\Delta x} = \frac{3500 - 1100}{50 - 10} = \frac{2400}{40} = 60$$

variable cost per chair = $60

FIGURE 1-43

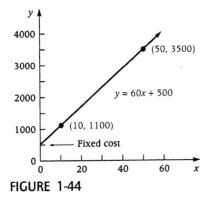

FIGURE 1-44

cost function (see Figure 1-44). Note that only the first quadrant portion of the graph of the cost function is shown since the function has meaning only for non-negative values of *x*.

Since fixed cost is not directly attributed to the cost of the product, it can be defined as the cost of producing 0 units. It is determined by substituting $x = 0$ into the cost equation and solving for *y* to obtain $y = 60(0) + 500 = 500$. Note that the fixed cost equals the *y*-intercept (see Figure 1-44).

The variable cost is the product of the variable cost per unit (i.e., the slope, $m = 60$) and the number of units produced (*x*).

SUMMARY

Linear Cost Function

In general, if total cost (*C*) and number of units produced (*x*) are linearly related, then the cost function is defined by

$$C(x) = vx + F \qquad (x \geq 0)$$

where $C(x)$ = cost of producing *x* units, v = variable cost per unit, and F = fixed cost. The graph of such a cost function appears in Figure 1-45.

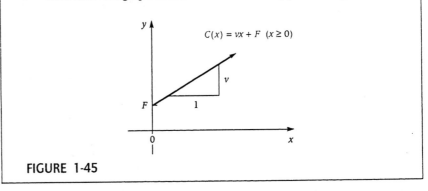

FIGURE 1-45

Revenue Function

Suppose the chair manufacturer of the above illustrative example sells the chairs that he produces for $110. If $R(x)$ = total sales revenue gained from selling *x* chairs, then

$$\text{sales revenue} = (\text{unit selling price})(\text{number of units sold})$$

or

$$R(x) = 110x$$

The function, *R*, which relates total sales revenue to number of units sold, is called a **sales revenue function.** Its graph appears in Figure 1-46. Note

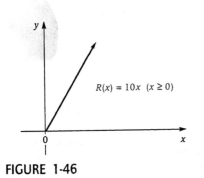

FIGURE 1-46

that only the first quadrant portion of the graph of the revenue function is shown since the function has meaning only for non-negative values of *x*.

■ SUMMARY

Sales Revenue Function

In general, if total sales revenue (*R*) and number of units sold (*x*) are linearly related, then the sales revenue function is given by

$$R(x) = sx \qquad (x \geq 0)$$

where $R(x)$ = total sales revenue gained from selling *x* units and *s* = unit selling price. Its graph is given in Figure 1-47.

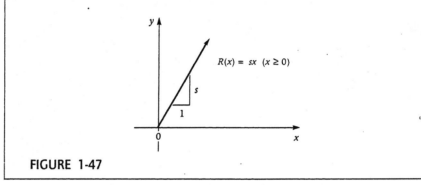

FIGURE 1-47

Profit Function

Suppose the chair manufacturer of the above illustrative examples wishes to determine the equation that relates total profit (*P*) to number of units sold (*x*). The function that defines this relationship is called a **profit function** and is found by the formula

$$\text{profit} = \text{revenue} - \text{cost}$$

Thus, if $P(x)$ = profit gained from selling *x* chairs, then

$$P(x) = R(x) - C(x)$$

Since, as determined in the previous illustrative examples, $R(x) = 110x$ and $C(x) = 60x + 500$, then substituting these results into the above equation gives

$$
\begin{aligned}
P(x) &= 110x - (60x + 500) \\
&= 110x - 60x - 500 \\
&= 50x - 500
\end{aligned}
$$

This result is graphed in Figure 1-48. Note that only the first and fourth quadrant portion of the graph of the profit function is shown since the function has meaning only for non-negative values of *x*.

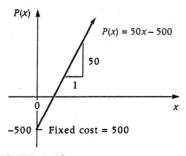

FIGURE 1-48

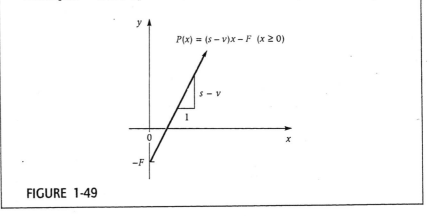

SUMMARY

Profit Function

In general, given a linear cost function $C(x) = vx + F$ and a sales revenue function $R(x) = sx$ where $x =$ number of units produced and sold, $v =$ variable cost per unit, $F =$ fixed cost, and $s =$ unit selling price, the profit function is determined as follows:

$$P(x) = R(x) - C(x)$$
$$= sx - (vx + F)$$
$$P(x) = (s - v)x - F \qquad (x \geq 0)$$

The slope, $s - v$, of the profit function is called the *unit contribution margin*.

FIGURE 1-49

Demand Function

Demand (q) for a product is sometimes linearly related to the product's unit price (p). The equation describing such a relationship between demand and unit price is called a **demand equation,** and its associated function is called a **demand function.**

Consider a case where 20 units of some commodity are demanded by the marketplace when the unit price of that commodity is $45, whereas 40 units are demanded at a unit price of $30. We must determine the linear equation relating demand (q) to unit price (p).

Typically, demand (q) is a function of unit price (p), or, in other words, $q = f(p)$. However, since most economists graph the relationship between demand (q) and unit price (p) by writing (p) on the vertical axis and (q) on the horizontal axis, we will also follow this convention. Thus, we summarize the information of the previous paragraph in Table 1-7 by listing first q and then p.

To determine the linear equation relating q and p, we first find the slope

$$m = \frac{\Delta p}{\Delta q} = \frac{30 - 45}{40 - 20} = \frac{-15}{20} = -\frac{3}{4}$$

Rewriting the point-slope form

$$y - y_1 = m(x - x_1)$$

TABLE 1-7

q	p	Ordered pairs (q, p)
20	$45	(20, 45)
40	$30	(40, 30)

with p replacing y and q replacing x, we have

$$p - p_1 = m(q - q_1)$$

Arbitrarily selecting $(q_1, p_1) = (40, 30)$, we substitute this result into the above equation along with $m = -3/4$ to obtain

$$p - 30 = -\frac{3}{4}(q - 40)$$

Solving for p, we first multiply $q - 40$ by $-3/4$ (using the distributive law) to obtain

$$p - 30 = -\frac{3}{4}q - \left(-\frac{3}{4}\right)(40)$$

$$= -\frac{3}{4}q + 30$$

and then we add 30 to both sides to obtain the demand equation

$$p = -\frac{3}{4}q + 60$$

which is graphed in Figure 1-50. Observing the graph of the demand function in Figure 1-50, note that its slope is negative. This is typically the case for demand functions since an increase in unit price usually results in a decrease in demand. Note that only the first quadrant portion of the graph of the demand function is shown since the function has meaning only for non-negative values of q and p.

We also note that a demand equation can be written in the form $q = f(p)$. Specifically, if we were to solve the above demand equation for q, we would obtain

$$q = -\frac{4}{3}p + 80$$

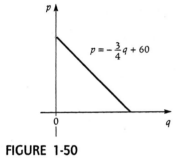

$p = -\frac{3}{4}q + 60$

FIGURE 1-50

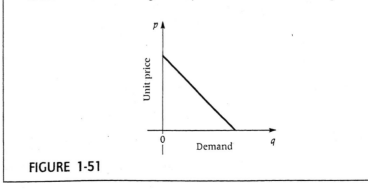

SUMMARY

Linear Demand Functions

A demand function expresses a relationship between demand (q) for some product and the product's unit price (p). The graph of a linear demand function has a *negative slope* and resembles that of Figure 1-51.

FIGURE 1-51

Supply Function

If a given commodity is selling at a unit price of $18, suppliers are willing to produce 30 units of this commodity. However, if the commodity is selling at a unit price of $28, then suppliers are willing to produce 60 units of this commodity. Note that suppliers are willing to produce more of this commodity if it is selling at a higher price than if it is selling at a lower price. This is typical of what usually occurs in the marketplace for most commodities.

An equation that expresses the relationship between the supply for some product and the product's unit price is called a **supply equation,** and its associated function is called a **supply function.** Assuming that supply and demand are linearly related, we now determine the supply equation for the above commodity.

We let p denote unit price and q denote the number of units supplied. As with demand functions, we will consider p the dependent variable and q the independent variable. Thus, we summarize the information of the first paragraph in Table 1-8.

Finding the slope, we obtain

$$m = \frac{\Delta p}{\Delta q} = \frac{28 - 18}{60 - 30} = \frac{10}{30} = \frac{1}{3}$$

As with our previous demand problem, we rewrite the point-slope form

$$y - y_1 = m(x - x_1)$$

by replacing y with p and x with q to obtain

$$p - p_1 = m(q - q_1)$$

Arbitrarily selecting $(q_1, p_1) = (30, 18)$, we substitute this result into the above equation along with $m = 1/3$ to obtain

$$p - 18 = \frac{1}{3}(q - 30)$$

Solving for p, we first multiply $q - 30$ by $1/3$ to obtain

$$p - 18 = \frac{1}{3}q - 10$$

and then we add 18 to both sides to obtain the supply equation

$$p = \frac{1}{3}q + 8$$

which is graphed in Figure 1-52. Observing the graph of the supply function in Figure 1-52, note that its slope is positive. This is typically the case for supply functions since an increase in unit price usually results is an increase in supply. Note that only the first quadrant portion of the graph of the supply function is shown since the function has meaning only for non-negative values of q and p.

TABLE 1-8

q	p	Ordered pairs (q, p)
30	$18	(30, 18)
60	$28	(60, 28)

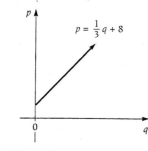

FIGURE 1-52

We also note that a supply equation can be written in the form $q = f(p)$. Specifically, if we were to solve the above supply equation for q, we would obtain

$$q = 3p - 24$$

SUMMARY

Linear Supply Functions

A supply function expresses a relationship between supply (q) for some product and the product's unit price (p). The graph of a linear supply function has a *positive slope* and resembles that of Figure 1-53.

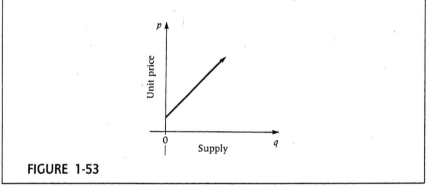

FIGURE 1-53

Consumption Function

TABLE 1-9

x	y
56	50
76	67.2

Table 1-9 exhibits a relationship between a nation's disposable income, x (in billions of dollars), and personal consumption expenditures, y (in billions of dollars). The equation that expresses the relationship between these two quantities defines a **consumption function.** If x and y are linearly related, the slope between the two points in Table 1-9 is

$$m = \frac{\Delta y}{\Delta x} = \frac{y_2 - y_1}{x_2 - x_1} = \frac{67.2 - 50}{76 - 56} = \frac{17.2}{20} = 0.86$$

Economists call this result the **marginal propensity to consume,** abbreviated **MPC.** Since MPC = 0.86, then for each dollar increase in disposable income, consumption increases by $0.86. In other words, 86% of each additional dollar earned is spent, and 14% is saved.

The linear equation relating x and y is determined below. We arbitrarily choose $(x_1, y_1) = (56, 50)$ and substitute this result along with $m = 0.86$ into the point-slope form

$$y - y_1 = m(x - x_1)$$

to obtain

$$y - 50 = 0.86(x - 56)$$

Solving for y, we obtain

$$y = 0.86x + 1.84$$

SUMMARY

Linear Consumption Function

A consumption function expresses a relationship between consumption (y) and income (x). For a linear consumption function, the *slope* is called the *marginal propensity to consume*, abbreviated MPC. The MPC indicates the portion spent of an additional dollar earned. The graph of a typical linear consumption function is given in Figure 1-54.

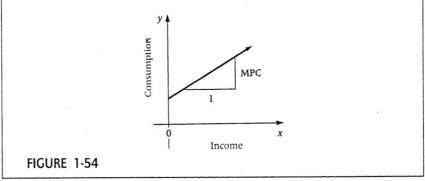

FIGURE 1-54

Linear Depreciation

Most assets decrease in value over a period of time. This decrease in value is called **depreciation.** Suppose a company spends $11,000 (total cost) for a truck expected to last 5 years **(economic life),** at which time it will probably be worth $1000 **(salvage value).** For tax purposes, such an asset may be considered to depreciate each year by a fixed amount determined as follows:

$$\frac{\text{depreciable amount}}{\text{economic life}} = \frac{\text{total cost} - \text{salvage value}}{\text{economic life}} = \frac{11,000 - 1000}{5}$$

$$= \$2000$$
$$\uparrow$$
$$\text{annual depreciation}$$

Therefore, after 1 year, the value of the truck, y, is

$$y = 11,000 - 2000 = \$9000$$

After 2 years, the value of the truck, y, is

$$y = 11,000 - 2000(2) = \$7000$$

After 3 years, the value of the truck, y, is

$$y = 11,000 - 2000(3) = \$5000$$

After x years, the value of the truck, y, is

$$y = 11,000 - 2000x$$

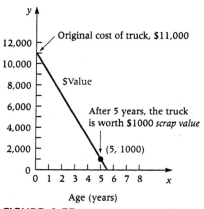

FIGURE 1-55

Thus, the linear equation $y = 11{,}000 - 2000x$ relates the value of the truck, y, to its age, x, in years. This method of depreciation is called the **straight-line method.** The equation is graphed in Figure 1-55.

We will now determine formulas for the y-intercept and slope of the linear equation relating the value of an asset with its age in years. Referring to the linear equation

$$y = 11{,}000 - 2000x$$

y-intercept   slope (annual
(total cost)   depreciation)

note that the y-intercept, 11,000, is the total cost of the asset and that the slope, -2000, indicates that the value of the truck decreases by $2000 per year.

We generalize as follows.

SUMMARY

Linear Depreciation

If

C = total cost of an asset

n = number of years of economic life of the asset

S = salvage value of the asset

then the linear equation relating the value, y, of the asset with its age, x, in years is given by

$$y = C - \left(\frac{C - S}{n}\right)x$$

Note that the y-intercept is C and the *slope* is

$$-\left(\frac{C - S}{n}\right)$$

• **EXAMPLE 1-17** _____

The Beefup Company buys a refrigerator for $20,000. The refrigerator has an economic life of 10 years, after which time it will probably have a salvage value of $2000. Find the linear equation relating the value, y, of the refrigerator to its age, x. Use the straight-line method of depreciation.

Solution

We know that $C = \$20{,}000$, $n = 10$, and $S = \$2000$. Substituting these values into the linear equation

$$y = C - \left(\frac{C - S}{n}\right)x$$

gives us

$$y = 20{,}000 - \left(\frac{20{,}000 - 2000}{10}\right)x$$
$$= 20{,}000 - 1800x$$

Exercises 1-4

Cost Functions

1. If 60 units of some product cost $1400 and 40 units cost $1200 to manufacture, then
   a) Determine the variable cost per unit.
   b) Determine the linear cost equation.
   c) Determine the fixed cost.
   d) Graph the cost function.

2. If 20 units of some product cost $2500 and 50 units cost $3400 to produce, then
   a) Determine the variable cost per unit.
   b) Determine the linear cost equation.
   c) Determine the fixed cost.
   d) Graph the cost function.

3. If 30 units of some commodity cost $2200 and 70 units cost $4200 to produce, then
   a) Determine the variable cost per unit.
   b) Determine the linear cost equation.
   c) Determine the fixed cost.
   d) Determine the total cost of producing 50 units.

4. If 30 units of some commodity cost $3100 and 50 units cost $3500 to manufacture, then
   a) Determine the variable cost per unit.
   b) Determine the linear cost equation.
   c) Determine the fixed cost.
   d) Determine the total cost of producing 70 units.

For each of the following, determine the equation of the linear cost function and also the total cost of producing 100 units.

5. Variable cost per unit = $20 and fixed cost = $1000
6. Variable cost per unit = $70 and fixed cost = $900
7. $F = \$8700$ and $v = \$15$
8. $F = \$5000$ and $v = \$90$

Cost, Sales Revenue, and Profit Functions

For each of the following, determine the linear cost, sales revenue, and profit equations. Graph each equation.

9. Variable cost per unit = $40, fixed cost = $900, and unit selling price = $70
10. Variable cost per unit = $90, fixed cost = $2000, and unit selling price = $100
11. $F = \$8000$, $v = \$100$, and $s = \$140$
12. $F = \$9000$, $v = \$50$, and $s = \$80$
13. $F = \$7500$, $v = \$25$, and $s = \$40$
14. $F = \$6000$, $v = \$90$, and $s = \$110$

Demand Functions

For each of the following, determine the equation defining the linear demand function. Graph the result.

15. If clocks are priced at $5 each, there will be a demand for 75 clocks; if clocks are priced at $10 each, the demand will decrease to 50 clocks.

16. At a unit price of $10, 500 units of some product will be demanded; at a unit price of $30, only 300 units will be demanded.

17.

q	p
50	$120
80	$60

18.

q	p
90	$40
30	$80

19.

q	p
300	$200
100	$600

Solve each of the following demand equations for q.

20. $4p + 3q = 12$ **21.** $6p + 5q = 30$

22. $p + 2q = 8$ **23.** $2p + q = 6$

Solve each of the following demand equations for p.

24. $6p + 4q = 24$ **25.** $p + 3q = 6$

26. $p + 5q = 20$ **27.** $8p + 5q = 40$

Supply Functions

For each of the following, determine the supply equation and graph the result.

28. If gadgets are priced at $9 each, suppliers are willing to produce 86 gadgets. If a gadget's price drops to $5, suppliers are willing to produce only 46 gadgets.

29. At a unit price of $20, suppliers are willing to produce 10 units of some product; at a unit price of $120, suppliers are willing to produce 30 units.

30.

q	p
50	$65
80	$80

31.

q	p
30	$100
90	$120

32.

q	p
20	$ 50
50	$110

Solve each of the following supply equations for q.

33. $4p - 3q = 12$ **34.** $5p - 4q = 20$

Solve each of the following supply equations for p.

35. $3p - 5q = 30$ **36.** $4p - 5q = 40$

Consumption Functions

For Exercises 37-39, if x denotes income and y denotes consumption, then
a) Calculate and interpret the MPC.
b) Determine the equation defining the linear consumption function.
c) Graph the result of part b.

37.

x	y
80	58
90	65

38.

x	y
50	44
80	68

39.

x	y
100	97
200	187

TABLE 1-10

x	y
48	44
68	60

TABLE 1-11

x	y
60	55
90	79

40. Table 1-10 presents the relationship between a nation's disposable income, x (in billions of dollars), and personal consumption expenditures, y (in billions of dollars).
   a) Calculate the MPC.
   b) According to the MPC of part a, for each dollar increase in disposable income, consumption increases by how much?
   c) Another rate of change is the *marginal propensity to save*, abbreviated MPS. It is defined as

$$MPS = 1 - MPC$$

   Calculate the MPS for the nation of this example.
   d) According to the MPS calculated in part c, for each dollar increase in disposable income, how many additional dollars are saved?
   e) Determine the equation defining the linear consumption function.
   f) Graph the result of part e.

41. Table 1-11 presents the relationship between a nation's disposable income, x (in billions of dollars), and personal consumption expenditures, y (in billions of dollars).
   a) Calculate and interpret the MPC.
   b) Calculate and interpret the MPS.
   c) Determine the equation defining the linear consumption function.
   d) Calculate the personal consumption expenditures corresponding to disposable income to $85 billion.

Linear Depreciation

In each of the following cases, determine the equation relating the value, y, of an asset to its age, x (in years).

42. $C = \$500,000$, $n = 5$, $s = \$50,000$
43. $C = \$90,000$, $n = 4$, $s = \$10,000$
44. $C = \$60,000$, $n = 6$, $s = 0$
45. $C = \$45,000$, $n = 3$, $s = 0$

46. A corporation buys an automobile for $10,500. The automobile's useful life is 5 years, after which time it will have a scrap value of $500.
   a) Find the linear equation relating the value of the automobile, y, to its age, x. Use the linear depreciation method.
   b) Sketch this linear equation.
   c) What is the value of the automobile after 3 years?

47. Made-Fresh Bakery buys an oven for $30,000. The useful life of the oven is 10 years, after which time it will have a scrap value of $1000.
   a) Find the linear equation relating the value of the oven, y, to its age, x.
   b) Graph the linear function defined by the equation of part a.
   c) What is the value of the oven after 6 years?

1-5 • BREAK-EVEN ANALYSIS; MARKET EQUILIBRIUM

Break-Even Analysis

Sally Adams, a recent college graduate, plans to start her own business manufacturing bicycle tires. After careful research, she concludes the following:

1. She will need $3000 for overhead (fixed cost).
2. Additionally, each tire will cost her $2 to produce (variable cost per unit).
3. To remain competitive, she must sell her tires for no more than $5 apiece.

Having compiled this information, Sally asks this crucial question:

How many tires must be produced and sold in order to break even?

This type of question is answered in the following manner. First, we must find the cost equation. If x represents the number of tires produced and sold, and $C(x)$ represents the total cost of producing x tires, then

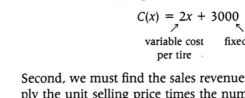

$$C(x) = 2x + 3000 \qquad \text{Cost equation}$$

variable cost per tire   fixed cost

Second, we must find the sales revenue equation. The sales revenue is simply the unit selling price times the number of units sold. If $R(x)$ represents the total sales revenue gained from selling x tires at $5 each, then

$$R(x) = 5x \qquad \text{Sales revenue equation}$$

Third, we sketch both cost and sales revenue functions on the same set of axes (see Figure 1-56). Observing Figure 1-56, note that the intersection of the graphs of a revenue function and a cost function is the **break-even point, (x_B, y_B).** Here,

$$\text{total sales revenue} = \text{total cost}$$

or

$$\text{profit} = 0$$

If $x < x_B$, then total cost is greater than total sales revenue, and the result is a loss. If $x > x_B$, then total sales revenue is greater than total cost, and the result is a profit. Thus, Sally's business will be profitable as long as x, the number of tires produced and sold, is greater than x_B, the x-coordinate of the break-even point.

To find the break-even point, (x_B, y_B), we equate $R(x)$ with $C(x)$. Thus,

$$R(x) = C(x)$$
$$5x = 2x + 3000$$

Solving for x, we obtain

$$3x = 3000$$
$$x = 1000 \qquad \text{Break-even}$$

Thus, x_B, the x-coordinate of the break-even point, is 1000. The corresponding y-coordinate, y_B, is determined by calculating either $C(1000)$ or $R(1000)$. Hence,

$$C(x) = 2x + 3000 \qquad \text{or} \qquad R(x) = 5x$$
$$C(1000) = 2(1000) + 3000 \qquad\qquad R(1000) = 5(1000)$$
$$= 5000 \qquad\qquad\qquad\qquad = 5000$$

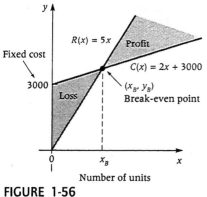

FIGURE 1-56

Therefore, the break-even point is (1000, 5000), and Sally must produce and sell 1000 tires to break even. If Sally produces and sells more than 1000 tires, she will make a profit.

Having determined the break-even point, Sally conducts a marketing research study which indicates that she can sell at least 10,000 tires at $5 apiece. Also, there is a strong possibility that she can sell as many as 20,000 tires at this price. Since both of these demand levels are greater than $x_B = 1000$, Sally knows she will make a profit. However, she wishes to determine the amount of profit corresponding to each of the demand levels of 10,000 and 20,000 tires.

One way of calculating profits is to find the profit equation. As discussed in the previous section, if

$P(x) = $ total profit from selling x tires

$R(x) = $ total sales revenue from selling x tires

$C(x) = $ total cost of producing x tires

then

$$P(x) = R(x) - C(x)$$
$$= 5x - (2x + 3000)$$
$$= 3x - 3000$$

Thus, the profit function is defined by

$$P(x) = 3x - 3000$$

Hence, if 10,000 tires are sold, the corresponding profit is

$$P(10,000) = 3(10,000) - 3000 = \$27,000$$

And if 20,000 tires are sold, the corresponding profit is

$$P(20,000) = 3(20,000) - 3000 = \$57,000$$

Since Sally is satisfied with either of these amount, she decides to start her tire-manufacturing business.

We note that the break-even point can also be determined by setting the profit equation equal to 0 and solving for x. This works because $P(x) = R(x) - C(x)$, and, therefore, setting $P(x) = 0$ gives $0 = R(x) - C(x)$ or $R(x) = C(x)$. Hence, for the above example, setting $P(x) = 0$ and solving for x gives

$$0 = 3x - 3000$$
$$x = 1000 \quad \text{Break-even}$$

The break-even analysis process is summarized on page 45. It should be studied before proceeding to the next example.

Break-Even Analysis

Linear Functions

In general, if s = unit selling price, v = variable cost per unit, F = fixed cost, and x = number of units produced and sold, then, as discussed in Section 1-4, the **cost function** is given by

$$C(x) = vx + F \qquad (x \geq 0)$$

the **sales revenue function** is given by

$$R(x) = sx \qquad (x \geq 0)$$

and the **profit function** is given by

$$P(x) = (s - v)x - F \qquad (x \geq 0)$$

The x-coordinate of the **break-even point,** the point where total sales revenue = total cost, can be determined by two methods.

Method 1 Set $R(x) = C(x)$ and solve for x. This gives

$$sx = vx + F$$
$$(s - v)x = F$$
$$x = \frac{F}{s - v}$$

Method 2 Set $P(x) = 0$ and solve for x. This gives

$$0 = (s - v)x - F$$
$$x = \frac{F}{s - v}$$

We now consider Example 1-18, which illustrates a format often used to present information on fixed and variable costs and sales revenue.

• **EXAMPLE 1-18**

This problem appeared on a past Uniform CPA Examination. In a recent period, the Zero Company had the following experience:

Sales (10,000 units @ $200 per unit)			$2,000,000
	Fixed	Variable	
Costs			
Direct material	$ —	$ 200,000	
Direct labor	—	400,000	
Factory overhead	160,000	600,000	
Administrative expenses	180,000	80,000	
Other expenses	200,000	120,000	
Total costs	$540,000	$1,400,000	1,940,000
			$ 60,000

a) Find the sales revenue equation.
b) Find the cost equation.
c) Find the break-even point.
d) How many units must be sold in order to generate a profit of $96,000?
e) What is the break-even point if management makes a decision that increases fixed costs by $18,000?

Solutions

a) If $R(x)$ is the sales revenue from selling x units at $200 each, then

$$R(x) = 200x$$

b) We have

$$\text{fixed cost} = \$540,000$$

The variable cost per unit is determined by dividing the total variable cost by the number of units. Hence,

$$\text{variable cost per unit} = \frac{\text{total variable cost}}{\text{number of units}}$$

$$= \frac{1,400,000}{10,000} = \$140$$

Thus, if $C(x)$ is the total cost of producing x units, then

$$C(x) = 140x + 540,000$$

c) At the break-even point,

$$R(x) = C(x)$$
$$200x = 140x + 540,000$$

Solving for x yields

$$60x = 540,000$$
$$x = 9000 \text{ units}$$

Thus, the Zero Company must produce and sell 9000 units in order to break even. Note that $R(9000) = C(9000) = \$1,800,000$.

d) If $P(x)$ is the profit from selling x units, then

$$P(x) = R(x) - C(x)$$
$$= 200x - (140x + 540,000)$$
$$= 60x - 540,000$$

If $P(x) = 96,000$, then

$$96,000 = 60x - 540,000$$

Solving for x yields

$$-60x = -636,000$$
$$x = 10,600 \text{ units}$$

Thus, the Zero Company must sell 10,600 units in order to generate a profit of $96,000.

e) The cost equation becomes

$$C(x) = 140x + \underbrace{540,000 + 18,000}_{\text{fixed cost}}$$

$$= 140x + 558,000$$

At the break-even point,

$$R(x) = C(x)$$

Thus,

$$200x = 140x + 558,000$$

Solving for x yields

$$60x = 558,000$$
$$x = 9300 \text{ units} \qquad \text{Break-even}$$

Therefore, the Zero Company must produce 9300 units to break even. Note that $R(9300) = C(9300) = \$1,860,000$.

• EXAMPLE 1-19 _____

Amtron, Inc., produces two products, AM50 and AM60, that are used in the computer industry. Projections for next year are given in Table 1-12.

a) Determine the profit function for AM50.
b) Determine the break-even point for AM50.
c) Because 3 AM50s are inserted into a part that also requires 2 AM60s, customers purchase composite units of 3 AM50s and 2 AM60s. Determine the composite profit function and break-even point.

Solutions

a) The unit selling price for AM50 is determined as follows:

$$s = \frac{\text{total sales revenue}}{\text{number of units}}$$
$$= \frac{\$100,000}{20,000} = \$5$$

The variable cost per unit for AM50 is determined as follows:

$$v = \frac{\text{total variable cost}}{\text{number of units}}$$
$$= \frac{\$30,000}{20,000} = \$1.50$$

The fixed cost for AM50 is $F = \$5100$.
The profit function is given by

$$P(x) = (s - v)x - F$$
$$= (5 - 1.5)x - 5100$$
$$= 3.5x - 5100$$

where x = number of units sold.

b) We determine the break-even point by setting $P(x) = 0$ and solving for x. Hence,

$$0 = 3.5x - 5100$$
$$-3.5x = -5100$$
$$x = 1457.14, \text{ which we round to } 1457$$

TABLE 1-12

	AM50		AM60	
	units	amount	units	amount
Sales	20,000	$100,000	12,000	$72,000
Costs				
Fixed		$ 5,100		$ 6,000
Variable		30,000		24,000
		$ 35,100		$30,000

c) We must determine the unit contribution margin for the composite: 3 AM50s and 2 AM60s. In part a, we determined the unit selling price and the variable cost per unit for AM50. Now we must determine the same for AM60. Hence, for AM60

$$\text{unit selling price} = \frac{\$72{,}000}{12{,}000} = \$6$$

$$\text{variable cost per unit} = \frac{\$24{,}000}{12{,}000} = \$2$$

Thus, for the composite units of 3 AM50s and 2 AM60s, the unit selling price (denoted by s_c) is determined below:

$$s_c = 3(\text{AM50 unit selling price}) + 2(\text{AM60 unit selling price})$$
$$= 3(\$5) + 2(\$6)$$
$$= \$27$$

Also, the variable cost per unit (denoted by v_c) for the composite is determined below:

$$v_c = 3\left(\frac{\text{AM50 variable cost}}{\text{per unit}}\right) + 2\left(\frac{\text{AM60 variable cost}}{\text{per unit}}\right)$$
$$= 3(\$1.50) + 2(\$2)$$
$$= \$8.50$$

The fixed cost (denoted by F_c) for the composite is the sum of the fixed costs of the two products. Hence,

$$F_c = \$5100 + \$6000 = \$11{,}100$$

Thus, the composite profit function is given by

$$P(x) = (s_c - v_c)x - F_c$$
$$= (27.00 - 8.50)x - 11{,}100$$
$$= 18.5x - 11{,}100$$

where x = number of composite units of 3 AM50s and 2 AM60s. To determine the break-even point, we set $P(x) = 0$ and solve for x. Hence,

$$0 = 18.5x - 11{,}100$$
$$-18.5x = -11{,}100$$
$$x = 600 \text{ composite units of 3 AM50s and 2 AM60s}$$

Note that the break-even point, $x = 600$ composite units, means that

3(600) or 1800 AM50s

and

2(600) or 1200 AM60s

must be sold in order to break even.

Market Equilibrium

In the previous section, we noted that the graph of a linear demand function has a negative slope, whereas the graph of a linear supply function has a positive slope. This implies that as the price of some product increases, its demand decreases and its supply increases. Conversely, as the price of the product decreases, its demand increases and its supply decreases. Figure 1-57 illustrates the graphs of typical linear supply and demand functions.

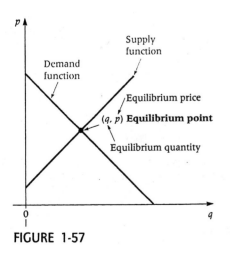

FIGURE 1-57

Economists often must determine the point where supply equals demand. Such a point is called the **equilibrium point.** Graphically, this is the intersection point of the graphs of the supply and demand functions, as illustrated in Figure 1-57. The first coordinate of the equilibrium point is called the **equilibrium quantity;** the second coordinate is called the **equilibrium price.** The equilibrium price is the unit price at which supply = demand for a given product.

We now consider the example below.

• **EXAMPLE 1-20** _____

The demand and supply equations for some commodity are given below.

$$\text{Demand equation:} \quad p = -2q + 100$$
$$\text{Supply equation:} \quad p = 3q$$

Determine the equilibrium point.

Solution

Since the equilibrium point is the intersection of the graphs of the demand and supply functions, it is found by equating the values of p given by the demand and supply equations. This gives

$$3q = -2q + 100$$

Solving for q gives

$$5q = 100$$
$$q = 20 \qquad \text{Equilibrium quantity}$$

The *equilibrium price* is determined by substituting the equilibrium quantity into either the supply or the demand equation. Arbitrarily selecting the supply equation, we get

$$p = 3q$$
$$p = 3(20) = \$60 \qquad \text{Equilibrium price}$$

If we had selected the demand equation, we would have gotten the same result, as is shown below.

$$p = -2q + 100$$
$$= -2(20) + 100$$
$$= \$60$$

The graphical illustration is given in Figure 1-58. Note that only the first quadrant portion of the graph of each function is shown since each function has meaning only for non-negative values of q and p.

•

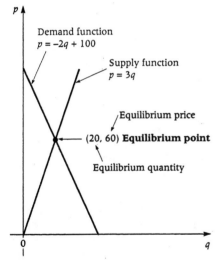

FIGURE 1-58

Exercises 1-5

Break-Even Point

For each of the following, determine the cost, sales revenue, and profit equations. Also, determine the x-coordinate of the break-even point by two methods.

1. $F = \$1000, v = \$5, s = \$9$
2. $F = \$8000, v = \$6, s = \$14$
3. $F = \$100,000, v = \$20, s = \$120$

4. $F = \$150,000$, $v = \$30$, $s = \$180$

5. $F = \$80,000$, $v = \$25$, $s = \$65$

6. $F = \$90,000$, $v = \$30$, $s = \$75$

7. A manufacturer has fixed costs of $2000 and a variable cost of $5 per unit. She sells her product for $15 apiece.
   a) Find the cost equation that relates cost to the number of units produced.
   b) Find the sales revenue equation that relates sales revenue to the number of units produced.
   c) Sketch both the cost and sales revenue equations on the same set of axes.
   d) Find the break-even point.
   e) Find the profit equation that relates profit to the number of units produced.
   f) Sketch the profit equation.
   g) Find the profit that results from producing and selling 300 units of this product.
   h) Find the profit that results from producing and selling 100 units of this product.
   i) How many units must be produced and sold in order to obtain a profit of $40,000?

8. The WVW Corporation has fixed costs of $5000. Its variable cost for producing 400 units is $16,000. The corporation sells its product for $60 apiece.
   a) Find the cost equation.
   b) Find the sales revenue equation.
   c) Sketch both the cost and sales revenue equations on the same set of axes.
   d) Find the break-even point.
   e) Find the profit equation.
   f) Sketch the profit equation.
   g) Find the profit that results from producing and selling 450 units.
   h) How many units must be produced and sold in order to yield a profit of $25,000?

9. The VUV Corporation has presented the information in Table 1-13 to its accountant.
   a) Find the variable cost per unit.
   b) Find the cost equation.
   c) Find the sales revenue equation.
   d) Sketch both the cost and sales revenue functions on the same graph.
   e) Find the break-even point.
   f) Find the profit equation.
   g) Sketch the profit equation.
   h) Find the profit that results from producing and selling of 1000 units.
   i) How many units must be produced and sold in order to obtain a profit of $104,000?

10. Envelex, Inc., produces two types of envelopes, EZ101 and EZ102. Projections for the next year are given in Table 1-14.
   a) Determine the profit equation for EZ101.
   b) Determine the break-even point for EZ101.
   c) How many units of EZ101 should be sold in order to yield a profit of $4000?
   d) Determine the profit equation for EZ102.
   e) Determine the break-even point for EZ102.
   f) How many units of EZ102 should be sold in order to yield a profit of $5000?

TABLE 1-13

Fixed costs	
Administrative	$200,000
Building and land	50,000
Other fixed overhead	10,000
Variable cost for 100 units of production	
Materials	$ 50,000
Labor	70,000
Selling expense	10,000
Selling price per unit	$ 1,800

TABLE 1-14

	EZ101		EZ102	
	units	amount	units	amount
Sales	10,000	$15,000	8,000	$16,800
Costs				
Fixed		$ 1,600		$ 5,100
Variable		7,000		3,200
		$ 8,600		$ 8,300

g) If customers purchase composite units of 4 EZ101s and 3 EZ102s, determine the composite profit equation and break-even point.

h) If customers purchase composite units of 1 EZ101 and 1 EZ102, determine the composite profit equation and break-even point.

11. *This problem appeared on a past Uniform CPA Examination.* Use the information in Table 1-15 to answer the following questions. Let x = number of units produced and sold.

a) Find the sales revenue equation.
b) Find the cost equation.
c) Find the break-even point.
d) Find the profit equation.
e) How many units should be sold in order to yield a profit of 4000?
f) What would be the operating income if sales increased by 25%?
g) What would be the break-even point if fixed factory overhead increased by $1700?

12. *This problem appeared on a past Uniform CPA Examination.* The Jarvis Company has fixed costs of $200,000. It has two products that it can sell: Tetra and Min. Jarvis sells these products at a rate of 2 units of Tetra to 1 unit of Min. The unit profit is $1 per unit for Tetra and $2 per unit for Min. How many units of Min would be sold at the break-even point?

13. The Algor Company markets two statistical software packages, Stat I and Stat

TABLE 1-15 **Full Ton Company financial projection for product USA for the year ended December 31, 19x7**

Sales (100 units @ $100 a unit)		$10,000
Manufacturing cost of goods sold		
Direct labor	$1,500	
Direct materials used	1,400	
Variable factory overhead	1,000	
Fixed factory overhead	500	
Total manufacturing cost of goods sold		4,400
Gross profit		5,600
Selling expenses		
Variable	600	
Fixed	1,000	
Administrative expenses		
Variable	500	
Fixed	1,000	
Total selling and administrative expenses		3,100
Operating income		$ 2,500

II, which account for 60% and 40%, respectively, of the total sales revenue of Algor. Stat I's variable cost is 60% of its sales revenue, and Stat II's is 85% of its sales revenue. Total fixed costs are $180,000.

a) Determine Algor's break-even point in sales dollars.
b) If Algor's total fixed costs increase by 40%, determine the sales revenue necessary to yield a profit of $105,000.

14. A company's projected sales volume for one of its products is 300,000 units. The fixed cost is $500,000, and the variable cost is 60% of the selling price. Determine the unit selling price necessary to yield a profit of $340,000.

Equilibrium Point

For each of the following, determine the equilibrium point. State the equilibrium price and the equilibrium quantity.

15. Demand equation: $p = \dfrac{-7}{3}q + 31$

Supply equation: $p = \dfrac{5}{3}q + 15$

16. Demand equation: $p = -5q + 68$
Supply equation: $p = 9q + 40$

17. Demand equation: $p = \dfrac{-1}{3}q + 13$

Supply equation: $p = \dfrac{1}{4}q + 6$

18. Demand equation: $p = -3q + 90$
Supply equation: $p = 5q + 42$

19. Susan Time can sell 150 watches at a price of $35 each. If the price drops to $20 apiece, Susan can sell 300 watches.

a) Find the linear demand equation.
Susan's suppliers are willing to supply only 125 watches if the price per watch is $25. However, if the price per watch increases to $40 per watch, the suppliers are willing to provide Susan with 350 watches.
b) Find the linear supply equation.
c) Sketch both the supply and demand equations on the same set of axes.
d) Find the equilibrium point.
e) For supply to equal demand, Susan's watches must be priced at how much apiece?

EXTRA DIVIDENDS

• Cost Accounting: Cost Segregation

Businesses usually collect data giving total costs associated with various levels of a given quantity. Such data are often used to segregate the fixed and variable portions of a total cost value. Table 1-16 gives equipment repair costs for various hours of operation of a particular machine used to make precision tools. The data span a time interval of 6 months. Note that we have indicated the highest and lowest monthly repair costs.

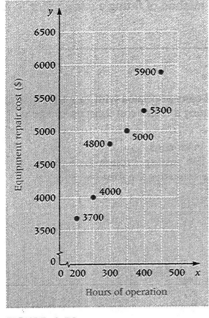

FIGURE 1-59

TABLE 1-16

	Hours of operation	Equipment repair cost ($)	
January	250	4000	
February	300	4800	
March	200	3700	Low
April	400	5300	
May	350	5000	
June	450	5900	High

The data are plotted to give a graph of cost versus hours of operation as illustrated in Figure 1-59. Observe that the data points are not collinear. In other words, they do not lie in the path of a straight line.

The firm's cost accountant is faced with the following problem.

PROBLEM

Determine the fixed monthly equipment repair cost and the variable equipment repair cost per hour of operation.

SOLUTION

Although the data points are not collinear, they seem to have a linear trend. If we can find the equation of a straight line that captures the trend of the data, then

1. Its y-intercept estimates the monthly fixed repair cost.
2. Its slope estimates the variable repair cost per hour of operation

One such straight line passes through the points of highest and lowest costs. Thus, the cost accountant determines the equation of the straight line passing through the points labeled High and Low in Table 1-16 and Figure 1-60. Accordingly, this method of segregating the fixed and variable portions of cost is called the **high-low point method**.

Using the points of highest and lowest costs, the cost accountant finds the slope (and also the estimated variable cost per hour) to be

$$\text{Slope} \qquad m = \frac{5900 - 3700}{450 - 200} = 8.80 \qquad \text{Variable cost per hour}$$

Using the point-slope form and choosing either the point of lowest cost or the point of highest cost gives

$$y - y_1 = m(x - x_1) \qquad \text{Point-slope form}$$
$$y - 3700 = 8.80(x - 200)$$

Solving for y gives the slope-intercept form

$$y = 8.80x + 1940$$

variable cost ↑   ↑ fixed monthly
per hour of   repair cost
operation

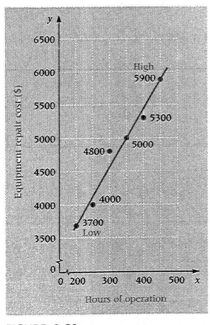

FIGURE 1-60

We summarize the high-low point method of fitting a straight line to a set of data points.

■ High-Low Point Method

Given a set of data points relating total costs associated with various levels of some quantity, an equation defining a linear cost function can be determined from the data as follows:

1. Choose the points of *highest* and *lowest* costs.
2. Find the equation of the straight line passing through these points.
3. The y-*intercept* of the straight line estimates the *fixed cost;* the *slope* estimates the *variable cost per unit.*

This is graphically illustrated in Figure 1-61.

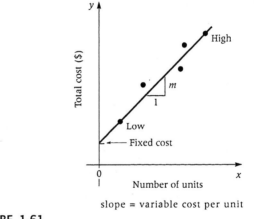

FIGURE 1-61

Note: This method works best when a plot of the data points reveals a linear trend.

The advantage of the high-low point method is that it is quick and easy to apply. A more accurate method of fitting a straight line to a set of data points will be presented in a later chapter.

■ *Exercises*

1. *Electric power costs.* Table 1-17 lists electric power costs associated with various hours of operation for some firm.
   a) Use the high-low point method to find the equation of the linear cost function that fits this set of data points.
   b) State the fixed cost.
   c) State the variable cost per hour.
2. *Office expense.* Table 1-18 lists office expenses associated with hours of operation for some firm.
   a) Use the high-low point method to find the equation of the linear cost function that fits this set of data points.

TABLE 1-17

Hours	Cost ($)
5800	7000
5000	6500
5600	6700
5900	7400

TABLE 1-18

Hours	Cost ($)
4000	41,000
5000	48,000
6000	59,000

TABLE 1-19

	Highest	Lowest
Cost per month	$39,200	$32,000
Machine hours	24,000	15,000

b) State the fixed cost.

c) State the variable cost per hour.

The following problems have appeared on past Uniform CPA Examinations. The questions have been adapted to conform to the format of these exercises.

3. *Maintenance expenses.* The maintenance expenses of a company are to be analyzed for purposes of constructing a flexible budget. Examination of past records disclosed the costs and volume measures listed in Table 1-19. Using the high-low point method of analysis,
   a) Determine the estimated variable cost per machine hour.
   b) Determine the estimated monthly fixed cost for maintenance expenditures.
   c) Use the result of part b to determine the estimated annual fixed cost for maintenance expenditures.

4. Paine Corporation wishes to determine the fixed portion of its electricity expense (a semivariable expense), as measured against direct labor hours, for the first 3 months of a given year. Information for the first 3 months is listed in Table 1-20. What is the fixed portion of Paine's electricity expense rounded to the nearest dollar?

TABLE 1-20

	Direct labor hours	Electricity expense ($)
January	34,000	610
February	31,000	585
March	34,000	610

EXTRA DIVIDENDS

• *Model Fitting: Goodness of Fit*

Table 1-21 gives a set of data that relates grades obtained on a mathematics exam by a very small class to the number of hours studied for the exam. Specifically, for each student, x denotes the number of hours that the student studied for the mathematics exam and y denotes the exam grade for that student.

Figure 1-62 gives a plot of the data points (x, y). Figure 1-63 gives a plot of the data and the graph of the straight line

$$y = 20x + 40$$

TABLE 1-21

x	Study time (in hours)	0.5	1.0	1.5	2.0	2.5	3.0
y	Exam grade	43	64	68	88	97	99

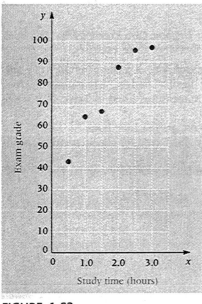

FIGURE 1-62

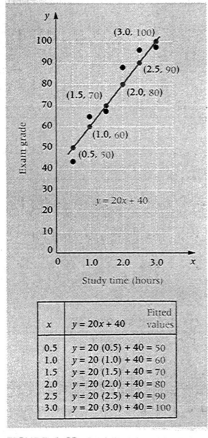

FIGURE 1-63

x	y = 20x + 40	Fitted values
0.5	y = 20 (0.5) + 40 = 50	
1.0	y = 20 (1.0) + 40 = 60	
1.5	y = 20 (1.5) + 40 = 70	
2.0	y = 20 (2.0) + 40 = 80	
2.5	y = 20 (2.5) + 40 = 90	
3.0	y = 20 (3.0) + 40 = 100	

that appears to capture the relationship between x and y. Observe, in Figure 1-63, that the fitted values are determined by substituting the x-values into the equation of the fitted linear model. Hence, the fitted values are simply the y-coordinates of points on the fitted line.

We will not be concerned with how the equation (or, in other words, the linear model) $y = 20x + 40$ was obtained. Such discussion is the topic of Section 15-4 in the calculus portion of this text. In this section, we address the issue of assessing the goodness of fit of a straight line fit to a set of data points.

• Goodness of Fit

To assess the goodness of fit of a model fit to a set of data, we determine, for each data point, the vertical distance between the given data point and the fitted line, as illustrated in Figure 1-64. Such vertical distances are called **residuals** and indicate the extent to which the fitted model does not fit the data points. An overall measure of the extent to which the fitted model (in this case, the straight line) does not fit the data is given by the sum of the squares of the residuals. This result is called the sum of squares error and is denoted by S, as is shown below.

Sum of Squares Error

$$S = (43 - 50)^2 + (64 - 60)^2 + (68 - 70)^2 + (88 - 80)^2 + (97 - 90)^2$$
$$+ (99 - 100)^2$$
$$= (-7)^2 + (4)^2 + (-2)^2 + (8)^2 + (7)^2 + (-1)^2$$
$$= 183 \quad \text{Sum of squares error}$$

If another straight line, say

$$y = 10x + 60$$

is fitted to the set of data points, it can be determined whether or not this line is a better fit to the data by computing the sum of squares error for this line and comparing the result with that of the previous line, $y = 20x + 40$. The better-fitting line is the one that has a smaller sum of squares error. The residuals for the new line, $y = 10x + 60$, are illustrated in Figure 1-65, and the sum of squares error is computed below.

Sum of Squares Error

$$S = (43 - 65)^2 + (64 - 70)^2 + (68 - 75)^2 + (88 - 80)^2 + (97 - 85)^2$$
$$+ (99 - 90)^2$$
$$= (-22)^2 + (-6)^2 + (-7)^2 + (8)^2 + (12)^2 + (9)^2$$
$$= 858 \quad \text{Sum of squares error}$$

Since the sum of squares error for the first line is less than that for the second line, the first line, $y = 20x + 40$, better-fits this set of data than does the second line, $y = 10x + 60$.

We summarize as follows.

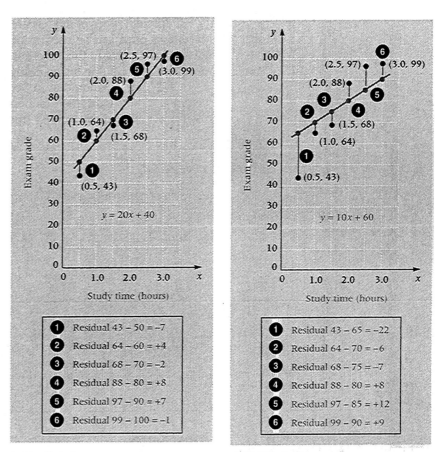

FIGURE 1-64   FIGURE 1-65

To Determine Goodness of Fit

The **goodness of fit** of a model fitted to a given set of data points is determined as follows:

1. Compute the **fitted values** by substituting the *x*-values of the data points into the equation of the fitted model.
2. Compute the **residual** for each data point in accordance with the formula.

$$\text{residual} = \text{data value} - \text{fitted value}$$

3. Compute the **sum of squares error, S,** as given below.

$$S = \text{sum of the squares of the residuals}$$

Note: The sum of squares error is an overall measure of the extent to which the fitted model does not fit the data.

Note: If more than one model is fit to the same set of data points, then the model resulting in the **smallest** sum of squares error is the better-fitting model for the set of data point.

If different types of models are fit to a given set of data points, the sum of squares error can be used to determine which type of model better fits the data according to this criterion. The model resulting in the smaller sum of squares error is the better-fitting model.

Lastly, we mention that in Section 15-4, we will learn how to find the equation of a straight line that best fits a set of data points. This entails the use of calculus, which we will study in later chapters of this text.

Exercises

For each of the following sets of data, the equations of two fitted linear models are given.
a) Determine the sum of squares error for each fitted linear model.
b) Write the equation of the better-fitting linear model.

1.

x	2	4	6	8	9
y	7	9	13	16	25

$y = 2x + 1$
$y = 3x - 2$

2.

x	1	3	4	7	9
y	9	13	16	24	35

$y = 3x + 5$
$y = 4x + 1$

3.

x	2	3	7	8	9
y	6	9	19	28	35

$y = 4x - 3$
$y = 3x + 2$

4.

x	2	4	5	8	9
y	9	19	27	38	47

$y = 5x - 1$
$y = 4x + 5$

Applications

Time Series

A set of data that relates some quantity to time is called a **time series.** The data in Exercises 5, 6, and 7 constitute time series. For these exercises, the variable, x, denotes successive time periods, such as weeks, months, quarters, or years, and the variable, y, denotes the quantity related to time.

5. *Stock prices: S&P 500.* The following data give quarterly values of Standard & Poors 500 Composite Index (denoted S&P 500), which measures stock market movement. The S&P 500 values given here begin with the second quarter of 1985 and end with the third quarter of 1988. The successive quarters are denoted by $x = 1, x = 2, \ldots, x = 14$.

x	1	2	3	4	5	6	7
y S&P 500	153.18	166.10	167.24	180.66	191.85	182.08	211.28
x	8	9	10	11	12	13	14
y S&P 500	238.90	250.84	231.32	242.17	291.70	304.00	337.00

The following two linear models are fit to this set of data:

$$y = 13x + 130 \qquad y = 20x + 70$$

a) Determine the sum of squares error for each fitted linear model.
b) Write the equation of the better-fitting linear model.

6. *Stock prices: S&P 500.* The following data give quarterly values of Standard & Poors 500 Composite Index (denoted S&P 500), which measures stock market movement. The S&P 500 values given here begin with the fourth quarter of

1972 and end with the third quarter of 1974. The successive quarters are denoted by $x = 1, x = 2, \ldots, x = 8$.

x	1	2	3	4	5	6	7	8
y S&P 500	118.05	111.52	104.26	108.43	97.55	93.98	86.00	63.54

The following two linear models are fit to this set of data:

$$y = -7x + 130 \qquad y = -10x + 140$$

a) Determine the sum of squares error for each fitted linear model.
b) Write the equation of the better-fitting linear model.

7. *Systolic Blood Pressure (SBP).* A person's systolic blood pressure (SBP) is recorded weekly with the following results:

x Week	1	2	3	4	5	6	7	8	9
y SBP	125	128	130	129	135	138	140	146	145

The following two linear models are fit to this set of data:

$$y = 3x + 120 \qquad y = 4x + 115$$

a) Determine the sum of squares error for each fitted linear model.
b) Write the equation of the better-fitting linear model.

8. *Education.* The data below relate undergraduate grade point average (GPA) to starting salary (in thousands of dollars) for a sample of recent graduates at a small liberal arts college.

x GPA	2.5	3.0	2.4	3.5	2.1	2.6
y Starting salary	15.5	19.7	15.2	22.8	14.6	15.8

The following two linear models are fit to this set of data:

$$y = 6x + 1 \qquad y = 7x - 1$$

a) Determine the sum of squares error for each fitted linear model.
b) Write the equation of the better-fitting linear model.

9. *Medical science.* The data below relate serum cholesterol level (in milligrams/100 milliters) with age for a sample of adult males.

x Age	20	35	27	40	49	55
y Cholesterol	210	279	230	190	252	287

The following two linear models are fit to the set of data:

$$y = 2x + 170 \qquad y = 3x + 100$$

a) Determine the sum of squares error for each fitted linear model.
b) Write the equation of the better-fitting linear model.

CHAPTER 1 HIGHLIGHTS

• Concepts

Your ability to answer the following questions is one indicator of the depth of your mastery of this chapter's important concepts. Note that the questions are grouped under various topic headings. For any question that you cannot answer, refer to the section of the chapter indicated by the topic heading. Pay particular attention to the summary boxes within a section.

1-1 FUNCTIONS

1. Explain the following terms: function, domain, range, dependent variable, independent variable, ordered pair, x-coordinate, y-coordinate, x-axis, y-axis, origin, quadrant.
2. A function is usually defined by a (an) _____ that expresses a (an) _____ between two quantities.
3. How can we determine whether or not a given graph represents a function?
4. Draw a graph of the absolute value function.
5. If a function is defined by more than one formula, the function is said to be _____ defined.

1-2 SLOPE AND EQUATIONS OF STRAIGHT LINES

6. Which of the following do not represent slope?
   a) Steepness of a straight line.
   b) Rate of change of the dependent variable with respect to the independent variable.
   c) Vertical change/horizontal change.
   d) Horizontal change/vertical change.
7. A straight line, $y = mx + b$, has slope $= -5/3$. State the effect on y if x increases by 3 units.
8. Draw a graph that typifies a straight line with

   a) Positive slope.   b) Negative slope.
   c) Zero slope.   d) Undefined slope.
9. A straight line with an equation of the form $y = mx$ passes through the _____.
10. A horizontal straight line has an equation of the form _____.
11. A vertical straight line has an equation of the form _____.
12. A linear equation in slope-intercept form is easily graphed by first plotting the _____ and then drawing the straight line upward to the right if its slope is _____ or upward to the left if its slope is _____.
13. A tax function is an example of a piecewise-defined function. The different slopes of a tax function represent _____ _____.

1-3 GRAPHING LINEAR EQUATIONS

14. Explain the following terms: x-intercept, y-intercept.
15. An x-intercept has a y-coordinate that equals _____.
16. A y-intercept has an x-coordinate that equals _____.
17. State the procedure for graphing a linear equation of the form $ax + by = c$.
18. State the procedure for graphing a linear equation of the form $y = mx$.

1-4 LINEAR MODELS

Cost, Sales Revenue, and Profit Functions

19. A cost function expresses a relationship between what two quantities?
20. A sales revenue function expresses a relationship between what two quantities?
21. A profit function expresses a relationship between what two quantities?
22. Give an interpretation of the slope of a linear cost function.
23. The y-intercept of a cost function is the _____ _____ ; explain this term.

Supply and Demand Functions

24. A demand equation relates the quantities _____ and _____.

25. A supply equation relates the quantities _____ and _____.

Consumption Function and MPC

26. A consumption function relates the quantities _____ and _____.

27. Give an interpretation of the MPC.

Linear Depreciation

28. Give the linear equation that relates the value of an asset to its age. Interpret its y-intercept and slope.

1-5 BREAK-EVEN ANALYSIS; MARKET EQUILIBRIUM

Break-Even Point

29. Give an interpretation of a break-even point.
30. Given cost and sales revenue functions, state the procedure for finding the break-even point.
31. The x-intercept of a profit function equals the x-coordinate of the _____-_____ _____.
32. Given a profit function, state the procedure for finding the break-even point.

Market Equilibrium

33. Graphically, an equilibrium point is the _____ of a supply function and a (an) _____ function.
34. Give an interpretation of the coordinates of an equilibrium point.

REVIEW EXERCISES

• *Functions and Functional Notation*

For each of the following, calculate $f(0)$, $f(1)$, and $f(3)$.

1. $f(x = 4x - 2$
2. $f(x) = 5x + 3$
3. $f(x) = x^2 + 2x - 1$
4. $f(x) = \dfrac{3x + 5}{x + 1}$

For each of the following, calculate the difference quotient

$$\frac{f(x + h) - f(x)}{h}$$

5. $f(x) = 4x + 8$
6. $f(x) = x^2 + 6x - 5$
7. $f(x) = x^2 - 4x + 3$
8. $f(x) = x^3 - x^2 + 7$

Specify the domain of each of the following functions.

9. $f(x) = \sqrt{x - 4}$
10. $f(x) = \sqrt{x + 8}$
11. $f(x) = \dfrac{x + 6}{(x - 7)(x + 5)}$
12. $f(x) = \dfrac{4x + 10}{x - 2}$

• *Functions and Graphs*

State whether each of the following is the graph of a function.

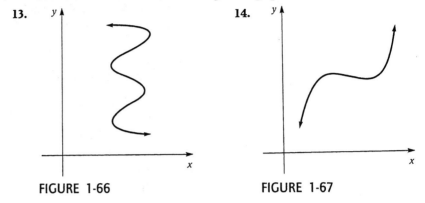

13.

FIGURE 1-66

14.

FIGURE 1-67

Graph each of the following.

15. $f(x) = \begin{cases} 2 & \text{if } x \le 3 \\ 5 & \text{if } 3 < x \le 8 \\ x & \text{if } x > 8 \end{cases}$

16. $g(x) = \begin{cases} -1 & \text{if } x \le 2 \\ x & \text{if } 2 < x \le 5 \\ 7 & \text{if } x > 5 \end{cases}$

17. *Call options.* An investor bought a call option entitling her to buy a specified number of shares of a stock for $20 per share during the next 3 months. The investor paid $4 per share for the call option. Determine the investor's profit function per share of stock. Graph the profit function.

• *Slope and Equations of Straight Lines*

Find the slope of the straight line passing through each of the following pairs of points.

18. $(3, -7)$ and $(-8, 26)$

19. $(6, 5)$ and $(4, -3)$

Find the equation of the straight line passing through each of the following pairs of points. Express the answer in slope-intercept form.

20. $(-1, 6)$ and $(4, 16)$

21. $(3, -2)$ and $(5, 8)$

For each of the following, determine which of the given points lie on the straight line.

22. $2x + 5y = 20$: $(0, 4), (10, 0), (2, 4), (5, 2), (3, 4)$
23. $4x - 2y = 10$: $(1, -3), (2, 5), (0, -5), (3, 0), (-1, -2)$

Draw the graph of a straight line that passes through the origin and has

24. Positive slope.

25. Negative slope.

Draw the graph of a straight line that passes through $(3, 4)$ and

26. Has slope $= 0$.

27. Has an undefined slope.

Write the equation of the straight line of

28. Exercise 26.

29. Exercise 27.

Which of the following pairs of straight lines are parallel?

30. $y = 5x + 7$, $y = 4x - 9$

31. $2x + 6y = 30$, $-4x - 12y = 24$

32. *Defects: U.S. automobiles.* The number of defects per 100 vehicles for Chrysler's North American operations declined from 810 to 175 during the years from 1979 to 1989.
  a) Find the slope of the straight line that indicates this trend.
  b) Interpret the slope.
  c) Find the equation of the straight line. Express the final answer in slope-intercept form.
  d) If Chrysler's defects continue to decline at the same rate, predict its defects per 100 vehicles (North America) for the year 1991.

• *Graphing Linear Equations*

Graph each of the following by finding the x- and y-intercepts.

33. $5x - 2y = 20$ **34.** $y = 7x - 14$
35. $f(x) = 6x$ **36.** $3x - 6y = 0$

• *Cost, Sales Revenue, and Profit Functions*

For Exercises 37 and 38, determine the linear cost, sales revenue, and profit equations. Graph each on the same set of axes. Determine the break-even point.

37. Variable cost per unit = $30, fixed cost = $1200, and unit selling price = $50
38. Variable cost per unit = $80, fixed cost = $1600, and unit selling price = $120

This problem is adapted from a past Uniform CPA Examination. The Dooley Company manufactures two products, baubles and trinkets. The Table 1-22 lists projections for the coming year:

39. Determine the profit equation for baubles.
40. Determine the break-even point for baubles.
41. Determine the profit equation for trinkets.
42. Determine the break-even point for trinkets.
43. If customers purchase composite units of 4 baubles and 3 trinkets, determine the composite profit equation and break-even point.

44. *Population.* The suburban population of a state is currrently 6,500,000 and is decreasing at the rate of 200,000 per year. The urban population is currently 3,700,000 and is increasing at the rate of 150,000 per year. How many years from now will both populations be equal?

45. *Market share.* The U.S. market share of Ford Motor Company was 20.8% for 1979 and 22.0% for 1989. The U.S. market share of Japanese automobiles was 15.2% for 1979 and 25.6% for 1989. Determine the break-even year.

TABLE 1-22

	Baubles		Trinkets	
	units	amount	units	amount
Sales	10,000	$10,000	7500	$10,000
Costs				
Fixed		$ 2000		$ 5600
Variable		6000		3000
		$ 8000		$ 8600
Income Before Taxes		$ 2000		$ 1400

• Supply, Demand, and Equilibrium Point

Determine the supply and demand equations and the equilibrium point. Graph the results.

46. *Demand:* If a given product is priced at $7 per unit, there is a demand for 4 units; if the product is priced at $6 per unit, there is a demand for 8 units.
   Supply: If the product is priced at $9 per unit, suppliers are willing to produce 4 units; if the product is priced at $23 per unit, suppliers are willing to produce 12 units.

• Consumption Function, MPC, and MPS

For Exercises 47 and 48, if x denotes income and y denotes consumption, then
a) Calculate and interpret the MPC.
b) Calculate and interpret the MPS.
c) Determine the equation defining the linear consumption function.
d) Graph the result of part C.

47.

x	y
50	85
60	94

48.

x	y
40	62
70	86

• Linear Depreciation

49. A construction company buys a truck for $80,000. The useful life of the truck is 5 years, after which time it will have a scrap value of $5000.
a) Find the linear equation relating the value of the truck, y, to its age, x.
b) Graph the result of part a.
c) What is the value of the truck after 3 years?

2

GRAPHING POLYNOMIAL AND RATIONAL FUNCTIONS

Introductory Application

Revenue and Cost Functions and Break-Even Points

Revenue Function

In Chapter 1, we learned that if the unit selling price of a particular product is constant, the resulting revenue function is linear. However, for some businesses, the unit selling prices of their products depend on the demand levels of the products. Such a relationship between unit selling price and demand is given by a demand equation

$$p = f(x)$$

where p denotes the unit price and x denotes the number of units demanded of the product. The sales revenue function is defined as follows:

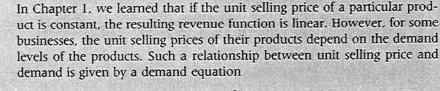

$$R(x) = xp$$
$$= xf(x)$$

If the demand equation is linear, the sales revenue function usually resembles the curve of Figure 2-A. Studying the graph of the revenue function of Figure 2-A, notice that sales revenue increases up to a certain point and then decreases as the number of units sold increases. In Section 2-3, we will explain in greater detail why this occurs.

Break-Even Analysis

If a business's cost function is linear, then a graph of both the cost and sales revenue functions is typified by that of Figure 2-B⁰. Note, in Figure 2-B, that the intersection points of the graphs of the cost and revenue functions are the points where sales revenue = cost. As in Chapter 1, these points are called break-even points. We will discuss such cases more fully in Section 2-3.

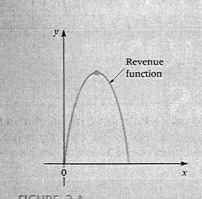

FIGURE 2-A

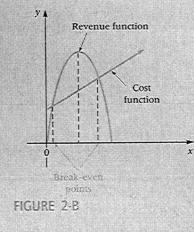

FIGURE 2-B

2-1 • GRAPHING CONCEPTS

In this section, we discuss graphing concepts that enable us to quickly sketch the graphs of functions whose equations are derived from equations of functions with known graphs. Also, we will use these graphing concepts to explain the graphs of functions, where appropriate, in this chapter.

Vertical Shifts

We begin with the graph of the absolute value function

$$f(x) = |x|$$

that was discussed in Chapter 1. Recall that to each non-negative number, the absolute value function associates the non-negative number; to each negative number, the absolute value function associates the negative number's additive inverse.

We now consider the graph of the function

$$y = |x| + 4$$

The y-values of this new function are 4 greater than those of the absolute value function. Thus, the graph of $y = |x| + 4$ is obtained from the graph of $y = |x|$ by *lifting the graph* of $y = |x|$ *vertically by 4 units*. This is called a **vertical shift** and is illustrated in Figure 2-1.

Also, the graph of

$$y = |x| - 4$$

is obtained from the graph of $y = |x|$ by *lowering the graph* of $y = |x|$ *vertically by 4 units* as the y-values of $y = |x| - 4$ are 4 less than those of $y = |x|$. This *vertical shift* is also illustrated in Figure 2-1.

We generalize as follows.

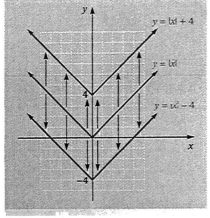

FIGURE 2-1

 SUMMARY

Vertical Shifts

Assume the graph of $y = f(x)$ is known.

1. The graph of $y = f(x) + c$, where $c > 0$, is obtained by *lifting the graph* of $y = f(x)$ *vertically by* c *units*, as illustrated in Figure 2-2.

2. The graph of $y = f(x) - c$, where $c > 0$, is obtained by *lowering the graph* of $y = f(x)$ *vertically by* c *units*, as illustrated in Figure 2-2.

continues

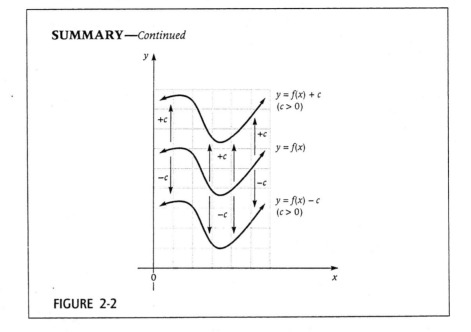

FIGURE 2-2

Horizontal Shifts

Consider the graph of

$$y = |x - 5|$$

as illustrated in Figure 2-3. Note that for any given value of y, the x-coordinates of points on $y = |x - 5|$ are 5 greater than those of $y = |x|$. Thus, the graph of $y = |x - 5|$ is obtained by *shifting the graph* of $y = |x|$ *horizontally to the right by 5 units*, as illustrated in Figure 2-3. This is an example of a **horizontal shift.**

Observe also in Figure 2-3 that the graph of the function

$$y = |x + 5|$$

is obtained by *shifting the graph* of $y = |x|$ *horizontally to the left by 5 units*. This is because for any given value of y, the x-coordinates of points on $y = |x + 5|$ are 5 less than those of $y = |x|$.

We generalize as follows.

SUMMARY

Horizontal Shifts

Assume that the graph of $y = f(x)$ is known.
1. The graph of $y = f(x - c)$, where $c > 0$, is obtained by *shifting the graph of $y = f(x)$ horizontally to the right by* c *units*, as illustrated in Figure 2-4.
2. The graph of $y = f(x + c)$, where $c > 0$, is obtained by *shifting the graph of $y = f(x)$ horizontally to the left by* c *units*, as illustrated in Figure 2-4.

continues

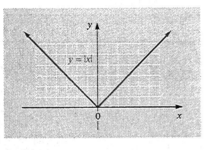

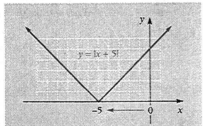

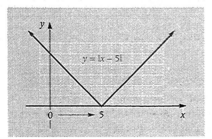

FIGURE 2-3

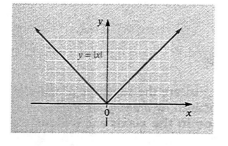

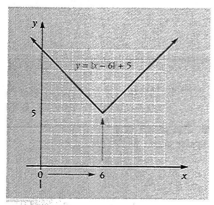

FIGURE 2-5

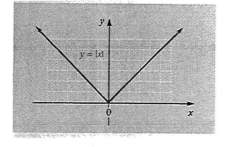

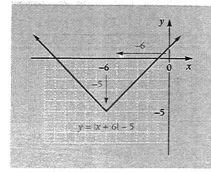

FIGURE 2-7

SUMMARY—*Continued*

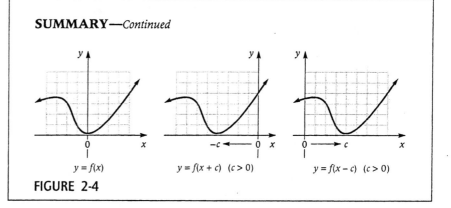

FIGURE 2-4

• **EXAMPLE 2-1** _____

Graph $y = |x - 6| + 5$.

Solution

This graph involves a horizontal shift followed by a vertical shift. First, the graph of $y = |x - 6|$ is obtained by shifting the graph of $y = |x|$ horizontally to the right by 6 units. Then the graph of $y = |x - 6| + 5$ is obtained by lifting the graph of $y = |x - 6|$ vertically by 5 units. This is illustrated in Figure 2-5.   •

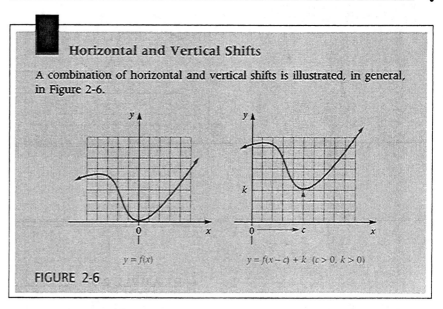

Horizontal and Vertical Shifts

A combination of horizontal and vertical shifts is illustrated, in general, in Figure 2-6.

FIGURE 2-6

• **EXAMPLE 2-2** _____

Graph $y = |x + 6| - 5$.

Solution

The graph of $y = |x + 6|$ is obtained by shifting the graph of $y = |x|$ horizontally to the left by 6 units. Then the graph of $y = |x + 6| - 5$ is obtained by lowering the graph of $y = |x + 6|$ vertically by 5 units. This is illustrated in Figure 2-7.   •

FIGURE 2-8

Reflections in the *x*-Axis

Consider the function

$$y = -|x|$$

Since the *y*-values of the function $y = -|x|$ are the negatives of those of $y = |x|$, then the graph of $y = -|x|$ is obtained by *drawing the graph* of $y = |x|$ *upside down*. This is called a **reflection in the *x*-axis** and is illustrated in Figure 2-8.

We generalize as follows.

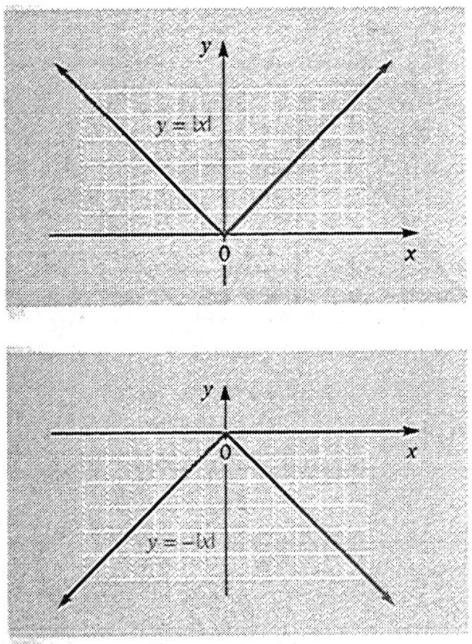

■ SUMMARY

Reflections in the *x*-Axis

Assume the graph of $y = f(x)$ is known. The graph of $y = -f(x)$ is obtained by *drawing the graph* of $y = f(x)$ *upside down*, as illustrated in Figure 2-9.

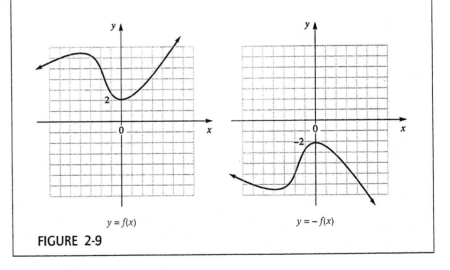

$y = f(x)$ $y = -f(x)$

FIGURE 2-9

• EXAMPLE 2-3

Graph $y = -|x - 3| + 5$.

Solution

We begin with the graph of $y = |x|$ and shift it horizontally to the right 3 units to obtain the graph of $y = |x - 3|$. Then we draw the graph of $y = |x - 3|$ upside down (reflection in the *x*-axis) to obtain the graph of $y = -|x - 3|$. Finally, we lift the graph of $y = -|x - 3|$ vertically 5 units (vertical shift) to obtain the graph of $y = -|x - 3| + 5$. This is illustrated in Figure 2-10.

Horizontal shift

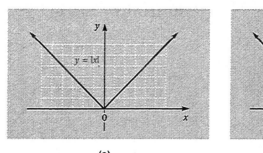

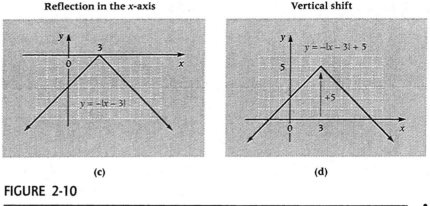

(a)

(b)

Reflection in the x-axis

Vertical shift

(c)

(d)

FIGURE 2-10

Symmetry with respect to the vertical axis (even functions)

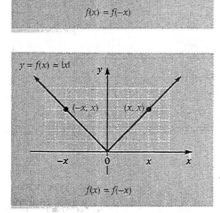

$y = f(x)$

$(-x, y)$ (x, y)

$-x$ 0 x x

$f(x) = f(-x)$

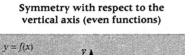

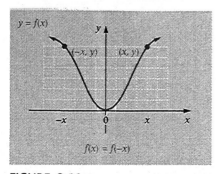

$y = f(x)$

$(-x, y)$ (x, y)

$-x$ 0 x x

$f(x) = f(-x)$

FIGURE 2-11

Symmetry

Observe the graphs of Figure 2-11. Note that for any of these graphs, if (x, y) is on the graph, then $(-x, y)$ is also on the graph. In other words, $f(-x) = f(x)$ for such functions. If a function f satisfies the above condition, it is called an **even function,** and its graph is **symmetrical with respect to the vertical axis.**

Observe the graphs of Figure 2-12 on page 72. Note that for any of these graphs, if (x, y) is on the graph, then $(-x, -y)$ is on the graph. In other words, $f(-x) = -f(x)$ for such functions. If a function satisfies this condition, it is called an **odd function,** and its graph is **symmetrical with respect to the origin.**

We generalize as follows.

SUMMARY

Symmetry

1. *Symmetry with respect to the vertical axis.* If $f(-x) = f(x)$, then f is an **even function,** and its graph is symmetrical with respect to the vertical axis, as illustrated in Figure 2-13.

continues

Symmetry with respect to the orgin
(odd functions)

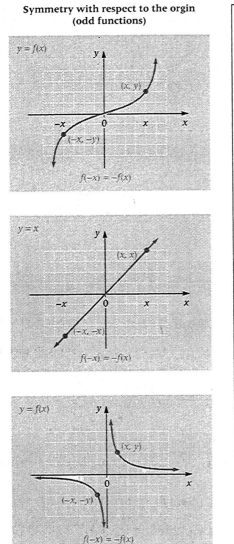

FIGURE 2-12

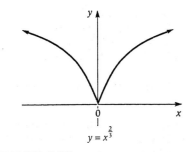

$$y = x^{\frac{2}{3}}$$

FIGURE 2-15

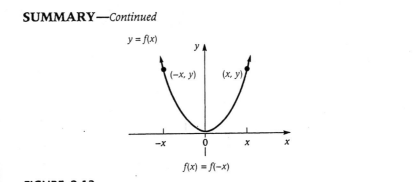

FIGURE 2-13

2. *Symmetry with respect to the origin.* If $f(-x) = -f(x)$, then f is an **odd function,** and its graph is symmetrical with respect to the origin, as illustrated in Figure 2-14.

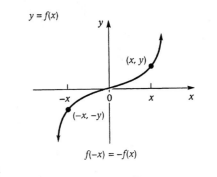

FIGURE 2-14

• **EXAMPLE 2-4**

Note that

$$f(x) = x^{2/3}$$

is an even function, as indicated by its table of x- and y-values below. Specifically, $f(-x) = f(x)$, and the graph of f is symmetrical with respect to the y-axis, as illustrated in Figure 2-15.

x	-3	-2	-1	0	1	2	3
$f(x)$	2.08	1.59	1	0	1	1.59	2.08

• **EXAMPLE 2-5**

Note that

$$f(x) = x^{1/3}$$

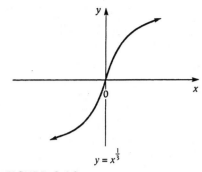

FIGURE 2-16

is an odd function, as indicated by its table of x- and y-values below. Specifically, $f(-x) = -f(x)$, and the graph of f is symmetrical with respect to the origin, as illustrated in Figure 2-16.

x	-3	-2	-1	0	1	2	3
$f(x)$	-1.44	-1.26	-1	0	1	1.26	1.44

Exercises 2-1

Graph each of the following.

1. $y = -|x - 2|$ **2.** $y = -|x + 6|$ **3.** $y = |x - 8| + 2$
4. $y = -|x - 6| + 4$ **5.** $y = -|x + 3| - 8$ **6.** $y = -|x + 7| - 9$

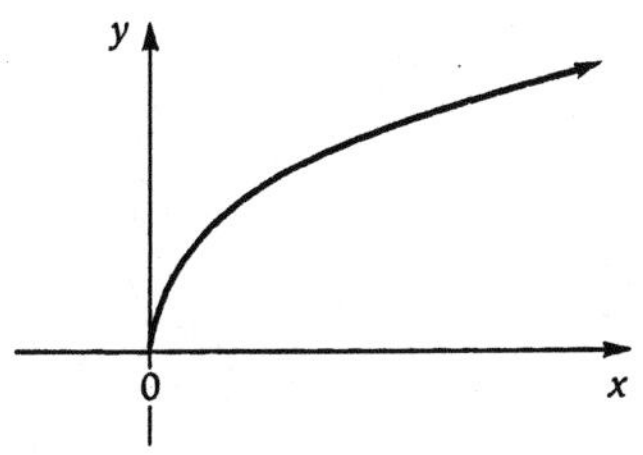

Observe the graph of $f(x) = x^{2/3}$ of Figure 2-15, Example 2-4. Then graph each of the following.

7. $f(x) = (x - 3)^{2/3}$ **8.** $f(x) = (x + 4)^{2/3}$
9. $f(x) = (x + 7)^{2/3} + 5$ **10.** $f(x) = (x - 6)^{2/3} - 2$
11. $f(x) = -(x - 5)^{2/3}$ **12.** $f(x) = -(x + 2)^{2/3}$
13. $f(x) = -(x - 3)^{2/3} - 1$ **14.** $f(x) = -(x + 2)^{2/3} + 4$

Observe the graph of $f(x) = x^{1/3}$ of Figure 2-16, Example 2-5. Then graph each of the following.

15. $f(x) = (x + 2)^{1/3}$ **16.** $f(x) = (x - 5)^{1/3}$
17. $f(x) = (x - 2)^{1/3} + 9$ **18.** $f(x) = (x + 1)^{1/3} - 2$
19. $f(x) = -(x - 1)^{1/3}$ **20.** $f(x) = -(x + 2)^{1/3}$
21. $f(x) = -(x - 5)^{1/3} + 2$ **22.** $f(x) = -(x - 4)^{1/3} + 7$

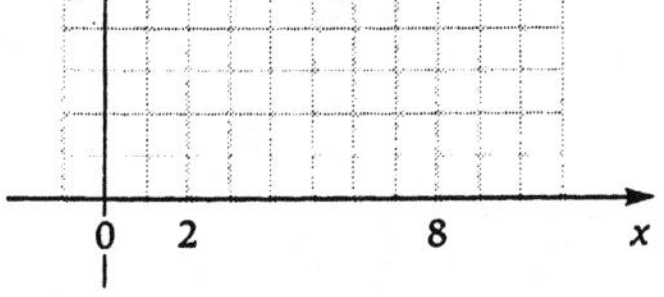

The graph of $f(x) = \sqrt{x}$ is given in Figure 2-17. Graph each of the following.

23. $f(x) = \sqrt{x - 5}$ **24.** $f(x) = \sqrt{x + 2}$
25. $f(x) = \sqrt{x + 9} + 2$ **26.** $f(x) = \sqrt{x - 4} - 6$
27. $f(x) = -\sqrt{x}$ **28.** $f(x) = -\sqrt{x + 1}$
29. $f(x) = -\sqrt{x - 3}$ **30.** $f(x) = -\sqrt{x + 1} - 2$

The graph of some function f is given in Figure 2-18. Graph each of the following.

31. $y = f(x - 2)$ **32.** $y = f(x + 4)$ **33.** $y = -f(x)$
34. $y = -f(x - 6)$ **35.** $y = f(x - 1) + 4$ **36.** $y = -f(x) + 5$
37. $y = -f(x - 2) + 1$ **38.** $y = -f(x + 1) - 2$ **39.** $y = -f(x) - 6$

FIGURE 2-17

FIGURE 2-18

For each of the graphs below, state whether the function is odd, even, or neither.

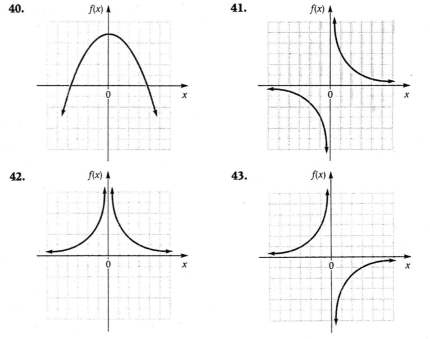

40.   **41.**

42.   **43.**

For each of the following:
a) Determine whether the function is odd, even, or neither by filling in the indicated table of x- and $f(x)$-values. Use a calculator if necessary.
b) Sketch a graph by plotting the points from part a.

44. $f(x) = x^2$

x	−3	−2	−1	0	1	2	3
$f(x)$							

45. $f(x) = x^3$

x	−3	−2	−1	0	1	2.	3
$f(x)$							

46. $f(x) = 1/(1 + x^2)$

x	−3	−2	−1	−1/2	0	1/2	1	2	3
$f(x)$									

47. $f(x) = 1/x$

x	−3	−2	−1	−1/2	0	1/2	1	2	3
$f(x)$									

48. $f(x) = (x - 2)^2$

x	-3	$-2.$	-1	0	1	2	3
$f(x)$							

Applications

Cost, Revenue, and Profit Functions

The graphs of cost, revenue, and profit functions for some product are given in Figure 2-19.

49. Indicate the effect on the graph of the cost function of a $100 increase in the fixed cost.

50. Indicate the effect on the graph of the profit function of a $100 increase in the fixed cost.

Market Dynamics: Supply, Demand, Equilibrium

In Chapter 1, we learned that a demand function relates the unit price of some product to the demand for that product. Also, a supply function relates the unit price of some product to the number of units supplied of the product. In Chapter 1, we worked with linear supply and demand functions. Thus, their corresponding graphs were straight lines. If the graph of a demand function is nonlinear, its graph is usually referred to as a **demand curve**. Analogously, if the graph of a supply function is nonlinear, its graph is called a **supply curve.**

51. The graphs of the supply and demand functions for some product are given in Figure 2-20. If the demand for this product increases by 5 units, then the graph of the demand function will shift horizontally to the right by 5 units, as illustrated. State the new equilibrium price.

52. Consider the supply and demand curves of Figure 2-21. If the supply of this product increases by 4 units, then the graph of the supply function will shift horizontally to the right by 4 units. State the new equilibrium price.

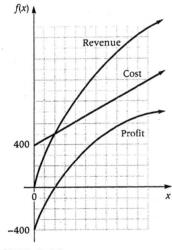

FIGURE 2-19

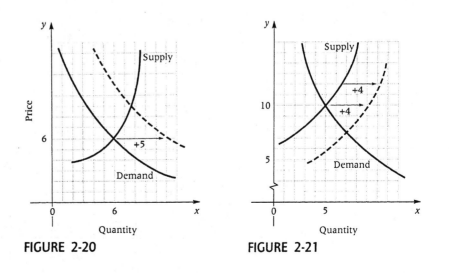

FIGURE 2-20　　　　　　　　　　**FIGURE 2-21**

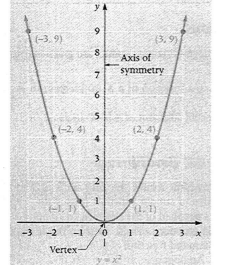

FIGURE 2-22

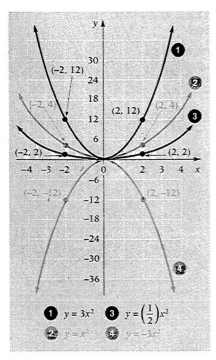

FIGURE 2-23

2-2

• QUADRATIC FUNCTIONS AND THEIR GRAPHS

In this and the next section, we will learn to graph equations like

$$y = 3x^2 - 4x + 7$$

Such an equation defines a **quadratic function.** Note that the highest-powered term of a quadratic equation is of the **second degree.**

$$y = f(x) = 3x^2 - 4x + 7$$

second-degree   first-degree   constant
term   term   term

In general, any equation of the form

$$y = ax^2 + bx + c$$

where a, b, and c are constant real numbers and $a \neq 0$, is called a **quadratic equation.** Without the restriction $a \neq 0$, the equation becomes the linear equation $y = bx + c$.

If the quadratic equation

$$y = 3x^2 - 4x + 7$$

is compared with the general form

$$y = ax^2 + bx + c$$

then $a = 3$, $b = -4$, and $c = 7$.

As a start in learning to graph quadratic functions, we consider the simplest of all quadratic equations, which is

$$y = x^2$$

Comparing this equation with the general quadratic form, $y = ax^2 + bx + c$, we have $a = 1$, $b = 0$, and $c = 0$.

A sketch of $y = x^2$ may be obtained by finding some ordered pairs (x, y) satisfying the equation and plotting their corresponding points on the rectangular coordinate system. Arbitrarily choosing values of x and finding their corresponding y-values, we have the following:

x-Value	Equation $(y = x^2)$	Ordered Pair (x, y)
If $x = -3$, then	$y = (-3)^2 = 9$	$(-3, 9)$
If $x = -2$, then	$y = (-2)^2 = 4$	$(-2, 4)$
If $x = -1$, then	$y = (-1)^2 = 1$	$(-1, 1)$
If $x = 0$, then	$y = 0^2 = 0$	$(0, 0)$
If $x = 1$, then	$y = 1^2 = 1$	$(1, 1)$
If $x = 2$, then	$y = 2^2 = 4$	$(2, 4)$
If $x = 3$, then	$y = 3^2 = 9$	$(3, 9)$

Plotting the ordered pairs (x, y) and sketching the curve through them, we obtain the graph of Figure 2-22. This graph form is called a **parabola.** In

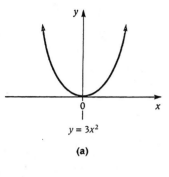

$y = 3x^2$

(a)

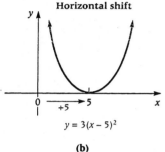

Horizontal shift

$y = 3(x - 5)^2$

(b)

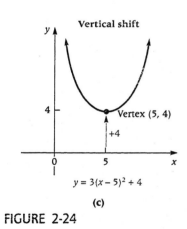

Vertical shift

Vertex (5, 4)

+4

$y = 3(x - 5)^2 + 4$

(c)

FIGURE 2-24

fact, the graph of any quadratic function is a parabola. Note that the origin, $(0, 0)$, is the lowest point on the parabola $y = x^2$ of Figure 2-22. The lowest point on the parabola is called the **vertex.** Thus, $(0, 0)$ is the vertex of $y = x^2$.

Still referring to the parabola $y = x^2$ of Figure 2-22 note that the y-axis separates the parabola into two symmetrical parts, each the mirror image of the other. Such a vertical line passing through the vertex is called the **axis of symmetry.**

We now consider quadratic equations of the form

$$y = ax^2$$

with $a \neq 1$. If $a > 0$, then the parabola has the same general shape as $y = x^2$ of Figure 2-22, but it is narrowed if $a > 1$ and widened if $a < 1$. If $a < 0$, then the y-coordinates are negative, and the parabola appears below the x-axis. To illustrate these comments, see the graphs of $y = x^2$ $y = 3x^2$, $y = (1/2)x^2$, and $y = -3x^2$ in Figure 2-23.

The graphs of quadratic functions with $a > 0$ are said to *open up*, whereas those with $a < 0$ are said to *open down*. Thus, the graphs of $y = x^2$, $y = 3x^2$, and $y = (1/2)x^2$ of Figure 2-23 are described as opening up, while the graph of $y = -3x^2$ is said to open down. Note that for a parabola that *opens down*, its **vertex** is the *highest point* on the parabola.

We now consider the graph of the quadratic function defined by

$$y = 3(x - 5)^2 + 4$$

The graph of this function can be sketched by drawing the graph of $y = 3x^2$, shifting it horizontally to the right by 5 units, and then shifting the result vertically by 4 units. This is illustrated in Figure 2-24.

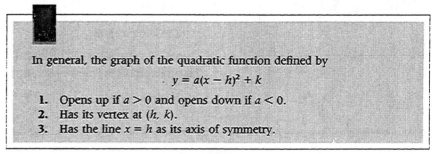

In general, the graph of the quadratic function defined by

$$y = a(x - h)^2 + k$$

1. Opens up if $a > 0$ and opens down if $a < 0$.
2. Has its vertex at (h, k).
3. Has the line $x = h$ as its axis of symmetry.

We now consider quadratic equations of the form

$$y = f(x) = ax^2 + bx + c$$

We will derive a formula for the $x =$ coordinate of the vertex, (h, k), in terms of a, b, and c by expressing the equation $y = a(x - h)^2 + k$ in the form $y = ax^2 + bx + c$. We begin with $y = a(x - h)^2 + k$ and replace $(x - h)^2$ with its equivalent expression, $x^2 - 2hx + h^2$, to obtain

$$y = a(x^2 - 2hx + h^2) + k$$

Simplifying this expression, we get

$$y = ax^2 - 2ahx + ah^2 + k$$

Comparing this result with the general quadratic form, $y = ax^2 + bx + c$, we have

$$b = -2ah \quad \text{and} \quad c = ah^2 + k$$

Solving the equation $b = -2ah$ for h, we obtain

$$h = \frac{-b}{2a} \qquad \text{x-coordinate of vertex}$$

Of course, the corresponding y-coordinate of the vertex is obtained by substituting the above result into the quadratic equation. Thus, the y-coordinate of the vertex is given by

$$f(-b/2a) \qquad \text{y-coordinate of vertex}$$

We now consider the following example.

• **EXAMPLE 2-6** ———————————————————————————

Graph $y = f(x) = 3x^2 + 5x + 2$.

Solution

Comparing this equation with the form $y = f(x) = ax^2 + bx + c$, we have $a = 3$, $b = 5$, and $c = 2$. Since a is positive, the parabola opens up. The $x =$ coordinate of the vertex, (h, k), is

$$h = -\frac{b}{2a} = -\frac{5}{2(3)} = -\frac{5}{6} \qquad \text{x-coordinate of vertex}$$

The y-coordinate of the vertex is

$$f\left(-\frac{b}{2a}\right) = f\left(-\frac{5}{6}\right) = 3\left(-\frac{5}{6}\right)^2 + 5\left(-\frac{5}{6}\right) + 2 = -\frac{1}{12} \qquad \text{y-coordinate of vertex}$$

Thus, the vertex is $(-5/6, -1/12)$.

The y-intercept is

$$y = f(0) = 3(0^2) + 5(0) + 2 = 2$$

The x-intercepts are found by setting $y = 0$ and solving for x. Hence,

$$0 = 3x^2 + 5x + 2$$
$$0 = (3x + 2)(x + 1)$$
$$3x + 2 = 0 \qquad\qquad x + 1 = 0$$
$$x = -\frac{2}{3} \qquad\qquad x = -1$$

Therefore, the x-intercepts are $(-2/3, 0)$ and $(-1, 0)$. The graph appears in Figure 2-25.

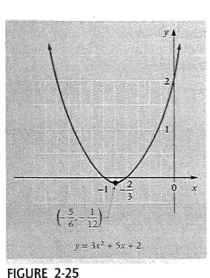

FIGURE 2-25

Quadratic Formula

When finding the x-intercepts of a parabola, we must often solve a quadratic equation of the form

$$ax^2 + bx + c = 0$$

where a, b, and c are constant real numbers and $a \neq 0$. Sometimes such an equation may be solved by factoring, as was the case in Example 2-6. A more general method is given by the **quadratic formula.***

Quadratic Formula

$$x = \frac{-b \pm \sqrt{b^2 - 4ac}}{2a}$$

We will review the use of the quadratic formula by calculating the x-intercepts of the parabola of Example 2-6. Substituting $a = 3$, $b = 5$, and $c = 2$ into the quadratic formula

$$x = \frac{-b \pm \sqrt{b^2 - 4ac}}{2a}$$

gives us

$$x = \frac{-5 \pm \sqrt{5^2 - 4(3)(2)}}{2(3)}$$

$$= \frac{-5 \pm \sqrt{25 - 24}}{6} = \frac{-5 \pm \sqrt{1}}{6}$$

$$= \frac{-5 \pm 1}{6} = \begin{cases} \dfrac{-5 + 1}{6} = -\dfrac{2}{3} \\[2mm] \dfrac{-5 - 1}{6} = -1 \end{cases}$$

Thus, the x-intercepts are $(-2/3, 0)$ and $(-1, 0)$.

The expression $b^2 - 4ac$, which appears under the square root sign in the quadratic formula, determines the character of the solutions. Hence, it is called the **discriminant.** Specifically,

1. If $b^2 - 4ac > 0$, there are two real solutions (two x-intercepts).
2. If $b^2 - 4ac = 0$, there is one real solution (one x-intercept).
3. If $b^2 - 4ac < 0$, there are no real solutions (no x-intercepts).

Each of the above situations is illustrated in Figure 2-26.

We now give a procedure for graphing a quadratic function.

Two *x*-intercepts: $b^2 - 4ac > 0$

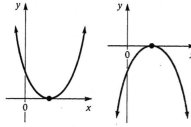

One *x*-intercept: $b^2 - 4ac = 0$

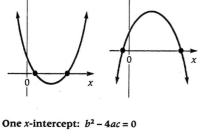

No *x*-intercepts: $b^2 - 4ac < 0$

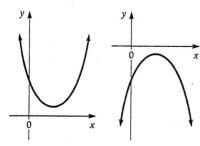

FIGURE 2-26

---

*A derivation of the quadratic formula is given in Appendix B.

To Graph a Quadratic Function

To graph a quadratic function whose equation is in the form

$$y = f(x) = ax^2 + bx + c$$

1. Determine whether the parabola *opens up* or *down*.
   Rule: If $a > 0$, parabola opens up $\cup$.
   If $a < 0$, parabola opens down $\cap$.

2. Find the y-*intercept*.

$$y = f(0) = a(0)^2 + b(0) + c = c$$

   Hence, the y-intercept is always $(0, c)$.

3. Find the coordinates of the *vertex* (_____, _____).
   $$-b/2a \qquad f(-b/2a)$$

4. Find any x-*intercepts*. Set $y = 0$ and solve the resulting equation for x.
   Note:
   • You might have to factor.
   • You might have to use the quadratic formula.
   • There will be two, one, or no x-intercept.

• **EXAMPLE 2-7** _____

Graph $f(x) = x^2 - 2x - 8$.

Solution

Note that $a = 1$, $b = -2$, and $c = -8$.

1. The parabola opens up since $a > 0$ ($a = 1$).
2. The y-intercept is $(0, c) = (0, -8)$.
3. Vertex (_____, _____)

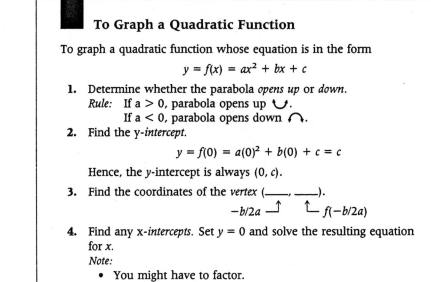

4. x-intercepts

$$0 = x^2 - 2x - 8$$
$$0 = (x + 2)(x - 4)$$
$$x + 2 = 0 \qquad \text{or} \qquad x - 4 = 0$$
$$\boxed{x = -2} \qquad\qquad \boxed{x = 4}$$

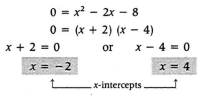
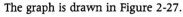

The graph is drawn in Figure 2-27.

• **EXAMPLE 2-8** _____

Graph $f(x) = -x^2 + 6x$.

Solution

Note that $a = -1$, $b = 6$, and $c = 0$.

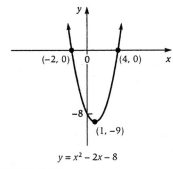

$y = x^2 - 2x - 8$

FIGURE 2-27

1. The parabola opens down since $a < 0$ $(a = -1)$.
2. The y-intercept is $(0, c) = (0, 0)$.
3. Vertex (_____, _____)

$$x\text{-coordinate:} \quad -b/2a = -6/2(-1) = 3$$
$$y\text{-coordinate:} \quad f(3) = -(3)^2 + 6(3) = 9$$

4. x-intercepts

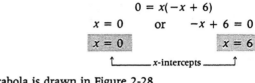

$$0 = -x^2 + 6x$$
$$0 = x(-x + 6)$$
$$x = 0 \quad \text{or} \quad -x + 6 = 0$$
$$\boxed{x = 0} \qquad\qquad \boxed{x = 6}$$

↑—————— x-intercepts —————↑

The parabola is drawn in Figure 2-28.

$f(x) = -x^2 + 6x$

(3, 9)

0   6 x

FIGURE 2-28

• **EXAMPLE 2-9** _____

Graph $f(x) = x^2 - 6x + 9$.

Solution

Note that $a = 1$, $b = -6$, and $c = 9$.

1. The parabola opens up since $a > 0$ $(a = 1)$.
2. The y-intercept is $(0, c) = (0, 9)$.
3. Vertex (_____, _____)

$$x\text{-coordinate:} \quad -b/2a = -(-6)/2(1) = 3$$
$$y\text{-coordinate:} \quad f(3) = 3^2 - 6(3) + 9 = 0$$

4. x-intercepts

$$0 = x^2 - 6x + 9$$
$$0 = (x - 3)^2 \qquad \text{Perfect square}$$
$$0 = x - 3$$
$$x = 3 \qquad \text{Only one } x\text{-intercept}$$

The parabola is drawn in Figure 2-29.

$f(x) = x^2 - 6x + 9$

9

0   3 x

FIGURE 2-29

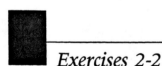

Exercises 2-2

1. Graph each of the following:
   a) $y = 5x^2$
   b) $y = -5x^2$
   c) $y = (1/2)x^2$
   d) $y = -(1/2)x^2$

2. Graph the following on the same set of axes: $y = x^2$, $y = 6x^2$, $y = (1/4)x^2$.
3. Graph the following on the same set of axes: $y = -x^2$, $y = -4x^2$, $y = -(1/3)x^2$.
4. Graph the following on the same set of axes: $f(x) = x^2$, $f(x) = 3x^2$, $f(x) = 7x^2$.

Graph each of the following by using a vertical shift.

5. $y = x^2 + 7$
6. $f(x) = 3x^2 + 5$
7. $y = x^2 - 9$
8. $y = -x^2 + 9$
9. $f(x) = 2x^2 - 8$
10. $y = -4x^2 + 36$

Graph each of the following by using a horizontal shift.

11. $y = (x - 3)^2$

12. $y = (x + 3)^2$

13. $y = 4(x - 1)^2$

14. $y = 4(x + 1)^2$

15. $f(x) = -2(x + 5)^2$

16. $f(x) = -2(x - 3)^2$

Graph each of the following by shifting.

17. $y = 2(x - 1)^2 + 3$

18. $y = -(x - 4)^2 - 1$

19. $f(x) = 3(x - 2)^2 - 1$

20. $f(x) = -3(x - 2)^2 + 4$

21. $y = -3(x + 2)^2 - 5$

22. $y = 4(x + 3)^2 - 2$

23. $f(x) = (x + 3)^2 - 1$

24. $f(x) = (x - 2)^2 + 4$

25. $f(x) = -(x + 2)^2 + 1$

26. $f(x) = -(x - 3)^2 + 2$

Graph each of the following.

27. $y = 2x^2 + 8x$

28. $f(x) = -3x^2 + 7x$

29. $f(x) = x^2 - 5x$

30. $y = -x^2 + 8x$

31. $y = -2x^2 + 6x$

32. $y = 3x^2 - 2x$

33. $y = x^2 - 6x + 5$

34. $y = x^2 - 2x - 3$

35. $f(x) = x^2 - 6x - 16$

36. $f(x) = x^2 - 8x + 7$

37. $y = x^2 - 2x - 15$

38. $y = x^2 - 8x + 15$

39. $y = x^2 - 4x - 5$

40. $y = x^2 + 7x + 6$

41. $f(x) = -5x^2 + 6x + 4$

42. $y = x^2 - 8x + 16$

43. $y = -x^2 + 8x - 16$

44. $f(x) = x^2 + x + 1$

45. $f(x) = x^2 - 10x + 26$

46. $y = 2x^2 - 3x + 6$

47. $f(x) = 2x^2 + 4x + 1$

48. $f(x) = x^2 - 6x + 7$

49. $f(x) = x^2 - 10x + 25$

50. $f(x) = x^2 + 10x + 25$

51. $y = x^2 - 6x + 9$

52. $f(x) = x^2 + 6x + 9$

Equations in Factored Form

If the equation of a quadratic function is given in factored form, such as

$$f(x) = a(x - x_1)(x - x_2)$$

where a, x_1, and x_2 are constants, then the x-intercepts are easily determined as shown below.

$$0 = a(x - x_1)(x - x_2)$$

$x - x_1 = 0$ or $x - x_2 = 0$

$$\boxed{x = x_1} \qquad \boxed{x = x_2}$$

$\llcorner\!\!\_\_\_\_\_$ x-intercepts $\_\_\_\_\_\!\!\lrcorner$

Then, since the x-coordinate of the vertex lies midway between the x-intercepts (due to symmetry), it is determined as shown below.

$$x\text{-coordinate of vertex} = \frac{x_1 + x_2}{2}$$

The y-coordinate of the vertex is determined as indicated below.

$$y\text{-coordinate of vertex} = f\left(\frac{x_1 + x_2}{2}\right)$$

The sign of coefficient a indicates whether the parabola opens up or down. Specifically, if a is positive, the parabola opens up, and if a is negative, the parabola opens down. The y-intercept is determined by setting $x = 0$ and solving for y.

Using the above comments, graph each of the following.

53. $y = (x - 2)(x + 3)$

54. $f(x) = (x + 1)(x - 5)$

55. $y = 4(x - 2)(x + 3)$

56. $y = -2(x + 1)(x - 5)$

57. $f(x) = (x - 6)^2$ **58.** $y = -(x - 6)^2$
59. $y = -5(x + 1)^2$ **60.** $f(x) = (x + 6)(x - 6)$
61. $y = (x - 2)(x + 2)$ **62.** $f(x) = (x + 6)(x + 6)$
63. $y = -3(x - 2)(x + 2)$ **64.** $f(x) = 4(x + 1)(x - 1)$

2-3

• APPLICATIONS OF QUADRATIC FUNCTIONS

Revenue, Cost, and Profit Functions

Revenue Function. We begin this section by discussing, in greater detail, the introductory application to this chapter. Recall that sometimes the unit selling price of a firm's product depends on the demand level of the product. Such a relationship is given by a demand equation

$$p = f(x)$$

where p denotes the unit price and x denotes the number of units demanded of the product. The sales revenue function is determined as follows.

$$\text{sales revenue} = (\text{number of units sold})(\text{unit price})$$
$$R(x) = xp$$
$$= xf(x)$$

As an example, suppose we are given the demand equation

$$p = -20x + 14{,}100$$

and asked to find the sales revenue function $R(x)$. We proceed as follows.

$$R(x) = xp$$
$$= x(-20x + 14{,}100)$$
$$= -20x^2 + 14{,}100x$$

This revenue function is graphed in Figure 2-30(a). Observe that the vertex point gives the maximum sales revenue. Thus, the maximum sales revenue of $2,485,125 is realized when 352.5 units of the product are sold. Later in this text, we will use calculus concepts to maximize or minimize quantities.

Studying the graph of the revenue function of Figure 2-30(a), observe that after the vertex point, sales revenue decreases as the number of units sold increases. This is because of the nature of the relationship between unit price and demand as given by the demand equation. Note that as demand increases, unit price decreases. Thus, as more and more units of this product are sold, they are sold at lower and lower unit prices. This ultimately results in decreases in sales revenue as the number of units sold increases.

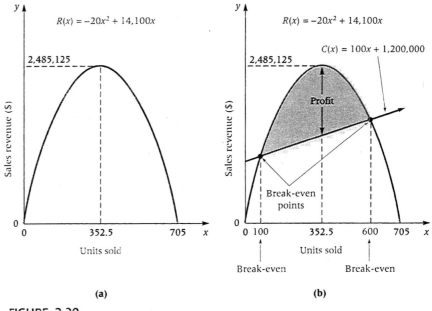

FIGURE 2-30

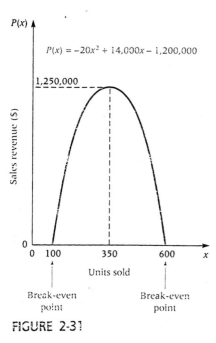

FIGURE 2-31

Cost Function. If this product has a fixed cost of $1,200,000 and a unit variable cost of $100, then the cost function is given by

$$C(x) = 100x + 1,200,000$$

Figure 2-30(b) gives a graph of both the cost and sales revenue functions on the same set of axes.

Break-Even Analysis. Note that the intersection points of the graphs of the cost and revenue functions of Figure 2-30(b) are the points where sales revenue = cost. As in Chapter 1, these points are called the **break-even points.** Also note that a positive profit results if the number of units sold lies between the x-coordinates of the break-even points. We will use the profit function to determine the break-even points.

Profit Function: Break-Even Analysis. Using the revenue and cost functions discussed above, we find the equation of the profit function as follows.

$$\text{profit} = \text{revenue} - \text{cost}$$
$$P(x) = R(x) - C(x)$$

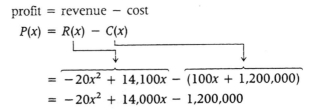

$$= -20x^2 + 14,100x - (100x + 1,200,000)$$
$$= -20x^2 + 14,000x - 1,200,000$$

The graph of the profit function is given in Figure 2-31.

Since the break-even points are the points where sales revenue = cost, or, in other words, profit = 0, we find the break-even points by finding the

x-intercepts of the profit function. Thus, we set $P(x) = 0$ and solve for x to obtain

$$0 = -20x^2 + 14,000x - 1,200,000$$
$$0 = -20(x^2 - 700x + 60,000)$$
$$0 = -20(x - 100)(x - 600)$$
$$x - 100 = 0 \quad \text{or} \quad x - 600 = 0$$
$$x = 100 \qquad\qquad x = 600 \qquad x\text{-intercepts}$$

break-even points

Thus, a positive profit is realized as long as the number of units sold, x, lies within the interval $100 < x < 600$.

Studying the graph of the profit function of Figure 2-31 note also that the vertex point gives the maximum profit. Thus, the maximum profit of $1,250,000 occurs when 350 units of this product are sold. We will, in later chapters, use calculus concepts to find maximum or minimum quantities.

Optimal Unit Price. If $x = 350$ units of this product are sold, then profit is maximized at $1,250,000. Substituting $x = 350$ into the demand equation

$$p = -20x + 14,100$$

gives the unit price that yields the maximum profit for this product. Hence,

$$p = -20(350) + 14,100$$
$$= \$7100 \qquad \text{optimal unit price}$$

Supply, Demand, and Market Equilibrium

In Chapter 1, we learned that a demand function relates the unit price of some product to the corresponding demand; a supply function relates the unit price to the corresponding supply. Given the *supply function*

$$p = x^2 + 1 \qquad (x > 0)$$

and the *demand function*

$$p = (x - 5)^2 \qquad (0 < x \le 5)$$

where p denotes the unit price in dollars and x denotes the number of units of the product supplied or demanded in millions of units, find the equilibrium point.

Remember, from Chapter 1, that the equilibrium point is the intersection of the graphs of the supply and demand functions. In other words, the equilibrium point is the point at which supply equals demand. Thus, to find the equilibrium point, we set the supply equation equal to the demand equation. Hence,

$$\text{supply} = \text{demand}$$
$$(x - 5)^2 = x^2 + 1$$
$$x^2 - 10x + 25 = x^2 + 1$$
$$-10x = -24$$
$$x = 2.4 \qquad \text{equilibrium quantity}$$

We find the equilibrium price by substituting $x = 2.4$ into either the supply or the demand equation.

Supply Function

$$p = (2.4 - 5)^2 = \$6.76 \leftarrow$$

Demand Function } —— equilibrium price

$$p = (2.4)^2 + 1 = \$6.76 \leftarrow$$

Equilibrium Point.   Thus, when supply = demand = 2.4 million units, the equilibrium price is $6.76 per unit. The graphs of the supply and demand functions are given in Figure 2-32.

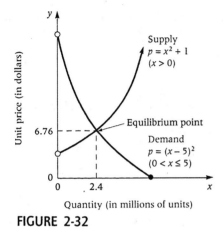

Supply
$p = x^2 + 1$
$(x > 0)$

Equilibrium point

6.76

Demand
$p = (x - 5)^2$
$(0 < x \le 5)$

2.4

Unit price (in dollars)

Quantity (in millions of units)

FIGURE 2-32

• EXAMPLE 2-10   Quality Control and Profits. ————

This problem is adapted from one that appeared on a past Uniform CPA Examination. MacKenzie Park sells its trivets for $0.25 per unit. The variable cost is $0.10 per trivet. Production capacity is limited to 15,000 trivets per day.

The company does not maintain an inspection system, but has an agreement to reimburse the wholesaler $0.50 for each defective unit the wholesaler finds. The wholesaler uses a method of inspection that detects all defective units. The number of defective units in each lot of 300 units is equal to the daily unit production rate divided by 200. Let x = daily production in units.

a)   Determine the algebraic expression that represents the number of defective units per day.

b)   Determine the function that expresses the total daily contribution to profit, including the reimbursement to the wholesaler for defective units.

c)   What is the maximum daily profit? How many units are produced daily in order to yield the maximum daily profit?

Solutions

a)   If x = daily production in units and a lot contains 300 units, then $x/300$ lots are produced in a day. Each of the $x/300$ lots contains $x/200$ defective units. Thus, the number of defective units per day is

$$\frac{x}{200} \cdot \frac{x}{300} = \frac{x^2}{60,000}$$

b)   First, we have

$$\text{profit} = \text{sales revenue} - \text{cost} - \text{reimbursement}$$

$$P(x) = 0.25x - 0.10x - 0.50\left(\frac{x^2}{60,000}\right)$$

$$= 0.15x - \frac{x^2}{120,000}$$

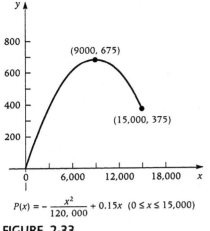

$$P(x) = -\frac{x^2}{120,000} + 0.15x \quad (0 \le x \le 15,000)$$

FIGURE 2-33

Thus, the profit function is defined by

$$P(x) = -\frac{x^2}{120,000} + 0.15x \quad (0 \le x \le 15,000)$$

Its graph appears in Figure 2-33. Since $0 \le x \le 15,000$, the parabola is drawn as a solid line over this interval.

c) As seen in Figure 2-33, the vertex, (9000, 675), is the maximum point on the parabola. Thus, when 9000 units are produced daily, the daily profit will be maximized at $675.

• **EXAMPLE 2-11   Time Series.**

A company's annual profits, P (in millions of dollars), are related to the time, t (in years), since its incorporation by the function

$$P(t) = 0.4t^2 + 30 \quad (t > 0)$$

Graph the function P and find the company's annual profit for the third year.

Solution

The graph of P is drawn by beginning with the graph of $0.4t^2$ and shifting it vertically by 30 units, as is illustrated in Figure 2-34

The company's annual profit for the third year is given by

$$P(3) = 0.4(3)^2 + 30$$
$$= \$33.6 \text{ million}$$

This corresponding point is illustrated in Figure 2-34.

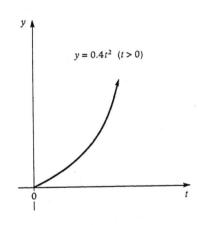

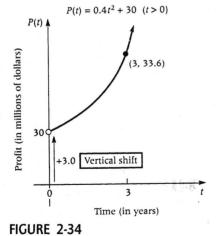

FIGURE 2-34

Light: Parabolic Reflectors

Parabolas possess the following properties when used as reflectors of light.

SUMMARY

Properties of Parabolic Reflectors

Property 1 If light rays (from some light source such as the sun or some other object) parallel to the axis of symmetry are directed toward a parabola, then such light rays will focus at a single point called the **focus,** as illustrated in Figure 2-35. The vertical distance along the axis of symmetry from the vertex of the parabola to the focus is given by

$$p = \frac{1}{4a}$$

where a is the coefficient of the x^2-term in the equation of the parabola.
continues

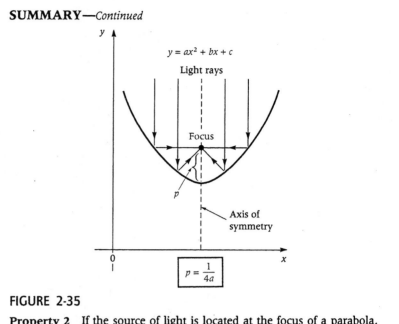

FIGURE 2-35

Property 2   If the source of light is located at the focus of a parabola, then light rays will reflect parallel to the axis of symmetry. This is graphically illustrated by reversing the direction of the arrows in Figure 2-35.

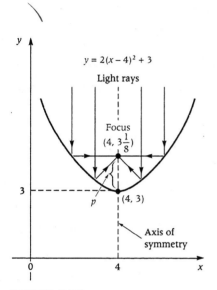

FIGURE 2-36

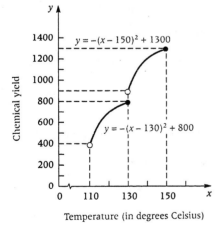

$$y = f(x) = \begin{cases} -(x - 130)^2 + 800 \text{ if } 110 < x \le 130 \\ -(x - 150)^2 + 1300 \text{ if } 130 < x \le 150 \end{cases}$$

FIGURE 2-37

Because they possess the above properties, parabolic reflectors are used for TV dishes, solar collectors, satellite communications, flashlights, automobile headlights, and more.

As an example, if the light rays are directed toward the parabola

$$y = 2(x - 4)^2 + 3$$

as illustrated in Figure 2-36, then the distance, p, from the vertex to the focus is

$$p = \frac{1}{4a} = \frac{1}{4(2)} = \frac{1}{8}$$

Thus, the focus is given by the point $(4, 3\frac{1}{8})$, as illustrated in Figure 2-36

Productivity: Chemical Process Yield

The productivity of a chemical process is measured in terms of its yield. After running a chemical process many times, a chemical company discovered that the yield, y, of the process is dependent on the temperature, x (in degrees Celsius), as given by the function

$$y = f(x) = \begin{cases} -(x - 130)^2 + 800 & \text{if } 110 < x \le 130 \\ -(x - 150)^2 + 1300 & \text{if } 130 < x \le 150 \end{cases}$$

Since this function is defined by more than one formula, then, as was discussed in Section 1-1, it is said to be **piecewise defined.** The parabola

$y = -(x - 130)^2 + 800$ over the interval $110 < x \le 130$ constitutes the first piece; the parabola $y = -(x - 150)^2 + 1300$ over the interval $130 < x \le 150$ constitutes the second piece. The graph of f is given in Figure 2-37.

Exercises 2-3

Revenue Functions

For each of the following demand dequations, p denotes the unit price in dollars, and x denotes the number of units demanded of some product.
a) Determine the equation of the revenue function, $R(x)$.
b) Graph the revenue function.
c) State the maximum sales revenue.
d) How many units must be sold in order to achieve the maximum sales revenue?
e) Substitute the result of part d into the demand equation to determine the unit price that maximizes sales revenue.

  1. Demand function: $p = -2x + 100$
  2. Demand function: $p = -3x + 180$
  3. Demand function: $p = -4x + 320$
  4. Demand function: $p = -5x + 1000$
  5. Demand function: $p = -6x + 1800$
  6. Demand function: $p = -3x + 240$

Revenue, Cost, and Profit Functions; Break-Even Analysis

For each of the following, p denotes the unit price in dollars, and x denotes the number of units produced and sold of some product.
a) Determine the equation of the revenue function, $R(x)$.
b) Graph both the revenue and cost functions on the same set of axes.
c) How many units of the product should be produced and sold in order to break even?
d) State the interval over which profit is positive.
e) Determine the equation of the profit function.
f) Graph the profit function.
g) Using the profit function, determine the break-even points. Verify that they agree with the answer to part c.
h) Using the profit function, state the interval over which profit is positive. Verify that this answer agrees with that of part d.
i) State the maximum profit.
j) How many units of the product should be produced and sold in order to maximize profit?
k) Find the unit price that yields the maximum profit.

  7. Demand function: $p = -x + 1200$
     Cost function: $C(x) = 200x + 160,000$
  8. Demand function: $p = -2x + 2400$
     Cost function: $C(x) = 400x + 180,000$
  9. Demand function: $p = -2x + 2700$
     Cost function: $C(x) = 300x + 540,000$
 10. Demand function: $p = -x + 2200$
     Cost function: $C(x) = 800x + 240,000$

Supply, Demand, and Market Equilibrium

For each of the following supply and demand functions, p denotes the unit price in dollars, and x denotes the number of units supplied or demanded of some product in millions of units.

a) Determine the equilibrium quantity.
b) Determine the equilibrium price.
c) Graph both the supply and demand functions on the same set of axes.

11. Supply function: $p = x^2 + 12$ $(x > 0)$
Demand function: $p = (x - 6)^2$ $(0 < x \le 6)$

12. Supply function: $p = x^2 + 3$ $(x > 0)$
Demand function: $p = (x - 3)^2$ $(0 < x \le 3)$

13. Supply function: $p = x^2 + 16$ $(x > 0)$
Demand function: $p = (x - 8)^2$ $(0 < x \le 8)$

14. Supply function: $p = x^2 + 20$ $(x > 0)$
Demand function: $p = (x - 10)^2$ $(0 < x \le 10)$

15. *Quality control and profits.* The Container Corporation manufactures wooden barrels. Each barrel costs $200 to produce and sells for $270. The barrels are manufactured in production lots. Each production lot contains 500 barrels. Quality control procedures have revealed that there are $x/20$ defective barrels per lot where x = the number of barrels produced per month. Each defective barrel costs the company an additional $50 to repair.

a) Find the equation that relates profit, P, with monthly production volume.
b) Graph the equation of part a.
c) Determine the maximum profit.
d) Determine the monthly production volume, x, that maximizes profit.

Time Series

16. A company's annual profits, P (in millions of dollars), are related to the time, t (in years), since its incorporation by the function

$$P(t) = 0.6t^2 + 20 \qquad (t > 0)$$

a) Graph the function P.
b) Find the company's annual profit for the second year.
c) Find the company's annual profit for the fourth year.
d) Find the company's annual profit for the fifth year.

17. A company's annual profits, P (in millions of dollars), are related to the time, t (in years), since its incorporation by the function

$$P(t) = 0.8(t - 2)^2 + 40 \qquad (t > 0)$$

a) Graph the function P.
b) Find the company's annual profit for the second year.
c) Find the company's annual profit for the fourth year.
d) Find the company's annual profit for the fifth year.

18. *Earnings per share.* The annual earnings per share (abbreviated EPS and expressed in dollars) of a corporation is calculated by dividing the corporation's annual earnings by the number of shares of its stock outstanding. That is,

$$\text{EPS} = \frac{\text{annual earnings}}{\text{number of shares of stock outstanding}}$$

The EPS is helpful in evaluating the performance of a corporation.

Assume that the EPS, denoted by y, for a corporation is related to the time, t (in years), since its incorporation by the function

$$y = 0.9(t - 3)^2 + 35 \qquad (t > 0)$$

a) Graph the function defined by the above equation.
b) Find the EPS for the second year.
c) Find the EPS for the third year.
d) Find the EPS for the fifth year.
e) Find the EPS for the sixth year.

19. *Production possibility curve.* A textile company produces amounts x and y of two different jeans using the same production process. The amounts x and y are related by the equation

$$y = -0.10x^2 + 30 \qquad (0 \le x \le 17)$$

Since the amounts x and y give the production possibilities for the two different jeans, the graph of the above equation is called a **production possibility curve.**
a) Graph the production possibility curve defined by the above equation.
b) Determine the production possibility for $x = 5$.
c) Determine the production possibility for $x = 10$.
d) If the company wants to produce an amount x such that it is twice as much as amount y (i.e., $x = 2y$), what amounts x and y should be produced?

20. *Cost.* The Haskins Company produces ornamental bells. The equation

$$C(x) = x^2 - 100x + 2900 \qquad (x \ge 0)$$

relates total daily production cost, C, to daily production, x, of bells.
a) Graph the cost function C.
b) Find the total daily production cost for a daily production level of $x = 650$ bells.
c) How many bells should the company produce daily in order to minimize daily production cost?
d) State the minimum daily production cost.

21. *Projectile.* A ball is projected vertically into the air. The function defined by

$$s(t) = -16t^2 + 192t \qquad (0 \le t \le 12)$$

gives the height of the ball (in feet) above the ground t seconds after it is projected into the air.
a) Graph the function S.
b) When does the ball reach maximum height? What maximum height does it reach?
c) When is the ball at zero height?

Parabolic Reflectors

Assume that for each of the following parabolas, rays of light parallel to the axis of symmetry are directed toward the parabola, as illustrated in Figure 2-38. Find the coordinates of the focus for each parabola.

22. $y = x^2$
23. $y = 0.5(x - 7)^2$
24. $y = (x - 2)^2 + 6$
25. $y = 2(x - 1)^2 + 3$
26. $y = 0.5(x - 3)^2 + 1$
27. $y = 0.1(x - 4)^2 + 5$

28. *Satellite dish.* Satellite dishes are used to transmit and receive radio signals. The cross-sectional center of a parabolic satellite dish is given by the equation

$$y = 0.5x^2$$

Give the x- and y-coordinates of the location of the transmitter and receiver.

29. *Solar collector.* A parabolic solar collector focuses sunlight into a container

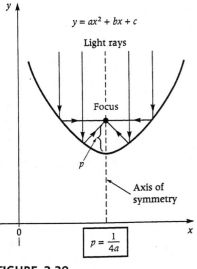

FIGURE 2-38

called a furnace. If the cross-sectional center of the solar collector is given by the equation

$$y = 0.25x^2$$

find the x- and y-coordinates of the location of the furnace.

30. *Flashlight.* The cross-sectional center of a parabolic reflector used in a flashlight is given by the equation

$$y = 0.125x^2$$

Determine the x- and y-coordinates of the location of the bulb.

31. *Productivity: Chemical process yield.* A chemical company has discovered that the yield, y, of a chemical process depends on its reaction time, t (in hours), as given by the function

$$y = f(t) = \begin{cases} (t-5)^2 + 40 & \text{if } 1 < t \le 5 \\ (t-10)^2 + 12 & \text{if } 5 < t \le 10 \end{cases}$$

a) Graph $f(t)$.

Compute the process yield for

b) $t = 3$ c) $t = 4$ d) $t = 6$ e) $t = 8$

32. *Delivery time.* The delivery time, y (in hours), for a manufacturer's product depends on the distance to be shipped, x (in thousands of miles), and the mode of transportation as given by the function

$$y = f(x) = \begin{cases} -(x-2)^2 + 50 & \text{if } 0 < x \le 2 \text{ (by truck)} \\ -(x-4)^2 + 60 & \text{if } 2 < x \le 4 \text{ (by rail)} \end{cases}$$

a) Graph $f(x)$.

According to the above function

b) For what shipping distances does the manufacturer ship by rail?

c) For what shipping distances does the manufacturer ship by truck?

Determine the delivery time for each of the following shipping distances

d) $x = 0.5$ e) $x = 1$ f) $x = 2.5$ g) $x = 3$

2-4 • SOME SPECIAL POLYNOMIAL AND RATIONAL FUNCTIONS

Polynomial Functions

In Chapter 1, we discussed linear functions. Recall that a linear function is defined by an equation of the form

$$f(x) = mx + b$$

Since the highest-powered term, mx, is of the first degree, linear functions are sometimes called **first-degree polynomial functions.** The graphs of first-degree polynomial functions are straight lines, as we learned in Chapter 1.

In Sections 2-2 and 2-3, we discussed quadratic functions. Recall that a quadratic function is defined by an equation of the form

$$f(x) = ax^2 + bx + c \qquad (a \ne 0)$$

Since the highest-powered term, ax^2, is of the second degree, quadratic functions are sometimes called **second-degree polynomial functions.**

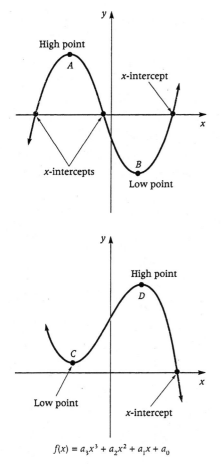

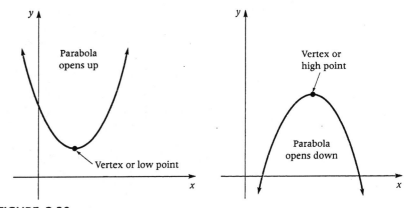

FIGURE 2-39

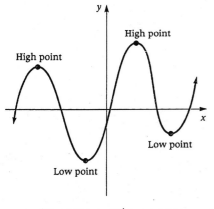

$$f(x) = a_3x^3 + a_2x^2 + a_1x + a_0$$

FIGURE 2-40

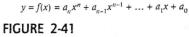

$$y = f(x) = a_nx^n + a_{n-1}x^{n-1} + \ldots + a_1x + a_0$$

FIGURE 2-41

The graphs of second-degree polynomial functions are parabolas (see Figure 2-39), as we learned in Sections 2-2 and 2-3. Note that a second-degree quadratic function (a parabola) has one point, the vertex, where its graph changes direction (see Figure 2-39). Also, a second-degree polynomial function has at most two x-intercepts.

An equation such as

$$f(x) = x^3 - 5x^2 + 3x + 9$$

defines a **third-degree polynomial function** since the highest-powered term, x^3, is of the third degree. The general form of the equation of a third-degree polynomial function is

$$f(x) = a_3x^3 + a_2x^2 + a_1x + a_0$$

where a_3, a_2, a_1, and a_0 are constant real numbers and $a_3 \neq 0$. Figure 2-40 illustrates possible shapes of graphs of third-degree polynomial functions. The points labeled A, B, C, and D, called high/low points, in Figure 2-40 are places where the graph of $f(x)$ changes direction. A third-degree polynomial function has at most two high/low points and at most three x-intercepts.

In general, an equation of the form

$$f(x) = a_nx^n + a_{n-1}x^{n-1} + \ldots + a_2x^2 + a_1x + a_0$$

where n is a positive integer, and a_n, a_{n-1}, . . ., a_2, a_1, and a_0 are constant real numbers, and $a_n \neq 0$, defines the **nth-degree polynomial function.** *An nth-degree polynomial function has at most* n − 1 *high/low points and at most* n x-*intercepts.*

• EXAMPLE 2-12

The graph of a polynomial function appears in Figure 2-41. Its degree must be at least what number?

Solution

The graph has 4 high/low points. Since the graph of a polynomial function of degree n has at most $n - 1$ such points, then the degree of the polynomial function in Figure 2-39 is at least 5. Also, the graph has 5 x-intercepts, which implies that the degree of the polynomial function is at least 5.

We now turn our attention to the graphs of some special case polynomial functions.

Special Case Polynomial Functions

We first consider the graphs of polynomial functions defined by equations of the form

$$f(x) = ax^n$$

where a is a constant coefficient and n is a positive integer. We consider the following two cases and their graphs in the following summary box.

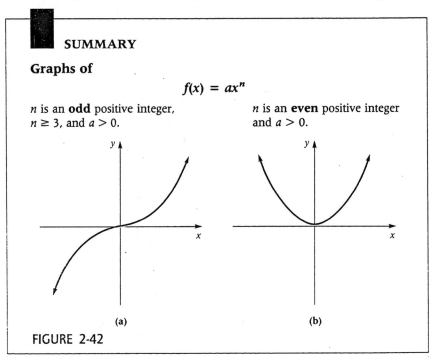

SUMMARY

Graphs of

$$f(x) = ax^n$$

n is an **odd** positive integer, $n \geq 3$, and $a > 0$.

n is an **even** positive integer and $a > 0$.

(a)   (b)

FIGURE 2-42

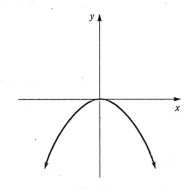

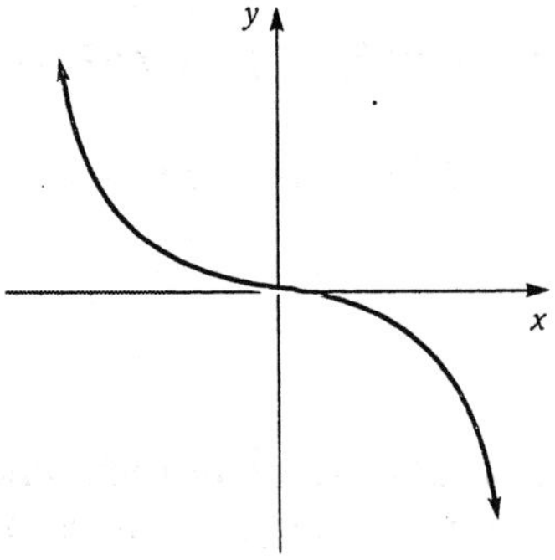

FIGURE 2-43

Thus, the graphs of $y = 2x^3$, $y = 3x^7$, and $y = 10x^9$ resemble those of Figure 2-42(a), whereas the graphs of $y = 3x^2$, $y = 7x^4$, and $y = 8x^{10}$ resemble those of Figure 2-42(b).

Also, the graphs of $y = -3x^5$, $y = -2x^7$, and $y = -8x^9$ are reflections in the x-axis of those resembling Figure 2-42(a). These resemble the graph of Figure 2-43.

The graphs of $y = -3x^4$, $y = -5x^8$, and $y = -6x^{10}$ are reflections in the x-axis of those resembling Figure 2-42(b). These resemble the graph of Figure 2-44.

Graphs of Some Rational Functions

If a function $f(x)$ is defined as the quotient of two polynomials, it is called a **rational function**. Thus, a rational function $f(x)$ is defined by

$$f(x) = \frac{g(x)}{h(x)}$$

$f(x) = ax^n$
($a < 0$, n is an even positive integer)

FIGURE 2-44

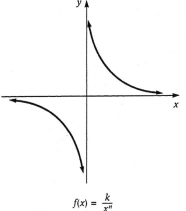

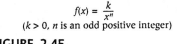

$$f(x) = \frac{k}{x^n}$$
($k > 0$, n is an odd positive integer)

FIGURE 2-45

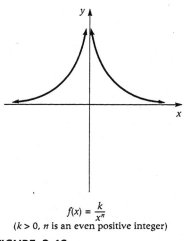

$$f(x) = \frac{k}{x^n}$$
($k > 0$, n is an even positive integer)

FIGURE 2-46

where $g(x)$ and $h(x)$ are polynomials and $h(x) \neq 0$. In this section, we will discuss the graphs of a special category of rational functions defined by equations of the form

$$y = f(x) = \frac{k}{x^n}$$

where k is a constant real number, n is a positive integer, and $x \neq 0$. We begin with rational functions defined by equations of the form

$$y = f(x) = \frac{k}{x^n}$$

where $k > 0$ and n is an *odd positive integer*. The graphs of such functions are typified by the graph in Figure 2-45. Observing Figure 2-45, note that as x takes on values closer and closer to 0, the graph of $f(x)$ gets closer and closer to the vertical line $x = 0$ (i.e., the y-axis). Such a vertical line is called a **vertical asymptote**. *Vertical asymptotes occur at values of* x *for which the denominator of a rational function = 0 and the numerator $\neq$ 0.* Note that the graph of $f(x)$ approaches different ends of the vertical asymptote from different sides. Further study of the graph in Figure 2-45 reveals that as x takes on values of larger and larger magnitude, the graph of $f(x)$ gets closer and closer to the horizontal line $y = 0$ (i.e., the x-axis). Such a horizontal line is called a **horizontal asymptote.**

For example, the graphs of $y = 2/x^5$, $y = 3/x^7$, and $y = 6/x^3$ resemble that in Figure 2-45.

Now we consider rational functions defined by equations of the form

$$y = f(x) = \frac{k}{x^n}$$

where $k > 0$ and n is an *even positive integer*. The graphs of such functions are typified by the graph in Figure 2-46. Studying this graph, note that the y-axis is a vertical asymptote and that the graph of $f(x)$ approaches the same end of this vertical asymptote from different sides. Also, the x-axis is a horizontal asymptote. For example, the graphs of $y = 5/x^4$, $y = 8/x^6$, and $y = 3x^8$ resemble that in Figure 2-46.

We summarize as follows.

SUMMARY

Graphs of

$$f(x) = \frac{k}{x^n} \qquad (k > 0)$$

n is an **odd** positive integer. n is an **even** positive integer.

continues

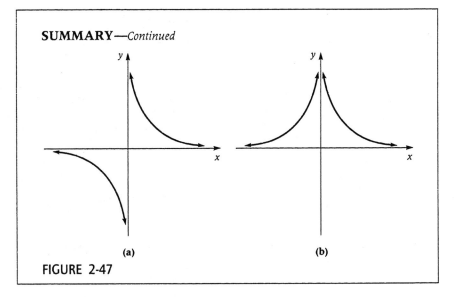

SUMMARY—*Continued*

(a)   (b)

FIGURE 2-47

Of course, if $k < 0$, then the resulting graphs are reflections about the x-axis of those in Figure 2-47.

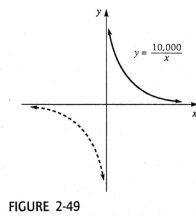

Applications

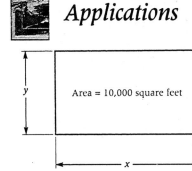

Area = 10,000 square feet

FIGURE 2-48

FIGURE 2-49

$y = \dfrac{10,000}{x}$

• **EXAMPLE 2-13   Area.**

A rectangular pasture must be enclosed so that the enclosed area equals 10,000 square feet, as illustrated in Figure 2-48. Draw a graph showing the possible x and y dimensions.

Solution

Since the enclosed area must be 10,000 square feet, then

$$xy = 10,000$$

Solving for y gives

$$y = \frac{10,000}{x}$$

Note that this equation is of the form $f(x) = k/x^n$, where n is an odd positive integer and $k > 0$. Thus, its graph resembles that of Figure 2-47(a). The graph of y versus x is drawn in Figure 2-49. Since x and y must be positive, we have drawn the portion of the graph in the first quadrant as a solid curve.

• **EXAMPLE 2-14   Production Possibility Curve.** _____

A firm produces x units of Product A and y units of Product B. The equation

$$y = \frac{2,000,000}{x^2} \qquad (00 \leq x \leq 500)$$

relates x and y and thus gives the production possibilities between these two products. The graph of y versus x is therefore called a **production possibility curve.**

a)   Graph the production possibility curve.
b)   State the production possibility for $x = 200$.

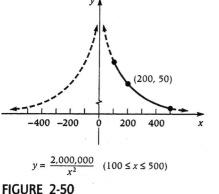

$y = \dfrac{2,000,000}{x^2}$ $(100 \le x \le 500)$

FIGURE 2-50

Solutions

a) The equation

$$y = \frac{2,000,000}{x^2}$$

is of the form $y = k/x^n$, where n is even and $k > 0$. Its graph is drawn in Figure 2-50.

b) When $x = 200$,

$$y = \frac{2,000,000}{(200)^2} = 50$$

Thus, when $x = 200$ units of Product A are produced, $y = 50$ units of Product B are produced. This is illustrated in Figure 2-50.

Average Cost Per Unit. If $C(x)$ denotes the total cost of producing x units of some product, then the *average cost per unit* is given by

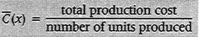

$$\overline{C}(x) = \frac{\text{total production cost}}{\text{number of units produced}}$$

or, in other words,

$$\overline{C}(x) = \frac{C(x)}{x} \qquad (x > 0)$$

The function $\overline{C}$ is called an **average cost function.**
   As an example, if

$$C(x) = 80x + 120,000$$

then the *average cost per unit* is given by

$$\overline{C}(x) = \frac{80x + 120,000}{x} \qquad (x > 0)$$

Dividing each term of the numerator by x, we obtain the equivalent expression for $\overline{C}(x)$ given below.

$$\overline{C}(x) = 80 + \frac{120,000}{x} \qquad (x > 0)$$

We graph the function $\overline{C}$ by noting that the term $120,000/x$ is of the form $f(x) = k/x^n$, where n is an odd positive integer and $k > 0$. Thus, we draw the graph of $\overline{C}$ by beginning with the graph of $y = 120,000/x$ and shifting it vertically by 80 units, as illustrated in Figure 2-51. Since $x > 0$, only that corresponding portion of the graph is drawn as a solid curve.

   Studying the graph of Figure 2-51, note that the average cost per unit approaches the variable cost per unit, 80 (the horizontal asymptote), as the number of units, x, gets larger and larger. This is because the fixed cost is averaged out over the x units and becomes rather insignificant when x is

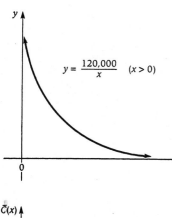

$y = \dfrac{120,000}{x}$ $(x > 0)$

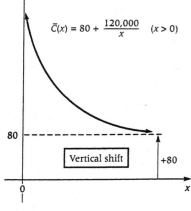

$\overline{C}(x) = 80 + \dfrac{120,000}{x}$ $(x > 0)$

Vertical shift +80

FIGURE 2-51

very large. We illustrate this numerically by computing the average cost per unit for each of the following production levels. Hence,

$$\overline{C}(10,000) = 80 + \frac{120,000}{10,000}$$

$$= 80 + 12 = \$92 \text{ per unit}$$

$$\overline{C}(100,000) = 80 + \frac{120,000}{100,000}$$

$$= 80 + 1.2 = \$81.20 \text{ per unit}$$

Exercises 2-4

State the degree of each polynomial function.

1. $y = -6x + 7$
2. $f(x) = 6x^4 - 8x + 9$
3. $f(x) = 9x^8 + 4x^6 - 8x^3 + 6$
4. $y = -x^2 + 3x + 4$
5. $y = 4x^3 - 8x^2 + 7x + 3$
6. $f(x) = x^5 - 8x^4 + x^3$

7. The graph of a polynomial function appears in Figure 2-52. Its degree must be at least what number?

8. The graph of a polynomial function appears in Figure 2-53. Its degree must be at least what number?

9. Show why graphs of equations of the form $f(x) = ax^n$, where $n \geq 3$ is an odd positive integer and $a > 0$, resemble that of Figure 2-42(a). Use $f(x) = x^3$ as an example and fill in the following table:

x	-4	-3	-2	-1	0	1	2	3	4
$f(x)$									

10. Show why graphs of equations of the form $f(x) = ax^n$, where n is an even positive integer and $a > 0$, resemble that of Figure 2-42(b). Use $f(x) = x^4$ as an example and fill in the following table:

x	-4	-3	-2	-1	0	1	2	3	4
$f(x)$									

Graph each of the following.

11. $f(x) = x^2$
12. $f(x) = 5x^2$
13. $f(x) = x^4$
14. $y = x^6$
15. $y = -4x^2$
16. $y = -x^6$
17. $y = x^3$
18. $f(x) = -2x^3$
19. $f(x) = x^5$
20. $f(x) = 4x^7$
21. $f(x) = -2x^5$
22. $y = -4x^7$

23. Show why graphs of equations of the form $f(x) = k/x^n$, where n is an odd positive integer and $k > 0$, resemble that of Figure 2-47(a). Use $f(x) = 1/x^3$ as an example and fill in the following table:

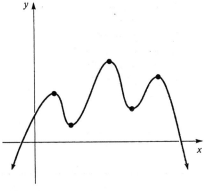

$y = f(x) = a_n x^n + a_{n-1} x^{n-1} + \dots + a_1 x + a_0$

FIGURE 2-52

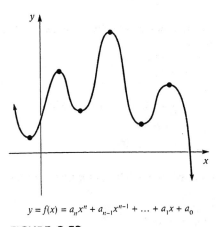

$y = f(x) = a_n x^n + a_{n-1} x^{n-1} + \dots + a_1 x + a_0$

FIGURE 2-53

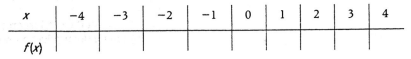

x	-4	-3	-2	-1	0	1	2	3	4
$f(x)$									

24. Show why graphs of equations of the form $f(x) = k/x^n$, where n is an even positive integer and $k > 0$, resemble that of Figure 2-47(b). Use $f(x) = 1/x^4$ as an example and fill in the following table:

x	-4	-3	-2	-1	0	1	2	3	4
$f(x)$									

Graph each of the following:

25. $y = 3/x^2$ **26.** $f(x) = 4/x^3$
27. $f(x) = 5/x^7$ **28.** $y = 6/x^4$
29. $f(x) = 2/x^5$ **30.** $y = 7/x^2$
31. $y = 5/x^3$ **32.** $f(x) = 8/x^7$
33. $y = 6/x^8$ **34.** $y = 10/x^{12}$
35. $f(x) = 4/x^5$ **36.** $f(x) = 3/x$
37. $y = -6/x^8$ **38.** $y = -3/x^4$
39. $y = -5/x^3$ **40.** $y = -3/x$
41. $y = -7/x^6$ **42.** $y = -4/x^5$

Use horizontal and vertical shifts to graph the following.

43. $y = 2(x - 5)^4$ **44.** $y = 2(x - 4)^5$
45. $y = 5(x + 2)^3$ **46.** $y = 3(x - 1)^6$
47. $y = (x - 2)^4 + 5$ **48.** $y = (x - 3)^6 + 7$
49. $y = (x + 5)^3 - 2$ **50.** $y = (x + 7)^5 - 1$
51. $y = 3/(x - 5)$ **52.** $y = 4/(x - 2)^2$
53. $y = 2/(x + 5)^6$ **54.** $y = 1/(x + 7)^3$
55. $y = \dfrac{7}{(x - 2)^4} + 3$ **56.** $y = \dfrac{3}{(x - 5)^2} - 4$

57. $y = \dfrac{2}{(x - 3)^5} - 1$ **58.** $y = \dfrac{1}{(x + 1)^5} + 2$

Applications

59. *Area.* A rectangular pasture of dimensions x feet by y feet must be enclosed so that the enclosed area equals 30,000 square feet. Draw a graph of y versus x.

60. *Production possibility curve.* A company produces x units of Product A and y units of Product B. The equation

$$y = \frac{4{,}000{,}000}{x^2} \qquad (100 \le x \le 400)$$

relates x and y and thus gives the production possibilities for these two products.
a) Graph the production possibility curve.
b) State the production possibility for $x = 100$.
c) State the production possibility for $x = 200$.
d) State the production possibility for $x = 400$.

61. *Production possibility curve.* A company produces x units of Product A and y units of Product B. The equation

$$y = \frac{200{,}000}{x} \qquad (1000 \le x \le 5000)$$

relates x and y and thus gives the production possibilities for these two products.

a) Graph the production possibility curve.
b) State the production possibility for $x = 1000$.

c)   State the production possibility for $x = 2000$.
d)   State the production possibility for $x = 4000$.
e)   State the production possibility for $x = 5000$.

62.   *Demand curve*. The equation

$$p = \frac{10,000}{x - 3} \quad (3 < x \le 4003)$$

gives the relationship between the unit price, p, and the number of units demanded, x, for some product.
a)   Graph the demand curve.
b)   Find the unit price when the demand is 1003 units.
c)   Find the unit price when the demand is 2003 units.
d)   Find the unit price when the demand is 4003 units.

63.   *Demand curve*. The equation

$$p = \frac{20,000}{x - 10} \quad (10 < x \le 5010)$$

gives the relationship between the unit price, p, and the number of units demanded, x, for some product.
a)   Graph the demand curve.
b)   Find the unit price when the demand is 1010 units.
c)   Find the unit price when the demand is 2010 units.
d)   Find the unit price when the demand is 4010 units.
e)   Find the unit price when the demand is 5010 units.

Average Cost Functions

For each of the following, $C(x)$ denotes the total cost (in dollars) of producing x units of some product.
a)   Determine the equation of the average cost function.
b)   Graph the result of part a.
c)   Evaluate $\overline{C}(1000)$, $\overline{C}(10,000)$, and $\overline{C}(100,000)$, and interpret the results.
d)   As the production level increases, the average cost per unit is approaching what value?

64. $\overline{C}(x) = 40x + 80,000$
65. $\overline{C}(x) = 50x + 40,000$
66. $\overline{C}(x) = 100x + 90,000$
67. $\overline{C}(x) = 20x + 60,000$

68.   *Quality/productivity: Loss functions*. The graphs of Figures 2-54 and 2-55 give the loss in dollars to a producer of some product. The notations LSL and USL denote lower specification limit and upper specification limit, respectively. As an example, if a product, say, a disk, must be made to diameter specification limits of

3.50 inches ± 0.10 inches

then the LSL = 3.50 − 0.10 = 3.40 inches, and the USL = 3.50 + 0.10 = 3.60 inches. Thus, such a disk is considered to be within specification if

3.40 inches < disk diameter < 3.60 inches

a)   According to the loss function of Figure 2-54, does the company incur a loss if its product remains within the specification limits?
b)   According to the loss function of Figure 2-54, if the product deviates from the average, but remains within the specification limits, does the company incur a loss?
Note: Experts in the field of quality/productivity refer to this type of loss function as "the old thinking."

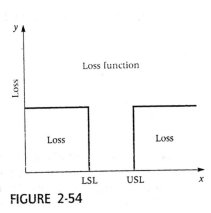

FIGURE 2-54

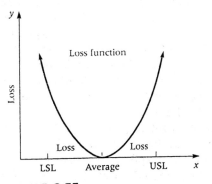

FIGURE 2-55

c) According to the loss function of Figure 2-55, does the company incur a loss as soon as its product deviates from the average?

d) According to the loss function of Figure 2-55, if the product deviates from the average, but remains within the specification limits, does the company incur a loss?

Note: Experts in the field of quality/productivity refer to this type of loss function as "the new thinking."

2-5   • GRAPHING POLYNOMIAL FUNCTIONS (OPTIONAL)

As was discussed in Section 2-4, an equation of the form

$$f(x) = a_n x^n + a_{n-1} x^{n-1} + \ldots + a_2 x^2 + a_1 x + a_0$$

where n is a positive integer, and $a_n, a_{n-1}, \ldots, a_2, a_1,$ and a_0 are constant real numbers, and $a_n \neq 0$, defines the **nth degree polynomial function.** In this section, we will develop and illustrate a procedure for sketching the graphs of factorable polynomial equations of at least the third degree.

We now consider the function defined by

$$f(x) = 2x^3 + 2x^2 - 10x + 6$$

This equation can be written in factored form as

$$f(x) = 2(x + 3)(x - 1)^2$$

Note that the y-intercept is $f(0) = 6$. To determine the x-intercepts, we set $f(x) = 0$. Hence,

$$0 = 2(x + 3)(x - 1)^2$$

Setting each factor equal to 0 and solving for x yields

$$x + 3 = 0 \qquad (x - 1)^2 = 0$$
$$x = -3 \qquad\qquad x = 1$$

Thus, the x-intercepts are $(-3, 0)$ and $(1, 0)$.

The x-intercepts divide the x-axis into the subintervals $x < -3$, $-3 < x < 1$, and $x > 1$. Important information about the graph of $f(x)$ is obtained by analyzing the sign of $f(x)$ on these subintervals. Figure 2-56 gives a sign chart that shows the sign of each factor of $f(x)$ and the sign of $f(x)$ for values of x. Studying this figure, note that the sign of $x + 3$ is negative for $x < -3$ and positive for $x > -3$. Of course, $x + 3 = 0$ at $x = -3$. Observe that the sign of $(x - 1)^2$ is positive at all values of x except $x = 1$, where it is 0. Multiplying the sign of $x + 3$ by the sign of $(x - 1)^2$, we obtain the sign of $(x + 3)(x - 1)^2$. The sign of $(x + 3)(x - 1)^2$ is the same as the sign of $f(x) = 2(x + 3)(x - 1)^2$ since the positive constant multiplier 2 does not change the sign of the original product, $(x + 3)(x - 1)^2$. Thus, $f(x)$ is non-negative for $x > -3$ and negative for $x < -3$.

Notice that $f(x)$ changes sign at the x-intercept of $x = -3$. Thus, the graph of $f(x)$ *crosses* the x-axis at $x = -3$. However, since $f(x)$ does not change sign at the x-intercept of $x = 1$, the graph of $f(x)$ *is tangent to,* and does not cross, the x-axis at $x = 1$ (see Figure 2-57). Note that $f(x)$ does not

Sign chart

Sign of $x + 3$ $-----0+++++++++$
                              -3 x

Sign of $(x - 1)^2$ $+++++++++++0+++$
                                  1 x

Sign of $(x + 3)(x - 1)^2$ $-----0+++++0+++$
                              -3 1 x

FIGURE 2-56

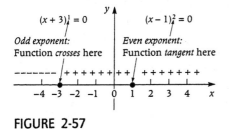

$(x + 3)^1 = 0$ $(x - 1)^2 = 0$
Odd exponent: *Even exponent:*
Function *crosses* here   Function *tangent* here

FIGURE 2-57

change sign at $x = 1$ because the corresponding factor $(x - 1)^2$ has an *even exponent*. Similarly, $f(x)$ does change sign at $x = -3$ because the factor $x + 3$ has an *odd exponent*. In general, we state the following rule to determine whether the graph of a function either crosses or is tangent to the x-axis at an x-intercept.

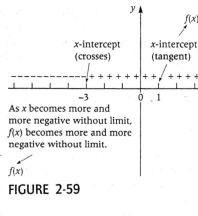

FIGURE 2-58

> ### x-Intercept Rule
>
> If the factor yielding the x-intercept has an *odd exponent*, then the graph of the function *crosses* the x-axis at that x-intercept. If the factor yielding the x-intercept has an *even exponent*, then the graph of the function *is tangent to*, and does not cross, the x-axis at that x-intercept.

Lastly, we determine the behavior of $f(x)$ as x increases without limit and as x becomes more and more negative without limit. We will show that the highest-powered term determines the behavior of a polynomial function at such values of x. We begin by factoring out $2x^3$, the highest-powered term of

$$f(x) = 2x^3 + 2x^2 - 10x + 6$$

and obtain

$$f(x) = 2x^3\left(1 + \frac{1}{x} - \frac{5}{x^2} + \frac{3}{x^3}\right)$$

As x takes on larger and larger positive values, the terms $1/x$, $-5/x^2$, and $3/x^3$ all approach 0. Thus, the highest-powered term, $2x^3$, determines the behavior of $f(x)$ as x increases without limit. Since the highest-powered term, $2x^3$, takes on larger and larger positive values as x takes on larger and larger positive values, $f(x)$ gets larger and larger as x gets larger and larger. This implies that for positive values of x far away from the origin, the graph of $f(x)$ is located in the upper right-hand corner of the first quadrant, as illustrated in Figure 2-58.

As x takes on negative values of larger and larger magnitude, the highest-powered term, $2x^3$, takes on negative values of larger and larger magnitude. Thus, $f(x)$ becomes more and more negative without limit as x becomes more and more negative without limit. This implies that for negative values of x far away from the origin, the graph of $f(x)$ is located in the lower left-hand corner of the third quadrant, as is shown in Figure 2-59.

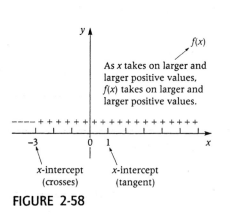

FIGURE 2-59

Using the information gained in the previous paragraphs, we sketch the graph of $f(x)$ in Figure 2-60. In Figure 2-60, we have labeled as A and B the high and low points. In subsequent chapters, we will use calculus to determine the locations of such points.

We summarize the following.

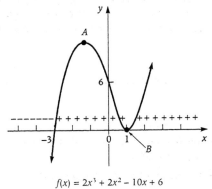

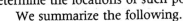
$$f(x) = 2x^3 + 2x^2 - 10x + 6$$

FIGURE 2-60

> ### To Graph a Polynomial Function
> To graph a polynomial function whose equation is in factored form:
> 1. Find the y-intercept.
>   - Set $x = 0$ and solve for y.
> 2. Find the x-intercept(s).
>   - Set $y = 0$ and solve for x.
>   - Apply the x-intercept rule to determine tangency or crossing.
>   - Draw a sign chart (optional).
> 3. Determine the behavior of the function
>   As x gets more and more positive.
>   As x gets more and more negative.
>   - Use the highest-powered term for this analysis.

Sign chart

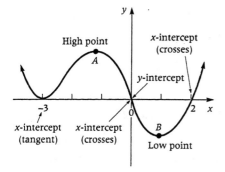

FIGURE 2-61

$$y = f(x) = x^4 + 4x^3 - 3x^2 - 18x$$

FIGURE 2-62

• **EXAMPLE 2-15**

Graph $f(x) = x^4 + 4x^3 - 3x^2 - 18x = x(x - 2)(x + 3)^2$.

Solution

The y-intercept is $f(0) = 0$. To determine the x-intercepts, we set $f(x) = 0$. Hence,

$$0 = x(x - 2)(x + 3)^2$$

Thus, the x-intercepts are $(0, 0)$, $(2, 0)$, and $(-3, 0)$. Since the factors yielding the x-intercepts $(0, 0)$ and $(2, 0)$ have odd exponents, the graph of $f(x)$ crosses the x-axis at these x-intercepts. Since the factor yielding the x-intercept $(-3, 0)$ has an even exponent, the graph of $f(x)$ is tangent to the x-axis at $(-3, 0)$. The sign chart of Figure 2-61 shows the sign of each factor of $f(x)$ and the sign of $f(x)$ for values of x.

Then, we determine the behavior of $f(x)$ as x increases without limit. Note that the highest-powered term, x^4, takes on larger and larger positive values as x takes on larger and larger positive values. This implies that for positive values of x far away from the origin, the graph of $f(x)$ is located in the upper right-hand corner of the first quadrant.

Also, as x takes on negative values of larger and larger magnitude, the highest-powered term, x^4, takes on larger and larger positive values. This implies that for negative values of x far away from the origin, the graph of $f(x)$ is located in the upper left-hand corner of the second quadrant.

Combining all of the preceding information, we sketch the graph of $f(x)$ in Figure 2-62. Observe that we have labeled as A and B the high and low points whose coordinates are unknown. In forthcoming chapters, we will use calculus to determine the locations of such points.

Application

• **EXAMPLE 2-16   Volume.**

A company manufactures open boxes by beginning with a square piece of tin 16 inches on each side, cutting equal squares from the corners of this piece of tin, and folding up the flaps to form sides (see Figure 2-63).

a) Express the volume, V, of the box as a function of x, the length of each side of the cut-out square.

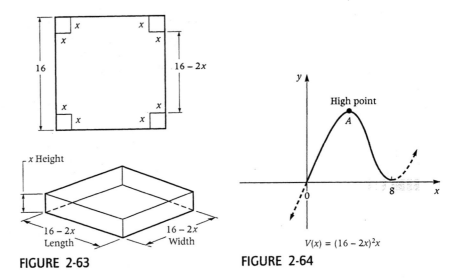

FIGURE 2-63   FIGURE 2-64

$V(x) = (16 - 2x)^2 x$

b) Referring to Figure 2-64, for what values of x is $V(x)$ non-negative? Does this make sense in terms of Figure 2-63?

Solutions

a) The volume of a box is the product of its length, width, and height (see Figure 2-63). Thus

$$V(x) = (\text{length})(\text{width})(\text{height})$$
$$= (16 - 2x)(16 - 2x)(x)$$
$$= (16 - 2x)^2 x$$

The graph of this function appears in Figure 2-64.

b) If $x \geq 0$, then $V(x) \geq 0$. However, referring to Figure 2-63, note that if $x = 8$, then all the tin would be cut away. And if $x > 8$, then more tin would be cut away than exists—an impossibility. Hence, the function "makes sense" only for $0 \leq x \leq 8$. Thus, that portion of the graph is drawn with a solid curve in Figure 2-64.

c) We note that volume is maximal at the x-coordinate of point A. As mentioned earlier, we will use calculus in forthcoming chapters to determine the locations of such points.

Exercises 2-5

Graph each of the following.

1. $f(x) = x^3 - 7x + 6 = (x - 1)(x + 3)(x - 2)$
2. $y = x^4 + x^3 - 21x^2 - x + 20 = (x - 1)(x - 4)(x + 1)(x + 5)$
3. $f(x) = x^3 - 7x^2 + 11x - 5 = (x - 1)^2(x - 5)$
4. $f(x) = x^3 - 4x^2 - 3x + 18 = (x - 3)^2(x + 2)$
5. $y = 3x^4 - 3x^3 - 9x^2 + 15x - 6 = 3(x - 1)^3(x + 2)$
6. $y = 5x^6 + 10x^5 - 15x^4$
7. $f(x) = x^3 + 3x^2 - 9x + 5 = (x - 1)^2(x + 5)$
8. $y = x^4 + 2x^3 - 15x^2$
9. $f(x) = -x^3 + 36x$
10. $f(x) = x^4 - 2x^3 + 15x^2$
11. $f(x) = x^3 - 19x - 30 = (x + 2)(x - 5)(x + 3)$

12. $f(x) = x^3 - 4x^2 - 3x + 18 = (x + 2)(x - 3)^2$
13. $f(x) = x^3 + x^2 - 5x + 3 = (x - 1)^2(x + 3)$
14. $f(x) = x^5 + x^4 - 5x^3 + 3x^2$
15. $y = x^3 + 3x^2 - 16x + 12 = (x - 1)(x + 6)(x - 2)$
16. $f(x) = x^4 + 6x^3 - 7x^2 - 60x = x(x - 3)(x + 4)(x + 5)$

Each of the following is a polynomial equation $f(x) = a_n x^n + a_{n-1} x^{n-1} + \ldots + a_2 x^2 + a_1 x + a_0$ expressed in factored form. Graph each one.

17. $f(x) = (1/2)(x - 2)^3(x + 5)$ **18.** $y = -(1/4)(x - 3)^2(x + 1)$
19. $f(x) = -3x^5(x - 2)^3(x + 4)$ **20.** $f(x) = x^2(x - 2)(x + 5)$
21. $f(x) = 2x^3(x - 5)(x + 6)^2$ **22.** $f(x) = x^2(x - 5)^4(x - 2)$
23. $y = (x - 2)(x + 3)^4(x - 1)$ **24.** $y = (x - 1)^2(x + 3)(x + 1)^2$

Applications

25. *Batch process and unit profits.* The Super Oar Company manufactures plastic paddles using the batch process (i.e., no production takes place until enough orders are received to produce a batch). The size of a batch is variable and may range from 0 to 30 paddles. The company statistician has found unit profit, p, and batch size, x, to be related by the polynomial equation

$$p(x) = -0.0001x^4 + 0.005x^3 - 0.07x^2 + 0.3x \qquad (0 \le x \le 30)$$

When factored, this becomes

$$p(x) = -0.0001x(x - 10)^2(x - 30)$$

a) Graph the function.
b) For which batch sizes will the company make zero unit profit?
c) Will Super Oar Company make a positive unit profit if batch size, x, falls within the interval $0 < x < 10$?
d) Will Super Oar Company make a positive unit profit if batch size, x, falls within the interval $10 < x < 30$?
e) Calculate the profit per paddle at a batch size of $x = 20$.

26. *Batch process and unit profits.* The factored polynomial equation

$$p(x) = \left(\frac{1}{10,000}x^2\right)(x - 20)(x - 30)^2 \qquad (0 \le x \le 40)$$

relates unit profit, p, with batch size, x, for Supergo Corporation.
a) Sketch the graph of this function.
b) For which batch sizes will Supergo Corporation make zero unit profit?
c) Will Supergo make a unit profit if batch size, x, falls within the interval $0 \le x \le 20$?
d) Will Supergo make a unit profit if batch size, x, falls within the interval $20 < x < 30$?
e) Will Supergo make a unit profit if batch size, x, falls within the interval $30 < x \le 40$?
f) Calculate the unit profit at each of the following batch sizes: $x = 25$, $x = 35$, $x = 40$.

27. *Volume.* A company manufactures open boxes from rectangular pieces of tin of dimensions 10 inches by 20 inches. The process involves cutting equal squares from the corners of each piece of tin and folding up the flaps to form sides.
a) Express the volume, V, of the box as a function of x, the length of each side of the cut-out square.
b) Graph the function $V(x)$ of part a.
c) For which values of x is volume, V, non-negative? Does this make sense?

d) Graphically indicate the location of the value of x at which volume will be maximal.

28. *Sales revenue.* A company manufactures electric switches. The equation

$$p(x) = -\frac{1}{400}x^2 + 90 \qquad (0 \le x \le 185)$$

represents the selling price per case, p, as a function of the number of cases sold, x.

a) Determine the sales revenue, R, as a function of x.
b) Graph the revenue function, $R(x)$.
c) For which values of x is sales revenue non-negative?
d) Graphically indicate the location of the value of x at which sales revenue is maximal.

29. *Particle movement.* A particle starts at point 0 and moves along a horizontal line as illustrated in Figure 2-65. The equation $S(t) = t^3 - 16t^2$ expresses the distance, $S(t)$, between the particle and its starting point, 0, after t seconds have elapsed.

a) Graph $S(t)$.
b) Where is the particle in relation to its starting point after 5 seconds have elapsed?
c) Where is the particle after 20 seconds have elapsed?
d) At what points in time is the particle at the starting point?

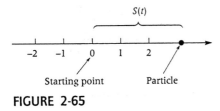

FIGURE 2-65

2-6 • GRAPHING RATIONAL FUNCTIONS (OPTIONAL)

In this section, we will learn to graph equations like

$$y = f(x) = \frac{6x + 12}{2x - 1}$$

Such an equation defines a **rational function** since it is a quotient of two polynomial functions.

A graph of $y = f(x) = (6x + 12)/(2x - 1)$ may be obtained by finding some ordered pairs (x, y) that satisfy the equation $y = (6x + 12)/(2x - 1)$ and plotting their corresponding points on the rectangular coordinate system. Table 2-1 shows values of y, or $f(x)$, for various values of x. The corresponding ordered pairs (x, y) are plotted in Figure 2-66. Studying the graph of Figure 2-66, note that this rational function is undefined at $x = 1/2$. As x takes on values closer and closer to $1/2$, $f(x)$ gets larger and larger in magnitude. The graph of $f(x)$ gets closer and closer to the vertical line $x = 1/2$. Such a vertical line is called a **vertical asymptote.** Note that vertical asymptotes occur at values of x for which the denominator of a rational function $= 0$ and the numerator $\ne 0$.

Further study of the graph of Figure 2-66 shows us that as x takes on larger and larger positive values, $f(x)$ gets closer and closer to 3. Thus, for positive values of x far away from the origin, the graph of $f(x)$ approaches the horizontal line $y = 3$. As x takes on negative values of larger and larger magnitude, $f(x)$ again gets closer and closer to 3. Thus, for negative values of x far away from the origin, the graph of $f(x)$ also approaches the hori

TABLE 2-1

x	$f(x)$
-50	2.85
-10	2.29
-3	0.86
-2	0
0	-12
1/3	-42
1	18
3	6
50	3.15

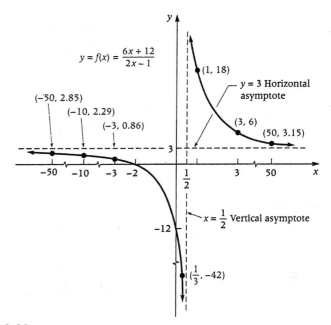

FIGURE 2-66

zontal line $y = 3$. Such a horizontal line is called a **horizontal asymptote.** Given the equation of a rational function, the horizontal asymptote (if it exists) is found by determining the behavior of the rational function at values of x far away from the origin. We will see that the behavior of a rational function at values of x far away from the origin is determined by the quotient

$$\frac{\text{highest-powered term of numerator}}{\text{highest-powered term of denominator}}$$

We begin by factoring out the highest-powered term of the numerator and also the highest-powered term of the denominator of our rational function

$$y = f(x) = \frac{6x + 12}{2x - 1}$$

This operation gives us

$$y = f(x) = \frac{6x\left(1 + \dfrac{2}{x}\right)}{2x\left(1 - \dfrac{1}{2x}\right)}$$

As x takes on larger and larger positive values, the terms $2/x$ and $1/2x$ approach 0. Thus, the quotient

$$\frac{\text{highest-powered term of numerator}}{\text{highest-powered term of denominator}} = \frac{6x}{2x} = 3$$

determines the behavior of $f(x)$ as x takes on larger and larger positive values. Also, as x takes on negative values of larger and larger magnitude, the quotient of the highest-powered terms of both the numerator and denominator determines the behavior of the graph of $f(x)$ at negative values of x far away from the origin. For this example, the quotient is the constant 3, indicating that the horizontal asymptote is $y = 3$.

Although we sketched the rational function $y = f(x) = (6x + 12)/(2x - 1)$ by choosing arbitrary x-values and plotting their corresponding points, there is a more methodical procedure, outlined by the following steps:

Step 1   Find the y-intercept.

Step 2   Find the x-intercept(s).

Step 3   Find the vertical asymptote(s).

Step 4   Determine the behavior of the function as x takes on values farther and farther away from the origin.

We now illustrate this procedure by sketching the graph of the rational function defined by

$$y = f(x) = \frac{2(x - 1)^3(x + 4)}{(x - 3)^2(x + 1)}$$

Step 1   Find the y-intercept. Here, we use

$$y = f(0) = \frac{2(0 - 1)^3(0 + 4)}{(0 - 3)^2(0 + 1)} = \frac{2(-1)^3(4)}{(-3)^2(1)} = \frac{-8}{9}$$

Thus, the y-intercept is $(0, -8/9)$.

Step 2   Find the x-intercept(s). Set $y = 0$. Hence,

$$0 = \frac{2(x - 1)^3(x + 4)}{(x - 3)^2(x + 1)}$$

$$0 = 2(x - 1)^3(x + 4)$$

$$(x - 1)^3 = 0 \qquad\qquad (x + 4)^1 = 0$$

$$x = 1 \qquad\qquad\qquad x = -4$$

odd exponent: ↑   *odd exponent:*   ↑
graph crosses   graph crosses
x-axis here ⌐ x-axis here ⌐

Step 3   Find the vertical asymptote(s). Vertical asymptotes exist at those values of x for which the denominator of a rational function equals 0. Thus, we set the denominator equal to 0. This gives us

$$0 = (x - 3)^2(x + 1)$$

$$(x - 3)^2 = 0 \qquad x + 1 = 0$$

$$x = 3 \qquad\qquad x = -1$$

↑   ↗

vertical asymptotes

Note that the numerator $2(x - 1)^3(x + 4)$, does not equal 0 at $x = 3$ and $x = -1$.

Before leaving step 3, we must determine whether the function approaches the *same end* of the vertical asymptote from both sides, or whether it approaches *different ends* of the vertical asymptote from both sides (see Figures 2-67 and 2-68). The behavior of a rational function at a vertical asymptote is determined by noting whether the exponent of the factor from which the vertical asymptote was calculated is odd or even. The following rule is applied.

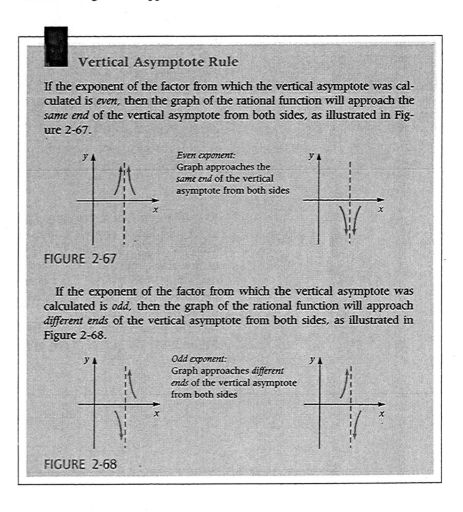

Vertical Asymptote Rule

If the exponent of the factor from which the vertical asymptote was calculated is *even*, then the graph of the rational function will approach the *same end* of the vertical asymptote from both sides, as illustrated in Figure 2-67.

Even exponent:
Graph approaches the *same end* of the vertical asymptote from both sides

FIGURE 2-67

If the exponent of the factor from which the vertical asymptote was calculated is *odd*, then the graph of the rational function will approach *different ends* of the vertical asymptote from both sides, as illustrated in Figure 2-68.

Odd exponent:
Graph approaches *different ends* of the vertical asymptote from both sides

FIGURE 2-68

Returning to our example, note that the vertical asymptotes were calculated as follows:

$$(x - 3)^2 = 0 \qquad\qquad (x + 1)^1 = 0$$
$$x = 3 \qquad\qquad\qquad x = -1$$

even exponent: *odd exponent:*
graph approaches the *same end*   graph approaches *differents ends*
of the vertical asymptote $x = 3$ of the vertical asymptote $x = -1$
from both sides   from both sides

One can see why this rule works by noting that for the rational function defined by

$$f(x) = \frac{2(x - 1)^3(x + 4)}{(x - 3)^2(x + 1)}$$

the values of $f(x)$ do not change sign as x takes on values from either side of 3 since the exponent of the factor $(x - 3)^2$ is 2, an even number. Hence, $f(x)$ approaches the vertical asymptote $x = 3$ from the same end. However, for values of x smaller than -1, the factor $x + 1$ is negative, whereas for values of x larger than -1, the factor $x + 1$ is positive, thereby causing a sign change in $f(x)$. Hence, $f(x)$ approaches the vertical asymptote $x = -1$ from different ends.

Step 4   Determine the behavior of the function as x takes on values farther and farther away from the origin. The quotient of the highest-powered terms of both numerator and denominator determines the behavior of $f(x)$ at values of x far away from the origin. In our example, this quotient is

$$\frac{2x^4}{x^3} = 2x$$

As x takes on larger and larger positive values, the quotient $2x$ takes on larger and larger positive values. Thus, for positive values of x far away from the origin, the graph of $f(x)$ is located in the upper right-hand corner of the first quadrant. As x takes on negative values of larger and larger magnitude, the quotient $2x$ becomes more and more negative. Thus, for negative values of x, the graph of $f(x)$ is located in the lower left-hand corner of the third quadrant.

The information obtained in the preceding four steps is illustrated in Figure 2-69. The graph of $f(x)$ appears in Figure 2-70.

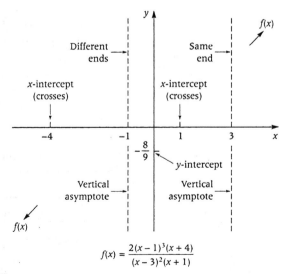

$$f(x) = \frac{2(x - 1)^3(x + 4)}{(x - 3)^2(x + 1)}$$

FIGURE 2-69

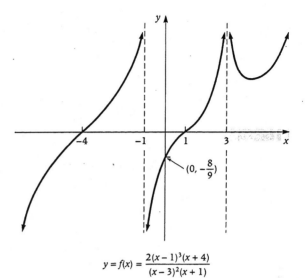

$$y = f(x) = \frac{2(x-1)^3(x+4)}{(x-3)^2(x+1)}$$

FIGURE 2-70

We now give a codified procedure for graphing rational functions.

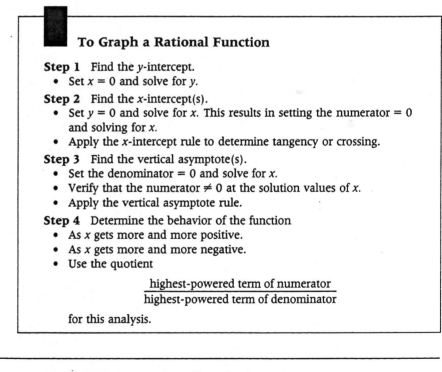

To Graph a Rational Function

Step 1 Find the y-intercept.
- Set $x = 0$ and solve for y.

Step 2 Find the x-intercept(s).
- Set $y = 0$ and solve for x. This results in setting the numerator $= 0$ and solving for x.
- Apply the x-intercept rule to determine tangency or crossing.

Step 3 Find the vertical asymptote(s).
- Set the denominator $= 0$ and solve for x.
- Verify that the numerator $\neq 0$ at the solution values of x.
- Apply the vertical asymptote rule.

Step 4 Determine the behavior of the function
- As x gets more and more positive.
- As x gets more and more negative.
- Use the quotient

$$\frac{\text{highest-powered term of numerator}}{\text{highest-powered term of denominator}}$$

for this analysis.

Application

• **EXAMPLE 2-17   Cost-Benefit Curve.**

The equation

$$y = f(x) = \frac{20x}{104 - x} \qquad (0 \le x \le 100)$$

expresses the cost, *y* (in thousands of dollars), of removing *x*% of a certain pollutant from the atmosphere of a large city. The graph of such a function is called a **cost-benefit curve.**

a) Sketch the cost-benefit curve.
b) Find the cost of removing 90% of the pollutant.
c) Find the cost of removing 95% of the pollutant.
d) Find the cost of removing 100% of the pollutant.

Solutions

a) **Step 1** *Find the* y-*intercept.* If $x = 0$, then

$$y = \frac{20(0)}{104 - 0} = \frac{0}{104} = 0$$

Thus, the *y*-intercept is $(0, 0)$

Step 2 *Find the* x-*intercept(s).* Set $y = 0$ and solve for *x*. This leads to

$$0 = \frac{20x}{104 - x}$$
$$0 = 20x^1 \longleftarrow$$
$$x = 0 \qquad \underline{\quad} \text{— } odd\ exponent:$$
$$\uparrow \qquad\qquad \text{graph } crosses \text{ x-axis}$$
$$x\text{-intercept} \qquad \text{here}$$

Step 3 *Find the vertical asymptote(s).* Set the denominator equal to 0. Hence,

$$104 - x = 0$$
$$x = 104$$

and the line $x = 104$ is a vertical asymptote. Since the exponent of the factor $104 - x$ is odd, the graph of $f(x)$ approaches different ends of the vertical asymptote from both sides.

Step 4 *Determine the behavior of* f(x) *as* x *takes on values farther and farther away from the origin.* The quotient of the highest-powered terms of both the numerator and denominator is

$$\frac{20x}{-x} = -20$$

Since this quotient is the constant -20, then $y = -20$ is a horizontal asymptote.

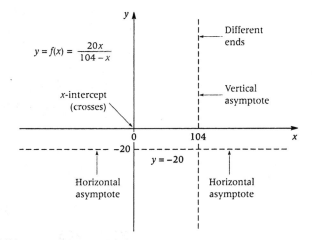

FIGURE 2-71

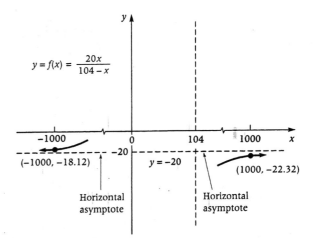

FIGURE 2-72

The information in steps 1 through 4 is summarized in Figure 2-71.

Since this function has a horizontal asymptote, we must determine whether the graph of $f(x)$ approaches the horizontal asymptote from *above* or *below* as x takes on larger and larger positive values, and also as x takes on negative values of larger magnitude. This is accomplished by evaluating the function at relatively large values of x.

Specifically, to get some idea of whether the function approaches the horizontal asymptote from above or below as x takes on larger and larger positive values, we will evaluate $f(x)$ at $x = 1000$. Here,

$$y = f(1000) = \frac{20(1000)}{104 - 1000} = \frac{20{,}000}{-896} = -22.32$$

Since $-22.32 < -20$, then, for large positive values of x, the graph of $f(x)$ appears to approach the horizontal asymptote, $y = -20$, from below (see Figure 2-72).

Similarly, to get some idea of whether the graph approaches the horizontal

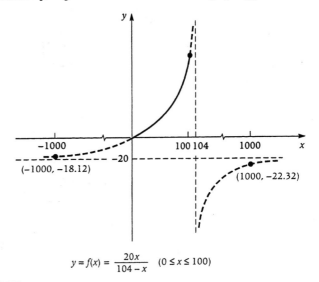

$$y = f(x) = \frac{20x}{104 - x} \quad (0 \le x \le 100)$$

FIGURE 2-73

asymptote from above or below as x takes on negative values of larger and larger magnitude, we evaluate $f(x)$ at $x = -1000$. In this case,

$$y = f(-1000) = \frac{20(-1000)}{104 - (-1000)} = \frac{-20,000}{1104} = -18.12$$

Since $-18.12 > -20$, then, as x takes on negative values far away from the origin, the graph of $f(x)$ appears to approach the horizontal asymptote, $y = -20$, from above (see Figure 2-72).

The completed graph is sketched in Figure 2-73. Note that the graph of the function is drawn as a solid curve for values of x within the interval $0 \le x \le 100$.

b) The cost of removing 90% of the pollutant is

$$y = f(90) = \frac{20(90)}{104 - 90} = \frac{1800}{14} \approx \$129 \text{ thousand*}$$

c) The cost of removing 95% of the pollutant is

$$y = f(95) = \frac{20(95)}{104 - 95} = \frac{1900}{9} \approx \$211 \text{ thousand}$$

d) The cost of removing 100% of the pollutant is

$$y = f(100) = \frac{20(100)}{104 - 100} = \frac{2000}{4} = \$500 \text{ thousand}$$

Note that it gets increasingly expensive to remove the last small portion of the pollutant.

Exercises 2-6

Graph each of the following.

1. $y = \dfrac{(x-3)^2(x+8)}{(x-1)^2}$

2. $f(x) = \dfrac{(x+5)(x-1)^4}{x(x-2)}$

3. $f(x) = \dfrac{(x-1)(x+3)^2}{(x+1)^3(x+4)}$

4. $y = \dfrac{(x-1)(x+3)^2}{x^4(x+4)}$

5. $y = \dfrac{1}{x-4}$

6. $f(x) = \dfrac{5}{(x+3)^2}$

7. $y = \dfrac{3x+12}{x-2}$

8. $f(x) = \dfrac{2x-10}{x+3}$

9. $f(x) = \dfrac{2x-16}{x+1}$

10. $f(x) = \dfrac{5x-30}{x^2-81}$

11. $y = \dfrac{x^2-9x}{3x-15}$

12. $f(x) = \dfrac{x^3-8x^2}{x^2-36}$

13. Graph the function defined by

$$f(x) = \frac{(x-3)(x+3)}{x^2+1}$$

This rational function does not have any vertical asymptotes. Why not? Also, use a calculator to fill in the table below by computing the indicated $f(x)$-

---

*The symbol $\approx$ means "approximately equal to."

values. Plot the corresponding points on the graph to determine the behavior of the graph of f over the interval $-3 < x < 3$.

x	-2	-1	$-1/2$	0	$1/2$	1	2
$f(x)$							

14. Graph the function defined by

$$f(x) = \frac{x^2 - 16}{x^2 + 2}$$

This rational function does not have any vertical asymptotes. Why not? Also, use a calculator to fill in the table below by computing the indicated $f(x)$-values. Plot the corresponding points on the graph to determine the behavior of the graph of f over the interval $-4 < x < 4$.

x	-3	-2	-1	$-1/2$	0	$1/2$	1	2	3
$f(x)$									

Applications

15. *Production possibility curve.* The Strong Steel Company produces two types of steel beams: I shaped and T shaped. The rational function defined by

$$y = \frac{420(x - 200)}{x - 210} \qquad (0 \le x \le 200)$$

relates the number, x, of I-shaped beams and the number, y, of T-shaped beams produced during a month. Such a function's graph is called a **production possibility curve.**
a) Sketch this production possibility curve.
b) If no I-shaped beams are produced, how many T-shaped are produced?
c) If no T-shaped beams are produced, how many I-shaped beams are produced?
d) If 70 I-shaped beams are produced, how many T-shaped beams are produced?

16. *Production possibility curve.* Keep-Cool Corporation manufactures two types of air conditioners: Model SM401 and Model LG535. The production possibility curve with equation

$$y = \frac{500(x - 300)}{x - 320} \qquad (0 \le x \le 300)$$

expresses the relationship between the number, x, of Model SM401 and the number, y, of Model LG535 produced during a month.
a) Sketch this production possibility curve.
b) If Keep-Cool Corporation produces no Model SM401s, how many Model LG535s can it produce?
c) If Keep-Cool Corporation produces no Model LG535s, how many Model SM401s can it produce?
d) If Keep-Cool Corporation produces 220 Model SM401s, how many Model LG535s can it produce?

17. *Cost-benefit curve.* The rational function defined by

$$y = \frac{40x}{110 - x} \qquad (0 \le x \le 100)$$

expresses the relationship between the cost, y (in millions of dollars), of removing $x\%$ of a pollutant from the atmosphere. This is an example of a cost-benefit curve.

a) Sketch the graph of this function.

b) Find the cost of removing the following amounts of pollution: 10%, 20%, 50%, 80%, 100%.

18. *Cost-benefit curve.* The rational function defined by

$$y = \frac{20x}{100 - x} \qquad (0 \le x < 100)$$

expresses the relationship between the cost, y (in thousands of dollars), of removing $x\%$ of a pollutant.

a) Sketch this cost-benefit curve.

b) Find the cost of removing the following amounts of pollution: 10%, 20%, 50%, 80%, 90%.

c) According to this function, is it possible to remove 100% of the pollutant?

EXTRA DIVIDENDS

• *Model Fitting: Goodness of Fit*

In the Extra Dividends section entitled "Model Fitting: Goodness of fit" following Chapter 1, we discussed how to determine the goodness of fit of linear models fit to given sets of data. This section applies the same concepts to nonlinear models. Specifically, if we are given a nonlinear model fit to a set of data, its goodness of fit is determined as it was in the previously mentioned section—by computing the sum of squares error. Although these concepts were summarized in the previous Extra Dividends, we repeat the summary here for completeness. We also note, as in the earlier section, that we are not concerned with how the fitted model is obtained. Such discussion is the topic of Section 15-4 in the calculus portion of this text.

To Determine Goodness of Fit

The **goodness of fit** of a model fitted to a given set of data points is determined as follows:

1. Compute the **fitted values** by substituting the x-values of the data points into the equation of the fitted model. These are simply the y-coordinates of points on the graph of the fitted model.

2. Compute the **residual** for each data point in accordance with the formula

    residual = data value − fitted value

3. Compute the **sum of squares error, S,** as given below.

    S = sum of the squares of the residuals

Note: The sum of squares error is an overall measure of the extent to which the fitted model does not fit the data.

Note: If more than one model is fit to the same set of data points, then the model resulting in the **smallest** sum of squares error is the better-fitting model for the set of data points.

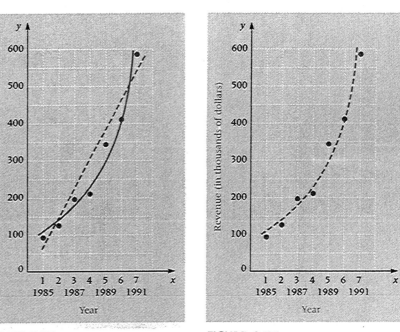

FIGURE 2-74

FIGURE 2-75

We now consider Table 2-2, a set of data relating annual sales revenues (in thousands of dollars) with time (in years). We learned in a previous Extra Dividends section that a set of data that relates some quantity to time is called a **time series**. For time series data, the successive time periods are denoted by $x = 1$, $x = 2$, . . . , etc. Although we use the variable x to denote the successive time periods, the letter t is also often used.

TABLE 2-2

Years	1985	1986	1987	1988	1989	1990	1991
x	1	2	3	4	5	6	7
y revenues	90	120	190	220	340	420	580

The data of Table 2-2 are plotted in Figure 2-74. Observe that the data appear to exhibit a nonlinear trend. This is made more explicit in Figure 2-75, where it is observed that a nonlinear model might be a better fit to the data than a linear model.

Figure 2-76 gives a plot of the data and the fitted quadratic model (i.e., a parabola)

$$y = 10x^2 + 70$$

that appears to capture the relationship between x and y. Observe, in Figure 2-76, that the fitted values are determined by substituting the x-values into the equation of the fitted model. As mentioned earlier, we will not be concerned with how the quadratic model, $y = 10x^2 + 70$, was obtained as

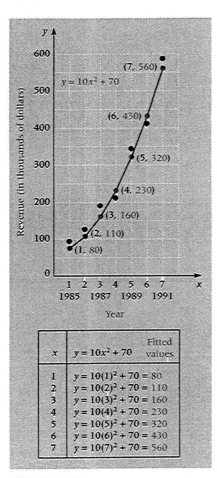

x	$y = 10x^2 + 70$	Fitted values
1	$y = 10(1)^2 + 70 = 80$	
2	$y = 10(2)^2 + 70 = 110$	
3	$y = 10(3)^2 + 70 = 160$	
4	$y = 10(4)^2 + 70 = 230$	
5	$y = 10(5)^2 + 70 = 320$	
6	$y = 10(6)^2 + 70 = 430$	
7	$y = 10(7)^2 + 70 = 560$	

FIGURE 2-76

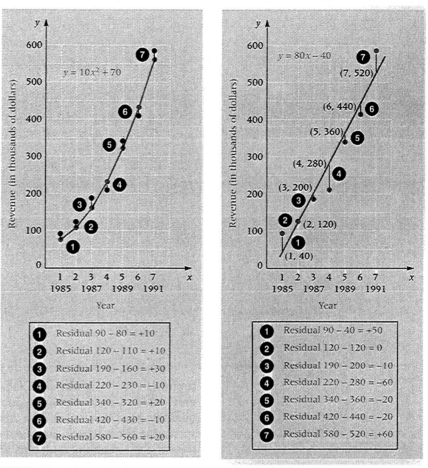

FIGURE 2-77   FIGURE 2-78

this will be discussed in Section 15-4 in the calculus portion of this text. Here we address the issue of assessing the goodness of fit of a nonlinear model fit to a set of data points.

• Goodness of Fit

As discussed in the previous Extra Dividends section at the end of Chapter 1, to assess the goodness of fit of a model fit to a set of data points, we determine, for each data point, the vertical distance between the given data point and the graph of the fitted model, as illustrated in Figure 2-77. Recall that these vertical distances are called **residuals** and indicate the extent to which the fitted model does not fit the data points. Also, as discussed earlier, an overall measure of the extent to which the fitted model (in this case, the parabola $y = 10x^2 + 70$) does not fit the data is given by the sum of squares error and is denoted by S, as is shown below.

Sum of Squares Error

$$S = (90 - 80)^2 + (120 - 110)^2 + (190 - 160)^2 + (220 - 230)^2$$
$$+ (340 - 320)^2 + (420 - 430)^2 + (580 - 560)^2$$
$$= (10)^2 + (10)^2 + (30)^2 + (-10)^2 + (20)^2 + (-10)^2 + (20)^2$$
$$= 2100 \quad \text{Sum of squares error}$$

Figure 2-78 illustrates the goodness of fit of the linear model.

$$y = 80x - 40$$

to the set of data points in Table 2-2. The sum of squares error is computed below.

Sum of Squares Error

$$S = (90 - 40)^2 + (120 - 120)^2 + (190 - 200)^2 + (220 - 280)^2$$
$$+ (340 - 360)^2 + (420 - 440)^2 + (580 - 520)^2$$
$$= (50)^2 + (0)^2 + (-10)^2 + (-60)^2 + (-20)^2 + (-20)^2 + (60)^2$$
$$= 10,600 \quad \text{Sum of squares error}$$

Comparing the sum of squares error of the linear model, 10,600, with that of the quadratic model, 2100, it is apparent that the quadratic model, having a smaller sum of squares error, is the better-fitting model for this set of data.

• Best-Fitting Models

We have stated that in Section 15-4 of this text, we will learn how to fit models to data. Actually, we will learn more than that. We will learn how to determine the best-fitting linear model for a set of data, how to determine the best-fitting quadratic model for a set of data, etc. We caution that the linear model fit to the data of Table 2-2 is not necessarily the best-fitting linear model for the data. The quadratic model $y = 10x^2 + 70$ is not necessarily the best-fitting quadratic model for this set of data. Thus, when our comparison of the goodness of fit of both models indicated the quadratic model to be the better-fitting model, that does not necessarily imply that the best-fitting quadratic model fits this set of data better than the best-fitting linear model does. This determination can be made by comparing the sum of squares error for both best-fitting models.

Exercises

For each of the following sets of data, the equations of two fitted models are given.
a) Determine the sum of squares error for each fitted model.
b) Select the better-fitting model.

1.

x	1	2	3	4	5
y	40	80	200	300	530

$y = 20x^2 + 10$
$y = 100x - 90$

2.

x	2	3	5	7	10
y	35	60	150	240	530

$y = 5x^2 + 20$
$y = 45x - 40$

Application

3. *Time series: GNP.* Figure 2-79 gives a MINITAB plot of quarterly U.S. gross national product (GNP) from 1970 through 1980. Also given are the equations of two fitted models and their associated sum of squares errors. Select the better-fitting model.

Fitted Model	Sum of Squares Error
$y = 48.4x + 768$	1,568,435
$y = 1.2x^2 + 1111$	1,596,801

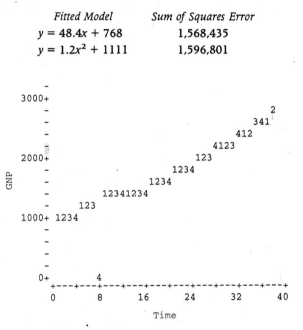

Each digit 1, 2, 3, and 4 indicates which quarter of a particular year's GNP is plotted at that location.

* This graph was drawn using the MINITAB statisitical software package. The annotations have been added.

FIGURE 2-79

CHAPTER 2 HIGHLIGHTS

• *Concepts*

Your ability to answer the following questions is one indicator of the depth of your mastery of this chapter's important concepts. Note that the questions are grouped under various topic headings. For any question that you cannot answer, refer to the section of the chapter indicated by the topic heading. Pay particular attention to the summary boxes within a section.

2-1   GRAPHING CONCEPTS

Explain each of the following terms, and indicate how it is related to the equation of a graph.

1. Vertical shift
2. Horizontal shift
3. Reflection in the x-axis
4. Symmetry with respect to the vertical axis
5. Symmetry with respect to the origin

2-2   QUADRATIC FUNCTIONS AND THEIR GRAPHS

6. Write the general form of a quadratic equation; write the formula for the x-coordinate of the vertex; the y-intercept is given by (0, ____).
7. Give the rule for determining whether a parabola opens up or down.
8. Give the procedure for finding the x-intercept(s) of a parabola.
9. A parabola may have as many as ____ x-intercepts.
10. If a parabola has exactly one x-intercept, then the x-intercept is also the _____.

2-3   APPLICATIONS OF QUADRATIC FUNCTIONS

11. Sales revenue is determined by beginning with the formula

    sales revenue = (_____)(_____)

12. A profit equation is determined by beginning with the formula

    profit = (_____) − (_____)

13. Given a profit equation, state the procedure for determining the break-even points.
14. Given the supply and demand equations, state the procedure for determining the equilibrium point.
15. If an equation relates some quantity to time, its graph is called a(an) _____.

2-4   SOME SPECIAL POLYNOMIAL AND RATIONAL FUNCTIONS

16. Write the general form for the equation of an nth-degree polynomial function.
17. An nth-degree polynomial function has at most ____ high/low points and at most ____ x-intercepts.
18. Draw the graph that typifies equations of the form $f(x) = ax^n$, where n is an odd positive integer, $n > 3$, and $a > 0$.
19. Draw the graph that typifies equations of the form $f(x) = ax^n$, where n is an even positive integer and $a > 0$.
20. Draw the graph that typifies equations of the form $f(x) = k/x^n$, where n is an odd positive integer and $k > 0$.
21. Draw the graph that typifies equations of the form $f(x) = k/x^n$, where n is an even positive integer and $k > 0$.
22. Give the procedure for determining vertical asymptotes of rational functions.
23. If $C(x)$ denotes the total cost of producing x units of some product, write the equation that gives the average cost per unit.

2-5   GRAPHING POLYNOMIAL FUNCTIONS (OPTIONAL)

24. Given a polynomial equation in factored form, state the rule for determining whether its graph crosses or is tangent to the x-axis at a particular x-intercept.

25. Give the procedure for graphing a polynomial function whose equation is given in factored form.

2-6   GRAPHING RATIONAL FUNCTIONS (OPTIONAL)

26. Give the procedure for graphing a rational function.
27. Give the vertical asymptote rule for rational functions.

REVIEW EXERCISES

• Graphing Concepts

Graph each of the following.

1. $y = |x - 7|$ **2.** $y = |x + 5| - 3$ **3.** $y = -|x + 2| + 1$

For Exercises 4-6, determine whether the function is odd, even, or neither by filling in the indicated table of x- and $f(x)$-values.

4. $f(x) = x^4$

x	−3	−2	−1	0	1	2	3
$f(x)$							

5. $f(x) = 1/x^3$

x	−3	−2	−1	0	1	2	3
$f(x)$							

6. $f(x) = 3x - 4$

x	−3	−2	−1	0	1	2	3
$f(x)$							

• Quadratic Functions

Graph Exercises 7-18.

7. $f(x) = x^2 - 25$ **8.** $f(x) = -x^2 + 36$
9. $f(x) = -3(x + 2)^2 + 4$ **10.** $f(x) = (x - 5)^2 - 3$
11. $y = -4x^2 + 24x$ **12.** $y = 5x^2 - 30x$
13. $f(x) = x^2 + 2x - 15$ **14.** $f(x) = x^2 - 9x + 8$
15. $f(x) = x^2 - 8x + 16$ **16.** $f(x) = x^2 + 10x + 25$
17. $y = (x + 4)(x - 6)$ **18.** $y = (x - 7)(x - 9)$

19. *Revenue function.* Given the demand equation $p = -2x + 140$, where p denotes the unit price in dollars and x denotes the number of units demanded of some product,
a) Determine the equation of the revenue function, $R(x)$.
b) Graph the revenue function.
c) State the maximum sales revenue.
d) How many units must be sold in order to achieve the maximum sales revenue?
e) Substitute the result of part d into the demand equation to determine the unit price that maximizes sales revenue.

20. *Revenue, cost, and profit functions; Break-even analysis.* Given the following:

$$\text{Demand function: } p = -2x + 2700$$
$$\text{Cost function: } C(x) = 300x + 400{,}000$$

where p denotes the unit price in dollars and x denotes the number of units produced and sold of some product,

a) Determine the equation of the revenue function, $R(x)$.
b) Graph both the revenue and cost functions on the same set of axes.
c) How many units of the product should be produced and sold in order to break even?
d) State the interval over which profit is positive.
e) Determine the equation of the profit function.
f) Graph the profit function.
g) Using the profit function, determine the break-even points. Verify that they agree with the answer to part c.
h) Using the profit function, state the interval over which profit is positive. Verify that this answer agrees with that of part d.
i) State the maximum profit.
j) How many units of the product should be produced and sold in order to maximize profit?

21. *Supply, demand, and market equilibrium.* For the following supply and demand functions, p denotes the unit price in dollars and x denotes the number of units supplied or demanded of some product in millions of units.

$$\text{Supply function: } p = x^2 + 8 \qquad (x > 0)$$
$$\text{Demand function: } p = (x - 4)^2 \qquad (0 < x \leq 4)$$

a) Determine the equilibrium quantity.
b) Determine the equilibrium price.
c) Graph both the supply and demand functions on the same set of axes.

22. *Time series.* A company's annual profits, P (in millions of dollars), are related to the time, t (in years), since its incorporation by the function

$$P(t) = 0.8t^2 + 40 \qquad (t > 0)$$

a) Graph the function $P(t)$.
b) Find the company's annual profit for the third year.
c) Find the company's annual profit for the sixth year.

• *Some Special Polynomial and Rational Functions*

Graph Exercises 23-32.

23. $y = x^6$ **24.** $y = x^5$ **25.** $y = 5x^8$ **26.** $y = -7x^4$
27. $y = 3/x^4$ **28.** $y = 6/x^7$ **29.** $y = -8/x^3$ **30.** $y = -2/x^2$
31. $y = -4(x - 2)^4 + 3$ **32.** $y = 2/(x - 5)^5$

33. *Production possibility curve.* A company produces x units of Product A and y units of Product B. The equation

$$y = 8{,}000{,}000/x^2 \qquad (200 \leq x \leq 800)$$

relates x and y and thus gives the production possibilities for the two products.

a) Graph the production possibility curve.
b) State the production possibility for $x = 200$.
c) State the production possibility for $x = 600$.
d) State the production possibility for $x = 800$.

34. *Demand curve.* The equation

$$p = 40{,}000/(x - 20) \qquad (20 < x < 8020)$$

gives the relationship between the unit price, p, and the number of units demanded, x, of some product.

a) Graph the demand curve.
b) Find the unit price when the demand is 1020 units.
c) Find the unit price when the demand is 6020 units.

35. *Average cost function.* The total cost in dollars of producing x units of some product is given by

$$C(x) = 800x + 480{,}000 \qquad (x > 0)$$

a) Determine the equation of the average cost function.
b) Graph the result of part a.
c) Evaluate $\overline{C}(2000)$, $\overline{C}(10{,}000)$, and $\overline{C}(100{,}000)$, and interpret the results.
d) As the production level increases, the average cost per unit is approaching what value?

• Polynomial Functions

Graph Exercises 36-39.

36. $f(x) = (x + 3)(x - 1)^2(x - 8)$

37. $f(x) = (x + 2)^3(x - 6)^2$

38. $f(x) = x^4 - 4x^2$

39. $f(x) = x^3 - 4x^2 + 4x$

40. *Volume.* A company makes open boxes from square pieces of tin of dimensions 20 inches by 20 inches. Equal squares are cut from the corners of each piece of tin, and the remaining flaps are folded up to form the sides.

a) Express the volume, V, of the box as a function of x, the length of each side of the cut-out square.
b) Graph the function $V(x)$ of part a.
c) For which values of x is volume, V, non-negative? Does this make sense?

• Rational Functions

Graph the following.

41. $f(x) = \dfrac{(x + 2)(x - 5)^2}{(x - 1)}$

42. $f(x) = \dfrac{(x + 4)(x - 7)}{(x - 3)^3}$

43. $f(x) = \dfrac{5x - 40}{x - 2}$

44. $f(x) = \dfrac{x^2 - 25}{x^2 - 4}$

45. $f(x) = \dfrac{x^2 - 36}{x - 8}$

46. $f(x) = \dfrac{x^3 - 4x^2 + 4x}{(x - 1)^2}$

3

EXPONENTIAL AND LOGARITHMIC FUNCTIONS

Introductory Application

Market Penetration: Long-Range Forecasting

The exponential function defined by

$$y = A - Be^{-mx}$$

where A, B, and m are positive constants, is used to model market penetration of a product that exhibits rapid sales growth upon introduction into the marketplace. The above function is called the **modified exponential model.** Its graph appears in Figure 3-A. Note that x denotes time (in years), y denotes the percentage of the market penetrated by the product, and the constant, A, denotes the market saturation level—not to exceed 100% ($A = 100$). Observe that the graph of Figure 3-A indicates rapid sales growth upon introduction of the product (at $x = 0$). This sales growth continues for some time until it eventually slows as the market reaches saturation level.

• **EXAMPLE**

The market penetration for television sets has followed the modified exponential model.

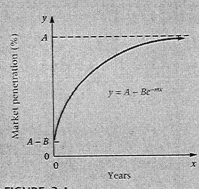

FIGURE 3-A

In this chapter, we discuss exponential and logarithmic functions, including the modified exponential model and the logistic growth model, along with other applications.

In this chapter, we will discuss functions used to describe growth and decay of various quantities. Such functions are called **exponential functions.** We will also consider **logarithms** and **logarithmic functions.** The derivatives of exponential and logarithmic functions will be discussed along with various applications.

3-1 • EXPONENTIAL FUNCTIONS AND THEIR GRAPHS

Consider two quantities, y and x, related by the equation

$$y = 2^x$$

Since the variable x is an exponent, such an equation defines an exponential function. The constant 2, is called the **base.** A graph and a table of x- and y-values are illustrated in Figure 3-1 and Table 3-1, respectively. Observing the graph of Figure 3-1, note that $(0, 1)$ is the y-intercept. Since 2^x approaches 0 as x takes on negative values of larger and larger magnitude, the graph of $y = 2^x$ approaches the x-axis as x takes on negative values far away from the origin. Thus, the x-axis is a horizontal asymptote.

Note that Table 3-1 shows values of 2^x for rational values of x. It is possible to evaluate 2^x for irrational values of x by approximating each irrational value of x by rational values. For example, $2^{\sqrt{3}}$ may be approximated to varying degrees of accuracy by considering the sequence of rational powers

$$2^1, 2^{1.7}, 2^{1.73}, 2^{1.732}, \ldots$$

Recall that $\sqrt{3} \approx 1.732$. Thus, as the exponents get closer and closer to $\sqrt{3}$, the corresponding powers of 2 get closer and closer to $2^{\sqrt{3}}$. Therefore, the exponential function defined by $y = 2^x$ has all of the real numbers as its domain, and its graph is the continuous curve illustrated in Figure 3-1.

We now consider the function defined by the equation

$$y = 2^{-x}$$

Again, since the variable x appears as an exponent, this equation defines an exponential function. Note that the exponent, $-x$, has a negative sign. The graph of $y = 2^{-x}$ and a table of $x-$ and $y-$ values are given on page 128 in Figure 3-2 and Table 3-2, respectively.

Studying the graph of Figure 3-2, we see that $(0, 1)$ is the y-intercept. Note that 2^{-x} approaches 0 as x takes on larger and larger positive values. Thus, the x-axis is a horizontal asymptote. The graphs of $y = 2^x$ and $y = 2^{-x}$ are reflections of one another through the y-axis.

We now consider the function defined by

$$y = 5 \cdot 2^x$$

TABLE 3-1

x	$y = 2^x$
-4	$y = 2^{-4} = (1/2)^4 = 1/$
-3	$y = 2^{-3} = (1/2)^3 = 1/$
-2	$y = 2^{-2} = (1/2)^2 = 1/$
-1	$y = 2^{-1} = (1/2)^1 = 1/$
0	$y = 2^0 \;\;\;= 1$
1	$y = 2^1 \;\;\;= 2$
2	$y = 2^2 \;\;\;= 4$
3	$y = 2^3 \;\;\;= 8$
4	$y = 2^4 \;\;\;= 16$

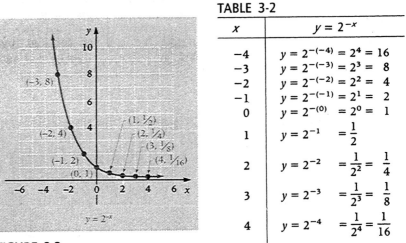

FIGURE 3-2

TABLE 3-2

x	$y = 2^{-x}$
-4	$y = 2^{-(-4)} = 2^4 = 16$
-3	$y = 2^{-(-3)} = 2^3 = 8$
-2	$y = 2^{-(-2)} = 2^2 = 4$
-1	$y = 2^{-(-1)} = 2^1 = 2$
0	$y = 2^{-(0)} = 2^0 = 1$
1	$y = 2^{-1} = \dfrac{1}{2}$
2	$y = 2^{-2} = \dfrac{1}{2^2} = \dfrac{1}{4}$
3	$y = 2^{-3} = \dfrac{1}{2^3} = \dfrac{1}{8}$
4	$y = 2^{-4} = \dfrac{1}{2^4} = \dfrac{1}{16}$

Since the variable x appears as an exponent, this equation also defines an exponential function. Its graph and a table of x- and y-values are illustrated in Figure 3-3 and Table 3-3, respectively. Looking at Figure 3-3, note that $(0, 5)$ is the y-intercept and that the x-axis is a horizontal asymptote.

If we compare the graphs of $y = 2^x$ and $y = 5 \cdot 2^x$ by sketching both functions on the same axis system, we obtain Figure 3-4. Note that the x-axis is the horizontal asymptote for both functions. Also, $(0, 1)$ is the y-intercept of $y = 2^x$, whereas $(0, 5)$ is the y-intercept of $y = 5 \cdot 2^x$. Observe that the graph of $y = 5 \cdot 2^x$ is similar to the graph of $y = 2^x$. The only effects of the constant multiplier, 5, on the graph of $y = 2^x$ are changes in its y-intercept and curvature. This is because the y-values of $y = 5 \cdot 2^x$ are 5 times those of $y = 2^x$.

TABLE 3-3

x	$y = 5 \cdot 2^x$
-3	$y = 5 \cdot 2^{-3} = 5 \cdot (1/2)^3 = 5/8$
-2	$y = 5 \cdot 2^{-2} = 5 \cdot (1/2)^2 = 5/4$
-1	$y = 5 \cdot 2^{-1} = 5 \cdot (1/2)^1 = 5/2$
0	$y = 5 \cdot 2^0 = 5 \cdot 1 = 5$
1	$y = 5 \cdot 2^1 = 5 \cdot 2 = 10$
2	$y = 5 \cdot 2^2 = 5 \cdot 4 = 20$
3	$y = 5 \cdot 2^3 = 5 \cdot 8 = 40$
4	$y = 5 \cdot 2^4 = 5 \cdot 16 = 80$

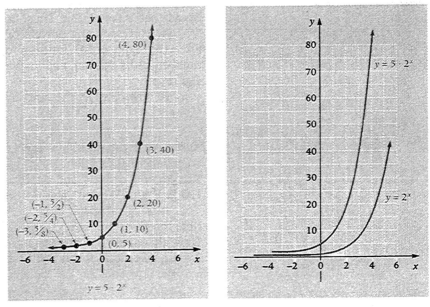

FIGURE 3-3

FIGURE 3-4

Step 1
Begin with the graph $y = 5 \cdot 2^x$.

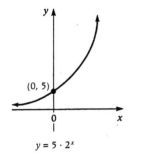

$y = 5 \cdot 2^x$

Step 2
Draw the graph of $y = 5 \cdot 2^x$ upside down to obtain the graph of $y = -5 \cdot 2^x$.

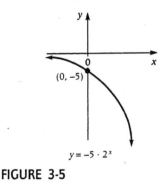

$y = -5 \cdot 2^x$

FIGURE 3-5

We note that if the constant multiplier is negative—say, -5,—then the y-values of the function $y = -5 \cdot 2^x$ are the negatives of those of $y = 5 \cdot 2^x$, and, therefore, the graph of $y = -5 \cdot 2^x$ is a reflection on the x-axis of the graph of $y = 5 \cdot 2^x$, as illustrated in Figure 3-5. In other words, the graph of $y = -5 \cdot 2^x$ can be obtained by drawing the graph of $y = 5 \cdot 2^x$ upside down.

Base e

The following discussion will involve values of the expression

$$\left(1 + \frac{1}{x}\right)^x$$

as x gets larger and larger. This expression occurs so often in mathematics that we use a calculator to evaluate it for larger and larger values of x as illustrated below.

$$\left(1 + \frac{1}{1000}\right)^{1000} = 2.716923924. . .$$

$$\left(1 + \frac{1}{10,000}\right)^{10,000} = 2.718145918. . .$$

$$\left(1 + \frac{1}{100,000}\right)^{100,000} = 2.718268237. . .$$

$$\left(1 + \frac{1}{1,000,000}\right)^{1,000,000} = 2.718281828. . .$$

$$\left(1 + \frac{1}{10,000,000}\right)^{10,000,000} = 2.718281828. . .$$

Note how $(1 + 1/x)^x$ is approaching a single value close to 2.718281828 to nine decimal places. Mathematicians have assigned the letter e to the limiting value of the expression $(1 + 1/x)$ as x gets larger and larger. In other words,

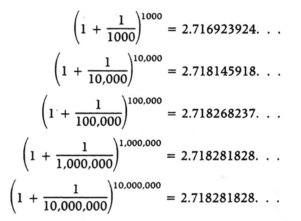

as x gets larger and larger, and e denotes the irrational number whose decimal expansion to nine decimal places is given as follows.

$$e = 2.718281828$$

We note that powers of e (i.e., e^2, e^3, $e^{1.5}$, $e^{-1.67}$, etc.) can be computed by using a calculator. Also, Appendix C gives values of e^x and e^{-x} for various values of x.

Up to this point, we have graphed exponential functions with base 2. However, we often encounter exponential functions with base e. Some examples include $y = e^x$, $y = e^{-x}$, $y = 5e^x$, and $y = -5e^x$. Since we have already graphed $y = 2^x$, $y = 2^{-x}$, $y = 5 \cdot 2^x$, and $y = -5 \cdot 2^x$, we note that the graphs of these equations resemble those of $y = e^x$, $y = e^{-x}$, $y = 5e^x$, and $y = -5e^x$, respectively.

We now summarize the concepts discussed up to this point in this section.

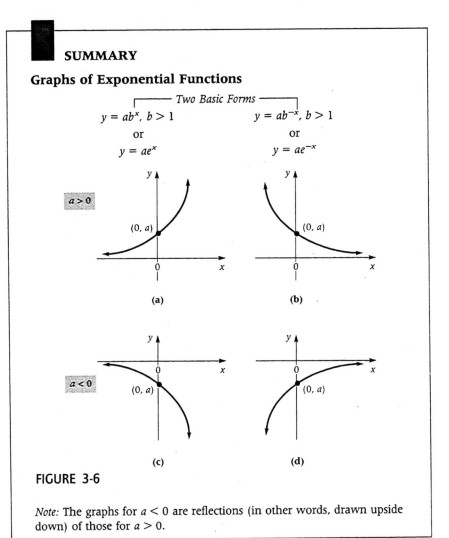

SUMMARY

Graphs of Exponential Functions

Two Basic Forms

$y = ab^x$, $b > 1$ $y = ab^{-x}$, $b > 1$

or   or

$y = ae^x$ $y = ae^{-x}$

FIGURE 3-6

Note: The graphs for $a < 0$ are reflections (in other words, drawn upside down) of those for $a > 0$.

• **EXAMPLE 3-1**

a) The graphs of $y = 5 \cdot 3^x$, $y = e^x$, and $y = 4e^x$ resemble that of Figure 3-6(a).

b) The graphs of $y = 5 \cdot 3^{-x}$, $y = e^{-x}$, and $y = 7e^{-x}$ resemble that of Figure 3-6(b).

c) The graphs of $y = -4 \cdot 2^x$, $y = -e^x$, and $y = -8e^x$ resemble that of Figure 3-6(c).

d) The graphs of $y = -5 \cdot 3^{-x}$. $y = -e^{-x}$, and $y = -6e^{-x}$ resemble that of Figure 3-6(d).

$y = ab^x + c$ and $y = ab^{-x} + c$ Where $b > 1$

Sometimes we encounter an exponential function defined by an equation such as

$$y = 3e^x + 2$$

Step 1
Begin with the graph of $y = 3e^x$.

Step 2 *Vertical shift*
Lift the graph of $y = 3e^x$ vertically by 2 units to obtain the graph of $y = 3e^x + 2$.

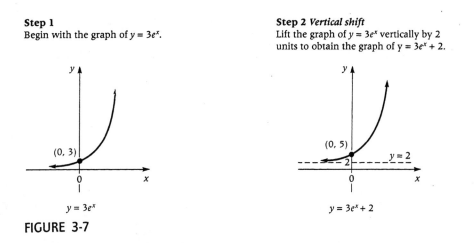

$y = 3e^x$ $y = 3e^x + 2$

FIGURE 3-7

Since the constant 2 is added to $y = 3e^x$, the y-values of $y = 3e^x + 2$ are 2 *greater than* those of $y = 3e^x$. Hence, $y = 3e^x + 2$ may be sketched by beginning with the graph of $y = 3e^x$ and *lifting it vertically by 2 units* (see Figure 3-7). As discussed in Chapter 2, this is called a **vertical shift**. Note that the horizontal line $y = 2$ is the horizontal asymptote for $y = 3e^x + 2$.

To Graph Exponential Functions

$$y = ab^x + c \quad \text{or} \quad y = ab^{-x} + c$$
$$\text{where } b > 1$$

Step 1   Begin with the graph of $y = ab^x$ or $y = ab^{-x}$.

Step 2   Vertical Shift

If $c > 0$, lift the graph of Step 1 vertically by c units.
If $c < 0$, lower the graph of Step 1 vertically by $|c|$ units.

• **EXAMPLE 3-2** _____

Sketch $f(x) = -2e^x - 1$.

Solution

Compare this equation with the general form $y = ab^x + c$, where $a = -2$ (a negative number), $b = e$, and $c = -1$. The graph is sketched in Figure 3-8.

• **EXAMPLE 3-3** _____

Sketch $y = -4e^{-x} + 6$.

Solution

This function is of the form $y = ab^{-x} + c$, where $a = -4$ (a negative number), $b = e$, and $c = 6$. Its graph is sketched in Figure 3-9 on page 132.

Step 1
Begin with the graph of $y = -2e^x$.

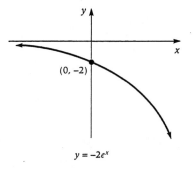

$y = -2e^x$

Step 2 *Vertical shift*
Lower the graph of $y = -2e^x$ vertically by 1 unit to obtain the graph of $y = -2e^x - 1$.

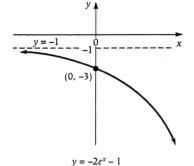

$y = -2e^x - 1$

FIGURE 3-8

Step 1
Begin with the graph of $y = -4e^{-x}$.

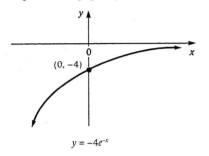

$$y = -4e^{-x}$$

Step 2 *Vertical shift*
Lift the graph of $y = -4e^{-x}$ vertically by 6 units to obtain the graph of $y = -4e^{-x} + 6$.

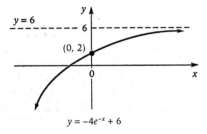

$$y = -4e^{-x} + 6$$

FIGURE 3-9

All of the equations defining exponential functions in this section have appeared in either of the following two forms:

$$y = ab^x + c \qquad (b > 1)$$

or

$$y = ab^{-x} + c \qquad (b > 1)$$

Note that for each form, $b > 1$. We now consider the cases for which $b \leq 1$. If $b = 1$, then $b^x = 1^x = 1$ for all finite x-values. Thus, the equation $y = ab^x + c$ becomes the horizontal line $y = a + c$. The same happens to the form $y = ab^{-x} + c$. We have little interest in such exponential functions.

We now show that the case in which $0 < b < 1$ is not really a new case at all. If $0 < b < 1$, then b^x may be written as b_1^{-x}, with $b_1 = 1/b$ and $b_1 > 1$. For example, $(1/2)^x = 2^{-x}$, $(1/3)^x = 3^{-x}$, $(2/5)^x = (5/2)^{-x}$, etc. Also, b^{-x} becomes b_1^x, with $b_1 = 1/b$ and $b_1 > 1$. For example, $(1/2)^{-x} = 2^x$, $(1/3)^{-x} = 3^x$, $(2/5)^{-x} = (5/2)^x$, etc. Thus, the equation $y = ab^x + c$, with $0 < b < 1$, may be written as $y = ab_1^{-x} + c$, with $b_1 > 1$, since $b_1 = 1/b$. Also, the equation $y = ab^{-x} + c$, with $0 < b < 1$, may be rewritten as $y = ab_1^x + c$, with $b_1 > 1$, since $b_1 = 1/b$.

If $b \leq 0$, we have little interest in equations of the form $y = ab^x + c$ or $y = ab^{-x} + c$ since the function is not defined at many x-values. Specifically, if $b = 0$ and $x = -1$, then $y = ab^x + c$ is undefined; if $b = -4$ and $x = 1/2$, then $y = ab^x + c$ is undefined.

We state the following property.

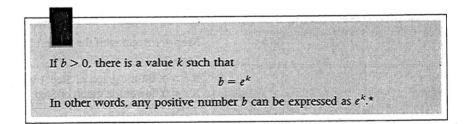

If $b > 0$, there is a value k such that

$$b = e^k$$

In other words, any positive number b can be expressed as e^k.*

Exponential Functions with Terms e^{kx} and e^{-kx}

Since

$$b^x = (e^k)^x = e^{kx}$$

equations of the forms

$$y = ab^x + c \qquad (b > 1)$$

and

$$y = ab^{-x} + c \qquad (b > 1)$$

---

*We will learn how to find k in Section 3-2.

Step 1
Begin with the graph of $y = -3e^{-0.05x}$.

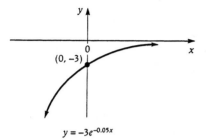

$y = -3e^{-0.05x}$

Step 2 *Vertical shift*
Lift the graph of $y = -3e^{-0.05x}$ vertically by 7 units to obtain the graph of $y = -3e^{-0.05x} + 7$.

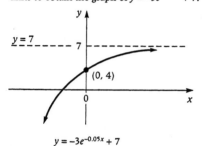

$y = -3e^{-0.05x} + 7$

FIGURE 3-10

may be restated as

$$y = ae^{kx} + c \qquad (k > 0)$$

and

$$y = ae^{-kx} + c \qquad (k > 0)$$

respectively. Therefore, the procedures of this section also apply to sketching exponential functions expressed in the latter forms that contain the terms e^{kx} and e^{-kx}.

• **EXAMPLE 3-4**

Sketch $y = -3e^{-0.05x} + 7$.

Solution

The graph is sketched in Figure 3-10.

Before ending this section, we state the following property.

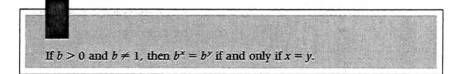

If $b > 0$ and $b \neq 1$, then $b^x = b^y$ if and only if $x = y$.

For example, if $3^{18} = 3^{2x}$, then $2x = 18$ and $x = 9$. If $5^{40} = 5^{4x}$, then $4x = 40$ and $x = 10$.

Applications

Radioactive Decay

A radioactive substance loses its mass (or, if you prefer, weight) as time passes. Specifically, its mass, y, is related to the time elapsed, t, by an equation of the form

$$y = ae^{-kt} \qquad (k > 0)$$

Note that at $t = 0$, the initial mass is

$$y = ae^{-k(0)}$$
$$= a \cdot 1$$
$$= a$$

The letter k represents a constant associated with the specific radioactive substance being considered. If, for a particular radioactive substance, the initial mass is $a = 1000$ grams and $k = 0.70$, then the equation

$$y = 1000e^{-0.70t}$$

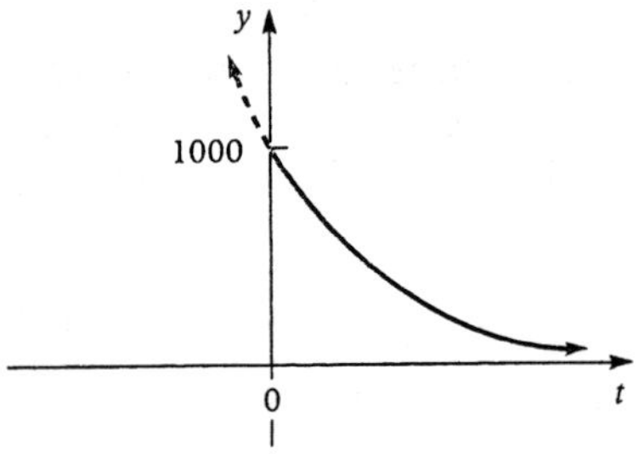

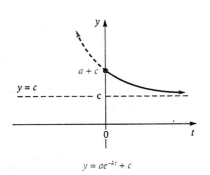

$y = 1000e^{-0.07t}$

FIGURE 3-11

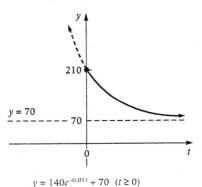

$y = ae^{-kt} + c$

FIGURE 3-12

$y = 140e^{-0.01t} + 70 \quad (t \geq 0)$

FIGURE 3-13

relates its mass, y (in grams), with the time elapsed, t (in minutes). Thus, at $t = 1$ (after 1 minute has elapsed), the mass is

$$y = 1000e^{-0.70(1)}$$
$$= 1000e^{-0.70}$$
$$\approx 1000(0.496585)$$
$$\approx 496.59 \text{ grams}$$

The graph of $y = 1000e^{-0.70t}$ is illustrated in Figure 3-11. Observe that the radioactive mass is decreasing as time is increasing.

Newton's Law of Cooling

Newton's law of cooling expresses the relationship between the temperature of a cooling object and the time elapsed since cooling first began. According to Newton's law of cooling, if

y = temperature of a cooling object after t units of time

c = temperature of the medium surrounding the cooling object

then the exponential function

$$y = ae^{-kt} + c$$

relates temperature, y, with time, t. The letters a and k represent constants associated with the cooling object. A sketch of the general function $y = ae^{-kt} + c$ appears in Figure 3-12. The constants a and k are non-negative. Studying Figure 3-12, we note that the temperature y of the cooling object approaches the temperature c of the surrounding medium as t gets larger and larger. Thus, the temperature of a cooling object will not fall below the temperature of the surrounding medium.

As a specific example, consider a cup of tea heated to 210°F. The room temperature is 70°F. Here, the exponential function

$$y = 140e^{-0.01t} + 70 \qquad (t \geq 0)$$

relates the temperature, y, of the tea with the time elapsed, t (in minutes). Hence, after 10 minutes have elapsed ($t = 10$), we find that

$$y = 140e^{-0.01(10)} + 70$$
$$= 140e^{-0.1} + 70$$
$$\approx 140(0.904837) + 70$$
$$\approx 126.67718 + 70$$
$$\approx 196.7$$

Thus, the object at this point in time has cooled to a temperature of approximately 197°F. The graph of $y = 140e^{-0.01t} + 70$ is sketched in Figure 3-13.

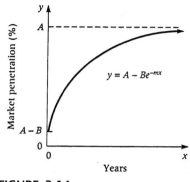

FIGURE 3-14

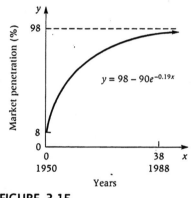

FIGURE 3-15

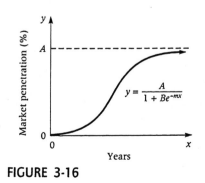

FIGURE 3-16

Market Penetration: Long-Range Forecasting

We discuss two exponential functions used to model and, thus, forecast the market penetration of products introduced into the marketplace. The first is called the modified exponential model, and the second is called the logistic growth model.

Modified Exponential Model. As discussed in the introductory application to this chapter, the exponential function defined by

$$y = A - Be^{-mx}$$

where A, B, and m are positive constants, is used to model market penetration of a product that exhibits rapid sales growth upon introduction into the marketplace. The above function is called the **modified exponential model.** Its graph appears in Figure 3-14. Note that x denotes time (in years), y denotes the percentage of the market penetrated by the product, and the constant, A, denotes the market saturation level—not to exceed 100% ($A = 100$). Observe that the graph of Figure 3-14 indicates rapid sales growth upon introduction of the product (at $x = 0$). This sales growth continues for some time until it eventually slows as the market reaches saturation level.

The market penetration for television sets has followed the modified exponential model, as illustrated in Figure 3-15. The equation

$$y = 98 - 90e^{-0.19x}$$

approximates the relationship between market penetration and time exhibited by the curve of Figure 3-15. Here $x = 0$ corresponds to the year 1950, and $x = 38$ corresponds to the year 1988.

USING THE MODEL TO FORECAST We forecast the percentage of the market penetrated by television sets for the year 1995 by substituting $x = 45$ into the equation of the model to obtain

$$y = 98 - 90e^{-0.19(45)} \qquad \text{Use a calculator}$$
$$\approx 97.98 \qquad \text{Forecast}$$

Thus, approximately 97.98% of all households are projected to have television sets in 1995.

Logistic Growth Model. The exponential function defined by

$$y = \frac{A}{1 + Be^{-mx}}$$

where A, B, and m are positive constants, is used to model market penetration of a product that exhibits slow sales growth when first introduced into the marketplace, then a period of rapid growth followed by a gradual decline in growth, and, finally, no growth as the market reaches saturation level. This is illustrated in Figure 3-16, which gives the graph of the above function. This function is called the **logistic growth model;** the variable,

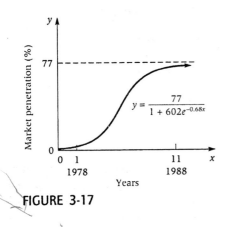

FIGURE 3-17

x, denotes time (in years), y denotes the percentage of the market penetrated by the product, and the constant, A, denotes the market saturation level—not to exceed 100% ($A = 100$).

The market penetration for videocassette recorders (VCRs) has followed the logistic growth model, as illustrated in Figure 3-17. The equation

$$y = \frac{77}{1 + 602e^{-0.68x}}$$

approximates the relationship between market penetration and time exhibited by the curve of Figure 3-17. Here $x = 1$ corresponds to the year 1978, and $x = 11$ corresponds to the year 1988.

USING THE MODEL TO FORECAST   We forecast the percentage of the market penetrated by videocassette recorders for the year 1995 by substituting $x = 18$ into the equation of the model to obtain

$$y = \frac{77}{1 + 602e^{-0.68(18)}} \qquad \text{Use a calculator}$$

$$\approx 76.77 \qquad \text{Forecast}$$

Thus, approximately 76.77% of all households are projected to have videocassette recorders in 1995.

Exercises 3-1

Sketch the following. Identify the y-intercept and the horizontal asymptote in each case.

1. $f(x) = 5^x$	**2.** $y = 3^x$	**3.** $y = 4^x$
4. $f(x) = 4 \cdot 5^x$	**5.** $y = 2 \cdot 3^x$	**6.** $y = 3 \cdot 4^x$
7. $f(x) = -4 \cdot 5^x$	**8.** $f(x) = -2 \cdot 3^x$	**9.** $y = -3 \cdot 4^x$
10. $y = 3e^x$	**11.** $f(x) = 7e^x$	**12.** $y = 10e^x$
13. $y = -3e^x$	**14.** $y = -7e^x$	**15.** $y = -10e^x$
16. $y = 2 \cdot 3^x + 5$		**17.** $f(x) = -3 \cdot 4^x + 8$
18. $f(x) = 4e^x + 1$		**19.** $y = 4e^x - 1$
20. $y = -2e^x + 8$		**21.** $f(x) = -2e^x - 5$
22. $y = 5^{-x}$		**23.** $f(x) = 3^{-x}$
24. $y = 4^{-x}$		**25.** $y = 4 \cdot 5^{-x}$
26. $f(x) = 2 \cdot 3^{-x}$		**27.** $y = 3 \cdot 4^{-x}$
28. $y = -4 \cdot 5^{-x}$		**29.** $f(x) = -2 \cdot 3^{-x}$
30. $y = -3 \cdot 4^{-x}$		**31.** $y = 3e^{-x}$
32. $y = 7e^{-x}$		**33.** $y = 10e^{-x}$
34. $y = -3e^{-x}$		**35.** $f(x) = -7e^{-x}$
36. $y = -10e^{-x}$		**37.** $y = 2 \cdot 3^{-x} + 5$
38. $f(x) = -3 \cdot 4^{-x} + 8$		**39.** $f(x) = 4e^{-x} + 1$
40. $y = 4e^{-x} - 1$		**41.** $y = -2e^{-x} + 30$
42. $f(x) = -2e^{-x} - 5$		**43.** $y = 30e^{-x} + 30$
44. $f(x) = 50 - 50e^{-x}$		**45.** $y = 10(1 - e^{-x})$
46. $f(x) = -5(1 - e^{-x})$		**47.** $y = (1/2)^x$
48. $y = (2/3)^x$		**49.** $y = (1/2)^{-x}$

50. $f(x) = (2/3)^{-x}$

51. $y = 5 \cdot (1/5)^x + 1$

52. $f(x) = -4 \cdot (1/6)^{-x} + 2$

53. $y = 3e^{2x} + 1$

54. $f(x) = 4e^{-3x} + 1$

55. $f(x) = -2e^{0.05x} + 1$

56. $y = 3e^{-0.02x} - 5$

57. $y = 10e^{0.07x}$

58. $y = -5e^{0.03x}$

59. $f(x) = 7e^{-0.10x}$

60. $y = -3e^{-0.06x}$

61. $y = 10(1 - e^{-0.20x})$

62. $y = -2e^{-0.3x} - 6$

63. $y = -8e^{-0.40x}$

64. $y = 70e^{-0.50x} + 10$

Applications

65. *Bacteria growth.* A certain type of bacteria triples its numbers each day. Initially, there were 500,000 such bacteria present. Let y represent the number of bacteria present and t represent the number of days elapsed.
   a) Find the equation that relates y and t.
   b) Sketch the graph of the equation of part a.
   c) How many bacteria are present after 4 days?
   d) How many bacteria are present after 6 days?

66. *Depreciation.* A certain car depreciates in such a way that it loses two-thirds of its value each year. The car initially cost $4000. Let y represent the car's value (in dollars) at the end of the xth year.
   a) Find the equation that relates y and x.
   b) Sketch the graph of the equation of part a.
   c) Find the car's value at the end of the fourth year.
   d) Find the car's value at the end of the fifth year.

67. *Time series.* The annual sales, y (in millions of dollars), of a particular company are related to time, t, by the equation

$$y = 3 \cdot 2^t$$

with $t = 0$ corresponding to the year 19x0, $t = 1$ corresponding to the year 19x1, etc.
   a) Sketch $y = 3 \cdot 2^t$.
   b) Find the annual sales for years 19x0, 19x1, and 19x2.

68. *Time series.* The annual earnings per share of AKD Corporation are related to time by the equation

$$y(t) = e^{0.1t}$$

where $y(t)$ represents the earnings per share for year t. Note that $t = 0$ corresponds to the year 19x0, $t = 1$ corresponds to the year 19x1, etc.
   a) Sketch $y(t) = e^{0.1t}$.
   b) Find the earnings per share for years 19x0, 19x1, 19x2, and 19x3.

69. *Maintenance cost.* The annual maintenance cost, y, of a machine is related to the number of years it is run, t, by the equation

$$y = 1000e^{0.05t} \qquad (t \geq 0)$$

   a) Sketch $y = 1000e^{0.05t}$, $t \geq 0$.
   b) Find the annual maintenance cost after the machine has run for 2 years.

70. *Population decline.* The population, $P(t)$, of a certain city is related to time, t (in years), by the exponential function

$$P(t) = 10,000e^{-0.03t}$$

Note that $t = 0$ corresponds to the year 19x0, $t = 1$ corresponds to the year 19x1, etc.
   a) Sketch $P(t) = 10,000e^{-0.03t}$.
   b) Find this city's population for 19x0, 19x1, 19x2, and 19x3.

71. *Radioactive decay.* A certain radioactive substance decays in accordance with the equation

$$y(t) = 2000e^{-0.60t} \qquad (t \geq 0)$$

where $y(t)$ represents the mass (in grams) related to time, t (in hours).
   a) Sketch $y(t) = 2000e^{-0.60t}$.
   b) Calculate the initial mass of the substance.
   c) Calculate the mass of the substance after 1/2 hour has elapsed.
   d) Calculate the mass of the substance after 3 hours have elapsed.

Learning Curve

Psychologists have found that when a person learns a new task, learning is rapid at first. Then, as time passes, learning tends to taper off. Once the task is mastered, the person's level of performance approaches an upper limit. The function that relates a learner's performance with the time elapsed is called a **learning curve.** Learning curves are often expressed by exponential functions.

72. *Learning curve.* Consider the learning curve expressed by the exponential function

$$y = 40 - 40e^{-0.2x} \qquad (x \geq 0)$$

Here, the performance, y, is the number of items produced by the worker during the xth day following the training period.
   a) Sketch $y = 40 - 40e^{-0.2x}$.
   b) How many items are produced during the third day following the training period?
   c) This worker's daily production will never exceed how many units?

73. *Learning curve.* The graph of the exponential function defined by

$$N(x) = 50 - 50e^{-0.3x} \qquad (x \geq 0)$$

is a learning curve, where $N(x)$ represents the number of items produced by an assembly line worker during the xth day after the training period.
   a) Sketch $N(x) = 50 - 50e^{-0.3x}$.
   b) How many items are produced during the fifth day following the training period?
   c) This worker's daily production will never exceed how many units?

74. *Newton's law of cooling.* The temperature, y, of a heated cup of coffee is related to the time elapsed, t (in minutes), by the equation

$$y = 150e^{-0.02t} + 65 \qquad (t \geq 0)$$

   a) Sketch $y = 150e^{-0.02t} + 65$.
   b) Calculate the temperature of the coffee before cooling began.
   c) Calculate the temperature of the coffee after 5 minutes have elapsed.
   d) What is the room temperature?
   e) The temperature of the coffee will not decline below what value?

75. *Newton's law of cooling.* A coroner determines that the temperature, T, of a murder victim's body is related to the time elapsed, t (in hours), since death by the equation

$$T = 38.6e^{-0.05t} + 60 \qquad (t \geq 0)$$

a) Sketch $T = 38.6e^{-0.05t} + 60$.
b) What is the room temperature?
c) Calculate the dead body's temperature after 2 hours have elapsed.

76. *Sales.* The function defined by

$$y = 3.6e^{0.02x} \qquad (x \geq 0)$$

approximates the relationship between sales, y (in billions of dollars), and advertising expenditure, x (in millions of dollars).
a) Sketch $y = 3.6e^{0.02x}$.
b) Calculate the expected sales for an advertising expenditure of $5 million.

77. *Market penetration: Long-range forecasting.* The percentage of market penetration for a product x years after it has been introduced is given by

$$y = 80 - 60e^{-0.70x}$$

a) Graph $y = 80 - 60e^{-0.70x}$ for $x \geq 0$.
b) Determine the percentage of market penetration for the second year.
c) Determine the percentage of market penetration for the tenth year.
d) Determine the saturation level.

78. *Market penetration: Long-range forecasting.* The percentage of market penetration for a product x years after it has been introduced is given by

$$y = \frac{80}{1 + 200e^{-0.90x}}$$

a) Determine the percentage of market penetration for the second, sixth, and twelfth years.
b) Determine the saturation level.

3-2 • LOGARITHMIC FUNCTIONS

> **Logarithm**
>
> If three numbers, L, b, and N (and $b > 0$, $b \neq 1$, and $N > 0$), are related in such a way that
>
> $$N = b^L$$
>
> then the exponent, L, is defined as "the logarithm of N to the base b." This definition is written in shorthand notation as
>
> $$L = \log_b N$$

Thus, the statement $N = b^L$ has the same meaning as the statement $L = \log_b N$. The statement $N = b^L$ is written in **exponential form**. The statement $L = \log_b N$ is written in **logarithmic form**. Specifically, the statement $9 = 3^2$ may be expressed in logarithmic form as $2 = \log_3 9$, read "2 equals the log of 9 to the base 3."

• EXAMPLE 3-5

Rewrite the statement $5^3 = 125$ in logarithmic form.

Solution

$3 = \log_5 125$, read "3 equals the log of 125 to the base 5."

• EXAMPLE 3-6

Rewrite the statement $10^4 = 10,000$ in logarithmic form.

Solution

$4 = \log_{10} 10,000$, read "4 equals the log of 10,000 to the base 10."

Studying the preceding examples, we note that a **logarithm** is an *exponent* of a number called the **base.** Thus, the statement

$$2 = \log_{10} 100$$

has the same meaning as the statement

$$10^2 = 100$$

Note that 2, the logarithm, is the exponent of 10, the base.

• EXAMPLE 3-7

Find y if $y = \log_2 8$.

Solution

Since $y = \log_2 8$ means $2^y = 8$, then $y = 3$. Thus, 3 is the log of 8 to the base 2.

• EXAMPLE 3-8

Find $\log_{10} 100$.

Solution

Let $y = \log_{10} 100$. Translated into exponential form, the statement becomes $10^y = 100$. Hence, $y = 2$. Thus, 2 is the log of 100 to the base 10.

Different Bases

We again emphasize that a logarithm is an exponent of a number called the base (study Examples 3-5 through 3-8). Two bases are most commonly used: **base 10** and **base e.** Base-10 logarithms are called **common logarithms.** Base-e logarithms are called **natural logarithms,** or **Napierian logarithms.** The following notation is used to distinguish between common logarithms and natural logarithms. Specifically, the common logarithm of x, $\log_{10} x$, is abbreviated $\log x$; the natural logarithm of x, $\log_e x$, is abbreviated $\ln x$. Thus, the statement $y = \log x$ means $10^y = x$; the statement $y = \ln x$ means $e^y = x$.

• EXAMPLE 3-9

Find $\log 10$.

Solution

Let $L = \log 10$. Rewriting the statement in exponential form, we have

$$10^L = 10$$

Hence, $L = 1$. Thus, the common logarithm of 10 is 1.

• EXAMPLE 3-10

Find $\ln e$.

Solution

Let $L = \ln e$. Rewriting this statement in exponential form gives us

$$e^L = e$$

Hence, $L = 1$. Thus, the natural logarithm of e is 1.

• EXAMPLE 3-11

In Section 3-1, we stated that for any positive number, b, there is a value k such that $b = e^k$. Find k.

Solution

Rewriting the statement $b = e^k$ in logarithmic form, we have

$$k = \ln b$$

Thus, $b = e^k = e^{\ln b}$

Calculators and Logarithms

Appendix C contains common logarithm tables to find common logarithms of numbers and natural logarithm tables to find natural logarithms of numbers. However, if a student has a calculator with "log" and "ln" buttons, then the common log of a number may be easily found by using the "log" button, and the natural log of a number may be determined by using the "ln" button.

• EXAMPLE 3-12

Use a calculator to determine each of the following:

a) $\ln 5396$ **b)** $\ln 8.43$
c) $\ln 0.765$ **d)** $\log 0.492$

Solutions

Enter		Key	Result
a) 5396		ln	8.593413
b) 8.43		ln	2.131796
c) 0.765		ln	−0.267879
d) 0.492		log	−0.308035

We note that the answers are truncated to six decimal places.

TABLE 3-4

$y = \log x$, or $x = 10^y$	Ordered pairs (x, y)
If $y = -3$, then $x = 10^{-3} = 1/1000$	$(1/1000, -3)$
If $y = -2$, then $x = 10^{-2} = 1/100$	$(1/100, -2)$
If $y = -1$, then $x = 10^{-1} = 1/10$	$(1/10, -1)$
If $y = 0$, then $x = 10^0 = 1$	$(1, 0)$
If $y = 1$, then $x = 10^1 = 10$	$(10, 1)$
If $y = 2$, then $x = 10^2 = 100$	$(100, 2)$
If $y = 3$, then $x = 10^3 = 1000$	$(1000, 3)$

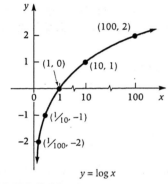

FIGURE 3-18

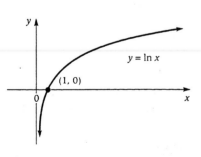

x-intercept
$y = \ln x$ means $x = e^y$.
If $y = 0$, then $x = e^0 = 1$.
Hence, $(1, 0)$ is the x-intercept.

FIGURE 3-19

• **EXAMPLE 3-13** _____

Find x for each of the following:

a) $\ln x = 0.783$ **b)** $\log x = 2.863$

Solutions

a) $\ln x = 0.783$
Rewriting this statement in exponential form, we have
$$x = e^{0.783}$$
$$\approx 2.188 \quad \text{Use the } \boxed{e^x} \text{ button on a calculator.}$$

b) $\log x = 2.863$
Rewriting this statement in exponential form gives
$$x = 10^{2.863}$$
$$\approx 729.458 \quad \text{Use the } \boxed{y^x} \text{ or } \boxed{x^y} \text{ button on a calculator.}$$

Logarithmic Functions

Consider two variables, x and y, related by the equation

$$y = \log x \qquad (x > 0)$$

Since this is an equation with two variables, it may be graphed by computing a table of x- and y-values. Such a table is easily obtained by rewriting the equation $y = \log x$ in exponential form as $10^y = x$ and then choosing arbitrary y-values (see Table 3-4). The graph is sketched in Figure 3-18.

The equation $y = \log x$ defines a logarithmic function. The graph of $y = \log x$, illustrated in Figure 3-18, is typical of the graph of a logarithmic function with a *base greater than 1*. Studying Figure 3-18, we see that $(1, 0)$ is the x-intercept and that the y-axis is a vertical asymptote. Also, note that $y = \log x$ is undefined for $x \leq 0$. A few trial values of x will indicate why. If $x = 0$, then $y = \log 0$ means $10^y = 0$. But no value of y exists such that $10^y = 0$. Thus, $\log 0$ is undefined. However, as y takes on negative values of larger magnitude, 10^y approaches 0, and the y-axis is a vertical asymptote. If x is a negative number, such as $x = -3$, then $y = \log -3$ means $10^y = -3$. Again, no value of y exists such that $10^y = -3$.

• **EXAMPLE 3-14** _____

Sketch the graph of $y = \ln x$.

Solution

Since this logarithmic function has base e (a number greater than 1), its graph will resemble that of $y = \log x$. See Figure 3-19.

Properties of Logarithms

Logarithms obey certain rules called **properties of logarithms.** These properties simplify much of our work with logarithms. They also enable us to perform certain arithmetic operations using logarithms. We now state the five properties of logarithms.

> ### Properties of Logarithms
>
> Let x, y, and b be any positive real numbers with $b \neq 1$. Also, let p be any real number.
>
> **Property 1** $\log_b xy = \log_b x + \log_b y$
>
> **Property 2** $\log_b \dfrac{x}{y} = \log_b x - \log_b y$
>
> **Property 3** $\log_b x^p = p \log_b x$
>
> **Property 4** $\log_b b = 1$
>
> **Property 5** $\log_b 1 = 0$

Since it is important to understand the meaning of these properties of logarithms, we will consider each in turn.

Property 1 $\log_b xy = \log_b x + \log_b y$

This property states that *the logarithm of a product of two numbers is equal to the sum of their logarithms*. The following are a few numerical illustrations of this property:

$$\log_2(8 \cdot 32) = \log_2 8 + \log_2 32$$
$$\log (5.23 \times 100) = \log 5.23 + \log 100$$
$$\ln (3 \cdot 7) = \ln 3 + \ln 7$$

Property 2 $\log_b \dfrac{x}{y} = \log_b x - \log_b y$

This property states that *the logarithm of a quotient of two numbers is equal to the difference of their logarithms*. The following are a few numerical illustrations of this property:

$$\log_2 \frac{64}{16} = \log_2 64 - \log_2 16$$
$$\log \frac{5.63}{100} = \log 5.63 - \log 100$$
$$\ln \frac{40}{3} = \ln 40 - \ln 3$$

Property 3 $\log_b x^p = p \log_b x$

This property states that *the logarithm of the* p*th power of a number is equal to* p *times the logarithm of the number*. The following are a few numerical illustrations of this property:

$$\log_2 4^3 = 3 \log_2 4$$
$$\ln 8^2 = 2 \ln 8$$
$$\log 3^{1/2} = \frac{1}{2}(\log 3)$$

Property 4 $\log_b b = 1$

This property states that *the logarithm of its base is 1*. Thus,

$$\log_5 5 = 1 \quad \log_3 3 = 1 \quad \log 10 = 1 \quad \ln e = 1$$

Property 5 $\log_b 1 = 0$

This property states that *the logarithm of 1 is 0*. Thus,

$$\log_5 1 = 0 \quad \log_3 1 = 0 \quad \log 1 = 0 \quad \ln 1 = 0$$

We now give the proofs of the properties of logarithms.

Proofs of Properties of Logarithms

Note that the properties of logarithms are simply translations of laws of exponents.

Property 1   Let $L_1 = \log_b x$ and $L_2 = \log_b y$. Rewriting these statements in exponential form, we have

$$x = b^{L_1} \qquad y = b^{L_2}$$

Thus,

$$xy = b^{L_1} \cdot b^{L_2}$$
$$= b^{L_1 + L_2}$$

Rewriting the statement $xy = b^{L_1 + L_2}$ in logarithmic form, we obtain

$$\log_b xy = L_1 + L_2$$

Since $L_1 = \log_b x$ and $L_2 = \log_b y$, the preceding statement may be rewritten as

$$\log_b xy = \log_b x + \log_b y$$

Property 2   Let $L_1 = \log_b x$ and $L_2 = \log_b y$. Rewriting these statements in exponential form results in

$$x = b^{L_1} \qquad y = b^{L_2}$$

Thus,

$$\frac{x}{y} = \frac{b^{L_1}}{b^{L_2}}$$
$$= b^{L_1 - L_2}$$

Rewriting the statement $x/y = b^{L_1 - L_2}$ in logarithmic form, we have

$$\log_b \frac{x}{y} = L_1 - L_2$$

Since $L_1 = \log_b x$ and $L_2 = \log_b y$, the preceding statement may be rewritten as

$$\log_b \frac{x}{y} = \log_b x - \log_b y$$

Property 3   Let $L = \log_b x$. Rewriting this statement in exponential form, we have

$$x = b^L$$

Raising both sides to the pth power, we obtain

$$x^p = (b^L)^p$$
$$= b^{Lp}$$
$$= b^{pL}$$

Rewriting the statement $x^p = b^{pL}$ in logarithmic form gives us

$$\log_b x^p = pL$$

Since $L = \log_b x$, this statement may be rewritten as

$$\log_b x^p = p \log_b x$$

Property 4   Let $L = \log_b b$. This statement is rewritten in exponential form as

$$b^L = b$$

Hence, $L = 1$ and

$$\log_b b = 1$$

Property 5   Let $L = \log_b 1$. This statement is rewritten as

$$b^L = 1$$

Hence, $L = 0$ and

$$\log_b 1 = 0$$

• **EXAMPLE 3-15** _____

Given that $\log 3 = 0.4771$ and $\log 5 = 0.6990$, find each of the following using the properties of logarithms:

a)   log 15   b)   log 625
c)   log $\sqrt{5}$ d)   log 0.6

Solutions

a) $\log 15 = \log (5 \cdot 3)$
            $= \log 5 + \log 3$ Property 1
            $= 0.6990 + 0.4771$
            $= 1.1761$

b) $\log 625 = \log 5^4$
            $= 4 \log 5$ Property 3
            $= 4(0.6990)$
            $= 2.7960$

c) $\log \sqrt{5} = \log 5^{1/2}$
            $= \frac{1}{2}(\log 5)$ Property 3
            $= \frac{1}{2}(0.6990)$
            $= 0.3495$

d) $\log 0.6 = \log \dfrac{3}{5}$

$= \log 3 - \log 5$ Property 2

$= 0.4771 - 0.6990$

$= -0.2219$

• **EXAMPLE 3-16** _____

Express each of the following in simpler form:

a) $\log\left(\dfrac{A}{BC}\right)$ **b)** $\log\left(\dfrac{A}{B}\right)^{.706}$

Solutions

a) $\log\left(\dfrac{A}{BC}\right) = \log A - \log (BC)$ Property 2

$= \log A - [\log B + \log C]$ Property 1

$= \log A - \log B - \log C$

b) $\log\left(\dfrac{A}{B}\right)^{.706} = .706 \log \dfrac{A}{B}$ Property 3

$= .706\,[\log A - \log B]$ Property 2

$= .706 \log A - .706 \log B$

We now state two more properties of logarithms that are useful in many applications. These properties are indicated by the graphs of logarithmic functions (Figures 3-18 and 3-19).

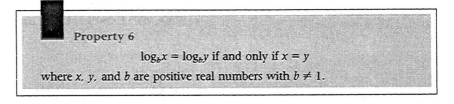

Property 6

$$\log_b x = \log_b y \text{ if and only if } x = y$$

where x, y, and b are positive real numbers with $b \neq 1$.

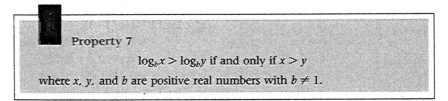

Property 7

$$\log_b x > \log_b y \text{ if and only if } x > y$$

where x, y, and b are positive real numbers with $b \neq 1$.

We now give an example where logarithms are used to solve for one quantity in terms of another.

• **EXAMPLE 3-17** _____

The demand, x (in millions), for a product is related to its unit price, p (in dollars), by the equation

$$p = e^{5-0.2x}$$

a) Express the demand, x, in terms of unit price, p.
b) Calculate the demand associated with a unit price of $6.

Solution

a) Taking the natural logarithm of each side, we have

$$\ln p = 5 - 0.2x$$

Solving for x yields

$$x = \frac{\ln p - 5}{-0.2}$$

b) Since $p = \$6$, then

$$x = \frac{\ln p - 5}{-0.2}$$
$$= \frac{\ln 6 - 5}{-0.2}$$
$$\approx \frac{1.791759 - 5}{-0.2}$$
$$\approx 16.04 \text{ million units}$$

Doubling Time: Exponential Growth

If a quantity, y, is related to time, t, by the exponential model

$$y = y_0 e^{kt}$$

where y_0 and k are positive constants, then the *initial value of y* (i.e., the value of y at $t = 0$) is

$$y = y_0 e^{k(0)}$$
$$= y_0 e^0$$
$$= y_0(1)$$
$$= y_0$$

The time it takes for the quantity y_0 to double itself is determined by setting $y = 2y_0$ and solving the resulting equation for t. Hence,

$$y = y_0 e^{kt}$$
$$2y_0 = y_0 e^{kt} \qquad \text{Set } y = 2y_0.$$
$$2 = e^{kt} \qquad \text{Multiply both sides by } 1/y_0.$$
$$kt = \ln 2 \qquad \text{Rewrite in logarithmic form.}$$
$$t = \frac{\ln 2}{k} \qquad \text{Doubling time}$$

For example, if

$$y = 1000e^{0.10t}$$

where t denotes time (in years), the initial value of y is 1000, and the doubling time is given by

$$t = \frac{\ln 2}{0.10}$$

$$= \frac{0.6931}{0.10}$$

$$= 6.931 \text{ years} \qquad \text{Doubling time}$$

Exercises 3-2

Rewrite each of the following statements in logarithmic notation:

1. $5^2 = 25$
2. $4^2 = 16$
3. $2^6 = 64$
4. $10^5 = 100,000$
5. $10^{-2} = 0.01$
6. $10^1 = 10$
7. $t^w = S$
8. $4^3 = 64$
9. $b^{x+y} = N$

Find y for each of the following:

10. $y = \log_3 9$
11. $y = \log_9 81$
12. $y = \log_2 8$
13. $y = \log_3 1$
14. $y = \log_2 16$
15. $y = \log_7 7$
16. $y = \log_{10} 1$
17. $y = \log_{10} 10$
18. $y = \log_{10} 100$
19. $y = \log_{10} 1000$
20. $y = \log_{10} 10,000$
21. $y = \log_{10} 100,000$
22. $y = \ln 1$
23. $y = \ln e^2$

Find each of the following logarithms:

24. $\log_3 81$
25. $\log_2 32$
26. $\log_4 16$
27. $\log_3 1$
28. $\log_5 1$
29. $\log_8 1$
30. $\log 1$
31. $\log 10$
32. $\log 100$
33. $\log 1000$
34. $\log 10,000$
35. $\log 100,000$

36. Sketch the graph of $y = \log_2 x$. What is the x-intercept?
37. Sketch the graph of $y = \log_3 x$. What is the x-intercept?

Given that $\log 2 = 0.3010$ and $\log 7 = 0.8451$, find each of the following using the properties of logarithms:

38. $\log 14$
39. $\log 3.5$
40. $\log \frac{2}{7}$
41. $\log 49$
42. $\log 98$
43. $\log 56$
44. $\log \sqrt{2}$
45. $\log \sqrt[3]{2}$
46. $\log \sqrt{7}$
47. $\log \sqrt{14}$
48. $\log \sqrt[5]{7}$
49. $\log \sqrt{98}$

Given that $\log 3.71 = 0.5694$, find each of the following using the properties of logarithms. (Remember that $\log 10 = 1$.)

50. $\log 37.1$
51. $\log 371$
52. $\log 3710$
53. $\log 37,100$
54. $\log 371,000$
55. $\log 0.371$
56. $\log 0.0371$
57. $\log 0.00371$
58. $\log 0.000371$

Given that ln 3 = 1.098612 and ln 2 = 0.693147, find each of the following using the properties of logarithms:

59. ln 6 **60.** ln 1.5 **61.** $\ln \frac{2}{3}$

62. ln 81 **63.** ln 8 **64.** ln 12

65. ln $\sqrt{3}$ **66.** ln $\sqrt[3]{2}$ **67.** ln 0.75

Using a calculator with a "log" button, find each of the following:

68. log 4.76 **69.** log 8.73 **70.** log 92.1

71. log 4760 **72.** log 0.0673 **73.** log 0.80

Using a calculator with an "ln" button, find each of the following.

74. ln 2.8 **75.** ln 10 **76.** ln 25

77. ln 0.15 **78.** ln 0.60 **79.** ln 80

Find x for each of the following:

80. log x = 0.7738 **81.** log x = 0.9047

82. log x = 2.7738 **83.** log x = 3.9047

84. log x = 1.4698 **85.** log x = 5.4099

86. ln x = 0.6419 **87.** log x = 1.3610

88. ln x = 3.6889 **89.** ln x = 1.7047

Express each of the following numbers as e^k:

90. 7 **91.** 3.4 **92.** 14 **93.** 5.5 **94.** 750

Use properties of logarithms to express each of the following in simpler form.

95. $\log \left(\frac{xy}{z} \right)$ **96.** $\log \left(\frac{x}{y} \right)^{5.83}$

97. $\log (x^2 y)$ **98.** $\log (xy)^7$

99. $\log \sqrt{xy}$

100. $\log \sqrt{\frac{xy}{z}}$

Applications

101. *Sales.* A company's sales, $S(x)$ (in thousands of dollars), are related to advertising expenditure, x (in thousands of dollars), by the equation

$$S(x) = 100{,}000 + 8000 \ln (x + 2)$$

  a) Calculate the sales associated with each of the following advertising expenditures: $1000, $3000, $10,000, and $20,000.
  b) Calculate $S(21) - S(20)$ and interpret the answer.
  c) If the company increases its advertising expenditures from $30,000 to $31,000, find the corresponding increase in sales.

102. *Sales.* A company's sales, $S(x)$ (in thousands), are related to advertising expenditures, x, (in thousands of dollars), by the equation

$$S(x) = 200{,}000 + 10{,}000 \ln x$$

  a) Calculate the sales associated with each of the following advertising expenditures: $2000, $5000, $10,000, and $30,000.
  b) Calculate $S(13) = S(12)$ and interpret the answer.
  c) If the company increases its advertising expenditure from $19,000 to $20,000, find the corresponding increase in sales.

103. *Revenue.* A company's sales revenue, $R(x)$ (in thousands of dollars), is related to the number of units sold, x, by the equation

$$R(x) = 10 \log(20x + 1)$$

a) Calculate and interpret each of the following: $R(1)$, $R(2)$, $R(5)$, and $R(10)$.
b) Calculate $R(11) - R(10)$ and interpret the answer.
c) If the company increases its sales from 20 units to 21 units, calculate the increase in sales revenue.

104. *Cost.* A company's total production cost, $C(x)$ (in dollars), is related to the number of units produced, x, by the equation.

$$C(x) = 9000 + 10 \ln(x + 1)$$

a) Calculate and interpret each of the following: $C(0)$, $C(1)$, $C(5)$, and $C(10)$.
b) Calculate $C(19) - C(18)$ and interpret the answer.
c) If the company increases its production from 12 units to 13 units, calculate the increase in total production cost.

105. *Tripling time: Exponential growth.* If a quantity, y, is related to time, t, by the exponential model

$$y = y_0 e^{kt}$$

where y_0 and k are positive constants, verify that the tripling time is given by

$$t = \frac{\ln 3}{k}.$$

If

$$y = 2000 e^{0.20t}$$

where t denotes time in days,
a) Determine the initial value of y.
b) Determine the tripling time.
c) Determine the quadrupling time.

106. *Doubling time.* If a quantity, y, is related to time, t, by the exponential model

$$y = y_0 b^{kt}$$

where y_0, k, and b are positive constants such that $b > 1$ and $b \neq e$, verify that the doubling time is given by

$$t = \frac{\ln 2}{k \ln b}$$

107. *Population growth.* The population, P, of a certain town is related to time, t (in years), by the exponential function

$$P = 1000 e^{0.05t}$$

a) How long will it take for the population to double itself?
b) How long will it take for the population to triple itself?

108. *Demand.* The demand, x (in billions), for a product is related to its unit price, p (in dollars), by the equation

$$p = e^{8-0.3x}$$

a) Express demand, x, in terms of unit price, p.
b) Find the demand associated with a unit price of $9.

109. *Supply.* The supply, y (in millions), for a product is related to its unit price, p (in dollars), by the supply equation

$$p = e^{1+0.3y}$$

a) Express supply, y, in terms of unit price, p.
b) Find the supply associated with a unit price of $10.

3-3 • FITTING EXPONENTIAL MODELS

In this section, we discuss fitting an exponential model of the form

$$y = ab^x$$

to a set of data points. First, we restate the above equation in logarithmic form by taking the natural logarithm of each side to obtain

$$\ln y = \ln ab^x \qquad \text{Logarithm property 6}$$
$$= \ln a + \ln b^x \qquad \text{Logarithm property 2}$$
$$= \ln a + x \ln b \qquad \text{Logarithm property 3}$$
$$= \ln a + (\ln b)x$$

Thus, the exponential equation $y = ab^x$ is restated in logarithmic form as $\ln y = \ln a + (\ln b)x$. Observe that the logarithmic form expresses a linear relationship between the variables $\ln y$ and x. This means that for points (x, y) on the graph of the exponential function $y = ab^x$, the graph of the corresponding points $(x, \ln y)$ is a straight line. In other words, if a plot of y-values versus x-values has the graph of an exponential function $y = ab^x$, then a plot of $\ln y$-values versus x-values has the graph of a straight line. Thus, given points (x, y) of an exponential model $y = ab^x$, the coefficients a and b are determined by fitting the linear model $\ln y = \ln a + (\ln b)x$ (straight line) to the points $(x, \ln y)$ and then by determining a and b, given their logarithms. We note that common logarithms can be used in place of natural logarithms.

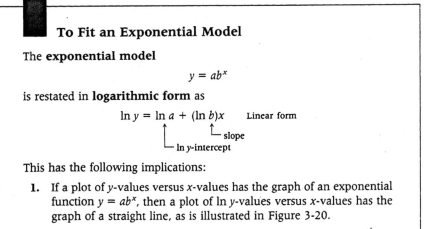

To Fit an Exponential Model

The **exponential model**

$$y = ab^x$$

is restated in **logarithmic form** as

$$\ln y = \ln a + (\ln b)x \qquad \text{Linear form}$$

slope

$\ln y$-intercept

This has the following implications:

1. If a plot of y-values versus x-values has the graph of an exponential function $y = ab^x$, then a plot of $\ln y$-values versus x-values has the graph of a straight line, as is illustrated in Figure 3-20.

continues

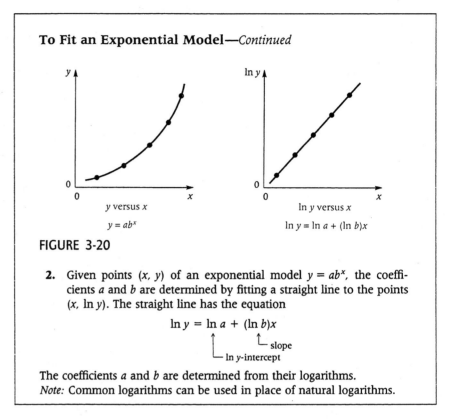

To Fit an Exponential Model—*Continued*

y versus x

$y = ab^x$

$\ln y$ versus x

$\ln y = \ln a + (\ln b)x$

FIGURE 3-20

2. Given points (x, y) of an exponential model $y = ab^x$, the coefficients a and b are determined by fitting a straight line to the points $(x, \ln y)$. The straight line has the equation

$$\ln y = \ln a + (\ln b)x$$

with labels: slope (pointing to $\ln b$) and $\ln y$-intercept (pointing to $\ln a$).

The coefficients a and b are determined from their logarithms.
Note: Common logarithms can be used in place of natural logarithms.

As an example, we will determine the coefficients a and b of the exponential model $y = ab^x$ whose graph contains the points $(1, 3)$ and $(5, 30)$. Use the following procedure.

Step 1 *Replace the y-value of each given data point with its logarithm.* Use either common or natural logarithms. We will use natural logarithms.

Using a calculator, we find that $\ln 3 \approx 1.10$ and $\ln 30 \approx 3.40$. This gives the corresponding points $(1, 1.10)$ and $(5, 3.40)$, which are plotted in Figure 3-21.

Step 2 *Find the equation of the straight line passing through the new points (x, ln y).* Begin by finding the slope.

$$\text{slope} = \frac{3.40 - 1.10}{5 - 1}$$

$$= \frac{2.30}{4} \approx 0.58$$

Using the point-slope form

$$y - y_1 = m(x - x_1)$$

with y replaced by $\ln y$, we choose the point $(1, 1.10)$ to obtain

$$\ln y - 1.10 = 0.58(x - 1)$$

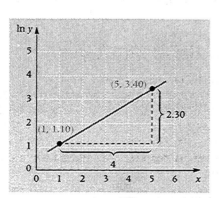

FIGURE 3-21

Simplifying, we get

$$\ln y - 1.10 = 0.58x - 0.58$$
$$= 0.58x - 0.58$$
$$\ln y = 0.58x - 0.58 + 1.10$$
$$\ln y = 0.58x + 0.52 \qquad \text{Logarithmic form}$$

This last equation is our answer in logarithmic form. However, it must be written in the exponential form $y = ab^x$.

Step 3 *Use the definition of a logarithm to determine the coefficients* a *and* b *of the exponential equation* y = ab^x. The above equation, when written as

$$\ln y = 0.52 + 0.58x$$

is of the form

$$\ln y = \ln a + (\ln b)x$$

where

$$\ln a = 0.52 \qquad \text{and} \qquad \ln b = 0.58$$

Rewriting the above in exponential form allows us to solve for a and b (with a calculator) as indicated below.

$$a = e^{0.52} \qquad\qquad b = e^{0.58}$$
$$\approx 1.68 \qquad\qquad\quad \approx 1.79$$

Thus, the exponential model

$$y = ab^x$$

containing the points (1, 3) and (5, 30) is given by

$$y = 1.68(1.79^x)$$

Application

Earnings Per Share

Annual earnings per share (EPS) in dollars of a corporation are determined by dividing the corporation's annual earnings by the number of shares of its stock outstanding. That is,

$$EPS = \frac{\text{annual earnings}}{\text{number of shares of stock outstanding}}$$

The EPS is used to evaluate the performance of a corporation.

The EPS for Lotus Development Corporation is given for the indicated years in Table 3-5 on page 154. Note that the years are coded, with $x = 1$ corresponding to 1986, $x = 2$ to 1987, . . ., $x = 5$ to 1990. Graphs of y-versus x-values and $\ln y$- versus x-values are given in Figure 3-22 on page 154. Observe that the graph of $\ln y$- versus x-values appears to have a linear trend. Thus, we fit the linear form

$$\ln y = \ln a + (\ln b)x$$

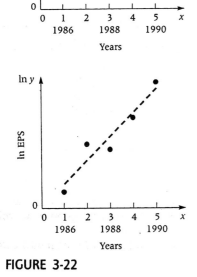

FIGURE 3-22

TABLE 3-5 Lotus Development Corporation: Earnings per share

Years	1986	1987	1988	1989	1990
x = coded years	1	2	3	4	5
y = EPS	1.03	1.58	1.29	1.61	2.30
ln y	0.0296	0.4574	0.2546	0.4762	0.8329

Step 1 We use the first and last data points with ln y-values, (1, 0.0296) and (5, 0.8329).

Step 2 The slope is given by

$$m = \frac{0.8329 - 0.0296}{5 - 1}$$
$$= \frac{0.8033}{4}$$
$$= 0.20 \quad \text{Slope}$$

Using the point-slope form

$$y - y_1 = m(x - x_1)$$

with y replaced by ln y, we choose the point (5, 0.8329) to obtain

$$\ln y - 0.8329 = 0.20(x - 5)$$
$$= 0.20x - 1$$

Solving for ln y gives

$$\ln y = 0.20x - 0.17 \quad \text{Logarithmic form}$$

Step 3 The above result, when rewritten as

$$\ln y = -0.17 + 0.20x$$

is of the form

$$\ln y = \ln a + (\ln b)x$$

where

$$\ln a = -0.17 \quad \text{and} \quad \ln b = 0.20$$

Hence,

$$a = e^{-0.17} \qquad\qquad b = e^{0.20}$$
$$\approx 0.84 \qquad\qquad \approx 1.22 \quad \text{Use a calculator}$$

Thus, the fitted exponential model, $y = ab^x$, is given by

$$y = 0.84(1.22^x)$$

Using the Model to Forecast. If the EPS for Lotus Development Corporation continue to grow in accordance with the above model, then the 1991 EPS are forecast by substituting $x = 6$ into the equation as given below.

$$y = 0.84(1.22^6)$$
$$\approx 0.84(3.2973)$$
$$\approx 2.77 \quad \text{1991 EPS}$$

Caution: Although we used the first and last data points to fit the linear model $\ln y = \ln a + (\ln b)x$, this does not necessarily give the best-fitting linear model. For this example, it does provide a reasonably good fit to the set of data points. Recall the goodness of fit of a model was discussed in the "Extra Dividends" following Chapters 1 and 2. Those concepts also apply to exponential models. Although we do not pursue the goodness of fit of exponential models here, we will learn how to determine the equation of a best-fitting model to a set of data points in Section 15-4.

Exercises 3-3

Determine the coefficients a and b of the exponential model $y = ab^x$ whose graph passes through the following given points.

1. (2, 6) and (8, 40)   **2.** (1, 8) and (5, 50)
3. (3, 20) and (6, 70)   **4.** (4, 10) and (7, 80)
5. (1, 15) and (5, 85)   **6.** (3, 27) and (8, 92)

Applications

Earnings Per Share

In exercises 7-9 the EPS of a company is given for a period. For each exercise
a) Fit the exponential model $y = ab^x$ by using the points appearing in color screen.
b) Assuming that the EPS continue to grow in accordance with the model determined in part a, forecast the next year's EPS.

7. Kellogg Company

Year	1981	1982	1983	1984	1985	1986	1987	1988	1989
x	1	3	4	5	6	7	8	9	10
EPS	1.35	1.49	1.59	1.68	2.28	2.58	3.20	3.90	3.46

8. Bristol-Myers Squibb Company

Year	1980	1981	1982	1983	1984	1985	1986	1987	1988	1989
x	1	2	3	4	5	6	7	8	9	10
EPS	1.02	1.15	1.30	1.50	1.73	1.93	2.07	2.47	2.88	1.43

9. Ford Motor Company

Year	1983	1984	1985	1986	1987	1988	1989
x	1	2	3	4	5	6	7
EPS	3.43	5.27	4.55	6.16	9.05	10.96	8.22

10. *Population growth.* The population of a particular town has grown exponentially from 20,000 in 1985 to 50,000 in 1990.
a) Determine the equation of the exponential model $y = ab^x$ whose curve passes through the two data points.
b) If the town's population continues to grow in accordance with the model derived in part a, forecast the town's population for 1991.

EXTRA DIVIDENDS

• *Stock Market Forecasting*

The *Value Line Investment Survey,* a reputable investment advisory newsletter, gave the following equation for predicting the Dow Jones Industrial Average (DJIA) for a given future year.

DJIA Forecast for t^{th} Year*

$$P_t = 1.021 P_{t-1} \cdot E^{0.236} \cdot D^{0.301} \cdot A^{-0.391}$$

Here, P_{t-1} = DJIA for the previous $(t-1)$ year

$$E = \frac{\text{earnings } t}{\text{earnings } (t-1)} = \text{ratio of } t^{th} \text{ to } (t-1) \text{ year earnings of the Dow Jones Industrial stocks}$$

$$D = \frac{\text{dividends } t}{\text{dividends } (t-1)} = \text{ratio of } t^{th} \text{ year to } (t-1) \text{ year dividends of the Dow Jones Industrial stocks}$$

$$A = \frac{\text{Aaa BOND YLD } t}{\text{Aaa BOND YLD } (t-1)} = \text{ratio of } t^{th} \text{ year to } (t-1) \text{ year yields of Aaa corporate bonds}$$

For example, if earnings are expected to increase by 8% next year, then

$$E = \frac{\text{earnings } t}{\text{earnings } (t-1)} = 1.08$$

If dividends are expected to increase by 5% next year, then

$$D = \frac{\text{dividends } t}{\text{dividends } (t-1)} = 1.05$$

If aaa corporate bond yields are expected to decrease by 3% next year, then

$$A = \frac{\text{Aaa BOND YLD } t}{\text{Aaa BOND YLD } (t-1)} = 1 - 0.03 = 0.97$$

PROBLEM

We will use the properties of logarithms to determine the effect on the DJIA forecast of

1. An increase in earnings
2. A decrease in earnings
3. An increase in dividends
4. A decrease in dividends
5. An increase in Aaa Bond yields
6. A decrease in Aaa Bond Yields

---

*Copyright © 1989 by Value Line, Inc.; used by permission.

SOLUTION

First, we must rewrite the equation in a form that is easier to analyze. We take the natural logarithm (or, if one prefers, the common logarithm) of each side to obtain

$$\ln P_t = \ln 1.021 + \ln P_{t-1} + \ln E^{0.236} + \ln D^{0.301} + \ln A^{-0.391}$$
property 1

$$\ln P_t = \ln 1.021 + \ln P_{t-1} + 0.236 \ln E + 0.301 \ln D + (-0.391) \ln A$$
property 3

At this point, we restate the following logarithmic property, which is determined by studying the graph of the logarithmic function illustrated in Figure 3-23.

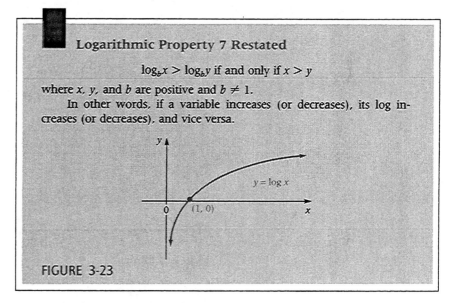

Logarithmic Property 7 Restated

$$\log_b x > \log_b y \text{ if and only if } x > y$$

where x, y, and b are positive and $b \neq 1$.

In other words, if a variable increases (or decreases), its log increases (or decreases), and vice versa.

$y = \log x$

$(1, 0)$

FIGURE 3-23

We now address our previously stated concerns.

1. If earnings are projected to increase for the next year, then the earnings ratio will be greater than 1, and, therefore, its natural logarithm (look at the graph of the logarithm function of Figure 3-23) will be positive. This result, when multiplied by 0.236, gives an increase in $\ln P_t$ which, by logarithmic property 7, implies an increase in P_t (the DJIA for the future year). This assumes that dividends and bond yields remain constant.

2. If earnings are projected to decrease for the next year, then the earnings ratio will be greater than 0, but smaller than 1, and, therefore, its natural logarithm (look at the graph of the logarithm function of Figure 3-23) will be negative. This result, when multiplied by 0.236, gives a decrease in $\ln P_t$ which, by logarithmic property 7, implies a decrease in P_t (the DJIA for the future year). This assumes that dividends and bond yields remain constant.

3. P_t will increase. The reasoning is the same as that for part 1.

4. P_t will decrease. The reasoning is the same as that for part 2.

5. If Aaa bond yields are projected to increase for the next year. Then the Aaa ratio will be greater than 1, and, therefore, its natural logarithm (look at the graph of the logarithm function of Figure 3-23) will be positive. This result, when multiplied by −0.391, gives a decrease in ln P_t which, by logarithmic property 7, implies a decrease in P_t (the DJIA for the future year). This assumes that earnings and dividends remain constant.

6. If Aaa bond yields are projected to decrease for the next year, then the Aaa ratio will be greater than 0, but smaller than 1, and, therefore, its natural logarithm (look at the graph of the logarithm function of Figure 3-23) will be negative. This result, when multiplied by −0.391, gives an increase in ln P_t which, by logarithmic property 7, implies an increase in P_t (the DJIA for the future year). This assumes that earnings and dividends remain constant.

FORECAST

We now forecast next year's DJIA under the following assumptions:

1. Previous year DJIA closing price: 2166
2. 7.5% increase in earnings
3. 10.2% increase in dividends
4. 1.5% increase in Aaa bond yields

Thus,

$$\ln P_t = \ln 1.021 + \ln 2166 + 0.236 \ln 1.075 \\ + 0.301 \ln 1.102 - 0.391 \ln 1.015$$

$$\ln P_t = 0.0208 + 7.6806 + 0.236(0.0723) \\ + 0.301(0.0971) - 0.391(0.0149)$$

$$\ln P_t = 7.7419$$

Rewriting this result in exponential form gives

$$P_t = e^{7.7419}$$
$$= 2302.84 \qquad \text{Use } e^x \text{ key on calculator.}$$

Thus, the DJIA forecast for the next year is 2302.84.

We note that, using statistical analysis techniques beyond the scope of this text, this forecast can be expanded into an interval within which the DJIA can be expected to fall with a predictable probability.

CHAPTER 3 HIGHLIGHTS

● *Concepts*

Your ability to answer the following questions is one indicator of the depth of your mastery of this chapter's important concepts. Note that the questions are grouped under various topic headings. For any question that you cannot answer, refer to the appropriate section of the chapter indicated by the topic heading. Pay particular attention to the summary boxes within a section.

3-1   EXPONENTIAL FUNCTIONS AND THEIR GRAPHS

For Exercises 1-4, draw the graph that typifies each function.

1. $y = ae^x, a > 0$ 2. $y = ae^{-x}, a > 0$
3. $y = ae^x, a < 0$ 4. $y = ae^{-x}, a < 0$
5. Give the procedure for graphing exponential functions of the form $y = ab^x + c$ or $y = ab^{-x} + c$, where $b > 1$.
6. Write the equation for Newton's law of cooling. Explain the dependent and independent variables.
7. Write the equations for the two market penetration models. Explain the dependent and independent variables.

3-2   LOGARITHMIC FUNCTIONS

8. A logarithm is a(an) _____ of a number that is called a base.
9. Base e logarithms are called _____ logarithms.
10. Base 10 logarithms are called _____ logarithms.
11. For any positive number b, there is a value k such that $b = e^k$, where $k = $ _____ .
12. Draw the graph of the logarithmic function $y = \ln x$. The x-intercept is (___, 0). Is there a y-intercept? Is the function defined for $x < 0$?
13. State the seven properties of logarithms. Explain each property using examples.

3-3   FITTING EXPONENTIAL MODELS

14. Write the linear form that corresponds to the exponential model $y = ab^x$.
15. For points (x, y) of the exponential function $y = ab^x$, the graph of the corresponding points $(x, \ln y)$ is a(an) _____ .

REVIEW EXERCISES

• *Exponential Functions*

Graph the following.

1. $y = 7^x$ 2. $y = 7^{-x}$ 3. $y = e^x$ 4. $y = e^{-x}$
5. $y = 8e^x$ 6. $y = -3e^x$ 7. $y = -5e^{-x}$ 8. $y = -e^x$
9. $f(x) = 4 + 2e^x$ 10. $f(x) = -2 + 5e^{-x}$
11. $f(x) = 9 - 2e^{-x}$ 12. $f(x) = 6 - 4e^x$
13. $f(x) = -1 + 5e^{-x}$ 14. $f(x) = 2 + e^{3x}$
15. $f(x) = 5 + e^{-2x}$ 16. $f(x) = 3 - e^{-x}$

17. *Time series*. The annual income, y (in millions of dollars), of a firm is related to time, t (in years), by the equation

$$y = 5e^t$$

where $t = 0$ denotes the year 19x0, $t = 1$ denotes the year 19x1, and so on.
a) Graph $y = 5e^t$ for $t \geq 0$.
b) Determine the annual earnings for the years 19x2, 19x3, and 19x5.

18. *Time series: Sales decay*. The annual sales, y (in millions of dollars), of a company are given by

$$y = 10e^{-t}$$

where $t = 0$ denotes the year 19x0, $t = 1$ denotes the year 19x1, and so on.
a) Graph $y = 10e^{-t}$ for $t \geq 0$.
b) Determine the annual sales for the years 19x0, 19x2, and 19x5.

19. *Market penetration: Long-range forecasting.* The percentage of market penetration for a product x years after it has been introduced is given by

$$y = 80 - 74e^{-0.27x}$$

a) Graph $y = 80 - 74e^{-0.27x}$ for $x \geq 0$.
b) Determine the percentage of market penetration for the third year.
c) Determine the percentage of market penetration for the tenth year.
d) Determine the saturation level.

20. *Market penetration: Long-range forecasting.* The percentage of market penetration for a product x years after it has been introduced is given by

$$y = \frac{90}{1 + 400e^{-0.80x}}$$

a) Determine the percentage of market penetration for the second, seventh, and twelfth years.
b) Determine the saturation level.

• *Logarithmic Functions*

Rewrite the following in logarithmic notation.

21. $10^4 = 10{,}000$ **22.** $5^3 = 125$
23. $y = e^x$

Find the logarithm for each of the following.

24. $\log_2 8$ **25.** $\log_3 9$ **26.** $\ln e^2$
27. $\log 1$ **28.** $\ln 1$ **29.** $\log 10$

Using a calculator with an "ln" button, find each the following.

30. $\ln 23$ **31.** $\ln 0.987$ **32.** $\ln 356$

Find x for the following.

33. $\log x = 0.8875$ **34.** $\ln x = 2.1576$
35. $\log x = 4.56$

Express each of the following as e^k.

36. 5   **37.** 4.6   **38.** 0.45

Use properties of logarithms to express the following in simpler form:

39. $\log (st/r)$ **40.** $\log (x^3 y)$ **41.** $\log (uv)^5$
42. $\log (x/y)^4$ **43.** $\log uv$ **44.** $\log uv/w$

45. Graph $y = \ln x$
46. *Demand.* The demand, x (in millions), for a product is related to its unit price, p (in dollars), by the equation

$$p = e^{4 - 0.2x}$$

a) Express demand, x, in terms of unit price, p.
b) Find the demand associated with a unit price of \$4.

• *Fitting Exponential Models*

47. Determine the coefficients a and b of the exponential model $y = ab^x$, whose graph passes through the points (2, 8) and (5, 60).

48. *Health care's share of GNP.* The U.S. health care industry's share of the gross national product (% of GNP) for the years 1965 to 2010 is given below: (Estimates are given for years beyond 1990.)

x = Coded Years	1	2	3	4	5	6	7
y = % of GNP	6	8	11	12	15.5	20	28

a) Fit the exponential model $y = ab^x$ by using the points appearing in color screens.

b) Assuming that each x-value denotes a time interval of approximately 7½ years, forecast health care's share of GNP for the next 7½ year time interval beyond the year 2010.

4

MATHEMATICS
OF FINANCE

Introductory Application

Amortization: Comparing Mortgage Terms

A couple plans to purchase a home for $200,000. They have put $50,000 down and will obtain a mortgage for $150,000 at an interest rate of 10.5% compounded monthly. They must decide whether to apply for either a 30-year or a 15-year mortgage. Find the monthly payment and the total interest for both a 30-year and a 15-year mortgage at an interest rate of 10.5% compounded monthly. Compare the total interest paid for each mortgage.

In this chapter, we will learn mathematics of finance concepts that enable us to solve problems such as the above and others. The above problem is solved in Example 4-33.

4-1 • SIMPLE INTEREST AND DISCOUNT

Interest is the price paid for the use of money. The amount of money lent (or borrowed or invested) is called the **principal.** After a given time period, the borrower must repay the principal plus interest. The interest is computed as a percentage of the principal. This percentage is called the **interest rate.** An interest rate is stated as a specified percentage per unit of time. In this section, the unit of time will be a year. Thus, an interest rate of 5% means 5% per year. Specifically, if Henry Orwell borrows $1000 for 2 years at an interest rate of 5%, then the principal is $1000, the interest rate is 5% per year, and the time period is 2 years. The following notation will be used:

P = principal (original amount lent, borrowed, or invested)

r = interest rate per year (annual rate)

t = time (duration of loan or investment in years)

I = amount of simple interest in dollars

S = total amount (principal + interest) due at the end of the time period

Simple interest is computed by the following formula.

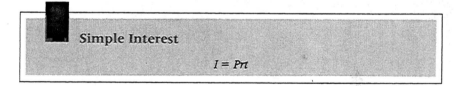

Simple Interest

$$I = Prt$$

Thus, the interest on Henry Orwell's 2-year, $1000 loan (at 5% per year) is

$$I = 1000(0.05)(2) = \$100$$

The total amount, S, that Henry must repay is calculated by the following formula.

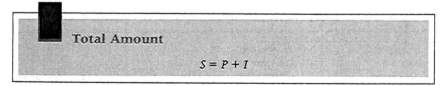

Total Amount

$$S = P + I$$

Hence, at the end of 2 years, Henry must repay

$$S = \$1000 + \$100 = \$1100$$

The bank views this loan as an investment. Its principal of $1000 is worth $1100 at the end of 2 years. Thus, the total amount (in this case, $1100) is often called the **future value,** whereas the principal (in this case, $1000) is called the **present value** (see the time diagram of Figure 4-1).

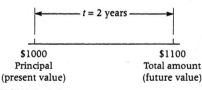

t = 2 years

$1000
Principal
(present value)

$1100
Total amount
(future value)

FIGURE 4-1

The formulas for I and S on page 165 can be combined to give one formula for S in terms of P, r, and t. If we begin with

$$S = P + I$$

and replace I with Prt, we get

$$S = P + Prt$$
$$= P(1 + rt)$$

We summarize below.

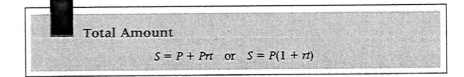

Total Amount

$$S = P + Prt \quad \text{or} \quad S = P(1 + rt)$$

• **EXAMPLE 4-1** _____

An investor lent \$10,000 to a business associate for 6 months at an interest rate of 8% per year.

a) Calculate the simple interest.
b) Calculate the total amount (future value) by two methods.

Solutions

Here $P = \$10,000$, $r = 0.08$, and $t = 1/2$ year.

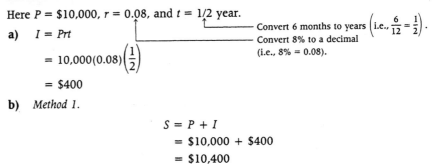

a) $I = Prt$

Convert 6 months to years $\left(\text{i.e., } \frac{6}{12} = \frac{1}{2}\right)$.
Convert 8% to a decimal (i.e., 8% = 0.08).

$$= 10,000(0.08)\left(\frac{1}{2}\right)$$

$$= \$400$$

b) *Method 1.*

$$S = P + I$$
$$= \$10,000 + \$400$$
$$= \$10,400$$

Method 2.

$$S = P(1 + rt)$$
$$= 10,000[1 + (0.08)(1/2)]$$
$$= 10,000(1.04) = \$10,400$$

Thus, the investor's \$10,000 is worth \$10,400 at the end of 6 months (see the time diagram of Figure 4-2).

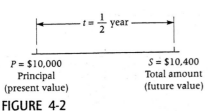

$t = \frac{1}{2}$ year

$P = \$10,000$
Principal
(present value)

$S = \$10,400$
Total amount
(future value)

FIGURE 4-2

Value of Money at Simple Interest

If a sum of money, P, is invested at simple interest, its value increases by the same amount each year. This can be shown by beginning with the formula for total amount

$$S = P + I$$

and replacing I with the equivalent expression Prt. The result is

$$S = P + Prt$$

Given values for P and r, this formula expresses a linear relationship between total amount, S, and time, t. The slope is Pr. Specifically, if a person invests $1000 at 8% per year, after 1 year,

$$S = 1000 + 1000(0.08)(1)$$
$$= \$1080$$

after 2 years,

$$S = 1000 + 1000(0.08)(2)$$
$$= \$1160$$

after 3 years,

$$S = 1000 + 1000(0.08)(3)$$
$$= \$1240$$

and after t years,

$$S = 1000 + 1000(0.08)t$$
$$= 1000 + 80t$$

Note that the slope, 80, is the yearly increase in S. The linear function defined by $S = 1000 + 80t$ is sketched in Figure 4-3.

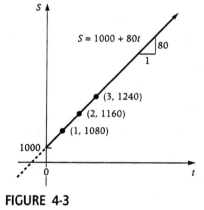

FIGURE 4-3

Calculating the Present Value

Sometimes it is necessary to calculate the present value (principal), given the future value (total amount). Thus, we now derive a formula for present value, P. We begin with

$$S = P(1 + rt)$$

and solve for P to get the equation in the box below.

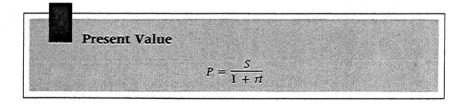

Present Value

$$P = \frac{S}{1 + rt}$$

• EXAMPLE 4-2

What amount of money should be invested now at 6% per year to yield a future value of $8000 7 months from now?

Solution

Since $S = \$8000$, $r = 0.06$, and $t = 7/12$ year, then

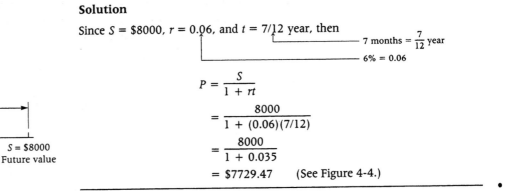

$$P = \frac{S}{1 + rt}$$

$$= \frac{8000}{1 + (0.06)(7/12)}$$

$$= \frac{8000}{1 + 0.035}$$

$$= \$7729.47 \qquad \text{(See Figure 4-4.)}$$

$t = \frac{7}{12}$ year

$P = \$7729.47$ $S = \$8000$
Present value   Future value

FIGURE 4-4

Sometimes a loan is transacted by the borrower giving the lender a signed paper promising to pay a specified amount by a given date. Such an instrument is called a **note.** The future value of the loan is called the **future value,** or the **maturity value,** of the note. To illustrate, suppose Henry Orwell transacted his 2-year, $1000 loan by giving the bank a note. Then, $1100, the future value of the loan, is also the future or maturity value of the note. The bank is called the **holder** of the note.

The holder of a note may sell the note prior to maturity. The buyer usually pays an amount less than the maturity value. When the borrower repays the loan (with the interest), the money (maturity value of the note) is automatically transferred to the buyer (now the present holder) of the note.

• **EXAMPLE 4-3** _____

Willis Harcase wishes to buy a note that has a maturity value of $3000. The note is due 9 months from today. If Willis wants to earn 8% per year on his invested money, how much should he pay for the note?

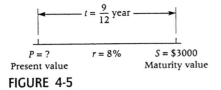

$t = \frac{9}{12}$ year

$P = ?$ $r = 8\%$ $S = \$3000$
Present value   Maturity value

FIGURE 4-5

Solution

The time diagram of Figure 4-5 illustrates this problem. Willis must calculate the present value of the note. Hence,

$$P = \frac{S}{1 + rt}$$

$$= \frac{3000}{1 + (0.08)(3/4)}$$

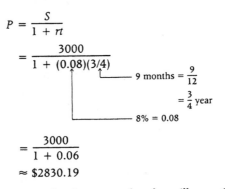

$$= \frac{3000}{1 + 0.06}$$

$$\approx \$2830.19$$

Thus, if Willis pays 2830.19 for the note today, he will earn 8% per year on his money when the note is repaid in 9 months.

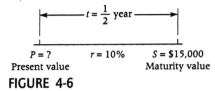

$P = ?$ $r = 10\%$ $S = \$15,000$
Present value   Maturity value

FIGURE 4-6

EXAMPLE 4-4

Melanie borrows a sum of money from Harry at 10% per year. She gives Harry a 6-month note with a maturity value of $15,000. How much did Melanie borrow from Harry?

Solution

See the time diagram of Figure 4-6. Calculating the present value, we have

$$P = \frac{S}{1 + rt}$$
$$= \frac{15,000}{1 + (0.10)(1/2)}$$
$$= \frac{15,000}{1.05}$$
$$\approx \$14,285.71$$

Therefore, Melanie borrowed $14,285.71 from Harry.

• EXAMPLE 4-5

Referring to Example 4-4, suppose Harry sold the note to Jacob 2 months before maturity. What amount did Jacob pay for the note if his invested money is earning 12% per year?

Solution

The time diagram of Figure 4-7 illustrates this problem. We must calculate the present value of $15,000 2 months before maturity. The simple interest rate is 12%. Hence,

$$P = \frac{S}{1 + rt}$$
$$= \frac{15,000}{1 + (0.12)(1/6)}$$
$$\approx \$14,705.88$$

Thus, Jacob paid $14,705.88 for the note. His profit is $15,000.00 − $14,705.88 = $294.12. Harry's profit is $14,705.88 − $14,285.71 = 420.17.

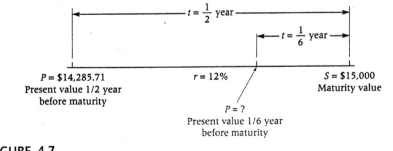

$P = \$14,285.71$ $r = 12\%$ $S = \$15,000$
Present value 1/2 year   Maturity value
before maturity

$P = ?$
Present value 1/6 year
before maturity

FIGURE 4-7

Simple Discount Note

In simple interest problems, the simple interest rate, r, is applied to the principal, P. Sometimes a loan is transacted by a **discount note.** In such a case, the cost of borrowing is called the **discount D.** The discount is computed as a percentage of the maturity value, S. This percentage is called the **discount rate, d.** Thus, if t is the length of time (in years) that the money is borrowed, then

discount = (maturity value)(discount rate)(length of time)

or

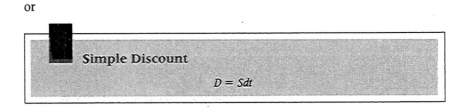

Simple Discount

$$D = Sdt$$

Specifically, consider the following example. Sam Schultz borrows a sum of money for 9 months by giving his bank a discount note for $1000. The discount rate is 8%. Thus, we have $S = \$1000$, $d = 0.08$, and $t = 9/12 = 3/4$ year. Hence, the discount is

$$D = Sdt$$
$$= 1000(0.08)(3/4)$$
$$= \$60$$

Although the note is written in terms of the maturity value of $1000, Sam only receives

$$\$1000 - \$60 = \$940$$

This amount is called the **proceeds, B,** of the note. In general, the proceeds of a discount note are calculated by the equation

proceeds = maturity value − discount

or

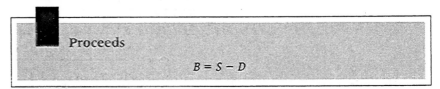

Proceeds

$$B = S - D$$

Of course, Sam will have to pay the bank $1000 (the maturity value) at the end of the 9-month time period to cancel the debt. This situation is illustrated by the time diagram of Figure 4-8.

When using a discount note, although the maturity value is referred to as the amount borrowed, the borrower actually receives only the proceeds after the discount is deducted from the maturity value.

If we use the above formula to determine the proceeds, we must first compute the discount by using the formula $D = Sdt$ and then compute the

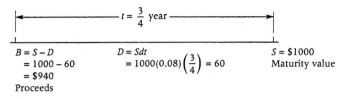

FIGURE 4-8

proceeds with the formula $B = S - D$. This is a two-step procedure. Since it is often easier to use a one-step procedure, we now derive such a formula for the proceeds. We begin with the formula for proceeds

$$B = S - D$$

and replace D with Sdt to get

$$B = S - Sdt$$
$$= S(1 - dt)$$

Thus, we now have an alternate formula for the proceeds. We summarize below.

Proceeds

$$B = S - D \quad \text{or} \quad B = S(1 - dt)$$

where

$$S = \text{maturity value}$$
$$d = \text{discount rate}$$
$$t = \text{time in years}$$
$$B = \text{proceeds}$$

• **EXAMPLE 4-6** _____

You give your bank a 4-month discount note for $12,000. The discount rate is 9%.

a) How much money do you receive from the bank?

b) How much money do you pay the bank at the end of 4 months to cancel your debt?

c) How much money does the bank earn on this transaction?

Solutions

a) We seek the proceeds, B. Since $S = \$12{,}000$, $d = 0.09$, and $t = 4/12 = 1/3$ year, then

$$B = S(1 - dt)$$
$$= 12{,}000[1 - (0.09)(1/3)]$$
$$= 12{,}000(1 - 0.03)$$
$$= 12{,}000(0.97)$$
$$= \$11{,}640 \quad \text{Proceeds}$$

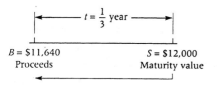

$B = \$11,640$
Proceeds

$S = \$12,000$
Maturity value

FIGURE 4-9

This situation is illustrated by the time diagram of Figure 4-9.

b) You must pay the bank the maturity value of the note, $12,000.

c) The bank earns the discount, D, which can be determined by either of the following methods:

Method 1.

$$D = Sdt$$
$$= 12,000(0.09)(1/3)$$
$$= \$360 \quad \text{Discount}$$

Method 2. The discount is also the difference between the maturity value and the proceeds, or, in other words,

$$D = S - B$$
$$= 12,000 - 11,640$$
$$= \$360 \quad \text{Discount}$$

Determining Maturity Value

Since a discount note is written in terms of its maturity value, but the borrower receives the lesser amount, called the **proceeds,** then the following problem arises when a discount note is written:

What should the maturity value, S, of a discount note be in order to yield a given amount of proceeds, B, at a specified discount rate, d?

To answer this question, we determine a formula for S in the following manner. We start with the formula

$$B = S(1 - dt)$$

and solve for S to obtain

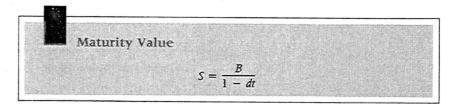

Maturity Value

$$S = \frac{B}{1 - dt}$$

We now return to our introductory example with Sam Schultz who gave his bank an 8%, 9-month discount note. If Sam wants to receive proceeds of $950 (instead of the original $940), the note must be written with the following maturity value:

$$S = \frac{950}{1 - (0.08)(3/4)}$$
$$= \frac{950}{1 - 0.06}$$
$$= \$1010.64$$

• **EXAMPLE 4-7**

You want to receive $8,000 for 6 months. Your bank offers you a 12% discount note.

a) Determine the maturity value of the discount note that you will sign.
b) How much does it cost you to use $8,000 for 6 months with this discount note?

Solutions

a) We seek S where $B = \$8,000$, $d = 0.12$, and $t = 6/12 = 1/2$ year. Hence,

$$S = \frac{B}{1 - dt}$$

$$= \frac{8000}{1 - (0.12)(1/2)}$$

$$= \frac{8000}{1 - 0.06}$$

$$= \frac{8000}{0.94} = \$8510.64 \qquad \text{Maturity value}$$

b) Since you must, at the end of 6 months, pay the bank the maturity value, $8,510.64, the cost of using $8,000 for 6 months is the discount, D. In this case, the easiest way of computing the discount is to subtract the proceeds from the maturity value. Hence,

$$D = S - B$$

$$= 8510.64 - 8000$$

$$= \$510.64 \qquad \text{Discount}$$

Of course, the discount is the amount earned by the bank. This situation is illustrated in the time diagram of Figure 4-10.

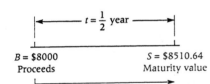

$B = \$8000$ Proceeds $S = \$8510.64$ Maturity value

FIGURE 4-10

Interest-Bearing Notes

Often, in the world of financial transactions, we encounter interest-bearing notes that are sold (or discounted) prior to their maturity dates. An interest-bearing note is written in terms of its face value, which is actually the principal, P, of a loan. The maturity value of such a note must first be determined by using the formula for total amount:

$$S = P(1 + rt)$$

Then the formulas for finding the proceeds, B, can be applied when discounting such a note. We illustrate the above comments in the next example.

• **EXAMPLE 4-8**

A 1¼-year, 7% simple-interest-bearing note has a face value of $6,000. The bank holding this note needs cash and, thus, sells (or discounts) this note at 8% to another bank 3 months prior to its maturity date. How much does the second bank pay for the note?

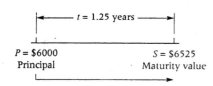

FIGURE 4-11

Solution

First, we find the maturity value, S, of the note. Since $P = \$6,000$, $r = 0.07$, and $t = 1.25$ years (we change 1¼ years to 1.25 years), then

$$S = P(1 + rt)$$
$$= 6000[1 + (0.07)(1.25)]$$
$$= 6000(1 + 0.0875)$$
$$= \$6525 \quad \text{Maturity value}$$

This is illustrated in the time diagram of Figure 4-11.

Next, we find the proceeds of the note 3 months prior to maturity. In other words, we discount the note at its discount rate, 8%, 3 months prior to maturity. This is illustrated in the time diagram of Figure 4-12. Thus, we use the formula

$$B = S(1 - dt)$$

where $S = 6525$, $d = 0.08$, and $t = 3/12 = 1/4$ year. Hence,

$$B = 6525[1 - (0.08)(1/4)]$$
$$= 6525 (1 - 0.02)$$
$$= 6525(.98)$$
$$= \$6394.50 \quad \text{Proceeds}$$

Thus, the second bank buys the note for $6,394.50 in order to receive $6,525 at the end of 3 months from the original borrower (or signer of the note).

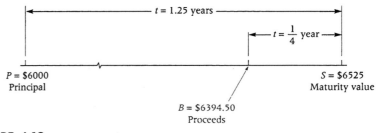

FIGURE 4-12

Simple Interest Rate

If a discount note is analyzed from a simple interest point of view, the simple interest rate is usually larger than the discount rate. For example, if we consider Sam Schultz's first discount rate for $1000 with proceeds of $940, we realize that Sam paid $60 interest to borrow $940 for 3/4 year. If we begin with the formula for simple interest

$$I = Prt$$

and solve for the simple interest rate, r, we have

$$r = \frac{I}{Pt}$$
$$= \frac{60}{940(3/4)}$$
$$= \frac{60}{705}$$
$$= 0.0851 = 8.51\% \quad \text{Simple interest rate}$$

Thus, a discount rate of 8% for 3/4 year is equivalent to a simple interest rate of 8.51% for the same time period.

Exercises 4-1

Find the simple interest and total amount of each of the following loans.

1. $1000 for 3 years at 7%
2. $10,000 for 2 years at 6%
3. $5000 for 6 months at 8%
4. $8000 for 3 months at 12%
5. $2000 for 4 months at 9%
6. $9000 for 1 year at 10%

7. A person invests $10,000 at 9% per year.
   a) Determine the equation that expresses total amount, S, as a function of time, t (in years).
   b) Graph the equation of part a.
   c) By how much does the total amount, S, increase each year? Relate this answer to the graph of part b.
8. A person invests $30,000 at 8% per year.
   a) Determine the equation that expresses total amount, S, as a function of time, t (in years).
   b) Graph the equation of part a.
   c) By how much does the total amount, S, increase each year? Relate this answer to the graph of part b.

Determine the present value (or principal), P, for each of the following.

9. $S = \$8,000$, $r = 0.09$, $t = 2$ years
10. $S = \$12,000$, $r = 0.10$, $t = 3$ years
11. $S = \$15,000$, $r = 0.08$, $t = 2.5$ years
12. $S = \$10,000$, $r = 0.07$, $t = 3.4$ years
13. Maturity value = $20,000, annual interest rate = 8%, time = 3 months
14. Maturity value = $30,000, annual interest rate = 9%, time = 8 months.

Determine the proceeds for each of the following discount notes.

15. Maturity value = $10,000, discount rate = 9%, time = 4 months
16. Maturity value = $90,000, discount rate = 8%, time = 9 months
17. Maturity value = $5,000, discount rate = 6%, time = 6 months
18. Maturity value = $20,000, discount rate = 8%, time = 3 months
19. $S = \$30,000$, $d = 0.09$, $t = 2/3$ year
20. $S = \$18,000$, $d = 0.10$, $t = 1/2$ year

21-26. For Exercises 9-14, determine the simple interest rate equivalent to the discount note.

For Exercises 27-32, determine the maturity value for each discount note.

27. Proceeds = $8,000, discount rate = 8%, time = 9 months
28. Proceeds = $5,000, discount rate = 6%, time = 8 months
29. Proceeds = $12,000, discount rate = 12%, time = 10 months
30. Proceeds = $10,000, discount rate = 9%, time = 8 months
31. $B = \$9,000$, $d = 0.10$, $t = 1/2$ year
32. $B = \$20,000$, $d = 0.06$, $t = 2/3$ year

Exercises 33-38 entail simple-interest-bearing notes discounted prior to maturity. Determine the proceeds of each note at the time of discount.

33. Face value = $10,000; 9-month note; annual interest rate = 8%; discounted at 6% 2 months prior to maturity

34. Face value = $9,000; 6-month note; annual interest rate = 7%; discounted at 8% 3 months prior to maturity

35. Face value = $14,000; 3-month note; annual interest rate = 8%; discounted at 6% 1 month prior to maturity

36. Face value = $20,000; 15-month note; annual interest rate = 8%; discounted at 9% 6 months prior to maturity

37. Face value = $30,000; 18-month note; annual interest rate = 9%; discounted at 8% 9 months prior to maturity

38. Face value = $15,000; 1.5-year note; annual interest rate = 7%; discounted at 6% 6 months prior to maturity

39. What amount of money should be invested now at 8% per year to yield a future value of $10,000 9 months from now?

40. A note with a maturity value of $1000 matures in 5 months. If one wishes to earn 9% per year, how much should be paid for the note now?

41. Sam Smith plans to buy a note with a maturity value of $10,000. The note is due 5 years from now. If Sam wishes to earn 10% per year on his invested money, how much should he pay for the note?

42. Helen borrows a sum of money from Tom at 9% per year by giving Tom a 6-month note with a maturity value of $9000.
    a) How much money did Helen borrow from Tom?
    b) Two years before maturity, Tom sells the note to Susan. What amount does Susan pay for the note if she is earning 10% per year?

43. Ellen Rydell borrows a sum of money for 5 years by giving her bank a discount note for $6000. The discount rate is 9%.
    a) Find the discount.
    b) Find the proceeds.
    c) Find the equivalent simple interest rate.

44. A woman borrows a sum of money for 6 months by giving her bank a discount note for $8000. The discount rate is 10%.
    a) Find the discount.
    b) Find the proceeds.
    c) How much money did the woman receive?
    d) Find the equivalent simple interest rate.

45. Glenn Nash receives $5000 for 4 months by giving his bank a discount note. The discount rate is 7%.
    a) Find the maturity value of the note.
    b) Find the equivalent simple interest rate.

46. A man receives $5000 from his bank for 9 months by using a discount note. The discount rate is 12%.
    a) Find the maturity value of the note.
    b) Find the equivalent simple interest rate.

47. Find the maturity value of an interest note for $600 issued for 4 months at an interest rate of 6% per year.

48. Find the present value of a 3-month interest note with a maturity value of $6000. Assume that the interest rate is 8% per year.

49. A 1½-year, 10% simple-interest-bearing note with a face value of $20,000 is sold to an investment firm 6 months prior to maturity at a discount rate of 9%.
    a) How much does the investment firm pay for the note?
    b) How much does the investment firm earn on the note?

50. A 21-month, 8% simple-interest-bearing note with a face value of $30,000 is sold to an investor 6 months prior to maturity at a discount rate of 7%.
   a) How much does the investor pay for the note?
   b) How much does the investor earn on the note?

The following problems have appeared on past Uniform CPA Examinations

51. Fay, Inc., received a $30,000, 6-month, 12% interest-bearing note from a customer. The note was discounted the same day by Carr National Bank at 15%. The amount of cash received by Fay from the bank was
   a) $30,000   b) $29,550
   c) $29,415   d) $27,750

52. Tallent Company received a $30,000, 6-month, 10% interest-bearing note from a customer. After holding the note for 2 months, Tallent was in need of cash and discounted the note at the United National Bank at a 12% discount rate. The amount of cash received by Tallent from the bank was
   a) $31,260   b) $30,870
   c) $30,300   d) $30,240

4-2 • COMPOUND INTEREST

In Section 4-1, we learned that the value of a sum of money, P, invested at simple interest increases by the same amount each year. This is due to the fact that the interest rate, r, is applied to the original principal, P. In this section, we will discuss a method of computing interest in which the value of a sum of money, P, increases by a larger amount each year. Here, the interest rate, r, will be applied to the original principal plus interest, rather than to just the original principal. Such a method of computing interest is called **compounding.** The result is **compound interest.**

Compound interest is usually computed periodically throughout the year. If compound interest is computed every month (12 times a year), it is said to be **compounded monthly.** Each month is called a **conversion period,** or **interest period.** If compound interest is computed every 3 months (4 times a year), it is said to be **compounded quarterly.** Thus, each 3-month time interval between successive compoundings is a conversion or interest period. If compound interest is computed every 6 months (2 times a year), it is said to be **compounded semiannually.** Hence, each 6-month time interval

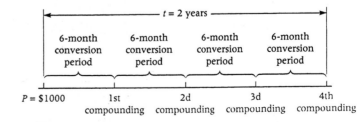

FIGURE 4-13

FIGURE 4-14

between successive compoundings is a conversion or interest period. Interest may also be compounded annually, weekly, daily, and continuously.

We now compute the total amount of $1000 invested for 2 years at 8% compounded semiannually. Note that $P = \$1000$ and $r = 0.08$. Since the interest is compounded semiannually, there will be two compoundings per year (see Figure 4-13 on page 177).

Thus, there will be four compoundings and four conversion periods during the 2-year time interval. We now show each compounding.

1. **First Compounding** (at End of First Conversion Period)—The interest is calculated and added to the original principal. Hence,

$$
\begin{aligned}
I &= Prt \\
&= 1000(0.08)(1/2) \\
&= 1000(0.04) \\
&= \$40 \\
S &= P + I \\
&= \$1000 + \$40 \\
&= \$1040
\end{aligned}
$$

Thus, the original investment is now worth $1040 (see Figure 4-14).

2. **Second Compounding** (at End of Second Conversion Period)—The total amount from the previous compounding becomes the *new principal*. Interest is calculated on the new principal. The total amount is calculated by adding the interest to the new principal. Hence, we have

$$
\begin{aligned}
I &= \text{new principal} \cdot r \cdot t \\
&= 1040(0.08)(1/2) \\
&= 1040(0.04) \\
&= \$41.60 \\
S &= \text{new principal} + I \\
&= \$1040.00 + \$41.60 \\
&= \$1081.60
\end{aligned}
$$

Thus, the original investment is now worth $1081.60 (see Figure 4-15).

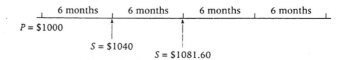

FIGURE 4-15

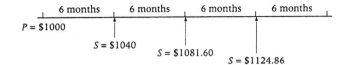

FIGURE 4-16

3. **Third Compounding** (at End of Third Conversion Period)—The process is repeated, and we obtain

$$I = \text{new principal} \cdot r \cdot t$$
$$= 1081.60(0.08)(1/2)$$
$$= 1081.60(0.04)$$
$$= \$43.26$$
$$S = \text{new principal} + I$$
$$= \$1081.60 + \$43.26$$
$$= \$1124.86$$

Hence, the original investment is now worth \$1124.86 (see Figure 4-16).

4. **Fourth Compounding** (at End of Fourth Conversion Period)—The process is repeated, giving us

$$I = \text{new principal} \cdot r \cdot t$$
$$= 1124.86(0.08)(1/2)$$
$$= 1124.86(0.04)$$
$$= \$44.99$$
$$S = \text{new principal} + I$$
$$= \$1124.86 + \$44.99$$
$$= \$1169.85$$

Thus, the original investment is now worth \$1169.85 (see Figure 4-17). This total is often called the **compound amount.**

Observe that, for each compounding in our example, the new principal is always multiplied by $(0.08)(1/2) = 0.04$. This value is called the **interest rate per conversion period.** In general, the interest rate per conversion period will be indicated by the symbol i. Hence, for the previous example, we write

$$i = 0.08(1/2) = 0.04$$

Thus, 8% compounded semiannually is equivalent to 4% per conversion period. Note that the interest rate per conversion period may be calculated

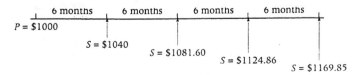

FIGURE 4-17

by dividing the quoted interest rate by the number of conversion periods per year. Thus, if

r = annual (or quoted) interest rate (or **nominal rate**)

m = number of conversion periods per year

then

$$i = \frac{r}{m}$$

Observe, also, that the number of conversion periods, n, may be calculated by multiplying the number of conversion periods per year, m, by the number of years, t. Hence,

$$n = mt$$

Thus, for the illustrated example,

m = 2 conversion periods per year

t = 2 years

n = 2(2) = 4 conversion periods

• EXAMPLE 4-9

A sum of money is invested for 4 years at 6% compounded monthly. Calculate i and n.

Solution

Since $r = 6\%$, $m = 12$ conversion periods per year, and $t = 4$ years, then

$$i = \frac{r}{m}$$

$$= \frac{6\%}{12} = \frac{1}{2}\% \text{ per month}$$

$$n = mt$$

$$= 12(4) = 48 \text{ conversion periods}$$

We will now derive a general formula for the compound amount, S. If

P = original principal

i = interest rate per conversion period

n = total number of conversion periods

S = compound amount (or total amount or maturity value or accumulated value)

then, at the end of the first conversion period,

$$I = Pi$$
$$S = P + I$$
$$= P + Pi$$
$$= P(1 + i)$$

At the end of the second conversion period,

new principal $= P(1 + i)$
$$I = \text{new principal} \cdot i$$
$$= P(1 + i)i$$
$$S = \text{new principal} + I$$
$$= P(1 + i) + P(1 + i)i$$
$$= P(1 + i)(1 + i)$$
$$= P(1 + i)^2$$

Use the distributive law.
$$P(1 + i) \cdot 1 + P(1 + i)i$$
$$= P(1 + i)(1 + i)$$

At the end of the third conversion period,

new principal $= P(1 + i)^2$
$$I = \text{new principal} \cdot i$$
$$= P(1 + i)^2 i$$
$$S = \text{new principal} + I$$
$$= P(1 + i)^2 + P(1 + i)^2 i$$
$$= P(1 + i)^2(1 + i)$$
$$= P(1 + i)^3$$

Use the distributive law.
$$P(1 + i)^2 \cdot 1 + P(1 + i)^2 i$$
$$= P(1 + i)^2(1 + i)$$

And at the end of the nth conversion period,

$$S = P(1 + i)^n$$

The time diagram of Figure 4-18 summarizes the preceding calculations.

Thus, if we invest P dollars for n periods at an interest rate per conversion period of i, the compound amount, S, is given by

Compound Amount

$$S = P(1 + i)^n$$

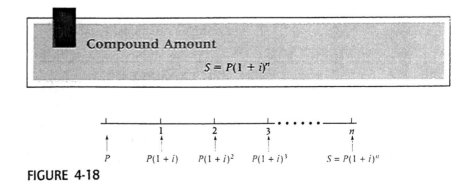

FIGURE 4-18

Returning to the introductory problem of this section where $P = 1000$, $n = 4$, and $i = 0.04$, we use the above formula to compute the compound amount. Hence,

$$S = P(1 + i)^n$$
$$= 1000(1 + 0.04)^4$$

Using a calculator, we evaluate $(1 + 0.04)^4 = (1.04)^4 \approx 1.169859$ to six decimal places. Thus,

$$S \approx 1000(1.169859)$$
$$\approx \$1169.86$$

We note that Table 4 in Appendix C gives values of $(1 + i)^n$ for various rates, i, and numbers of periods, n. Using Table 4 to determine the value of $(1.04)^4$, we locate the "$i = 4\%$" column and then move four periods down in that column to find $(1.04)^4 = 1.169859$.

• **EXAMPLE 4-10** _____

Find the compound amount of \$10,000 invested for 5 years at 8% compounded quarterly.

Solution

Here $P = \$10,000$, $r = 8\%$, $m = 4$, and $t = 5$ years. Thus,

$$i = \frac{r}{m} = \frac{8\%}{4} = 2\% \text{ per conversion period}$$

$$n = mt = 4(5) = 20 \text{ conversion periods}$$

$$S = P(1 + i)^n$$
$$= 10,000(1 + 0.02)^{20} \qquad \text{Using Appendix C, Table 4, or a}$$
$$\approx 10,000(1.485947) \qquad \text{calculator } (1 + 0.02)^{20} \approx 1.485947.$$
$$\approx \$14,859.47 \qquad \text{(See Figure 4-19.)}$$

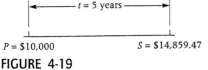

$t = 5$ years

$P = \$10,000$ $S = \$14,859.47$

FIGURE 4-19

Sometimes we must use the formula $S = P(1 + i)^n$ repeatedly for more complex situations. Example 4-11 illustrates such a case.

• **EXAMPLE 4-11** _____

A person deposits \$10,000 in a savings account that pays 6% compounded semiannually. Three years later, this person deposits an additional \$8,000 in the savings account. Also, at this time, the interest rate changes to 8% compounded quarterly. How much is in the account 5 years after the original \$10,000 deposit?

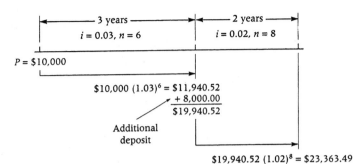

FIGURE 4-20

Solution

First, we find the compound amount of $10,000 after 3 years at 6% compounded semiannually (see Figure 4-20). This is given by

$$S = P(1 + i)^n$$
$$= 10,000(1 + 0.03)^6$$

$$n = 3(2) = 6$$
$$i = \frac{6\%}{2} = 0.03$$

$$\approx 10,000(1.194052)$$
$$= \$11,940.52$$

Second, since $8,000 is deposited in the account after 3 years, we add this amount to the compound amount of $11,940.52 to obtain $11,940.52 + 8,000.00 = \$19,940.52$. Now we find the compound amount of $19,940.52 after 2 years at 8% compounded quarterly to obtain

$$S = P(1 + i)^n$$
$$= 19,940.52(1 + 0.02)^8$$

$$n = 2(4) = 8$$
$$i = \frac{8\%}{4} = 0.02$$

$$\approx 19,940.52(1.171659)$$
$$= \$23,363.49 \qquad \text{Answer}$$

This situation is also illustrated in Figure 4-20.

Present Value at Compound Interest

The formula

$$S = P(1 + i)^n$$

accumulates or brings forward a principal (or present value), P, *for n* periods at an interest rate of i per period, as illustrated in the time diagram of Figure 4-21. Sometimes it is necessary to calculate the present value, P,

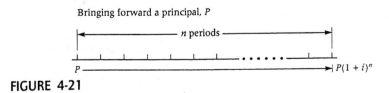

FIGURE 4-21

Bringing back a future value, S

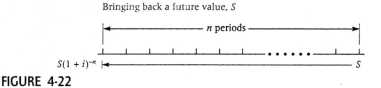

FIGURE 4-22

given the compound amount. A formula for P may be derived by beginning with the equation for compound amount

$$S = P(1 + i)^n$$

and solving for P. The result is

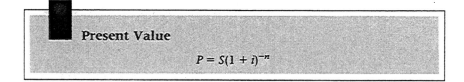

Present Value

$$P = S(1 + i)^{-n}$$

This formula is used to find the present value of a given compound amount. Table 5 in Appendix C gives values of $(1 + i)^{-n}$ for various values of i and n. A calculator can also be used to compute these values. We note that this formula brings back a future value of S for n periods at an interest rate of i per period, as shown in the time diagram of Figure 4-22.

• EXAMPLE 4-12

What sum of money should be invested for 4 years at 9% compounded monthly in order to provide a compound amount of $8000?

Solution

Here, $S = \$8000$, $r = 9\%$, $m = 12$, and $t = 4$ years. Thus,

$$i = \frac{r}{m} = \frac{9\%}{12} = \frac{3}{4}\% \text{ per month}$$

$$n = mt = 12(4) = 48 \text{ conversion periods}$$

$$P = S(1 + i)^{-n}$$
$$= 8000(1 + 0.0075)^{-48} \quad \text{Using a calculator or Appendix C,}$$
$$\approx 8000(0.698614) \quad \quad \text{Table 5, } (1 + 0.0075)^{-48} \approx 0.698614.$$
$$\approx \$5588.91 \quad \text{(See Figure 4-23.)}$$

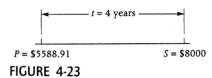

$P = \$5588.91$ $S = \$8000$

FIGURE 4-23

Equivalent Rates

Sometimes it is helpful to convert interest rates from, for example, a compounded quarterly basis to a compounded monthly basis, from a compounded monthly basis to a compounded annually basis, etc. This is easily accomplished as long as we understand the concept of *equivalent interest rates*, which we define as follows.

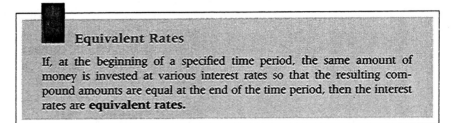

Equivalent Rates

If, at the beginning of a specified time period, the same amount of money is invested at various interest rates so that the resulting compound amounts are equal at the end of the time period, then the interest rates are **equivalent rates.**

Although we can use any length time period, we usually use a 1-year time interval. Thus, if P dollars are invested at annual rate r compounded m times a year, and another P dollars are invested at annual rate s compounded k times a year, then the rates are equivalent as long as

$$\underbrace{P(1 + r/m)^m} = \underbrace{P(1 + s/k)^k}$$

Compound amount of P dollars invested for 1 year at annual rate r compounded m times a year

Compound amount of P dollars invested for 1 year at annual rate s compounded k times a year

Dividing both sides of the above equation by P gives the equivalent rates equation which can be solved for either r or s, depending on which is the unknown.

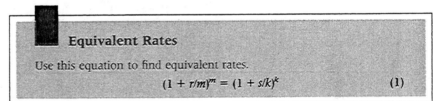

Equivalent Rates

Use this equation to find equivalent rates.

$$(1 + r/m)^m = (1 + s/k)^k \tag{1}$$

• **EXAMPLE 4-13**

What rate compounded monthly is equivalent to 8% compounded quarterly?

Solution

Let r be the equivalent rate compounded monthly. Then, using equation (1),

$$(1 + r/12)^{12} = (1 + 0.08/4)^4$$
$$= (1.02)^4$$

Solving for r, we take the 12th root of each side to obtain

$$1 + r/12 = ((1.02)^4)^{1/12}$$
$$= (1.02)^{1/3}$$
$$r/12 = (1.02)^{1/3} - 1 \qquad \text{Using a calculator,}$$
$$\approx 1.006622 - 1 \qquad (1.02)^{1/3} \approx (1.02)^{0.3333} \approx 1.006622.$$
$$= 0.006622$$
$$r = 12(0.006622)$$
$$\approx 0.079476$$
$$\approx 7.95\%$$

Thus, 7.95% compounded monthly is equivalent to 8% compounded quarterly.

Effective Rate

If we convert from an interest rate compounded m times a year (where $m > 1$) to an interest rate compounded annually (i.e., once a year), the resulting equivalent rate is called the *effective annual interest rate* or, simply, **effective rate.** Thus, to determine the effective rate, s, corresponding to the annual rate, r, compounded m times a year, we use equation (1) to obtain the equation

$$(1 + r/m)^m = 1 + s$$

which, when solved for s, gives the following formula for the effective rate.

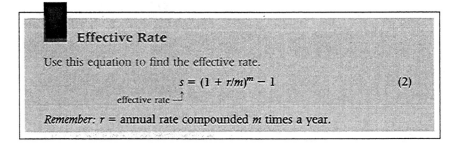

Effective Rate

Use this equation to find the effective rate.

$$s = (1 + r/m)^m - 1 \qquad (2)$$

effective rate —↑

Remember: r = annual rate compounded m times a year.

As an example, the effective rate corresponding to 8% compounded quarterly is given by

$$
\begin{aligned}
s &= (1 + r/m)^m - 1 \\
&= (1 + 0.08/4)^4 - 1 \\
&= (1.02)^4 - 1 && \text{Using a calculator,} \\
&\approx 1.082432 - 1 && (1.02)^4 \approx 1.082432. \\
&= 0.082432 \approx 8.24\% && \text{Effective rate}
\end{aligned}
$$

Thus, 8% compounded quarterly is equivalent to 8.24% compounded annually.

• EXAMPLE 4-14

Find the effective rate corresponding to 6% compounded monthly.

Solution

Using equation (2), we have

$$
\begin{aligned}
s &= (1 + r/m)^m - 1 \\
&= (1 + 0.06/12)^{12} - 1 \\
&= (1.005)^{12} - 1 && \text{Using a calculator,} \\
&\approx 1.061678 - 1 && (1.005)^{12} \approx 1.061678. \\
&= 0.061678 \approx 6.17\% && \text{Effective rate}
\end{aligned}
$$

Thus, 6% compounded monthly is equivalent to 6.17% compounded annually.

Effective rates are used to compare competing interest rates offered by banks and other financial institutions. The next example illustrates such a case.

• EXAMPLE 4-15 _____

One bank pays interest on its savings accounts at the rate of 8.65% compounded quarterly; another bank pays 8.70% compounded semiannually. Which pays its savers more interest?

Solution

We find the effective rate for each bank's rate by using a calculator as follows.

8.65% compounded quarterly: The *effective rate* is given by

$$(1 + 0.0865/4)^4 - 1 \approx 1.089347 - 1 = 0.089347 \approx 8.93\%$$

8.70% compounded semiannually: The *effective rate* is given by

$$(1 + 0.0870/2)^2 - 1 \approx 1.088892 - 1 = 0.088892 \approx 8.89\%$$

The bank that has the greater effective rate pays its savers more interest. Thus, the bank that pays 8.65% compounded quarterly has the greater effective rate and, therefore, pays more interest to its savers.

"Double, Triple, Quadruple . . . Your Money"

Consider the following question:

How long does it take a principal to double itself at 8% compounded quarterly?

The answer is found by beginning with the formula for compound amount

$$S = P(1 + i)^n$$

and substituting $2P$ for S. Hence,

$$2P = P(1 + i)^n$$

Dividing by P, we obtain

$$2 = (1 + i)^n$$

We must now solve the equation for n. Taking the natural logarithm of each side, we get

$$\ln 2 = \ln (1 + i)^n$$
$$= n \ln (1 + i)$$

Solving for n yields

$$n = \frac{\ln 2}{\ln (1 + i)}$$

Since $i = 8\%/4 = 2\% = 0.02$, then

$$n = \frac{\ln 2}{\ln 1.02}$$
$$\approx \frac{0.6931}{0.0198}$$
$$\approx 35 \text{ conversion periods}$$

Thus, the principal, P, will double itself after $n = 35$ conversion periods or $35/4 = 8\frac{3}{4}$ years (since there are 4 conversion periods per year). We note that the above procedure could also be employed by using common logarithms.

Daily Compounding

So far in this chapter we have worked examples where interest has been compounded annually, semiannually, quarterly, and monthly. Interest may also be compounded weekly, daily, and hourly. When interest is compounded daily, most financial institutions have used a 360-day year. However, with the increasing use of computers and calculators, many are using a 365-day year. In this text, we will employ a 365-day year. Hence, if interest is compounded daily, then $i = r/365$.

• EXAMPLE 4-16

A man invests $18,000 for 3 years at 10% compounded daily. Find the compound amount

Solution

Here, we use

$$S = P(1 + i)^n$$

where $P = \$18,000$, $i = 0.10/365$, and $n = 365(3) = 1095$. Hence,

$$S = 18,000\left(1 + \frac{0.10}{365}\right)^{1095}$$

Let us first evaluate $(1 + 0.10/365)^{1095}$. Using a calculator, we determine that $(1 + 0.10/365)^{1095} \approx 1.349803332$. Thus, the compound amount is

$$S \approx 18,000(1.349803332)$$
$$\approx \$24,296.46$$

• EXAMPLE 4-17

Find the effective annual interest rate corresponding to 12% compounded daily.

Solution

We must evaluate

$$\left(1 + \frac{0.12}{365}\right)^{365} - 1$$

Using a calculator, we determine that $(1 + 0.12/365)^{365} \approx 1.127475$. Hence, the effective annual interest rate is

$$\left(1 + \frac{0.12}{365}\right)^{365} - 1 \approx 1.127475 - 1$$
$$= 0.127475$$

Thus, 12% compounded daily is equivalent to 12.75% compounded annually.

Continuous Compounding

In Section 3-1, we learned that the expression

$$\left(1 + \frac{1}{x}\right)^x \boxed{\text{approaches}}\!\!\!> e$$

as x gets larger and larger. Also we used a calculator to compute $(1 + 1/x)^x$ for larger and larger values of x and determined that

$$e = 2.718281828. \; . \; .$$

We now show how this result is used in the continuous compounding of interest.

The previous two examples have involved daily compounding of interest. We may go further and compound every minute, every second, every half-second, etc. As the number of compoundings per year, m, increases without bound, the interest is said to be **compounded continuously.**

To determine the formula for the future value of an amount P that is compounded continuously, we begin with

$$S = P\left(1 + \frac{r}{m}\right)^{mt}$$

where r = nominal interest rate, m = number of conversion periods per year, and t = number of years. As m increases without bound, the preceding formula for S is rewritten as

$$S = P\left[\left(1 + \frac{1}{m/r}\right)^{m/r}\right]^{rt}$$

Hence, as m increases, m/r increases. Eventually, the factor

$$\left(1 + \frac{1}{m/r}\right)^{m/r}$$

approaches $e = 2.718281828$ . . . . Thus, when interest is compounded continuously at a nominal rate, r, the future value, S, is given by

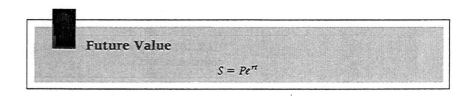

Future Value

$$S = Pe^{rt}$$

• **EXAMPLE 4-18** _____

A financial analyst invests $10,000 at 7% compounded continuously for 10 years. Find the compound amount.

Solution

Here $P = \$10,000$, $r = 0.07$, and $t = 10$ years.
Thus,

$$S = Pe^{rt}$$
$$= 10{,}000e^{0.07(10)} \qquad \text{Using a calculator or Appendix C,}$$
$$\approx 10{,}000(2.013753) \qquad \text{Table 3, } e^{0.70} \approx 2.013753.$$
$$= \$20{,}137.53$$

Effective Rate: Continuous Compounding

To determine a formula for the effective rate when compounding continuously at an annual rate, r, we find its equivalent rate, s, compounded annually by using the equation below.

$$e^{r(1)} = 1 + s$$

Compound amount of \$1 invested ⎯↑   ↑⎯ Compound amount of \$1 invested
for 1 year at annual rate r for 1 year at annual rate s
compounded continuously   compounded annually

Solving the above equation for s gives the following formula for the effective rate when compounding continuously.

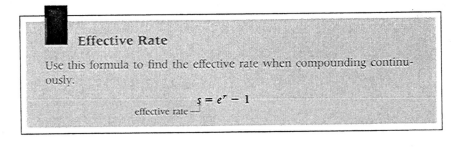

Effective Rate

Use this formula to find the effective rate when compounding continuously.

$$s = e^r - 1$$

effective rate ⎯

• **EXAMPLE 4-19** _____

Find the effective annual interest rate corresponding to 10% compounded continuously.

Solution

We seek the interest earned by investing \$1 at 10% compounded continuously for 1 year. This is given by

$$e^{0.10} - 1 \approx 1.105171 - 1$$
$$= 0.105171 \approx 10.52\%$$

Thus, 10% compounded continuously is equivalent to approximately 10.52% compounded annually.

•

Present Value at Continuous Compounding

The formula for present value at continuous compounding is found by beginning with the formula for compound amount

$$S = Pe^{rt}$$

and solving for P. Thus,

Present Value

$$P = Se^{-rt}$$

• EXAMPLE 4-20 _____

What sum of money should be invested for 5 years at 6% compounded continuously in order to provide a compound amount of $9000?

Solution

In this case, we have $S = \$9000$, $r = 0.06$, and $t = 5$ years. Therefore,

$$P = Se^{-rt}$$
$$= 9000e^{-0.06(5)}$$
$$\approx 9000(0.740818)$$
$$\approx \$6667.36$$

Using a calculator,
$e^{-0.30} \approx 0.740818$.

Exercises 4-2

Using a calculator or Appendix C, Table 4 (or both), find the compound amount and interest for each of the following situations:

1. $P = \$1000$, $r = 0.08$, $m = 4$, $n = 40$
2. $P = \$5000$, $r = 0.08$, $m = 2$, $n = 30$
3. $P = \$8000$, $r = 0.06$, $m = 1$, $n = 10$
4. $P = \$3000$, $r = 0.12$, $m = 3$, $n = 36$
5. $5000 invested at 4% compounded quarterly for 6 years
6. $10,000 invested at 8% compounded semiannually for 15 years
7. $3000 invested at 12% compounded monthly for 4 years
8. $20,000 invested at 6% compounded semiannually for 11 years

Determine the present value in each of the following situations.

9. $S = \$8,000$, interest rate is 8% compounded semiannually, time is 5 years
10. $S = \$10,000$, interest rate is 10% compounded semiannually, time is 6 years
11. $S = \$6,000$, interest rate is 8% compounded quarterly, time is 9 years
12. $S = \$15,000$, interest rate is 7% compounded quarterly, time is 3 years
13. $S = \$9,000$, interest rate is 8% compounded annually, time is 20 years
14. $S = \$12,000$, interest rate is 6% compounded annually, time is 15 years.

Find the present value of each of the following.

15. $8000 due in 4 years with money worth 8% compounded quarterly
16. $4000 due in 10 years with money worth 5% compounded annually
17. $20,000 due in 20 years with money worth 8% compounded semiannually
18. $10,000 due in 3 years with money worth 12% compounded monthly
19. A man borrows $10,000 from a bank. The bank charges interest at the rate of 8% compounded quarterly. Ten years later, the man repays the loan in a lump-sum payment.
    a) Find the lump-sum payment.
    b) Find the interest.
20. During a 10-year period, the population of a city increased at a rate of 4% a year (i.e., 4% compounded annually). If the initial population was 500,000, what was the population 10 years later? What was the increase?
21. The day a girl was born, her parents deposited $500 into a bank account paying 5% compounded annually. How much will be in this account on the girl's 20th birthday?
22. A woman deposits $10,000 into a bank account. During the first 4 years, the account earns interest at 5% compounded annually. During the last 6 years,

the account earns interest at 6% compounded semiannually. Find the total amount.

23. Jean Scott deposits $5000 into a bank account earning interest at the rate of 8% compounded semiannually. Three years later, Jean deposits an additional $6000. Also, at this time, the bank's interest rate is increased to 10% compounded semiannually. How much is in the account 10 years after the initial $5000 deposit was made? Assume that no withdrawals have been made.

24. Harry Mazzuri deposited $900 in a savings account that paid 6% compounded semiannually. Seven years later, the bank changed its interest rate to 10% compounded quarterly. How much will Harry's account be worth 10 years after the original deposit of $900?

25. Lucy Maceratta deposited $600 in a savings account. Six years later, she deposited an additional $300. How much will be in Lucy's account 11 years after the original deposit of $600 if the interest rate is 8% compounded quarterly?

26. How much money should be invested for 6 years at 8% compounded semiannually in order to provide a compound amount of $10,000?

27. An investment contract with a maturity value of $1000 matures in 5 years. If one wishes to earn interest at 6% compounded semiannually, how much should be paid for the investment contract now?

28. Hank Jackson plans to buy a note with a maturity value of $9000. The note is due 6 years from now. If Hank wishes to earn interest at 12% compounded monthly, how much should he pay for the note?

29. A 3-year note has a maturity value of $10,000. The interest rate is 12% compounded quarterly.
    a) How much money is needed to pay the debt now?
    b) How much money is needed to pay the debt 2 years from now?

30. How much money should be deposited now in order to accumulate into $8000 in 10 years at an interest rate of 12% compounded quarterly?

Find the effective annual interest rate corresponding to each of the following.

31. 6% compounded semiannually
32. 4% compounded quarterly
33. 12% compounded monthly
34. 8% compounded semiannually

How long will it take money to double itself at each of the following rates?

35. 6% compounded semiannually
36. 8% compounded semiannually
37. 8% compounded annually
38. 12% compounded monthly

How long will it take money to triple itself at each of the following rates?

39. 8% compounded quarterly
40. 6% compounded semiannually

How long will it take money to quadruple itself at each of the following rates?

41. 8% compounded quarterly
42. 6% compounded semiannually

Use a calculator to solve each of the following problems. Find the value of $(1 + i)^n$ for each of the following.

43. 7% compounded monthly for 3 years
44. 5% compounded monthly for 5 years
45. 10% compounded monthly for 4 years
46. 8% compounded monthly for 6 years

47. 9% compounded weekly for 2 years
48. 6% compounded weekly for 3 years
49. 9% compounded daily for 3 years
50. 5% compounded daily for 2 years
51. 8% compounded daily for 4 years
52. 6% compounded daily for 3 years
53. A person deposits $10,000 into a bank account that pays interest at 8% compounded daily. How much is in the account at the end of 5 years?
54. Determine the compound amount of $80,000 that earns interest at 10% compounded daily for 2 years.
55. How much should be invested now at 7% compounded daily in order to accumulate $50,000 at the end of 3 years?
56. How much should be invested now at 9% compounded daily in order to accumulate $10,000 at the end of 2 years?
57. What rate compounded semiannually is equivalent to 8% compounded quarterly?
58. What rate compounded quarterly is equivalent to 10% compounded semiannually?
59. What rate compounded monthly is equivalent to 6% compounded semiannually?
60. What rate compounded quarterly is equivalent to 10% compounded monthly?

Which would you rather earn?

61. 8.8% compounded annually or 8.5% compounded daily
62. 10% compounded annually or 9.75% compounded daily
63. 9% compounded annually or 8.75% compounded monthly

Find the compound amount of each of the following.

64. $1000 invested for 3 years at 6% compounded continuously
65. $5000 invested for 8 years at 5% compounded continuously
66. $10,000 invested for 10 years at 8% compounded continuously
67. $6000 invested for 5 years at 6% compounded continuously

Find the present value of each of the following.

68. $6000 due in 3 years at 6% compounded continuously
69. $10,000 due in 7 years at 10% compounded continuously
70. $8000 due in 10 years at 8% compounded continuously
71. $4000 due in 2 years at 7% compounded continuously

Find the effective annual interest rate corresponding to each of the following.

72. 6% compounded continuously
73. 7% compounded continuously
74. 8% compounded continuously
75. 9% compounded continuously

4-3 • GEOMETRIC SERIES AND ANNUITIES

Geometric Series

A **geometric series** is an expression of the form

$$a + ar + ar^2 + \ldots + ar^{n-1}$$

Each term is a constant multiple, r, of the preceding term. If S_n denotes the sum of the first n terms of a geometric series, then

$$S_n = a + ar + ar^2 + \ldots + ar^{n+1}$$

$$\underset{\substack{\text{1st} \\ \text{term}}}{\uparrow} \quad \underset{\substack{\text{2d} \\ \text{term}}}{\uparrow} \quad \underset{\substack{\text{3d} \\ \text{term}}}{\uparrow} \qquad \underset{\substack{n\text{th} \\ \text{term}}}{\uparrow}$$

An alternate formula for evaluating S_n is derived as follows. Take the equation

$$S_n = a + ar + ar^2 + \ldots + ar^{n-1}$$

and multiply both sides by r to obtain

$$rS_n = ar + ar^2 + \ldots + ar^{n-1} + ar^n$$

Now consider both equations:

$$S_n = a + ar + ar^2 + \ldots + ar^{n-1}$$
$$rS_n = ar + ar^2 + \ldots + ar^{n-1} + ar^n$$

Note that

$$S_n - rS_n = a - ar^n$$

Factoring both sides of this last equation gives us

$$S_n(1 - r) = a(1 - r^n)$$

Hence,

$$S_n = \frac{a(1 - r^n)}{1 - r}$$

Thus, for the geometric series

$$9 + \underbrace{9 \cdot 2} + \underbrace{9 \cdot 2^2} + \underbrace{9 \cdot 2^3} + \underbrace{9 \cdot 2^4} + \underbrace{9 \cdot 2^5}$$

$$\underset{\substack{\text{1st} \\ \text{term}}}{\uparrow} \quad \underset{\substack{\text{2d} \\ \text{term}}}{\uparrow} \quad \underset{\substack{\text{3d} \\ \text{term}}}{\uparrow} \quad \underset{\substack{\text{4th} \\ \text{term}}}{\uparrow} \quad \underset{\substack{\text{5th} \\ \text{term}}}{\uparrow} \quad \underset{\substack{\text{6th} \\ \text{term}}}{\uparrow}$$

$a = 9$, $r = 2$, and $n = 6$. Then

$$S_6 = \frac{a(1 - r^n)}{1 - r}$$
$$= \frac{9(1 - 2^6)}{1 - 2}$$
$$= \frac{9(1 - 64)}{1 - 2}$$
$$= \frac{9(-63)}{-1}$$
$$= 567$$

Note that if the series is added term by term, we will obtain the same result.

• EXAMPLE 4-21

Find the sum of the seven terms of the geometric series

$$5 + 5 \cdot 3 + 5 \cdot 3^2 + 5 \cdot 3^3 + 5 \cdot 3^4 + 5 \cdot 3^5 + 5 \cdot 3^6$$

Solution

Comparing this geometric series with the general form

$$a + ar + ar^2 + \ldots + ar^{n-1}$$

we have $a = 5$, $r = 3$, and $n = 7$. Hence,

$$S_7 = \frac{a(1 - r^n)}{1 - r}$$

$$= \frac{5(1 - 3^7)}{1 - 3}$$

$$= \frac{5(1 - 2187)}{1 - 3}$$

$$= \frac{5(-2186)}{-2}$$

$$= 5465$$

Annuities

An **annuity** is a series of equal payments made at equal intervals of time. Many everyday business transactions are annuities. Mortgage payments, premium payments on insurance plans, rental payments on a lease, and installment purchases are a few examples. In general, any series of equal payments made at equal intervals of time is an annuity. Each payment is called the **periodic payment,** or **period rent.** Periodic payment will be denoted by R. The total time during which these payments are made is called the **term** of the annuity.

Specifically, if a person deposits $100 at the end of each 6-month period for 2 years, then the periodic payment, R, is $100, the payment period is 6 months, and the term is 2 years (see Figure 4-24). Note that each payment is made *at the end* of the payment period. Such an annuity is called an **ordinary annuity.** If each payment were made *at the beginning* of the payment period, the annuity would be called an **annuity due.** In this section, we will begin with ordinary annuities. Annuities due will be covered later in the section.

Each payment, R, of an annuity earns compound interest. Here, and in Sections 4-4 through 4-5, we will discuss only those annuities for which

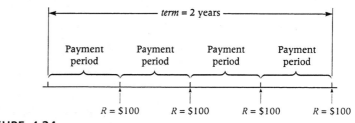

FIGURE 4-24

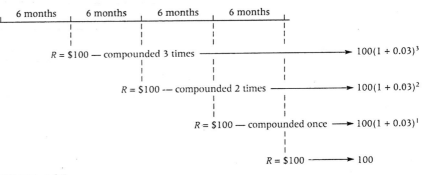

FIGURE 4-25

the payment period and conversion period coincide. Returning to our example, since each $100 payment is deposited semiannually, the interest will be compounded semiannually. We will use an interest rate of 6% compounded semiannually. Hence, $i = 3\%$ per conversion period.

The sum of all periodic payments, R, plus their interest is called the **total amount,** or **future value,** of the annuity. It will be denoted by S. To calculate the total amount, S, of an annuity, we must realize that each periodic payment, R, is made at a different point in time. Hence, each payment, R, earns compound interest for the duration of its term in the annuity. This is illustrated in Figure 4-25 for our previous annuity of $100 deposited semiannually for 2 years at an interest rate of 6% compounded semiannually. Studying Figure 4-25, note that the total amount, S, of the annuity is equal to the sum of the compound amounts of the payments of $100. Hence,

$$S = 100 + 100(1 + 0.03)^1 + 100(1 + 0.03)^2 + 100(1 + 0.03)^3$$

Observe that the expression for S is a geometric series with $a = 100$, $r = 1 + 0.03 = 1.03$, and $n = 4$. Using either Table 4 in Appendix C or a calculator, we evaluate the above.

$$S = 100 + 100(1.03) + 100(1.0609) + 100(1.09273)$$
$$= 100 + 103 + 106.09 + 109.27$$
$$= \$418.36$$

Now we will derive a general formula for the total amount (or future value), S, of an ordinary annuity. The time diagram of Figure 4-26 illustrates an ordinary annuity of n payments of R dollars each.

Thus, there are n payment periods (or conversion periods). As usual, $i =$ interest rate per conversion period. Studying Figure 4-26, we note that the total amount, S, of the annuity is equal to the sum of the compound amounts of the payments, R. Therefore,

$$S = R + R(1 + i) + R(1 + i)^2 + \ldots + R(1 + i)^{n-2} + R(1 + i)^{n-1}$$

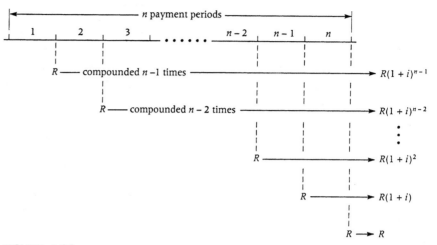

FIGURE 4-26

Observe that this expression is a geometric series of this form

$$a + ar + ar^2 . . . + ar^{n-1}$$

with $a = R$ and $r = 1 + i$. Recall that the sum of the n terms of this latter geometric series is given by the formula

$$\frac{a(1 - r^n)}{1 - r}$$

Substituting R for a and $1 + i$ for r yields

$$\frac{R[1 - (1 + i)^n]}{1 - (1 + i)}$$

which simplifies to

$$R\left[\frac{(1 + i)^n - 1}{i}\right]$$

Thus, the formula for the total amount, S, of an ordinary annuity of n payments of R dollars each is

$$S = R\left[\frac{(1 + i)^n - 1}{i}\right]$$

where i = interest rate per conversion period.

Appendix C, Table 6 lists the tabulations of the quantity $[(1 + i)^n - 1]/i$ for various values of i and n. For brevity, this quantity is usually denoted by the symbol $s_{\overline{n}|i}$, read "s angle n at i." This quantity can also be evaluated with a calculator. Thus, the preceding formula for the total amount, S, of an ordinary annuity is usually written

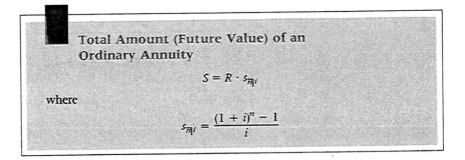

Total Amount (Future Value) of an Ordinary Annuity

$$S = R \cdot s_{\overline{n}|i}$$

where

$$s_{\overline{n}|i} = \frac{(1 + i)^n - 1}{i}$$

Returning to the previous example, where $R = \$100$, $i = 0.03$, and $n = 4$, the total amount is calculated as

$$S = R \cdot s_{\overline{4}|0.03}$$
$$\approx 100(4.183627)$$
$$\approx \$418.36$$

Using Appendix C, Table 6,
$s_{\overline{4}|0.03} \approx 4.183627$.
Using a calculator,
$s_{\overline{4}|0.03} = [(1.03)^4 - 1]/0.03 = 4.183627$.

• **EXAMPLE 4-22** _____

Mr. Haskins deposits $200 at the end of each quarter into a pension fund earning interest at 8% compounded quarterly.

a)   Find the total amount at the end of 10 years.
b)   How much interest was earned?

Solutions

Here we have $R = \$200$, $i = 8\%/4 = 2\% = 0.02$, and $n = 4(10) = 40$.

a)   The calculation is

$$S = R \cdot s_{\overline{n}|i}$$
$$= 200 \cdot s_{\overline{40}|0.02}$$
$$\approx 200(60.401983)$$
$$\approx \$12,080.40$$

Using a calculator,
$s_{\overline{40}|0.02} = [(1.02)^{40} - 1]/0.02 \approx 60.401983$.

b)   Mr. Haskins actually deposited 40 payments of $200 each, or 40($200) = $8000. Thus, the interest earned is

$$\$12,080.40 - \$8000.00 = \$4080.40$$

Note that, for the annuities discussed up to this point, the payment intervals are coincident with the interest (or conversion) periods. Such an annuity where the payment intervals coincide with the interest (or conversion) periods is called a **simple annuity.** All of the annuities of this chapter are simple annuities until Section 4-6.

Annuity Due

As was stated earlier, if each payment, R, of an annuity is made *at the beginning* of the payment period, the annuity is called an **annuity due.** The

Ordinary annuity

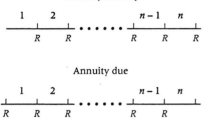

Annuity due

FIGURE 4-27

time diagram of Figure 4-27 compares an ordinary annuity and an annuity due.

Note that both annuities have n payments of R dollars each. Howver, since each payment of an annuity due is made at the beginning of the period, then each payment earns interest for one additional period. We now derive the formula for the total amount of an annuity due (see Figure 4-28).

Studying Figure 4-28, note that

$$S = R(1 + i) + R(1 + i)^2 + \cdots + R(1 + i)^{n-1} + R(1 + i)^n$$

$$= \underbrace{[R + R(1 + i) + R(1 + i)^2 + \cdots + R(1 + i)^n]}_{\text{geometric series}} - R$$

Applying the formula for the sum of a geometric series, we have

$$S = R\left[\frac{1 - (1 + i)^{n+1}}{1 - (1 + i)}\right] - R$$

$$= R\left[\frac{(1 + i)^{n+1} - 1}{i}\right] - R$$

$$= R \cdot s_{\overline{n+1}|i} - R$$

$$= R(s_{\overline{n+1}|i} - 1)$$

Thus, the formula for the total amount (or future value), S, of an annuity due is as follows.

Total Amount (Future Value) of an Annuity Due

$$S = R(s_{\overline{n+1}|i} - 1)$$

where

$$s_{\overline{n+1}|i} = \frac{(1 + i)^{n+1} - 1}{i}$$

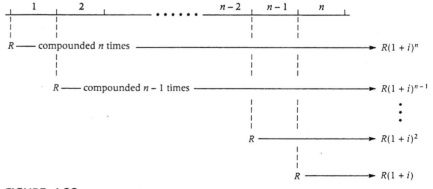

FIGURE 4-28

• **EXAMPLE 4-23** _____

Ms. Jones deposits $100 at the beginning of each quarter into a bank account earning interest at 8% compounded quarterly. Find the total amount at the end of 9 years.

Solution

Here, $R = \$100$, $i = 8\%/4 = 2\% = 0.02$, and $n = 4(9) = 36$. Therefore,

$$S = R(s_{\overline{n+1}|i} - 1)$$

$$= 100(s_{\overline{37}|0.02} - 1)$$

$$\approx 100(54.034255 - 1)$$

$$= 100(53.034255)$$

$$\approx \$5303.43$$

Using a calculator,
$s_{\overline{37}|0.02} = [(1.02)^{37} - 1]/0.02 \approx 54.034255.$

• **EXAMPLE 4-24** **Ordinary Annuity Versus Annuity Due.**

A person deposits $300 per month into a bank account earning interest at 6% compounded monthly. Find the total amount at the end of 4 years if each payment is made:

a) At the end of the month   **b)** At the beginning of the month

Solutions

a) If each payment is made at the end of the month, the annuity is an ordinary annuity, with $n = (12)(4) = 48$ and $i = 0.06/12 = 0.005$. The total amount of the annuity is determined as follows:

$$S = R \cdot s_{\overline{n}|i}$$

$$= 300 \, s_{\overline{48}|0.005}$$

$$\approx 300(54.097832)$$

$$\approx \$16,229.35$$

Using a calculator,
$s_{\overline{48}|0.005} = [(1.005)^{48} - 1]/0.005 \approx 54.097832.$

b) If each payment is made at the beginning of the month, the annuity is an annuity due, with $n = 48$, $n + 1 = 49$, and $i = 0.005$. The total amount is determined as follows:

$$S = R(s_{\overline{n+1}|i} - 1)$$

$$= 300(s_{\overline{49}|0.005} - 1)$$

$$\approx 300(55.368321 - 1)$$

$$= 300(54.368321)$$

$$\approx \$16,310.50$$

Using a calculator,
$s_{\overline{49}|0.005} = [(1.005)^{49} - 1]/0.005 \approx 55.368321.$

Note that, for the same interest rate and time period, the future value of the annuity due is greater than that of the corresponding ordinary annuity. This is because each deposit of the annuity due earns interest for an additional conversion period.

Exercises 4-3

For each of the following geometric series, find the sum of the indicated terms in two ways.

1. $2 + 2 \cdot 5 + 2 \cdot 5^2 + 2 \cdot 5^3$
2. $3 + 3 \cdot 2 + 3 \cdot 2^2 + 3 \cdot 2^3 + 3 \cdot 2^4 + 3 \cdot 2^5$
3. $7 + 7 \cdot 4 + 7 \cdot 4^2 + 7 \cdot 4^3 + 7 \cdot 4^4 + 7 \cdot 4^5 + 7 \cdot 4^6$

Find the total amount of each of the following ordinary annuities:

4. $100 each quarter for 5 years at 7% compounded quarterly
5. $1000 semiannually for 20 years at 6% compounded semiannually
6. $500 monthly for 4 years at 12% compounded monthly
7. $5000 annually for 20 years at 5% compounded annually
8. $900 monthly for 5 years at 6% compounded monthly
9. $1,500 quarterly for 6 years at 8% compounded quarterly

10-15. Repeat Exercises 4-9 under the assumption that each annuity is an annuity due.

16. A woman deposits $100 at the end of each quarter into a fund earning interest at 4% compounded quarterly.
    a) Find the total amount at the end of 12 years.
    b) How much interest was earned?

17. A man deposits $1500 at the end of each year into a pension fund earning interest at 5% compounded annually.
    a) Find the total amount at the end of 20 years.
    b) How much interest was earned?

18. Sally Smith deposits $1000 at the end of each 6-month period for 15 years into a fund earning interest at 6% compounded semiannually.
    a) Find the total amount at the end of 15 years.
    b) If Sally leaves the total amount in the fund for 5 more years without making any additional deposits, how much is her fund worth if it earns interest at 6% compounded semiannually?

19. For 4 years, a man deposits $100 into a retirement account at the beginning of each month. If the interest rate is 12% compounded monthly, how much is in the account after 4 years?

20. A woman deposits $1000 at the beginning of each quarter for 5 years. Each deposit earns interest at 12% compounded quarterly.
    a) Find the total amount at the end of 5 years.
    b) If the woman leaves the total amount in the fund for 4 more years without making any additional deposits, how much is her fund worth if the interest rate is 12% compounded quarterly?

21. Jane deposits $100 at the end of each month into a bank account earning interest at 12% compounded monthly. How much is in the account at the end of 4 years? Assume that no withdrawals have been made.

22. Referring to Exercise 21, suppose that Jane, after 4 years, deposits $200 at the end of each month for the next 3 years. If the $200 deposits earn interest at 12% compounded monthly and the accumulated amount of the $100 deposits also earns interest at 12% compounded monthly, how much does Jane have in her account at the end of 7 years (i.e., 7 years after she first opened the account)?

23. A man deposits $500 at the end of each 6-month period into a bank account for 4 years. At that time, his deposits are changed to $600 semiannually for the next 5 years. If all deposits earn interest at 12% compounded semiannually, how much is in the account at maturity?

24. Repeat Exercise 23 under the assumption that each payment is made at the beginning of the 6-month period.

Use a calculator and the following formula to solve problems 25-28.

$$s_{\overline{n}|i} = \frac{(1 + i)^n - 1}{i}$$

25. $s_{\overline{100}|0.015}$

26. $s_{\overline{360}|0.024}$

27. $s_{\overline{n}|i}$ for an interest rate of 20% compounded monthly for 10 years

28. $s_{\overline{n}|i}$ for an interest rate of 11% compounded monthly for 5 years

29. A person deposits $400 at the end of each month into a bank account that pays interest at the rate of 10% compounded monthly. How much is in the account after 7 years?

30. A person deposits $200 at the end of each month into a bank account that pays interest at 7% compounded monthly. How much is in the account after 5 years?

31. Repeat Exercise 29 under the assumption that the deposits are made at the beginning of each month.

32. Repeat Exercise 30 under the assumption that the deposits are made at the beginning of each month.

4-4 • PRESENT VALUE OF AN ANNUITY

The **present value of an annuity** is the sum of the present values of all the periodic payments R (see Figure 4-29).

Observing Figure 4-29, the present value, A, of an annuity is

$$A = R(1 + i)^{-n} + R(1 + i)^{-(n-1)} + R(1 + i)^{-(n-2)} + \cdots + R(1 + i)^{-2} + R(1 + i)^{-1}$$

Thus, an annuity of R dollars per period for n periods is worth A dollars now. In other words, a lump-sum investment of A dollars now will provide payments of R dollars per period for the next n periods.

The preceding formula for A may be simplified. Multiplying the right-hand side by $(1 + i)^n/(1 + i)^n$ yields

$$A = \frac{R + R(1 + i) + R(1 + i)^2 + \cdots + R(1 + i)^{n-2} + R(1 + i)^{n-1}}{(1 + i)^n}$$

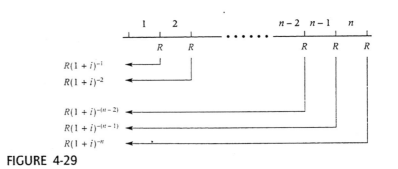

FIGURE 4-29

Note that the numerator is a geometric series. Applying the formula for its sum, we obtain

$$A = \frac{R\left[\dfrac{(1 + i)^n - 1}{i}\right]}{(1 + i)^n}$$

$$= R\left[\frac{1 - (1 + i)^{-n}}{i}\right]$$

Thus, the formula for the present value, A, of an ordinary annuity of n payments of R dollars each is

$$A = R\left[\frac{1 - (1 + i)^{-n}}{i}\right]$$

where i = interest rate per conversion period.

Appendix C, Table 7 lists the tabulations of the quantity $[1 - (1 + i)^{-n}]/i$ for various values of i and n. For brevity, this quantity will be denoted by the symbol $a_{\overline{n}|i}$, read "a angle n at i." This quantity can also be evaluated with a calculator. Thus, the preceding formula for the present value, A, of an ordinary annuity may be written as follows.

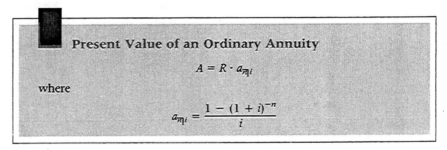

Present Value of an Ordinary Annuity

$$A = R \cdot a_{\overline{n}|i}$$

where

$$a_{\overline{n}|i} = \frac{1 - (1 + i)^{-n}}{i}$$

• EXAMPLE 4-25

A parent wishes to provide for quarterly payments of $400 each for the next 4 years. The payments will be made at the end of each quarter to a daughter who will be attending college. How much should the parent invest at 8% compounded quarterly?

Solution

The answer is the present value, A, of the annuity. Note that $R = \$400$, $i = 8\%/4 = 2\% = 0.02$, and $n = 4(4) = 16$. Thus,

$$A = R \cdot a_{\overline{n}|i}$$
$$= 400 \cdot a_{\overline{16}|0.02}$$
$$\approx 400(13.577709)$$
$$\approx \$5431.08$$

Using Appendix C, Table 7,
$a_{\overline{16}|0.02} \approx 13.577709$.
Using a calculator,
$a_{\overline{16}|0.02} = [1 - (1.02)^{-16}]/0.02 \approx 13.577709$

Thus, the parent's investment of $5431.08 will provide for 16 payments of $400, or 16($400) = $6400, over the next 4 years.

• EXAMPLE 4-26

This problem is adapted from one that appeared on a past Uniform CPA Examination. Cause Company is planning to invest in a machine with a useful life of 5 years and no salvage value. The machine is expected to produce cash flow from operations, net of income taxes, of $20,000 in each of the 5 years. Cause's expected rate of return is 10% compounded annually. How much will the machine cost?

Solution

We seek the present value of this annuity. Here $i = 0.10$, $n = 5$, and $R = 20,000$. Thus,

$$A = R \cdot a_{\overline{n}|i}$$
$$= 20,000 \cdot a_{\overline{5}|0.10}$$
$$\approx 20,000(3.790787)$$
$$\approx \$75,815.74$$

Using a calculator,
$a_{\overline{5}|0.10} = (1 - (1.10)^{-5})/0.10 \approx 3.790787$

Thus, the machine cost $75,815.74.

We should also understand that the present value of an annuity, A, if invested for the duration of the annuity, will yield the same total amount, S, as the annuity. In other words, if Mr. Johnson deposits n payments of R dollars each and Mr. Thomas deposits a lump sum of A dollars now, then after n conversion periods, both will have the same total amount (assuming that the interest rate, i, is the same for both). The time diagrams of Figure 4-30 illustrate this example.

Observe that if we equate the formulas for the total amount, S, we have

$$A(1 + i)^n = R\left[\frac{(1 + i)^n - 1}{i}\right]$$

Solving for A yields

$$A = R\left[\frac{1 - (1 + i)^{-n}}{i}\right]$$

Note that this is the formula for the present value of an annuity.

• **EXAMPLE 4-27**

Henry deposits $100 at the end of each month for 3 years into a savings account. If Cindy wishes to have the same amount in her account at the end of 3 years, what single sum of money should she deposit now? Assume that both accounts earn interest at 6% compounded monthly.

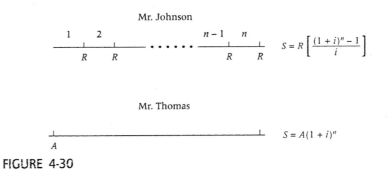

FIGURE 4-30

Solution

The answer is the present value, A, of the annuity. Note that $R = \$100$, $i = 6\%/12 = (1/2)\% = 0.005$, and $n = 12(3) = 36$. Thus,

$$A = R \cdot a_{\overline{n}|i}$$
$$= 100 \cdot a_{\overline{36}|0.005}$$
$$\approx 100(32.871016)$$
$$\approx \$3287.10$$

• EXAMPLE 4-28   Leases.

A corporation can either lease a machine with a 5-year useful life for $2000 per year or buy it for a lump sum of $8000.

a)   If money is worth 7% compounded annually, which alternative is preferable?
b)   If money is worth 8% compounded annually, which alternative is preferable?

Solutions

a)   The leasing alternative involves an annuity with $R = \$2000$, $n = 5$, and $i = 0.07$. The present value of this annuity is

$$A = R \cdot a_{\overline{n}|i}$$
$$= 2000 \cdot a_{\overline{5}|0.07}$$
$$\approx 2000(4.100197)$$
$$\approx \$8200.39$$

Since this amount exceeds the purchase price, purchasing the machine is cheaper.

b)   In this case,

$$A = R \cdot a_{\overline{n}|i}$$
$$= 2000 \cdot a_{\overline{5}|0.08}$$
$$\approx 2000(3.992710)$$
$$\approx \$7985.42$$

Since this amount is less than the purchase price, leasing the machine is cheaper.

• EXAMPLE 4-29   Capital Expenditure Analysis.

A corporation wants to modernize its equipment in order to reduce labor costs. It has a chance of purchasing two machines for a certain assembly operation. Machine A costs $7000, will save $1600 annually, and has a useful life of 6 years. Machine B costs $9000, will save $1900 annually, and has a useful life of 7 years. If money is worth 8% compounded annually, which machine should the company buy?

Solution

Machine A saves $1600 annually for 6 years. The present value of this annuity at 8% compounded annually is

$$A = R \cdot a_{\overline{n}|i}$$
$$= 1600 \cdot a_{\overline{6}|0.08}$$
$$\approx 1600(4.622880)$$
$$\approx \$7396.61$$

Thus, the annual savings of $1600 for 6 years are equivalent to a lump-sum savings of $7396.61 now. Since Machine A costs $7000, the net saving is

$$\$7396.61 - \$7000 = \$396.61$$

Machine B saves $1900 annually for 7 years. The present value of this annuity at 8% compounded annually is

$$
\begin{aligned}
A &= R \cdot a_{\overline{n}|i} \\
&= 1900 \cdot a_{\overline{7}|0.08} \\
&\approx 1900(5.206370) \\
&\approx \$9892.10
\end{aligned}
$$

Thus, the annual savings of $1900 for 7 years are equivalent to a lump-sum savings of $9892.10 now. Since Machine B costs $9000, the net saving is

$$\$9892.10 - \$9000 = \$892.10$$

Since Machine B has the larger net saving, this is the one the corporation should buy.

•

Present Value of an Annuity Due

The formula for the present value of an annuity due is derived by observing the time diagram of Figure 4-31 and equating the total amounts. Thus, we have

$$
\begin{aligned}
A(1+i)^n &= R\left[\frac{(1+i)^{n+1} - 1}{i} - 1\right] \quad \text{Replace 1 with } \frac{i}{i}, \text{ and} \\
&= R\left[\frac{(1+i)^{n+1} - 1 - i}{i}\right] \quad \begin{array}{l}\text{then add the numerators} \\ \text{to obtain}\end{array} \\
&= R\left[\frac{(1+i)^{n+1} - (1+i)}{i}\right]
\end{aligned}
$$

Dividing both sides by $(1+i)^n$ yields

$$
\begin{aligned}
A &= R\left[\frac{(1+i) - (1+i)^{-(n-1)}}{i}\right] \\
&= R\left[1 + \frac{1 - (1+i)^{-(n-1)}}{i}\right]
\end{aligned}
\qquad
\begin{aligned}
&\quad \frac{1}{i} + \frac{i}{i} - \frac{(1+i)^{-(n-1)}}{i} \\
&= 1 + \frac{1}{i} - \frac{(1+i)^{-(n-1)}}{i} \\
&= 1 + \frac{1 - (1+i)^{-(n-1)}}{i}
\end{aligned}
$$

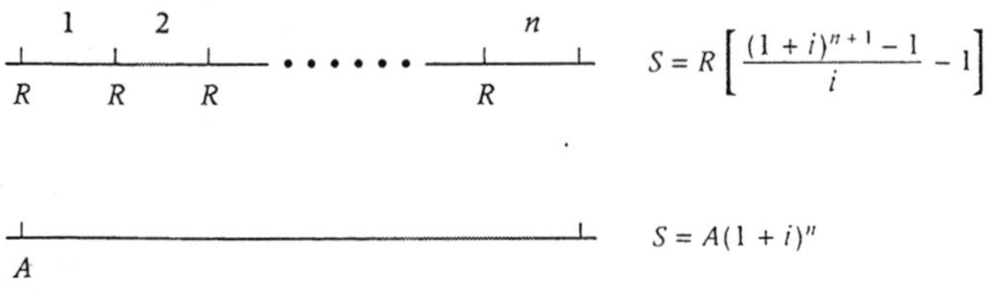

$$
\begin{array}{ccccccc}
& 1 & 2 & & & n & \\
\vdash & \vdash & \vdash & \cdots & \vdash & \vdash & \quad S = R\left[\frac{(1+i)^{n+1} - 1}{i} - 1\right] \\
& R & R & R & & R &
\end{array}
$$

$$
\begin{array}{cc}
\vdash \rule{3cm}{0.4pt} \vdash & \quad S = A(1+i)^n \\
A &
\end{array}
$$

FIGURE 4-31

Since

$$\frac{1 - (1 + i)^{-(n-1)}}{i} = a_{\overline{n-1}|i}$$

then the present value of an annuity due is found by the following formula.

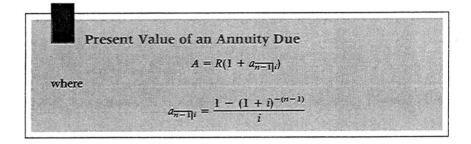

Present Value of an Annuity Due

$$A = R(1 + a_{\overline{n-1}|i})$$

where

$$a_{\overline{n-1}|i} = \frac{1 - (1 + i)^{-(n-1)}}{i}$$

• EXAMPLE 4-30

Find the present value of an annuity due of $1000 quarterly for 5 years at 8% compounded quarterly.

Solution

Here we have $R = \$1000$, $i = 8\%/4 = 2\% = 0.02$, and $n = 4(5) = 20$. Thus,

$$\begin{aligned}
A &= R(1 + a_{\overline{n-1}|i}) \\
&= 1000(1 + a_{\overline{19}|0.02}) \\
&\approx 1000(1 + 15.678462) \\
&= 1000(16.678462) \\
&\approx \$16{,}678.46
\end{aligned}$$

Using a calculator,
$a_{\overline{19}|0.02} = [1 - (1.02)^{-19}]/0.02 \approx 15.678462.$

• EXAMPLE 4-31   Ordinary Annuity Versus Annuity Due.

Determine the present value of an annuity of $300 per month for 4 years at an interest rate of 6% compounded monthly if each payment is made

a)   At the end of the month   **b)**   At the beginning of the month

Recall that we determined the future values of this annuity in Example 4-24.

Solutions

a)   If each payment is made at the end of the month, the annuity is an ordinary annuity, with $n = (12)(4) = 48$ and $i = 0.06/12 = 0.005$. The present value is determined as follows:

$$\begin{aligned}
A &= Ra_{\overline{n}|i} \\
&= 300\, a_{\overline{48}|0.005} \\
&\approx 300(42.580318) \\
&\approx \$12{,}774.10
\end{aligned}$$

Using a calculator,
$a_{\overline{48}|0.005} = [1 - (1.005)^{-48}]/0.005 \approx 42.580318.$

b) If each payment is made at the beginning of the month, the annuity is an annuity due, with $n = 48$, $n - 1 = 47$, and $i = 0.005$. The present value is determined as follows:

$$A = R(a_{\overline{n-1}|}\,i + 1)$$
$$= R(a_{\overline{47}|0.005} + 1)$$
$$\approx 300(41.793219 + 1)$$
$$= 300(42.793219)$$
$$\approx \$12,837.97$$

Using a calculator,
$a_{\overline{47}|0.005} = [1 - (1.005)^{-47}]/0.005 \approx 41.793219.$

Note that for the same interest rate and time period, the present value of an annuity due is greater than that of the corresponding ordinary annuity. This is because, in terms of a time diagram, each payment of an annuity due is brought back one less conversion period than that of an ordinary annuity.

We now provide a summary of the formulas used in the application of compound interest. Since it is most helpful to relate each formula to a time diagram, we have provided such in the following summary box. Thus, we urge you to visualize and relate the associated time diagram to each formula.

The summary box is followed by a box providing a problem-solving procedure for approaching mathematics of finance problems. As we have proceeded through this chapter, we have been given more and more formulas for various financial problems. Thus, at this point, when we begin to solve a problem, we need a procedure to guide our thinking in selecting an appropriate formula (or formulas) to solve the problem. Since it is difficult to provide a step-by-step procedure for solving all mathematics of finance problems, the boxed procedure is applicable to the types of problems that occur most often.

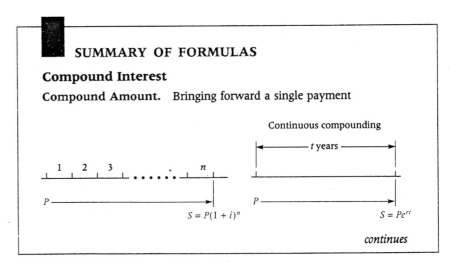

SUMMARY OF FORMULAS

Compound Interest

Compound Amount. Bringing forward a single payment

Continuous compounding

t years

1   2   3   . . . . .   *n*

P $S = P(1 + i)^n$

P $S = Pe^{rt}$

continues

SUMMARY OF FORMULAS—*Continued*

Present Value.   Bringing back a single payment

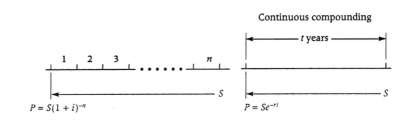

Future Value of Annuity.   Bringing forward a series of equal payments

Ordinary Annuity
   Each payment occurs at the end of the payment period.

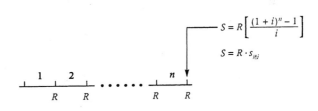

Annuity Due
   Each payment occurs at the beginning of the payment period.

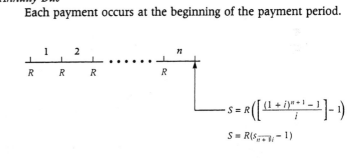

Present Value of an Annuity.   Bringing back a series of equal payments

Ordinary Annuity

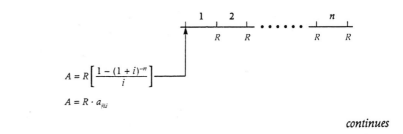

continues

SUMMARY OF FORMULAS—*Continued*

Annuity Due

$$A = R\left(\left[\frac{1 - (1 + i)^{-(n-1)}}{i}\right] + 1\right)$$

$$A = R(a_{\overline{n-1}|i} + 1)$$

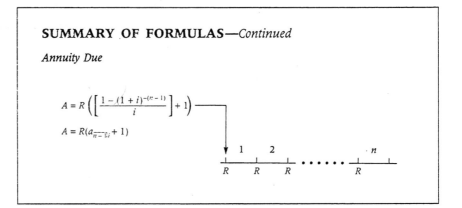

To Solve Problems Involving Compound Interest

1. Draw a time diagram of the problem. Determine the values of i and n.
2. Determine whether the problem involves a single payment or a series of equal payments.

Single Payment. If only a single payment is involved, you should be thinking of using the following formulas:

		Continuous Compounding
Future value	$S = P(1 + i)^n$	$S = Pe^{rt}$
Present value	$P = S(1 + i)^{-n}$	$P = Se^{-rt}$

Series of Equal Payments. If a series of equal payments is involved, you should be thinking of using the following annuity formulas:

	Ordinary Annuity	*Annuity Due*
Future value	$S = R \cdot s_{\overline{n}|i}$	$S = R(s_{\overline{n+1}|i} - 1)$
Present value	$A = R \cdot a_{\overline{n}|i}$	$A = R(a_{\overline{n-1}|i} + 1)$

3. Determine whether the solution to the problem involves a future value or a present value and then focus on the appropriate formulas. Occasionally, more than one formula may have to be used to solve the problem.

Exercises 4-4

Find the present value of each of the following ordinary annuities.

1. $3000 quarterly for 6 years at 8% compounded quarterly
2. $10,000 annually for 4 years at 5% compounded annually
3. $2000 semiannually for 10 years at 6% compounded semiannually
4. $6000 monthly for 3 years at 12% compounded monthly
5. $5,000 quarterly for 9 years at 12% compounded quarterly
6. $2,000 monthly for 3 years at 6% compounded monthly

7-12. Repeat Exercises 1-6 under the assumption that each annuity is an annuity due.

13. Maria Lopez wishes to provide for a semiannual payment of $2000 at the end of each 6-month period for the next 10 years. The payments will be made to her daughter who will be attending college and medical school. How much money should Maria invest now at 10% compounded semiannually?

14. Mr. Wang buys a car by agreeing to pay $500 at the end of each quarter for the next 5 years. This includes interest at 12% compounded quarterly. If instead of financing the car Mr. Johnson decides to pay cash now, how much should he pay?

15. Holly deposits $400 at the end of each quarter into a savings account. If Sara wishes to have the same amount in her account at the end of 5 years, what single sum of money should she deposit now? Assume that both accounts earn interest at 8% compounded quarterly.

16. A company is planning a project that will generate a cash inflow of $10,000 a year for 8 years. If the company wants a rate of return on its invested capital of at least 10% compounded annually, what should be the maximum amount invested in this project now?

17. An investment contract promises to pay its holder $500 at the beginning of each month for 3 years. If one wishes to earn 12% compounded monthly, how much should be paid for this contract now?

18. A certain investment contract promises to pay $1000 at the end of each quarter for the next 7 years. If we wish to buy this investment contract and earn 12% compounded quarterly, how much should we pay for it now?

19. Repeat Exercise 18 under the assumption that the payments are made at the beginning of each quarter.

20. Mr. Cambra wishes to provide for payments of $400 at the end of each quarter to his son for the next 5 years. What sum should be deposited now at 8% compounded quarterly to attain Mr. Cambra's objective?

21. Repeat Exercise 20 under the assumption that the payments are made at the beginning of each quarter.

Use a calculator and the following formula to solve problems 22-25.

$$a_{\overline{n}|i} = \frac{1 - \dfrac{1}{(1 + i)^n}}{i}$$

22. $a_{\overline{100}|0.016}$
23. $a_{\overline{365}|0.024}$
24. $a_{\overline{n}|i}$ for an interest rate of 15% compounded monthly for 10 years
25. $a_{\overline{n}|i}$ for an interest rate of 10% compounded monthly for 20 years

26. Parents of a college freshman wish to set up a fund that will pay $400 per month (at the end of the month) to their daughter for 4 years. How much should the parents deposit now if the fund earns interest at 5% compounded monthly?

27. Parents of a college freshman wish to set up a fund that will pay $600 per month (at the end of the month) to their son for 4 years. How much should the parents deposit now if the fund earns interest at 7% compounded monthly?

28. Repeat Exercise 26 assuming an annuity due.
29. Repeat Exercise 27 assuming an annuity due.
30. Repeat Exercise 26 assuming that the payments are to continue for 6 years.
31. Repeat Exercise 27 assuming that the payments are to continue for 6 years.
32. *This problem is adapted from one that appeared on a past Uniform CPA Examination. On January 1, 19xx, Liberty Company sold a machine to Bell Corpora-*

tion in an "arms length" transaction. Bell signed a noninterest-bearing note requiring payment of $20,000 annually for 10 years. The first payment was made on January 1, 19xx. The prevailing rate of interest for this type of note at the date of issuance was 12% (compounded annually). Liberty should record the above sale in January 19xx at what value?

4-5   • SINKING FUNDS AND AMORTIZATION

Often a person decides to accumulate a sum of money by making periodic deposits into a fund. At the end of a specified time period, the deposits plus the interest earned equal the desired accumulated amount. Such a fund is called a **sinking fund.**

Sinking Funds

As an example, consider a contractor foreseeing the need for a new truck 4 years from now. The price of the truck is forecasted to be $20,000. The contractor wishes to accumulate this amount by setting aside semiannual payments of R dollars each for 4 years. Each payment of this sinking fund earns interest at 10% compounded semiannually. The contractor must determine the semiannual payment, R. This situation is illustrated by the time diagram of Figure 4-32.

Since the semiannual payments constitute an annuity with a total amount of $20,000, then

$$S = R \cdot s_{\overline{n}|i}$$
$$20,000 = R \cdot s_{\overline{8}|0.05}$$

Solving for R yields

$$R = \frac{20,000}{s_{\overline{8}|0.05}}$$
$$\approx \frac{20,000}{9.549109}$$
$$\approx \$2094.44$$

Thus, the series of semiannual payments, R = $2094.44, plus interest will accumulate to S = $20,000. Note that the contractor will make eight payments of $2094.44 each, or 8($2094.44) = $16,755.52. Therefore, the interest earned is

$$\$20,000 - \$16,755.52 = \$3244.48$$

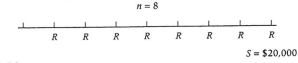

FIGURE 4-32

Sinking Fund Schedule

The accumulation of value in a sinking fund is illustrated by a sinking fund schedule. Such a schedule for the above problem is given in Table 4-1. The *interest* for a given period is the product of i and the total value of the fund at the beginning of the period, as is illustrated in Table 4-1. The *total* value of the fund for a given period is the sum of its payment, interest, and the previous period's total.

Studying the sinking fund schedule of Table 4-1, note that the interest for each period is determined by multiplying $i = 0.05$ times the previous period's total. Observe that the total interest is $3244.53. The $0.05 discrepancy from the previous calculation is due to round-off error.

TABLE 4-1   Sinking fund schedule

Payment number	Payment	Interest	Total
1	$2,094.44	$ 0	$2,094.44
2	2,094.44	104.72	4,293.60
3	2,094.44	214.68	6,602.72
4	2,094.44	330.14	9,027.30
5	2,094.44	451.37	11,573.11
6	2,094.44	578.66	14,246.21
7	2,094.44	712.31	17,052.96
8	2,094.44	852.65	20,000.05
		$3,244.53	

— 2094.44(0.05) = $104.72

— 4293.60(0.05) = $214.68

• **EXAMPLE 4-32** _____

A business executive wishes to set aside semiannual payments to purchase machinery 2 years from now. The machinery's estimated cost is $5000. Each payment earns interest at 12% compounded semiannually.

a) Find the semiannual payment.
b) Find the total interest earned.
c) Prepare a sinking fund schedule similar to that of Table 4-1.

Solutions

a) Here, $S = \$5000$, $i = 12\%/2 = 6\% = 0.06$, and $n = 2(2) = 4$. We must determine R. Since

$$S = R \cdot s_{\overline{n}|i}$$

then

$$5000 = R \cdot s_{\overline{4}|0.06}$$

Solving for R yields

$$R = \frac{5000}{s_{\overline{4}|0.06}}$$

$$\approx \frac{5000}{4.374616}$$

$$\approx \$1142.96$$

b) The business executive will make four payments of $1142.96 each, or 4($1142.96) = $4571.84. Thus, the interest earned is

$$\$5000.00 - \$4571.84 = \$428.16$$

c) The sinking fund schedule is shown in Table 4-2. Observing this sinking fund schedule, note that the interest for each period is determined by multiplying $i = 0.06$ times the previous period's total. Here, the total interest is $428.17. The $0.01 discrepancy from the previous calculation is due to round-off error.

TABLE 4-2

Payment number	Payment	Interest	Total
1	$1142.96	$ 0	$1142.96
2	1142.96	68.58	2354.50
3	1142.96	141.27	3638.73
4	1142.96	218.32	5000.01
		$428.17	

Amortization

Often a loan is repaid by a series of equal payments made at equal intervals of time—an annuity. The *amount of the loan* is the *present value of the annuity*. A portion of each payment is applied against the principal, and the remainder is applied against the interest. When a loan is repaid by an annuity, it is said to be **amortized.**

Consider a person borrowing $7000. The loan plus interest is to be repaid in equal quarterly installments made at the end of each quarter during a 2-year interval. The interest rate is 16% compounded quarterly. We must determine the quarterly payment, R. This situation is illustrated by the time diagram of Figure 4-33.

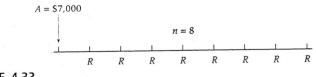

FIGURE 4-33

Since the quarterly payments constitute an annuity with a present value of $7000, then

$$A = R \cdot a_{\overline{n}|i}$$
$$7000 = R \cdot a_{\overline{8}|0.04}$$

Solving for R yields

$$R = \frac{7000}{a_{\overline{8}|0.04}}$$
$$\approx \frac{7000}{6.732745}$$
$$\approx \$1039.69$$

Thus, the borrower will make eight payments of $1039.69 each, or 8($1039.69) = $8317.52, to repay the $7000 loan. Thus, the interest is

$$\$8317.52 - \$7000.00 = \$1317.52$$

Amortization Schedule

The amortization of a loan on a payment-by-payment basis is illustrated in an amortization schedule. Such a schedule for the above problem is given in Table 4-3.

Studying the amortization schedule of Table 4-3, note that the interest for each period is determined by multiplying $i = 0.04$ times the previous period's balance. The amount of **principal reduction** for a period is the difference between the payment, R, and the interest for that period. Each entry in the *balance* column is the difference between the previous period's balance and the principal reduction for the given period. Note, in Table 4-3, that the last payment is increased by $0.04 in order to reduce the final balance to zero.

We also note that the balance of the loan after a given payment has been made can be determined by finding the present value of the remain-

TABLE 4-3 Amortization schedule

| Payment number | Payment R | Payment allocation | | Balance |
		interest	principal reduction	
0				$7000.00
1	$1039.69	$280.00	$759.69	$6240.31
2	1039.69	249.61	790.08	5450.23
3	1039.69	218.01	821.68	4628.55
4	1039.69	185.14	854.55	3774.00
5	1039.69	150.96	888.73	2885.27
6	1039.69	115.41	924.28	1960.99
7	1039.69	78.44	961.25	999.74
8	1039.73	39.99	999.74	0.00
		$1317.56		

7000(0.04)

6240.31(0.04)

ing annuity. To illustrate, the balance of the loan of Table 4-3 after the fifth payment is determined by computing the present value of the remaining three payments. Hence,

$$\text{balance} = 1039.69 a_{\overline{3}|0.04}$$
$$\approx 1039.69(2.775091)$$
$$\approx \$2,885.23$$

Notice that this agrees with the balance after the fifth payment given in Table 4-3 except for a $0.04 roundoff error.

• **EXAMPLE 4-33   Mortgage: Comparing Terms.** _____

A couple plans to purchase a home for $200,000. They have put $50,000 down and will obtain a mortgage for $150,000 at an interest rate of 10.5% compounded monthly. They must decide whether to apply for either a 30-year or a 15-year mortgage. Find the monthly payment and the total interest for both a 30-year and a 15-year mortgage at an interest rate of 10.5% compounded monthly. Compare the total interest paid for each mortgage.

Solution

For either mortgage, $i = 0.105/12 = 0.00875$.

30-year mortgage

$$n = (12)(30) = 360 \quad \text{and} \quad a_{\overline{360}|0.00875} = 109.3207656$$

Since the amount of the mortgage is the present value of the annuity, then the monthly payment is determined as follows:

$$A = R \cdot a_{\overline{n}|i}$$
$$150,000 = R \cdot a_{\overline{360}|0.00875}$$

Solving for R, we obtain

$$R \approx \frac{150,000}{109.3207656} \approx \$1372.11 \qquad \text{Monthly payment}$$

With this mortgage, the couple would make 360 payments of $1372.11 each, or 360($1372.11) = $493,959.60. Thus, the total interest is

$$\$493,959.60 - \$150,000.00 = \$343,959.60 \qquad \text{Total interest}$$

15-year mortgage

$$n = (12)(15) = 180 \quad \text{and} \quad a_{\overline{180}|0.00875} = 90.4650781$$

Again, since the amount of the mortgage is the present value of the annuity, then the monthly payment is determined as follows:

$$A = R \cdot a_{\overline{n}|i}$$
$$150,000 = R \cdot a_{\overline{180}|0.00875}$$

Solving for R, we obtain

$$R \approx \frac{150,000}{90.4650781} \approx \$1658.10 \qquad \text{Monthly payment}$$

With this mortgage, the couple would make 180 payments of $1658.10 each, or 180($1658.10) = $298,458.00. Thus, the total interest is

$$\$298,458 - \$150,000 = \$148,458 \qquad \text{Total interest}$$

Comparison

1. Note that the monthly payment for the 15-year mortgage is only $1658.10 − $1372.11 = $285.99 more than that for the 30-year mortgage. Thus, reducing the term of a mortgage by one-half does not double the monthly payment. Note that the monthly payment for the 15-year mortgage is much less than twice the monthly payment for the 30-year mortgage.

2. Note that the total interest for the 15-year mortgage is $148,458 versus $343,959.60 for the 30-year mortgage for a savings of $343,959.60 − $148,458.00 = $195,501.60.

SUMMARY

Sinking Fund Versus Amortization

1. *Sinking fund.* The future value of an annuity is usually given. The problem usually involves determining the periodic payment, R, by using the formula

$$S = R \cdot s_{\overline{n}|i}$$

and then solving for R to obtain

$$R = \frac{S}{s_{\overline{n}|i}}$$

2. *Amortization.* The present value of an annuity is usually given. The problem usually involves determining the periodic payment, R, by using the formula

$$A = R \cdot a_{\overline{n}|i}$$

and then solving for R to obtain

$$R = \frac{A}{a_{\overline{n}|i}}$$

Add-On Interest

Some lending institutions compute the periodic payment necessary to amortize a loan by the **add-on-interest method.** When using this method, the lender determines the periodic payment necessary to amortize the loan by the following procedure:

1. Compute the simple interest on the original loan amount (the principal) for the term of the loan.
2. Add the interest to the original loan amount.
3. Divide the resulting sum by the number of payments to obtain the periodic payment.

As an example, we consider the $7000 2-year loan with its amortization schedule appearing in Table 4-3. Recall, from Table 4-3 that, at 16% compounded quarterly, the periodic payment necessary to amortize this loan was $1039.69. We now compute the periodic payment by the add-on-interest method. We will use the same interest rate of 16%. However, we will use simple interest since the add-on-interest method uses simple interest. Thus, we compute the periodic payment as follows:

Step 1 Compute the simple interest.

$$I = Prt = 7000(0.16)(2) = \$2240$$

Step 2 Add the interest to the principal.

$$S = P + I = 7000 + 2240 = \$9240$$

Step 3 Divide the result of step 2 by the number of payments.

$$\text{Periodic payment} = 9240/8 = \$1155$$

Note that the periodic payment, $1155, is larger than $1039.69, the payment computed by using the annuity formula at 16% compounded quarterly. Thus, the interest rate on this loan, using the add-on-interest method, is greater than 16% compounded quarterly.

This is because the add-on-interest method entails computation of interest on the original loan amount for the entire term of the loan despite the fact that payments will begin, in this example, 3 months after the loan was granted. In contrast, the method using the annuity formula, $A = R \cdot a_{\overline{n}|i}$, computes interest only on the unpaid balance of the loan. In other words, the lender pays interest on the full loan amount only for the first payment period, and then the balance of the loan is reduced by the principal reduction portion of the periodic payment, so that interest for the second payment period is computed on a smaller balance. This process continues, with a smaller portion of each successive payment allocated to interest.

Exercises 4-5

Determine the periodic payment for each of the following sinking funds. Assume an ordinary annuity.

1. $S = \$35,000$; quarterly payments for 5 years; interest rate is 8% compounded quarterly

2. $S = \$18,000$; monthly payments for 4 years; interest rate is 12% compounded monthly.

3. $S = \$10,000$; semiannual payments for 6 years; interest rate is 6% compounded semiannually

4. $S = \$20,000$; annual payments for 9 years; interest rate is 7% compounded annually

5. $S = \$28,000$; annual payments for 6 years; interest rate is 9% compounded annually

6. $S = \$50,000$; quarterly payments for 5 years; interest rate is 6% compounded quarterly

7. $S = \$145,000$; monthly payments for 10 years; interest rate is 10.2% compounded monthly

8. $S = \$270,000$; monthly payments for 20 years; interest rate is 9.42% compounded monthly

Determine the periodic payment necessary to amortize each of the following loans. Assume an ordinary annuity.

9. $30,000 loan; annual payments for 5 years; interest rate is 9% compounded annually

10. $25,000 loan; quarterly payments for 7 years; interest rate is 7% compounded quarterly

11. $95,000 loan; monthly payments for 5 years; interest rate is 6% compounded monthly

12. $130,000 loan; monthly payments for 6 years; interest rate is 12% compounded monthly

13. $80,000 loan; semiannual payments for 10 years; interest rate is 8% compounded semiannually

14. $150,000 loan; annual payments for 20 years; interest rate is 9% compounded annually

15. $230,000 mortgage; monthly payments for 25 years; interest rate is 10.68% compounded monthly

16. $130,000 mortgage; monthly payments for 30 years; interest rate is 9.12% compounded monthly

17. A grocer anticipates a need for a new freezer 5 years from now. The price is expected to be $10,000. If the grocer wishes to accumulate this amount by setting aside quarterly payments earning interest at 8% compounded quarterly for the next 5 years, how much should be set aside at the end of each quarter?

18. A person wishes to accumulate $20,000 in 20 years by setting aside annual payments earning interest at 5% compounded annually. How much should be set aside at the end of each year?

19. Six years from now, Gerry Grumble must pay Brian Broker $5000. Gerry wishes to set aside into a bank account, at the end of each 6-month period, a payment earning interest at 6% compounded semiannually. How much should each payment be in order to retire the debt in 6 years?

20. Wan Li borrows $10,000. This loan will be repaid by a monthly installment at the end of each month over the next 4 years. If the interest rate is 12% compounded monthly, what is Wan's monthly payment?

21. Tom Thrift buys a house with a purchase price of $80,000. He makes a down payment of $20,000 and finances the remainder with a mortgage requiring a quarterly payment at the end of each quarter for the next 12 years. If the interest rate is 8% compounded quarterly, what is Tom's quarterly payment?

22. A debt of $20,000 is to be amortized over 10 years by a payment at the end of each 6-month period. If the interest rate is 6% compounded semiannually, how much is each payment?

23. A payment is made at the end of each year for 4 years into a sinking fund with a future value of $60,000. Each payment earns interest at 10% compounded annually.

    a) Determine the annual payment.
    b) Determine the total interest earned.
    c) Prepare a sinking fund schedule similar to that of Table 4-1.

24. A company sets aside a payment at the end of each 6-month period to provide for the replacement of equipment 3 years from now. Each payment earns interest at 10% compounded semiannually, and the equipment's projected cost is $20,000.

    a) Find the semiannual payment.
    b) Find the total interest earned.
    c) Prepare a sinking fund schedule similar to that of Table 4-1.

25. A 5-year mortgage for $90,000 is amortized with annual payments (at the end of the year). The interest rate is 9% compounded annually.
    a) Determine the annual payment.
    b) Determine the total interest.
    c) Prepare an amortization schedule similar to that of Table 4-3.
    d) What is the balance after 2 years?

26. Maria Diaz has purchased a car for $10,000. She has made a down payment of $4000 and will finance the balance by making a payment at the end of each quarter for 2 years. The interest rate is 12% compounded quarterly.
    a) Find the quarterly payment.
    b) How much will Maria pay out for the loan after 2 years, and what will the total interest be?
    c) What is the balance after 1¼ years?
    d) Prepare an amortization schedule similar to that of Table 4-3.

27. A 30-year mortgage for $100,000 is amortized with monthly payments (at the end of the month). The interest rate is 9% compounded monthly.
    a) Find the monthly payment.
    b) Find the balance after 4 years.

28. A 30-year mortgage for $150,000 is amortized with monthly payments (at the end of the month). The interest rate is 9.2% compounded monthly. Find the monthly payment.

29. Mr. and Mrs. Barrera have purchased a home for $120,000. They have put $30,000 down and will obtain a 15-year mortgage for $90,000 at an interest rate of 12% compounded monthly.
    a) Find the payment due at the end of each month.
    b) How much will the Barreras pay out for the loan after 15 years, and what will be the total interest?
    c) What is the balance after 10 years?

30. Verify that the quarterly payment necessary to amortize a $20,000 loan is twice that for a $10,000 loan. Assume an ordinary annuity, a 5-year time interval, and an interest rate of 8% compounded quarterly.

31. Show that for given values of i and n, the periodic payment necessary to amortize a loan of $2L$ dollars is twice that for a loan of L dollars. Also, show that, in general, the periodic payment necessary to amortize a loan of kL dollars is k times that of a loan of L dollars.

32. *Mortgage: Comparing terms.* Compare the monthly payments and total interest for 30-year and 15-year mortgages of $100,000 at an interest rate of 9.75% compounded monthly.

33. *Mortgage: Comparing interest rates.* Compare monthly payments and total interest for 30-year mortgages of $100,000 at interest rates of 9.75% and 10.75% compounded monthly.

34. *Mortgage: Comparing interest rates.* Compare monthly payments and total interest for 15-year mortgages of $100,000 at interest rates of 9.75% and 10.75% compounded monthly.

35. *This problem is adapted from one that appeared on a past Uniform CPA Examination.* On January 15, 1988, Carr Corporation adopted a plan to accumulate funds for environmental improvements beginning July 1, 1992, at an estimated cost of $2,000,000. Carr plans to make four equal annual deposits in a fund that will earn interest at 10% compounded annually. The first deposit was made on July 1, 1988. Find the annual deposit.

36-39. *Add-on interest.* Determine the periodic payments necessary to amortize the loans of Exercises 9-12 by the add-on-interest method.

4-6

• EQUATIONS OF VALUE; DEFERRED ANNUITIES; COMPLEX ANNUITIES

Equations of Value

Before going on, let us summarize some basic concepts from previous sections of this chapter. For any financial transaction, the value of an amount of money changes with time as a result of the application of interest. Thus, to *accumulate* or *bring forward* a single payment, R, for n periods at an interest rate of i per period, we multiply R by $(1 + i)^n$, as illustrated in Figure 4-34. To *bring back* a single payment, R, for n periods at an interest rate of i per period, we multiply R by $(1 + i)^{-n}$, as shown in Figure 4-35. To accumulate or bring forward an annuity of n payments of R dollars each, we multiply R by $s_{\overline{n}|i}$, where $s_{\overline{n}|i} = [(1 + i)^n - 1]/i$, as pictured in Figure 4-36 on page 222. To bring back an annuity of n payments of R dollars each, we multiply R by $a_{\overline{n}|i}$, where $a_{\overline{n}|i} = [1 - (1 + i)^{-n}]/i$, as illustrated in Figure 4-37 on page 222.

We now consider the following problem.

PROBLEM

A business person has a debt of $4000 due in 3 years. He wants to repay this debt by making a $3000 payment 2 years from now and a last payment 5 years from now. If the interest rate is 12% compounded annually, what must be the amount of the last payment?

SOLUTION

This situation is illustrated in the time diagram of Figure 4-38 on page 222. Note that the last payment is denoted by x. Thus, we want to determine x so that the value of the two payments on the lower time line is equivalent to the value of the single payment on the upper time line if the interest rate is 12% compounded annually.

Since the value of any amount of money changes with time as a result of the application of interest, we must choose a point on both time lines at

Bringing forward a single payment, R

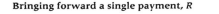
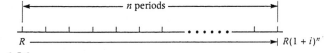

FIGURE 4-34

Bringing back a single payment, R

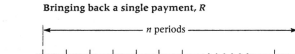

FIGURE 4-35

Bringing forward an annuity of *n* equal payments

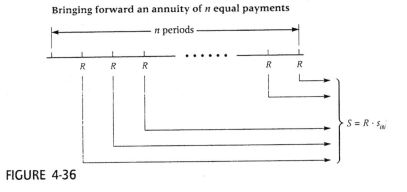

FIGURE 4-36

Bringing back an annuity of *n* equal payments

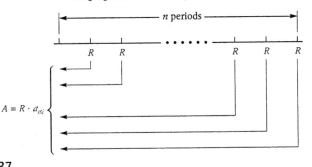

FIGURE 4-37

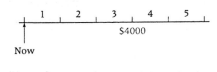

$4000

Now

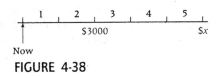

$3000 $x

Now

FIGURE 4-38

which we will equate the values of the payments of both time lines. Such a point is called a **comparison point** and may be chosen arbitrarily.

If, for the situation of Figure 4-38, we choose the comparison point to be "Now," we must

1. Bring back the $4000 payment on the upper time line three periods
2. Bring back the $3000 payment on the lower time line two periods and the unknown payment five periods (see Figure 4-39)

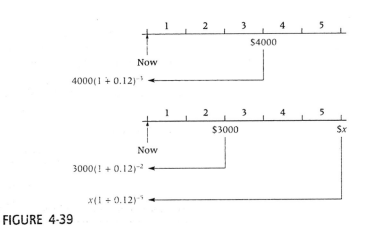

FIGURE 4-39

Equating the values of both time lines at the comparison point, "Now," we obtain the equation

$$4000(1 + 0.12)^{-3} = 3000(1 + 0.12)^{-2} + x(1 + 0.12)^{-5}$$

This equation is called an **equation of value.** Solving for x, we multiply both sides by $(1 + 0.12)^5$ to obtain

$$4000(1 + 0.12)^2 = 3000(1 + 0.12)^3 + x$$

Hence,

$$x = 4000(1 + 0.12)^2 - 3000(1 + 0.12)^3$$

Using Table 4 in Appendix C to obtain the needed powers of $(1 + 0.12)$, we have

$$x = 4000(1.254400) - 3000(1.404928)$$
$$= \$802.82$$

Thus, the last payment is $802.82.

As mentioned before, the comparison point may be chosen arbitrarily. If the comparison point for the preceding problem is chosen to be the end of the fifth year, then each payment must be brought forward to the end of the fifth year. The resulting equation of value is

$$4000(1 + 0.12)^2 = 3000(1 + 0.12)^3 + x$$

Note that this equation of value is equivalent to the first one. If we multiply both sides of the first equation of value by $(1 + 0.12)^5$ (which we did in order to solve it), we obtain the latter one. Again, the last payment, x, is $802.82.

• EXAMPLE 4-34 _____

A business person wishes to borrow $10,000 today and $6000 3 years from today. She wishes to repay both loans with equal annual payments at the end of each year for the next 4 years. If the interest rate is 15% compounded annually, what is the annual payment?

Solution

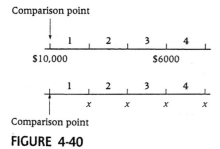

Comparison point

$10,000 $6000

Comparison point

FIGURE 4-40

This problem is illustrated by the time lines of Figure 4-40. The annual payment is denoted by x. If the beginning of the first year is chosen as the comparison point, then the annuity of four payments of x dollars each must be brought back to the comparison point. We do this by multiplying x by $a_{\overline{4}|0.15}$. Also, $6000 must be brought back to the comparison point. We do this by multiplying $6000 by $(1 + 0.15)^{-3}$. Hence, the equation of value is

$$10,000 + 6000(1 + 0.15)^{-3} = x \cdot a_{\overline{4}|0.15}$$

Solving for x, we have

$$x = \frac{10,000 + 6000(1 + 0.15)^{-3}}{a_{\overline{4}|0.15}}$$
$$= \$4884.48$$

Thus, the annual payment is $4884.48.

Variable Annuities

Some financial institutions offer graduated payment loans. The repayment of such a loan involves an annuity whose later payments are larger than its earlier ones. Such an annuity is called a **variable annuity.**

• EXAMPLE 4-35 _____

Mrs. Logan finances the purchase of a new car with a cash price of $10,000 by a variable annuity. During the first 3 years, she will make payments of a certain amount at the end of each year. During the last 4 years, her annual payment will be twice as large. If the interest rate is 12% compounded annually, what are the annual payments?

Solution

The time lines of Figure 4-41 illustrate this problem.

Observe that x denotes the first three annual payments and $2x$ denotes the remaining payments. If the comparison point is chosen to be the end of the third year, then the annuity consisting of three payments of x dollars each must be brought forward to the comparison point. This is done by multiplying x by $s_{\overline{3}|0.12}$. Also, the annuity consisting of four payments of $2x$ dollars each must be brought back to the comparison point. This is done by multiplying $2x$ by $a_{\overline{4}|0.12}$. Finally, $10,000 must be brought forward to the comparison point. This is done by multiplying $10,000 by $(1 + 0.12)^3$. Hence, the equation of value is

$$x \cdot s_{\overline{3}|0.12} + 2x \cdot a_{\overline{4}|0.12} = 10,000(1 + 0.12)^3$$

Using either tables or a calculator to determine $s_{\overline{3}|0.12}$, $a_{\overline{4}|0.12}$, and $(1 + 0.12)^3$, this equation becomes

$$x(3.374400) + 2x(3.037349) = 10,000(1.404928)$$

Solving for x, we have

$$3.3744x + 6.074698x = 14049.28$$
$$x = \$1486.84$$

Thus, the first three annual payments are $1486.84, and the remaining annual payments are $2(\$1486.84) = \$2973.68$.

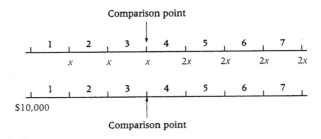

FIGURE 4-41

Deferred Annuities

A **deferred annuity** is an annuity whose payments begin later than at the end of the first period. For example, if a person finances the purchase of

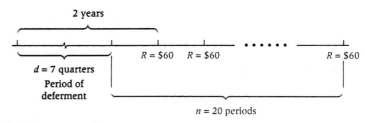

FIGURE 4-42

some item by agreeing to pay 20 quarterly payments of $60 each, *with the first payment due 2 years from now,* then this series of payments constitutes a deferred annuity. The length of time from the present to the beginning of the first payment time interval is called the **period of deferment.** If d = number of periods of deferment, then, as illustrated in Figure 4-42, $d = 7$, and the annuity consists of $n = 20$ payments, each payment made at the end of a quarter. Note that although eight payment periods precede the first payment, the period of deferment consists of one less period ($d = 8 - 1 = 7$) since the period of deferment is defined as the length of time from the present to the beginning of the first payment time interval. Thus, the period preceding the first payment is counted along with those of the annuity and not with the period of deferment.

The total amount of a deferred annuity is its future value at the end of n periods and is determined by the usual formula for the total amount of an annuity:

$$S = R \cdot s_{\overline{n}|i}$$

For the annuity of Figure 4-42, if the interest rate is 12% compounded quarterly, then $i = 0.03$ and

$$
\begin{aligned}
S &= 60 \cdot s_{\overline{20}|0.03} \\
&\approx 60(26.870374) \\
&\approx \$1612.22
\end{aligned}
$$

Present Value of a Deferred Annuity

In general, the present value, A, of a deferred annuity of n payments with d periods of deferment (see Figure 4-43) at an interest rate of i per conversion period may be determined by the following formula.

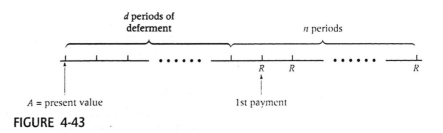

FIGURE 4-43

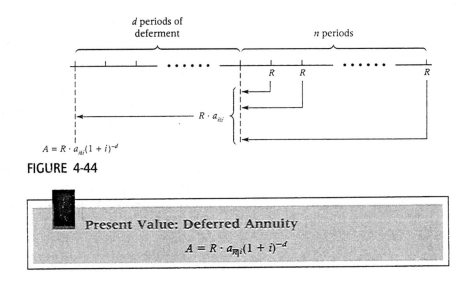

FIGURE 4-44

> **Present Value: Deferred Annuity**
>
> $$A = R \cdot a_{\overline{n}|i}(1 + i)^{-d}$$

Observing Figure 4-44, note that the term $R \cdot a_{\overline{n}|i}$ gives the present value of the annuity at the beginning of the first payment period. Multiplying $R \cdot a_{\overline{n}|i}$ by $(1 + i)^{-d}$ brings this result back d periods to yield the present value of the deferred annuity. Thus, for the deferred annuity of Figure 4-42, the present value is

$$
\begin{aligned}
A &= R \cdot a_{\overline{n}|i}(1 + i)^{-d} \\
&= 60 \cdot a_{\overline{20}|0.03}(1 + 0.03)^{-7} \\
&\approx 60(14.877475)(0.813092) \\
&\approx \$725.81
\end{aligned}
$$

• EXAMPLE 4-36

Sara Smith agrees to repay a loan by making \$200 payments at the end of each month for 3 years. The first payment is due at the end of 6 months. If the interest rate is 12% compounded monthly, then find the amount of the loan.

Solution

The amount of the loan is the present value of this deferred annuity. Observing Figure 4-45, note that $d = 5$, $n = 12(3) = 36$, and $R = \$200$. Also, $i = 0.12/12 = 0.01$. Hence, the present value is

$$
\begin{aligned}
A &= R \cdot a_{\overline{n}|i}(1 + i)^{-d} \\
&= 200 \cdot a_{\overline{36}|0.01}(1 + 0.01)^{-5} \\
&\approx 200(30.107505)(0.951466) \\
&\approx \$5729.25
\end{aligned}
$$

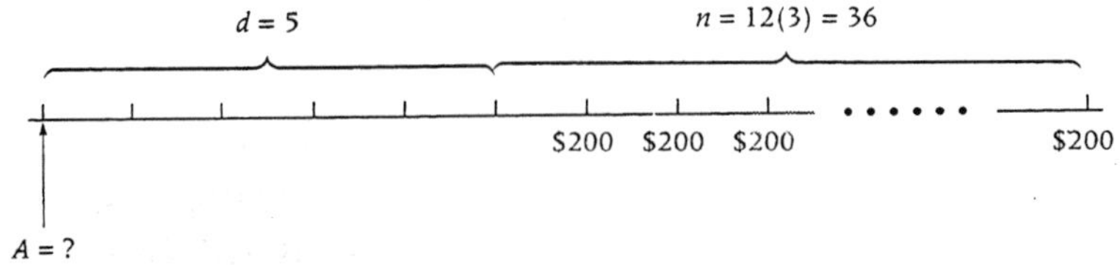

$d = 5$ $n = 12(3) = 36$

\$200 \$200 \$200   • • • • • •   \$200

$A = ?$

FIGURE 4-45

Complex Annuities

Up to this point, we have been considering annuities in which the payment periods coincide with the conversion (interest) periods. As stated earlier, such annuities are called simple annuities. If we have an annuity where the payment period does not coincide with the conversion (interest) period, we have a **complex annuity,** or **general annuity.** Here we will present a method for determining present and future values of complex annuities. Although there is more than one method for determining the present and future values of complex annuities, we will change the original interest rate to an equivalent interest rate such that its conversion (interest) period coincides with the payment period of the annuity. Thus, the annuity with an equivalent interest rate where the interest period coincides with the payment period becomes a simple annuity.

PROBLEM

As an example, we find the future and present values of an annuity of seven payments of $1000 each made at the end of each quarter with an interest rate of 12% compounded monthly.

SOLUTION

Since we have quarterly payment periods and monthly interest periods, we must change the interest rate to coincide with the quarterly payment periods. Specifically, we must find the equivalent interest rate compounded quarterly corresponding to 12% compounded monthly. Using equation (1) on page 185, we have

$$(1 + r/4)^4 = (1 + 0.12/12)^{12}$$

where r is the equivalent annual rate compounded quarterly. Since we need the interest rate per conversion period, $r/4$, for our computations, we solve for $r/4$ by taking the fourth root of each side of the above equation to obtain

$$1 + r/4 = [(1 + 0.01)^{12}]^{1/4}$$
$$= (1 + 0.01)^3$$
$$r/4 = (1 + 0.01)^3 - 1$$
$$\approx 0.030301 \qquad \text{Equivalent interest rate per quarter}$$

Now we use the formulas for the future and present values of simple annuities that we learned in the previous sections of this chapter. Thus, for this annuity, $n = 7$, $i = 0.030301$, and $R = 1000$.

Future Value

$$S = R \cdot s_{\overline{n}|i}$$
$$= 1000 s_{\overline{7}|0.030301}$$
$$\approx 1000(7.66944789)$$
$$\approx \$7669.45$$

Using a calculator,
$s_{\overline{7}|0.030301} = [1.030301)^7 - 1]/0.030301$
$\approx 7.66944789.$

Present Value

$$A = R \cdot a_{\overline{n}|i}$$
$$= 1000 a_{\overline{7}|0.030301}$$
$$\approx 1000(6.223221394)$$
$$\approx \$6223.22$$

Using a calculator,
$a_{\overline{7}|0.030301} = [(1 - (1.030301)^{-7}]/0.030301$
$\approx 6.223221394.$

This method is also used for complex annuities due by applying the respective formulas that we have learned in previous sections for annuities due.

• EXAMPLE 4-37   Complex Annuity Due. _____

A person deposits $800 at the beginning of each month for 3 years into a bank account that pays interest at 8% compounded semiannually. Find the total amount and present value of this annuity.

Solution

Since we have monthly payments and semiannual interest periods, we must change the interest rate to coincide with the monthly payment periods. Thus, we must find the equivalent interest rate compounded monthly corresponding to 8% compounded semiannually. If r denotes the annual rate compounded monthly, then, using equation (1) on page 185, we have

$$(1 + r/12)^{12} = (1 + 0.08/2)^2$$

Solving for $r/12$, the interest rate per conversion period, we take the 12th root of each side to obtain

$$1 + r/12 = [(1.04)^2]^{1/12}$$
$$= (1.04)^{1/6}$$
$$\approx 1.006558$$
$$r/12 \approx 1.006558 - 1$$
$$\approx 0.006558 \qquad \text{Equivalent interest rate per month}$$

Now we use formulas for the future and present values of annuities due that we learned in Sections 4-3 and 4-4. For this annuity, $n = (12)(3) = 36$, $i = 0.006558$, and $R = 800$.

Future Value

$$S = R(s_{\overline{n+1}|i} - 1)$$
$$= 800(s_{\overline{37}|0.006558} - 1)$$
$$\approx 800(41.721258 - 1)$$
$$= 800(40.721258)$$
$$\approx \$32,577.01$$

$n + 1 = 36 + 1 = 37$
Using a calculator,
$s_{\overline{37}|0.006558} = [(1.006558)^{37} - 1]/0.006558$
$\approx 41.721258.$

Present Value

$$A = R(a_{\overline{n-1}|i} + 1)$$
$$= 800(a_{\overline{35}|0.006558} + 1)$$
$$\approx 800(31.182828 + 1)$$
$$= 800(32.182828)$$
$$\approx \$25,746.26$$

$n - 1 = 36 - 1 = 35$
Using a calculator,
$a_{\overline{35}|0.006558} = [1 - (1.006558)^{-35}]/0.006558$
$\approx 31.182828.$

Exercises 4-6

Equations of Value

1. Mr. Evans has a debt of $8000 due in 4 years. He wants to repay this debt by making a $2000 payment 1 year from now, a $1000 payment 3 years from now, and a last payment 6 years from now. If the interest rate is 10% compounded annually, what must be the amount of the last payment?

2. A business person's debt is payable as follows: $2000 1 year from now and $5000 5 years from now. The business person wants to repay the debt as follows: a $1000 payment now, a $2000 payment 2 years from now, a $1000 payment 3 years from now, and the last payment 4 years from now. If the interest rate is 12% compounded annually, find the amount of the last payment.

3. A woman wishes to borrow $5000 now and $4000 2 years from now. She wishes to repay both loans with equal annual payments at the end of each year for the next 5 years. If the interest rate is 10% compounded annually, find the annual payment.

4. If money is worth 12% compounded annually, what single payment made 2 years from now can replace the following two payments: $3000 due 1 year from now and $5000 due 4 years from now.

5. A person wishes to borrow $6000 now and $5000 3 years from now. Both loans are to be repaid by equal annual payments at the end of each year for the next 7 years. If the interest rate is 8% compounded annually, determine the annual payment.

6. Mary Smith signed a mortgage for $10,000. The mortgage is to be repaid with equal monthly payments for the first 2 years and equal monthly payments twice as large for the next 3 years. If the interest rate is 12% compounded monthly, find the monthly payments. Assume each payment is made at the end of the month.

7. Find the present value of a variable annuity consisting of $500 at the end of each year for the first 4 years and $800 at the end of each year for the next 5 years. The interest rate is 10% compounded annually.

8. A man buys a car with a cash price of $12,000 by financing it over a 5-year period. At the end of each of the first 2 years, he will make equal payments. At the end of each of the next 3 years, his equal payments will be 1½ times as large. If the interest rate is 12% compounded annually, find his annual payments.

Use a calculator to solve each of the following problems.

9. A person plans to borrow $8,000 now and $5,000 3 years from now. Both loans will be repaid with equal monthly payments at the end of each month for the next 6 years. If the interest rate is 7% compounded monthly, determine the monthly payment.

10. A $20,000 loan is to be repaid with monthly payments (at the end of the month) over the next 5 years. If the monthly payments during the last 3 years are twice those of the first 2 years, determine the monthly payments, assuming an interest rate of 8% compounded monthly.

11. A $150,000 loan is to be amortized with equal monthly payments (at the end of the month) for the first 10 years and payments 1½ times as large for the last 15 years. If the interest rate is 10.08% compounded monthly, determine the monthly payments.

12. A $300,000 loan is to be amortized with equal monthly payments (at the end of the month) for the first 10 years, payments 1½ times as large for the next 10 years, and payments twice as large for the last 10 years. If the interest rate is 8.64% compounded monthly, find the monthly payments.

Deferred Annuities

For each of the following deferred annuities, determine d, the number of periods of deferment.

13. Quarterly payments with the first payment at the end of 2 years
14. Semiannual payments with the first payment at the end of 4 years
15. Monthly payments with the first payment at the end of 1½ years
16. Annual payments with the first payment at the end of 3 years
17. Quarterly payments with the first payment at the end of 5½ years
18. Semiannual payments with the first payment at the end of 7½ years

19. A loan is repaid by paying $500 at the end of each quarter for 10 years. The first payment is due 1 year from now. If the interest rate is 16% compounded quarterly, what is the amount of the loan?
20. If a person repays a loan with monthly payments of $400 at the end of each month for 3 years, what is the amount of the loan if the first payment is due in 6 months and the interest rate is 24% compounded monthly?
21. Ms. James is considering buying an investment contract that promises to pay $1000 at the end of each 6 months for 10 years. The first payment is due in 18 months. If Ms. James wishes to earn 16% compounded semiannually on her investment, how much should she pay for this investment contract?
22. Harry Morgan wishes to set up a fund to provide for $2000 payments at the end of each quarter for 4 years. The payments will be made to Harry's college-age daughter who will enter college 1 year from now. Thus, the first payment will be made 1 year from now. If Harry earns 16% compounded quarterly on his money, how much should be deposited into this fund now?
23. A loan of $50,000 will be repaid by quarterly payments made at the end of each quarter for 5 years. If the interest rate is 20% compounded quarterly and the first payment is due 1½ years from now, what is the quarterly payment?
24. A mortgage of $70,000 will be repaid by monthly payments made at the end of each month for 8 years. If the interest rate is 18% compounded monthly and the first payment is due in 1 year, find the monthly payment.

Complex Annuities

Use a calculator to solve each of the following problems.

25. Find the total amount and present value of an annuity of $1000 payable at the end of each quarter for 5 years at an interest rate of 12% compounded monthly.
26. Find the total amount and present value of an annuity of $3500 payable at the end of each 6 months for 10 years. The interest rate is 8% compounded quarterly.
27. Find the total amount and present value of an annuity of $5600 payable at the end of each month for 6 years. The interest rate is 12% compounded quarterly.
28. Find the total amount and present value of an annuity of $1300 payable at the end of each quarter for 10 years. The interest rate is 15% compounded annually.

29. A loan is to be repaid with quarterly payments of $650 at the end of each quarter for 6 years. If the interest rate is 12% compounded monthly, find the amount of the loan.

30. A loan is repaid by monthly payments of $250 at the end of each month for 5 years. If the interest rate is 6% compounded semiannually, find the amount of the loan.

31. A borrower will repay a loan with 21 monthly payments of $1000 each. The first payment is due 10 months from now. If the interest rate is 12% compounded quarterly, find the amount of the loan.

32. A loan will be repaid by six annual payments of $4500 each. The first payment is due 2 years from now. If the interest rate is 6% compounded quarterly, find the amount of the loan.

33. A loan of $12,500 is to be repaid by semiannual payments at the end of each 6 months for 7 years. If the interest rate is 6% compounded monthly, find the semiannual payment.

Complex Annuities Due

Use a calculator to solve each of the following problems.

34. Find the total amount and present value of an annuity of $1200 payable at the beginning of each half-year if the interest rate is 6% compounded monthly. The payments continue for 8 years.

35. Find the total amount and present value of an annuity due of $150 monthly for 4 years if the interest rate is 6% compounded semiannually.

36. Find the total amount and present value of an annuity due of $890 quarterly for 5 years if the interest rate is 12% compounded monthly.

37. Find the total amount and present value of an annuity due of $500 semiannually for 10 years if the interest rate is 9% compounded annually.

38. A loan of $8500 is to be repaid by semiannual payments at the beginning of each 6-month time period over a period of 8 years. If the interest rate is 9% compounded monthly, find the semiannual payment.

39. A loan of $4600 is to be repaid by monthly payments at the beginning of each month for 5 years. If the interest rate is 8% compounded quarterly, find the monthly payment.

40. A person wishes to accumulate $10,000 during a 5-year period by making monthly deposits into a fund earning interest at 16% compounded quarterly. Find the monthly deposit if payments are made at the beginning of each month.

41. A person wishes to accumulate $8000 over a 4-year period by making annual deposits into a fund earning interest at 6% compounded quarterly. Find the annual deposit if payments are made at the beginning of each year.

EXTRA DIVIDENDS

• Net Present Value (Capital Investment Decision)

Write Graphics, Inc., is planning to invest $350,000 in new computer equipment, which is expected to reduce labor costs by $100,000 per year (after taxes) for the next 5 years. The management of Write Graphics, Inc., wishes to determine if the investment is cost effective (assuming money is currently worth 10% compounded annually).

The time diagram of Figure 4-46 illustrates the cash flows involved in

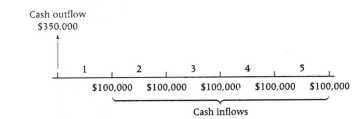

FIGURE 4-46

this investment decision. To determine whether the investment of $350,000 is cost effective at 10% compounded annually, management must determine the **net present value** (denoted by **NPV**) of the cash flows. The net present value is defined by

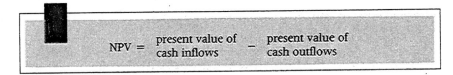

$$\text{NPV} = \frac{\text{present value of}}{\text{cash inflows}} - \frac{\text{present value of}}{\text{cash outflows}}$$

The present value of the cash outflow is the initial investment of $350,000. The present value of cash inflows at 10% compounded annually is determined by the formula for the present value of an annuity:

$$A = R \cdot a_{\overline{5}|0.10}$$
$$\approx 100{,}000(3.790787)$$
$$\approx \$379{,}078.70$$

Thus, the net present value of this investment is

$$\text{NPV} = \frac{\text{present value of}}{\text{cash inflows}} - \frac{\text{present value of}}{\text{cash outflows}}$$
$$= \$379{,}078.70 - \$350{,}000.00$$
$$= \$29{,}078.70$$

The net present value is positive because the present value of the cash inflows exceeds the present value of the cash outflow. Thus, the investment is cost effective at an interest rate of 10% compounded annually. This means that the investment of $350,000 is earning a rate of return greater than the quoted interest rate of 10% compounded annually.

If the present value of the cash inflows had been less than the present value of the cash outflow, the net present value would have been negative and the investment would not have been cost effective at the quoted interest rate of 10% compounded annually. In other words, the investment of $350,000 would be earning a rate of return less than the quoted interest rate of 10% compounded annually.

If the present value of the cash inflows had equaled the present value of the cash outflow, the net present value would have been 0, and the investment would have been cost effective at the quoted interest rate of 10% compounded annually. In other words, the investment of $350,000 would be earning a rate of return of 10% compounded annually.

The net present value concept is used in making decisions regarding capital investments, as summarized in the box below.

SUMMARY

Net Present Value and Rate of Return

For a net present value (NPV) for some capital investment computed at a given interest rate,

1. If NPV > 0, the rate of return on the invested capital is *greater than* the interest rate at which the NPV was computed.
2. If NPV = 0, the rate of return on the invested capital *equals* the interest rate at which the NPV was computed.
3. If NPV < 0, the rate of return on the invested capital is *less than* the interest rate at which the NPV was computed.

Exercises

1. If the preceding investment resulted in cash inflows of $70,000, $80,000, $100,000, $110,000, and $130,000 at the end of the first, second, third, fourth, and fifth years, respectively, calculate the net present value if money is worth 10% compounded annually. Is the investment earning a rate of return of at least 10% compounded annually?

2. Assume that the initial investment is changed to an amount different from $350,000 and that the resulting cash inflows are $80,000, $100,000, $110,000, $120,000, and $140,000 at the end of the first, second, third, fourth, and fifth years, respectively. If the net present value is −$1000, find the amount invested, assuming money is worth 12% compounded annually.

The following problems are adapted from some that have appeared on past Uniform CPA Examinations. For each of the following problems, assume interest rates are compounded annually.

3. On January 1, 19xx, Jenkins, Inc., purchased for $520,000 a new machine with a useful life of 8 years and no salvage value. The machine is expected to produce an annual cash flow from operations, net of income taxes, of $120,000. Assuming that Jenkins uses a rate of return of 14%, what is the net present value?

4. Hillsdale Company purchased a machine for $480,000. The machine has a useful life of 6 years and no salvage value. The machine is expected to generate cash flows from operations, net of income taxes, of $140,000 in each of the 6 years. Hillsdale's desired rate of return is 14%. Find the net present value.

5. Hamilton Company invested in a 2-year project having a rate of return of 12%. The project is expected to produce cash flows from operations, net of income taxes, of $60,000 in the first year and $70,000 in the second year. How much will the project cost?

6. Scott, Inc., is planning to invest $120,000 in a 10-year project. Scott estimates that the annual cash inflow from this project, net of income taxes, will be

$20,000. Scott's desired rate of return on an investment of this type is 10%. Information on present value factors is as follows:

	At 10%	At 12%
Present value of $1 for ten periods	0.386	0.322
Present value of an annuity of $1 for ten periods	6.145	5.650

Scott's expected rate of return on this investment is

a) Less than 10%, but more than 0%   b) 10%

c) Less than 12%, but more than 10%   d) 12%

7. Sant Company is planning to invest $40,000 in a machine with a useful life of 5 years and no salvage value. Sant estimates that the annual cash inflow from operations from using this machine, net of income taxes, will be $10,000. Sant's desired rate of return on investments of this type is 10%. The present value of an ordinary annuity of $1 for 5 years at 10% is 3.791. The present value of $1 for five periods at 10% is 0.621. Using the net present value method, Sant's true rate of return on this investment is

a) 0%   b) Less than 10%, but more than 0%

c) 10%   d) More than 10%

8. Virginia Company invested in a 4-year project. Virginia's expected rate of return is 10%. The cash inflows from operations resulting from this project are $4000 for the first year, $4400 for the second year, $4800 for the third year, and $5200 for the fourth year. Assuming a positive net present value of $1000, what was the amount of the original investment?

9. Hilltop Company invested $100,000 in a 2-year project. Hilltop's expected rate of return was 12%. The cash flow, net of income taxes, was $40,000 for the first year. Assuming that the rate of return was exactly 12%, what was the cash flow, net of income taxes, for the second year of the project?

10. Tracy Corporation is planning to invest $80,000 in a 3-year project. Tracy's expected rate of return is 10%. The cash flow, net of income taxes, will be $30,000 for the first year and $36,000 for the second year. Assuming that the rate of return is exactly 10%, what will the cash flow, net of income taxes, be for the third year?

CHAPTER 4 HIGHLIGHTS

• Concepts

Your ability to answer the following questions is one indicator of the depth of your mastery of this chapter's important concepts. Note that the questions are grouped under various topic headings. For any question that you cannot answer, refer to the appropriate section of the chapter indicated by the topic heading. Pay particular attention to the summary boxes within a section.

4-1   SIMPLE INTEREST AND DISCOUNT

1. Write the formula for simple interest, and explain each component.
2. Explain the term *total amount*, and write its formula.

3. Explain the term *present value*, and write its formula.
4. Explain the difference between simple interest and simple discount.
5. Write the formula for simple discount, and explain each component.
6. Explain the term *proceeds*, and write its formula.
7. When discounting an interest-bearing note, one must first compute its

_____ _____

4-2 COMPOUND INTEREST

8. Write the formula for compound amount, and explain its components. Use a time diagram.
9. Explain the term *interest rate per conversion period*, and write its formula.
10. Explain the term *total number of conversion periods*, and write its formula.
11. Write the formula for present value, and explain its components. Use a time diagram.
12. Explain the term *equivalent interest rates*. Write the equation used to find equivalent interest rates, and explain its components.
13. Explain the term *effective rate*, and give its formula.
14. Write the formula for future value when interest is compounded continuously, and explain its components. Use a time diagram.
15. Write the formula for present value when interest is compounded continuously, and explain its components. Use a time diagram.
16. Write the formula for the effective rate when interest is compounded continuously.

4-3 GEOMETRIC SERIES AND ANNUITIES

17. What is an annuity?
18. Explain the difference between an ordinary annuity and an annuity due.
19. Explain, using a time diagram, the term *total amount* (future value) of an ordinary annuity, and write its formula.
20. Write the formula for the total amount of an annuity due, and explain its components. Use a time diagram.

4-4 PRESENT VALUE OF AN ANNUITY

21. Explain, using a time diagram, the term *present value of an ordinary annuity*, and write its formula.
22. Write the formula for the present value of an annuity due, and explain its components. Use a time diagram.

4-5 SINKING FUNDS AND AMORTIZATION

23. What is a sinking fund? Write the formula to determine the periodic payment for a sinking fund, and explain its components.
24. In a sinking fund schedule, explain how the interest for a particular period is determined.
25. Explain the term *amortization*. Write the formula to determine the periodic payment for an amortization problem, and explain its components.
26. In an amortization schedule, explain how, for a particular period,
   a) The interest is determined   b) The balance is determined
27. Explain how to determine the balance of a loan after a particular payment has been made.
28. Explain the add-on-interest method of amortizing a loan. Contrast this method with the method that involves the annuity formula.

4-6 EQUATIONS OF VALUE; DEFERRED ANNUITIES; COMPLEX ANNUITIES

29. To bring forward a single payment on a time diagram, multiply by the expression _____. Explain the components of this expression.
30. To bring back a single payment on a time diagram, multiply by the expression _____. Explain the components of this expression.
31. To bring forward an annuity of n equal payments on a time diagram, multiply an individual payment by the expression _____. Explain the components of this expression.
32. To bring back an annuity of n equal payments on a time diagram, multiply an individual payment by the expression _____. Explain the components of this expression.
33. What is a variable annuity?
34. What is a deferred annuity? Write the formula for the present value of a deferred annuity, and explain its components.
35. What is a complex annuity? What is the difference between a complex annuity and a simple annuity?
36. To find the present and future values of complex annuities, we change the _____ and use the formulas for simple annuities.

REVIEW EXERCISES

• Simple Interest and Discount

1. A person invests $1000 at 9% per year for 6 years.
    a) Find the simple interest earned.
    b) Find the future value.
2. A person earns $20 on a principal of $500 during a 3-month time interval. Find the rate of interest.
3. A person invests $10,000 at 8% per year for 10 years.
    a) Find the simple interest earned.
    b) Find the future value.
4. The maturity value of a 9-month discount note is $10,000. The note is discounted at 8% by a bank.
    a) Find the discount.
    b) Find the proceeds.
5. Mary Jones wishes to receive $8000 for 6 months by using a discount note with a discount rate of 8%.
    a) Find the maturity value of the discount note.
    b) Mary's note is sold to a third party 2 months before maturity at a discount rate of 6%. How much does the third party pay for the note? How much did the original holder earn on the note?
6. A 9-month, 8% simple-interest-bearing note with a face value of $10,000 is sold to an investor 3 months prior to maturity at a discount rate of 7%.
    a) How much does the investor pay for the note?
    b) How much does the investor earn on the note?

• Compound Amount and Present Value

7. Carl Johnson deposits $10,000 into a bank that pays 8% compounded semi-annually. What amount will he have at the end of 11 years?
8. How much money does R. T. White need now if he can invest the money at

6% compounded quarterly for 7 years and receive $6000 at the end of the period?

9. A 5-year note has a maturity value of $10,000. If we wish to purchase this note now and earn 12% compounded quarterly on our investent, how much should we pay for the note now (5 years before maturity)?

10. A person invests $9000 at 8% compounded quarterly for 9 years. Find the maturity value.

11. How much money should be deposited now at 12% compounded monthly in order to accumulate $80,000 in 8 years?

12. Determine the compound amount of $15,000 invested for 2 years at 7% compounded daily.

13. Determine the compound amount of $8000 invested for 3 years at 6% compounded continuously.

14. What amount should be invested now at 8% compounded continuously in order to accumulate $20,000 at the end of 4 years?

Find the effective rate for Exercises 15-18.

15. 9% compounded monthly
16. 8.75% compounded continuously
17. 7.9% compounded daily
18. 8.4% compounded quarterly

19. A person deposits $10,000 into a bank account that earns interest at 6% compounded semiannually for 3 years. At the end of the 3-year time interval, the person reinvests the original $10,000 plus its interest and deposits an additional $5000. At this time the interest rate changes to 7% compounded continuously. How much is in the account 5 years after the original $10,000 deposit?

• Simple Annuities; Amortization; Sinking Funds

20. Miss Smith deposits $600 at the end of each quarter for 11 years. Each deposit earns interest at 12% compounded quarterly. Find the total amount in this account at the end of 11 years.

21. Mr. Jones wants to accumulate the same total amount as Miss Smith in Exercise 20. However, he wants to deposit one lump-sum payment now. Assuming that the interest rate and time period are the same as in Miss Smith's case, how much should Mr. Jones deposit now?

22. A man deposits $100 in a bank at the end of each month for 3 years and 4 months. If the money earns interest at 12% compounded monthly, how much money does he have in his account at the end of the period?

23. A woman wishes to withdraw $400 at the end of every 6 months for 10 years. If the money earns interest at 6% compounded semiannually, how much must she deposit now?

24. A certain investment contract promises to pay $1000 at the end of each quarter for the next 7 years. If we wish to buy this investment contract and earn 12% compounded quarterly on our money, how much should we pay for it now?

25. A grocer anticipates an expenditure of $10,000 for a new freezer 5 years from now. How much should he deposit at the end of each month into a sinking fund earning interest at 6% compounded monthly?

26. A woman buys a piece of real estate selling for $60,000 by putting $40,000 down and financing the balance with a 20-year mortgage having an interest rate of 16% compounded quarterly. Find the payment due at the end of each quarter.

27. A certain investment contract promises to pay $500 at the end of each quarter

for the next 2 years and a lump sum of $6000 3 years thereafter. How much is this investment contract worth now at 12% compounded quarterly?

28. Joan Hill deposits $100 at the end of each quarter for 12 years into a savings account paying interest at 8% compounded quarterly. How much money will be in her account at the end of 12 years? How much interest is earned?

29. John owes Harry $20,000 10 years from now. Instead of waiting 10 years, John wishes to pay an equal sum at the end of each quarter for the next 10 years. If the interest is compounded quarterly at 8%, find the quarterly payment.

30. A man has a 12-year mortgage of $20,000 at an interest rate of 8% compounded quarterly. If a payment is made at the end of each quarter, find the payment.

31. A company is considering purchasing new equipment that will result in an increased cash flow of $10,000 per year for the next 5 years. If the goal is a rate of return of 8% compounded annually on the investment, how much should be spent now on the new equipment?

32. A person borrows $7000 to buy a car. The loan is to be paid off by a payment at the end of each month over a 4-year period. The interest rate is 24% compounded monthly.
    a) Find the borrower's monthly payment.
    b) At the end of 4 years, how much did the borrower actually pay for the car?
    c) Find the amount of interest paid.

33. Mrs. Elipe purchased equipment that required a $1000 down payment, and she agreed to pay $100 at the end of each month for the next 5 years. If money is worth 12% compounded semiannually, what would have been the price had Mrs. Elipe decided to pay cash for the entire purchase?

34. In anticipation of an expenditure of $30,000 6 years from now, the H. J. Ellis Co. establishes a sinking fund into which a payment is made at the end of each month. Assuming that the interest rate is 12% compounded monthly, find the monthly payment.

35. A woman purchased a house for $70,000. She made a down payment of $20,000 and financed the balance with a 20-year mortgage calling for equal semiannual payments. If the interest rate is 8% compounded semiannually and the first payment is due in six months, find the semiannual payment.

36. A man desires to have a $12,000 fund at the end of 10 years. If his savings can be invested at 8% compounded quarterly, how much must he invest at the end of each quarter for 10 years?

37. A grocer anticipates an expenditure of $10,000 for a new freezer 5 years from now. How much should she deposit at the end of each month into a sinking fund earning interest at 12% compounded monthly?

38. A man deposits $100 in a bank at the end of each month for 3 years and 9 months. If the money earns interest at 12% compounded monthly, how much money does he have in his account at the end of the period?

39. A woman wishes to withdraw $600 at the end of every 6 months for 10 years. If the money earns interest at 6% compounded semiannually, how much must she deposit now?

40. A businessperson wants to accumulate $1 million in 10 years from now by depositing a payment at the end of each year into an account earning interest at the rate of 8% compounded annually. Find the annual payment.

41. Mr. Johnson deposits $100 at the beginning of each month into an account earning interest at 24% compounded monthly. How much is in the account at the end of 4 years?

42. Susan Sullivan wants to accumulate $40,000 10 years from now by depositing a payment at the end of each year into an account earning interest at the rate of 10% compounded annually. Find the annual payment.

• *Equations of Value; Deferred Annuities*

43. A person wishes to borrow $4000 now and $5000 1 year from now. Both loans are to be repaid by a $3000 payment 2 years from now and a final payment 3 years from now. If the interest rate is 8% compounded annually, determine the final payment.

44. A person wishes to borrow $5000 now and $6000 1 year from now. Both loans are to be repaid by equal annual payments at the end of each year for the next 5 years. If the interest rate is 9% compounded annually, determine the annual payment.

45. Find the present value of an annuity consisting of 12 semiannual payments of $1000, with the first payment due 3 years from now. The interest rate is 8% compounded quarterly.

46. A loan is to be repaid by making $400 payments at the end of each quarter for 5 years. The first payment is due 1 year from now. If the interest rate is 12% compounded quarterly, find the amount of the loan.

• *Complex Annuities*

47. Find the total amount and present value of an annuity of $600 payable at the end of each year for 5 years if the interest rate is 8% compounded quarterly.

48. Find the total amount and present value of an annuity of $800 payable at the beginning of each year for 3 years if the interest rate is 12% compounded monthly.

49. Find the total amount and present value of an annuity of $1000 payable at the end of each month for 4 years if the interest rate is 12% compounded semiannually.

50. Find the total amount and present value of an annuity of $1000 payable at the beginning of each month for 3 years if the interest rate if 10% compounded annually.

51. A loan of $35,000 is to be repaid by quarterly payments at the beginning of each quarter for 5 years. The first payment is due 1 year from now. If the interest rate is 6% compounded monthly, find the quarterly payment.

5

LINEAR SYSTEMS AND MATRICES

Introductory Application

Production Costs

The following problem appeared on a past Uniform CPA Examination.

PROBLEM

Total production costs for Gallop, Inc., are budgeted at $230,000 for 50,000 units of budgeted output and at $280,000 for 60,000 units of budgeted output. Because of the need for additional facilities, budgeted fixed costs for 60,000 units are 25% more than budgeted fixed costs for 50,000 units. How much is Gallop's budgeted variable cost per unit of output?

SOLUTION

In this chapter, we present a procedure for translating such word problems into an algebraic formulation. Then the chapter provides methods for solving such algebraic formulations.

5-1

• LINEAR SYSTEMS

We begin this section with a problem whose solution will lead us through the main concepts of this section. Additionally, we will develop a systematic procedure for translating word problems into an algebraic formulation and then methods for solving such a formulation.

PROBLEM

Nutrition: Diet

A dietician must determine how many ounces of each of two food types—food A and food B—to include in a diet to ensure that sufficient quantities of protein and calcium are derived from the diet. Specifically, each ounce of food A contains 3 milligrams of protein and 6 milligrams of calcium. Also, each ounce of food B contains 4 milligrams of protein and 5 milligrams of calcium. The nutritionist must ensure that the diet provides exactly 64 milligrams of protein and 98 milligrams of calcium. How many ounces of each food type should the diet include?

SOLUTION

Step 1 *Identify the unknowns. Use letters (or, in other words, variables) to denote these quantities.*
We must determine the number of ounces of food A and food B to include in a diet. Thus, we let

- x = number of ounces of food A to be included in the diet
- y = number of ounces of food B to be included in the diet

Step 2 *Organize the given information, and write the equations that express any relationships existing among the variables.*
The information is organized in the table below.

Milligrams per ounce of food type

	Food A	Food B		
Protein	3	4	64	} nutritional requirements
Calcium	6	5	98	} in milligrams

We now write the protein and calcium requirements as equations.

Protein Requirement

Since each ounce of food A contains 3 milligrams of protein and each ounce of food B contains 4 ounces of protein, then the expression

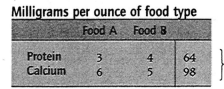

$$\underbrace{3(\text{number of ounces of food A})}_{\substack{\text{milligrams of protein} \\ \text{derived from food A}}} + \underbrace{4(\text{number of ounces of food B})}_{\substack{\text{milligrams of protein} \\ \text{derived from food B}}}$$

represents the number of milligrams of protein derived from both food A and food B. Since the diet must provide exactly 64 milligrams of protein, we set the above expression equal to 64 to obtain the equation

3(number of ounces of food A) + 4(number of ounces of food B) = 64

Since x = number of ounces of food A and y = number of ounces of food B, the above becomes

$$3x + 4y = 64$$

Calcium Requirement

Since each ounce of food A contains 6 milligrams of calcium and each ounce of food B contains 5 ounces of calcium, then the expression

6(number of ounces of food A) + 5(number of ounces of food B)

milligrams of calcium derived from food A   milligrams of calcium derived from food B

represents the number of milligrams of calcium derived from both food A and food B. Since the diet must provide exactly 98 milligrams of calcium, we set the above expression equal to 98 to obtain the equation

6(number of ounces of food A) + 5(number of ounces of food B) = 98

Since x = number of ounces of food A and y = number of ounces of food B, the above becomes

$$6x + 5y = 98$$

Thus, we seek values of x and y that simultaneously satisfy the two equations

$$3x + 4y = 64$$
$$6x + 5y = 98$$

Note that each of the above equations is of the form

$$ax + by = c$$

where a, b, and c real number constants. As we learned in Chapter 1, such equations are linear equations in two variables. The two equations constitute a **system** of two linear equations in two variables. A system of linear equations is often called a **linear system.**

Step 3 *Solve the linear system of step 2.*
A solution to a linear system of two equations is a sequence of numbers x and y that, when substituted into each equation, results in a true statement. In other words, the values of x and y must satisfy both equations. The solution may be written as the ordered pair (x, y).

Graphical Interpretation

Graphically, each equation of a linear system is a straight line. Figure 5-1 gives the graphs of both equations of the above linear system of our illus-

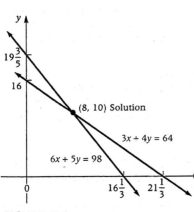

FIGURE 5-1

trative problem. Note that each point (x, y) on the straight line $3x + 4y = 64$, where x and y are non-negative, represents a possible diet that meets the protein requirement. Also, each point (x, y) on the straight line $6x + 5y = 98$, where x and y are non-negative, represents a possible diet that meets the calcium requirement.

Since both the protein and the calcium requirements must be met, then, graphically, the coordinates of any point that lies on both lines constitute a **solution** to the diet problem. In Figure 5-1, we see that a solution occurs at the intersection of both straight lines. The x- and y-coordinates of such a point satisfy both equations of the linear system. Thus, the x- and y-coordinates of the intersection point of the straight lines of our linear system constitute a solution to the linear system. As illustrated in Figure 5-1, the solution, determined by graphing both lines and noting the coordinates of the intersection point, is given by the ordered pair $(8, 10)$. In other words,

$x = 8$ ounces of food A should be included in the diet

$y = 10$ ounces of food B should be included in the diet

Note that this solution was obtained by sketching both straight lines on graph paper and using the grid to determine the coordinates of the intersection point. We check our solution by substituting the results into both equations of the linear system. Hence,

$$3x + 4y = 64 \qquad\qquad 6x + 5y = 98$$
$$3(8) + 4(10) \overset{2}{=} 64 \qquad\qquad 6(8) + 5(10) \overset{2}{=} 98$$
$$64 \overset{\checkmark}{=} 64 \qquad\qquad 98 \overset{\checkmark}{=} 98$$

This concludes the introductory problem to this section. We now summarize the problem-solving procedure used throughout this example. We will use this procedure to solve further applied examples in this section and chapter.

Problem-Solving Procedure

Step 1   Identify the unknown quantities to be found. Use letters to denote these quantities. Since these unknowns usually constitute an integral part of some decision-making process, they are often called **decision variables.**

Step 2   Reread the problem, over and over if necessary, to organize the given information. Write equations for the relationships among the variables. To obtain such equations, think of similar or related problems encountered in the past. At the completion of this step, the problem is formulated algebraically.

Step 3   Solve the equations of step 2 and check your results. This usually entails algebraic methods that have been previously learned. In this chapter, we will discuss such methods useful for solving many algebraic formulations.

Since the algebraic formulations of many word problems result in linear systems, we further discuss linear systems. Returning to the diet problem, we note that the solution to the diet problem was determined graphically. This was to provide insight and intuition regarding linear systems. However, in this section, we will discuss algebraic methods for solving linear systems. Such methods provide more efficient methods for solving linear systems.

We summarize as follows.

SUMMARY

Solution to a Linear System

The **solution** to a linear system of two equations in two variables is given by the coordinates of any point where the corresponding straight lines *intersect*.

Since a pair of straight lines can be drawn so that they intersect, are parallel, or coincide (see Figure 5-2), then three possibilities exist for a solution to a linear system. These are described in the following box.

Linear System Possibilities

Two Equations in Two Variables

1. The linear system has a **unique solution.** The straight lines *intersect* at one point [see Figure 5-2(a)].
2. The linear system has **no solution.** The straight lines are *parallel* and do not intersect [see Figure 5-2(b)].
3. The linear system has **infinitely many solutions.** The straight lines *coincide* [see Figure 5-2(c)].

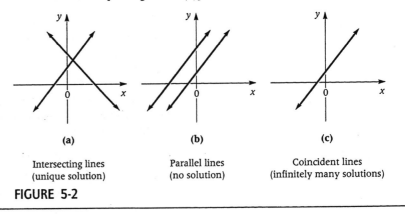

(a)	(b)	(c)
Intersecting lines (unique solution)	Parallel lines (no solution)	Coincident lines (infinitely many solutions)

FIGURE 5-2

Solving Linear Systems

We now discuss two algebraic methods for solving linear systems of two equations in two variables. The first method, which involves adding equations to eliminate variables, is called the **method of elimination.** The second method involves solving either equation for one variable in terms of the other variable and then substituting the result into the other equation. Hence, this method is called the **method of substitution.** Although these methods can be generalized to larger size linear systems, they are most efficient for linear systems of two equations in two variables, and, therefore, we present them from that perspective. In Section 5-2, we will learn a method that is very efficient for any size linear system.

Method of Elimination

We return to the linear system associated with the diet problem of this section. We restate the linear system below.

$$3x + 4y = 64$$
$$6x + 5y = 98$$

To solve a linear system by the method of elimination, the linear system must be written so that the coefficients of one of the variables are additive inverses. Then the two equations can be added with the result that the variable whose coefficients are additive inverses is *eliminated.* Thus, for the above linear system, we multiply the first equation by -2 to obtain

$$-2(3x + 4y) = (-2)64 \quad \longrightarrow \quad -6x - 8y = -128$$
$$6x + 5y = 98 \qquad\qquad\qquad 6x + 5y = 98$$

The resulting linear system has the same solution as the original linear system and is thus said to be equivalent to the original system. Thus, we add the resulting equations as indicated below.

$$
\begin{array}{l}
-6x - 8y = -128 \\
\underline{6x + 5y = 98} \\
0x - 3y = -30 \\
\quad\; -3y = -30 \\
\qquad\;\; y = 10
\end{array}
$$

Note how the variable x is eliminated when we add the two equations.

We now substitute the value $y = 10$ into either of the two original equations and solve for the remaining variable. Choosing the first equation, we obtain

$$3x + 4y = 64$$
$$3x + 4(10) = 64$$
$$3x + 40 = 64 \qquad \text{Add } -40 \text{ to each side.}$$
$$3x = 24 \qquad \text{Multiply each side by 1/3.}$$
$$x = 8$$

Thus, the solution is $x = 8$ and $y = 10$, or $(8, 10)$. This corresponds to what we obtained graphically at the beginning of this section. We refrain from checking this solution as we have already done so earlier.

• **EXAMPLE 5-1** _____

Solve the linear system below by the elimination method.

$$5x + 2y = 22$$
$$4x - 3y = -10$$

Solution

Multiplying the first equation by 3 and the second by 2 gives an equivalent linear system with coefficients of y that are additive inverses. Thus,

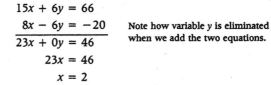

$$3(5x + 2y) = 3(22)$$
$$2(4x - 3y) = 2(-10)$$
$$\longrightarrow$$
$$15x + 6y = 66$$
$$8x - 6y = -20$$

Adding the two resulting equations gives

$$15x + 6y = 66$$
$$\underline{8x - 6y = -20}$$
$$23x + 0y = 46$$
$$23x = 46$$
$$x = 2$$

Note how variable y is eliminated when we add the two equations.

Now we substitute the value $x = 2$ into either equation of the original system and solve for y. Choosing the first equation, we obtain

$$5x + 2y = 22$$
$$5(2) + 2y = 22$$
$$10 + 2y = 22 \qquad \text{Add } -10 \text{ to both sides.}$$
$$2y = 12 \qquad \text{Multiply both sides by 1/2.}$$
$$y = 6$$

Thus, the solution to the linear system is $x = 2$ and $y = 6$. This is written as the ordered pair $(2, 6)$. The graph of this linear system is given in Figure 5-3. Also, we check our solution below.

$$5x + 2y = 22 \qquad\qquad 4x - 3y = -10$$
$$5(2) + 2(6) \stackrel{?}{=} 22 \qquad\qquad 4(2) - 3(6) \stackrel{?}{=} -10$$
$$22 \stackrel{\checkmark}{=} 22 \qquad\qquad -10 \stackrel{\checkmark}{=} -10$$

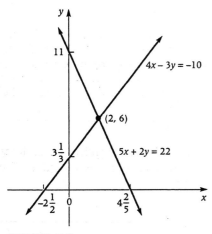

FIGURE 5-3

• **EXAMPLE 5-2** _____

Solve the linear system

$$3x - 2y = 8$$
$$-6x + 4y = 10$$

Solution

Multiplying the first equation by 2 gives an equivalent system with coefficients of y that are additive inverses. Hence,

$$6x - 4y = 16$$
$$-6x + 4y = 10$$

Adding the two equations of the equivalent system, we obtain

$$6x - 4y = 16$$
$$\underline{-6x + 4y = 10}$$
$$0 = 26$$

Inconsistent
(no solutions)

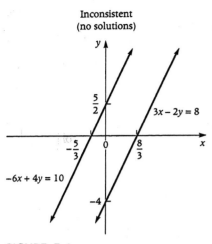

FIGURE 5-4

Infinitely many solutions

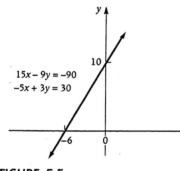

FIGURE 5-5

The statement $0 = 26$ is a false statement, indicating that the linear system has no solution. Such a linear system (having no solutions) is called **inconsistent.** The graph of this system appears in Figure 5-4. Note that the two straight lines are parallel and, therefore, do not intersect.

• **EXAMPLE 5-3** _____

Solve the linear system

$$-5x + 3y = 30$$
$$15x - 9y = -90$$

Solution

Multiplying the first equation by 3 yields the equivalent system

$$-15x + 9y = 90$$
$$15x - 9y = -90$$

Adding the two resulting equations, we obtain the true statement $0 = 0$. The statement $0 = 0$ indicates that both equations of the linear system are equivalent. Hence, they have the same graph. Thus, if we graph each equation on the same set of axes, we will draw one straight line on top of the other straight line. The intersection points consist of all points on either straight line, and, thus, there are infinitely many solutions (see Figure 5-5).

_____   •

The following example provides an additional application of linear systems. Example 5-4, in particular, demonstrates the determination of an equilibrium point by solving a linear system.

• **EXAMPLE 5-4   Equilibrium Point.** _____

The demand and supply equations for a given commodity are as follows:

$$\text{Demand equation} \rightarrow 5q + 2p = 50$$
$$\text{Supply equation} \rightarrow 4q - 3p = -52$$

where p is the unit price and q is the number of units in thousands. Find the equilibrium point.

Solution

Solving this system by the elimination method, we multiply the first equation by 3 and the second by 2 to obtain

$$15q + 6p = 150$$
$$8q - 6p = -104$$

Adding the resulting equations yields

$$23q = 46$$
$$q = 2$$

We may substitute $q = 2$ into either of the original equations. Choosing the first equation, we have

$$5q + 2p = 50$$
$$5(2) + 2p = 50$$
$$p = 20$$

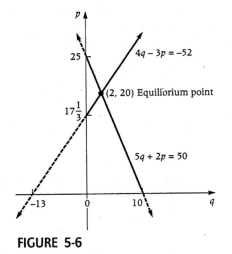

FIGURE 5-6

Thus, at a unit price of $20, supply = demand = 2 thousand units. The graphical interpretation appears in Figure 5-6.

Method of Substitution

Sometimes a linear system of two equations in two variables is most efficiently solved by the method of substitution. As mentioned earlier, this involves solving one of the equations for one variable in terms of the other variable and substituting the result into the other equation. For example, consider the linear system.

$$3x + 5y = 38$$
$$2x + y = 16$$

Since the second equation has a variable with a coefficient of 1, it is easy to solve for that variable and then substitute the result into the other equation. Thus, we solve the second equation for y to obtain

$$y = -2x + 16$$

and substitute this result into the first equation to get

$$3x + 5(-2x + 16) = 38$$

Solving for x gives

$3x - 10x + 80 = 38$	Combine the x-terms.
$-7x + 80 = 38$	Add -80 to both sides.
$-7x = -42$	Multiply both sides by $-1/7$.
$x = 6$	

Although we can substitute this result into either equation and solve for the other variable, the most efficient procedure is to substitute this result into the equation that gives one variable in terms of the other. Thus, we substitute $x = 6$ into the equation

$$y = -2x + 16$$

to obtain

$$y = -2(6) + 16$$
$$= 4$$

Thus, the solution to the linear system is $x = 6$ and $y = 4$. This can be written as the ordered pair $(6, 4)$. We check this solution below.

$$3x + 5y = 38 \qquad\qquad 2x + y = 16$$
$$3(6) + 5(4) \overset{?}{=} 38 \qquad\qquad 2(6) + 4 \overset{?}{=} 16$$
$$38 \overset{\checkmark}{=} 38 \qquad\qquad 16 \overset{\checkmark}{=} 16$$

We now consider an application.

• EXAMPLE 5-5

C.P. Realty, Inc., is planning to build a housing development consisting of two- and three-bedroom ranch-style houses. Public demand indicates a need for three times as many three-bedroom houses as two-bedroom houses. Each two-bedroom house provides a net profit of $15,000. Each three-bedroom house provides a new profit of $16,000. If C.P. Realty, Inc., must net a total profit of $6,300,000 from this development, how many of each type ranch house should be built?

Solution

Applying our problem-solving procedure yields the results below.

Step 1 *Identify the unknowns. Use letters to denote these quantities.*
We wish to determine the number of two-bedroom and three-bedroom houses to be built. Thus, we let

$$x = \text{number of two-bedroom houses}$$
$$y = \text{number of three-bedroom houses}$$

Step 2 *Organize the given information, and write the equations that express any relationships existing among the unknowns.*
The information is organized in the table below.

	Two-bedroom	Three-bedroom	
Profits	$15,000	$16,000	$6,300,000
Numbers	# of three-bedroom houses = 3(# of two-bedroom houses)		

Since each two-bedroom house provides a net profit of $15,000 and each three-bedroom a net profit of $16,000, then the expression

$$15,000x + 16,000y$$

represents the total net profit from building x two-bedroom and y three-bedroom houses. Since the desired total net profit must be $6,300,000, we set the above expression equal to 6,300,000 to obtain the equation

$$15,000x + 16,000y = 6,300,000$$

Also, since the number of three-bedroom houses must equal three times the number of two-bedroom houses, this relationship is expressed by the equation

$$y = 3x$$

Thus, we have the linear system

$$15,000x + 16,000y = 6,300,000$$
$$y = 3x$$

Step 3 *Solve the linear system of step 2.*
This system is most efficiently solved by the substitution method since the second equation expresses y in terms of x. *Substituting* $3x$ for y in the first equation yields

$$15,000x + 16,000(3x) = 6,300,000$$

Solving for x, we obtain

$$15,000x + 48,000x = 6,300,000$$
$$63,000x = 6,300,000$$
$$x = 100$$

We may substitute $x = 100$ into either of the two equations. Choosing the second equation, we obtain

$$y = 3(100)$$
$$= 300$$

Thus, C.P. Realty, Inc., should build $x = 100$ two-bedroom houses and $y = 300$ three-bedroom houses.

PROBLEM

We conclude this section by applying our problem-solving procedure to the Uniform CPA Examination problem encountered in the Introductory Application to this chapter.

SOLUTION

Step 1 *Identify the unknowns. Use letters to denote these quantities.*
For the above example, we must find the variable cost per unit. Thus, using notation developed in Chapter 1, we let

$$v = \text{variable cost per unit}$$

Step 2 *Organize the given information, and write the equations that express any relationships existing among the unknowns.*
In Chapter 1, we learned that a cost function is defined by the equation

$$C = vx + F$$

where C = total cost of producing x units, v = variable cost per unit, and F = fixed cost.

The first sentence of the problem indicates that if $x = 50,000$ units produced, then the total cost is $C = \$230,000$. Substituting these values for C and x into the cost equation

gives the equation

$$230,000 = v(50,000) + F$$

The first and second sentences of the problem indicate that if $x = 60,000$ units produced, then $C = \$280,000$, and the corresponding fixed costs are 25% more than those of the first equation. Substituting these values for C, x, and F into the cost equation gives

$$280,000 = v(60,000) + 1.25F$$

Thus, the two equations constitute a linear system such that

$$230,000 = v(50,000) + F$$
$$280,000 = v(60,000) + 1.25F$$

expresses the relationships among the various quantities of the problem.

Step 3 *Solve the linear system of step 2.*
The above linear system can be written as

$$50{,}000v + F = 230{,}000$$
$$60{,}000v + 1.25F = 280{,}000$$

To solve this system by the elimination method, we multiply the first equation by -6 and the second by 5 to obtain

$$-6(50{,}000v + F) = -6(230{,}000) \longrightarrow -300{,}000v - 6F = -1{,}380{,}000$$
$$5(60{,}000v + 1.25F) = 5(280{,}000) \qquad 300{,}000v + 6.25F = 1{,}400{,}000$$

Adding the two equations gives

$$-300{,}000v - 6F = -1{,}380{,}000$$
$$\underline{300{,}000v + 6.25F = 1{,}400{,}000}$$
$$0v + 0.25F = 20{,}000$$
$$0.25F = 20{,}000$$
$$F = 80{,}000$$

Now we choose either of the original equations and substitute 80,000 for F. Choosing the first equation, we have

$$50{,}000v + F = 230{,}000$$
$$50{,}000v + 80{,}000 = 230{,}000 \qquad \text{Subtract 80,000 from each side.}$$
$$50{,}000v = 150{,}000 \qquad \text{Divide both sides by 50,000.}$$
$$v = 3 \qquad \text{Answer}$$

Thus, the answer to the problem is that the variable cost per unit is \$3.

Exercises 5-1

Solve each of the following linear systems by the method of elimination.

1. $2x - 3y = 6$
$x - 7y = 25$

2. $4x - 5y = -2$
$3x + 2y = -13$

3. $4x + y = 8$
$6x - 2y = -9$

4. $2x + 3y = 3$
$12x - 15y = -4$

5. $-3x + 10y = 5$
$2x + 7y = 24$

6. $\frac{1}{2}x + 5y = 17$
$3x + 2y = 18$

7. $1.5x + 2y = 20$
$2.5x - 5y = -25$

8. $3.5x - y = 13$
$3x + 2y = 14$

Solve each of the following linear systems by the method of elimination. To eliminate the fractions, multiply each side of the equation by the common denominator of its fractions.

9. $\frac{1}{3}x - \frac{3}{2}y = -4$
$5x - 4y = 14$

10. $\frac{x}{5} + \frac{y}{4} = \frac{7}{10}$
$\frac{x}{3} - y = \frac{-5}{3}$

11. $\dfrac{x}{2} + \dfrac{y}{5} = \dfrac{8}{5}$

$\dfrac{x}{3} + \dfrac{y}{4} = \dfrac{17}{12}$

12. $\dfrac{x}{4} + \dfrac{3y}{5} = \dfrac{-7}{20}$

$5x - 3y = 8$

Solve each of the following by the method of substitution.

13. $2x + y = 21$
$\quad\quad y = 5x$

14. $x + 2y = 24$
$\quad\quad x = 4y$

15. $-5x + y = 13$
$\quad\quad\quad y = 7x - 1$

16. $2x + 3y = 36$
$\quad\quad y = -4x + 2$

17. $\quad\quad x = 2y - 5$
$3x + 4y = 5$

18. $\quad\quad y = -2x + 1$
$5x + 3y = 7$

Solve each of the following linear systems and include its graphical interpretation.

19. $x + 2y = 1$
$3x - 5y = -8$

20. $2x - y = -7$
$-x + 2y = 8$

21. $3x + 5y = 7$
$2x - 6y = 11$

22. $x + y = 11$
$x - y = 1$

23. $2x + y = 11$
$3x + 2y = 18$

24. $-3x + 4y = 23$
$2x - 5y = -20$

Solve each of the following linear systems. Choose the method that you feel is the more efficient.

25. $-3x + 4y = 23$
$2x - 5y = -20$

26. $x + 2y = 2$
$3x + 5y = 9$

27. $2x + 3y = -13$
$4x - 5y = 29$

28. $3x - 2y = -14$
$x + y = -3$

29. $x + y = -2$
$-2x + 3y = -11$

30. $6x + y = -4$
$4x - 2y = -8$

31. $4x - 3y = 2$
$x + 2y = -5$

32. $-2x + 5y = -9$
$3x - 2y = 8$

33. Try to solve the linear system

$$5x - 7y = 70$$
$$-10x + 14y = 120$$

Note that your result is the contradictory statement $0 = 260$. To explain this result, show that this linear system has no solution by expressing each linear equation in slope-intercept form. What do you observe? What are your conclusions? Include the graphical interpretation.

34. Try to solve the linear system

$$5x - 7y = 70$$
$$-10x + 14y = -140$$

Note that your result is the statement $0 = 0$. Show that this linear system has infinitely many solutions by expressing each linear equation in slope-intercept form. What do you observe? What are your conclusions? Include the graphical interpretation.

Determine which of the following have no solutions and which have infinitely many solutions.

35. $3x - 8y = 10$
$12x - 32y = 75$

36. $7x - 8y = -11$
$-35x + 40y = 55$

37. $2x - y = 1$ **38.** $x - 2y = 1$
           $-6x + 3y = 8$ $-3x + 6y = -3$

39. $3x - y = 9$ **40.** $2x - y = 3$
             $y = 3x$ $y = 2x + 3$

41. *Nutrition.* A diet must provide exactly 1200 milligrams of protein and 1000 milligrams of iron. These nutrients will be obtained by eating meat and spinach. Each pound of meat contains 500 milligrams of protein and 100 milligrams of iron. Each pound of spinach contains 200 milligrams of protein and 800 milligrams of iron. How many pounds of meat and spinach should be eaten in order to provide the proper amounts of nutrients?

42. *Agriculture.* A farmer wants to plant a combination of two crops, cabbage and corn, on 100 acres. Cabbage requires 60 person-hours of labor per acre, and corn requires 80 person-hours of labor per acre. If the farmer has 6600 person-hours available, how many acres of each crop should be planted?

43. *Product mix.* A toy company manufactures wagons and cars. The company usually sells four times as many wagons as cars. Each wagon provides a net profit of $6, and each car provides a net profit of $5. How many wagons and cars must be produced in order to give a total profit of $29,000?

44. *Equilibrium point.* The demand and supply equations for watches appear in the linear system

Demand equation	$5p + 4q = 650$
Supply equation	$3p - 7q = -1020$

where p is the unit price and q is the number of watches. Find the equilibrium point. Interpret the result.

45. *Break-even analysis.* A company's sales revenue and cost equations appear in the linear system

Revenue equation	$y = 25x$
Cost equation	$y = 10x + 6000$

where x is the number of units and y is the dollar amount. Find the break-even point. Interpret the result.

46. *Product mix.* A company manufactures bicycles and tricycles. Each bicycle and tricycle must pass through two departments: department I (Assembly) and department II (Finishing and Inspection). Each bicycle requires 3 hours in department I and 5 hours in department II. Each tricycle requires 4 hours in department I and 2 hours in department II. Each month, departments I and II have available 450 and 400 hours, respectively. All of the time in both departments must be used (i.e., there must be no idle time or slack time). How many bicycles and tricycles should the company produce each month?

47. *Investment.* A young executive has $100,000 earmarked for investment. A portion of the $100,000 will be invested in corporate bonds that yield 12%, and the remainder will be invested in U.S. Treasury bonds that yield 8%. If the executive wishes to earn a yield of 9% on the $100,000, how much should be invested in each type of bond?

48. *Production costs.* The total cost of producing 100,000 units of some product is $500,000. The total cost of producing 200,000 units of this product is $790,000. Because of the need for additional facilities, the fixed costs for 200,000 units are 30% more than those for 100,000 units. Determine the variable cost per unit for this product and the fixed costs for both 100,000 and 200,000 units of production.

49. *Mixture.* A 20-pound mixture of cashews and peanuts costs $60. If cashews cost $6 per pound and peanuts cost $2 per pound, then how many pounds of each kind are there in the mixture?

50. *Product mix.* A company produces gadgets and widgets. Each gadget requires 3 pounds of a particular raw material, and each widget requires 5 pounds of the same raw material. The company's inventory contains 22 pounds of this raw material. Also, each gadget and widget must pass through a production department that has 20 hours of time available for the manufacture of these two products. Each gadget requires 2 hours, and each widget requires 6 hours of time in the production department. How many gadgets and widgets should be produced if all available resources are to be used?

51. *Decision making: Equipment selection.* A company is considering purchasing one of two possible machines for its production facility. Machine 1 costs $300,000 and produces items at a unit cost of $5. Machine 2 costs $400,000 and produces items at a unit cost of $4. If the total cost of each machine is determined by the formula

total cost = (unit production cost)(production volume) + machine cost

a) What production volume yields the same total cost for each machine?
b) For production volume of 60,000 units, which machine results in a lower total cost? State the minimum cost.
c) For a production volume of 120,000 units, which machine results in a lower total cost? State the minimum cost.

5-2

• LINEAR SYSTEMS; TABLEAUS; PROBLEM FORMULATION

In Section 5-1, we discussed two methods of solving linear systems consisting of two equations in two variables. In this section, we set the stage for the application of a more structured method for solving linear systems of any size. This method, called the Gauss-Jordan method of solving linear systems, is discussed in the next section. This method consists of replacing an original linear system with a succession of equivalent linear systems (which have the same solution as the original linear system), the last of which is made up of equations that explicitly give the solution values of the variables. Additionally, we present applied problems whose algebraic formulations result in linear systems with more than two equations in two variables.

Notation

In Section 5-1, we encountered linear equations written in the form

$$ax + by = c$$

where a, b, and c are constant real numbers. In this and succeeding sections of this chapter, we will often use x_1 and x_2 in place of x and y, respectively. This allows for a smoother transition to linear systems with more than two variables.

Tableau Format

The Gauss-Jordan method for solving linear systems is most efficiently performed by writing the linear system in **tableau** form. We illustrate by considering the linear system

$$2x_1 + 3x_2 = 9$$
$$x_1 + 4x_2 = 17$$

After making certain that the x_1- and x_2-terms and the right-hand-side constants are arranged in their separate columns, we write a tableau consisting of the coefficients of x_1 and x_2 and the right-hand-side constants, as shown below.

$$\begin{array}{cc} x_1 & x_2 \end{array}$$

first equation $\longrightarrow$ $\begin{bmatrix} 2 & 3 & | & 9 \\ 1 & 4 & | & 17 \end{bmatrix}$ $\longleftarrow$ right-hand-side
second equation $\longrightarrow$ $\longleftarrow$ constants

$$\uparrow \quad \uparrow$$
$$\text{coefficients}$$

A tableau, such as the one above, consists of a rectangular array of numbers. Later in this chapter we will learn that a rectangular array of numbers is called a **matrix.** A tableau, such as the one above, that contains coefficients of variables as well as right-hand-side constants, is called an **augmented matrix.** Thus, we will use the terms *tableau* and *augmented matrix* interchangeably.

Studying the above tableau, note that the first column consists of the coefficients of x_1 of the linear system, the second column consists of the coefficients of x_2, the vertical line replaces the equal signs, and the column to the right of the vertical line consists of the right-hand-side constants of the linear system.

Since it is important to be able to write a tableau (or augmented matrix) corresponding to a linear system, we now consider the following examples.

• **EXAMPLE 5-6** _____

Write the tableau (or augmented matrix) for this linear system.

$$-2x + 7y = 80$$
$$x + 4y = 60$$

Solution

The tableau (or augmented matrix) is given below.

$$\begin{array}{cc} x & y \end{array}$$
$$\begin{bmatrix} -2 & 7 & | & 80 \\ 1 & 4 & | & 60 \end{bmatrix}$$

• **EXAMPLE 5-7** _____

Write the tableau (or augmented matrix) for this linear system.

$$6x_1 - 9x_2 = 45$$
$$x_2 = 50$$

Solution

The tableau (or augmented matrix) is given below.

$$\begin{array}{cc} x_1 & x_2 \\ \begin{bmatrix} 6 & -9 & | & 45 \\ 0 & 1 & | & 50 \end{bmatrix} \end{array}$$

Since it is as important to be able to write a linear system corresponding to a given tableau as it is to be able to write a tableau corresponding to a given linear system, we consider the next examples.

• **EXAMPLE 5-8** _____

Write the linear system corresponding to the tableau

$$\begin{bmatrix} -4 & 6 & | & 20 \\ 3 & 2 & | & 46 \end{bmatrix}$$

Solution

Using x_1 and x_2 for variables and remembering that each row of the tableau represents an equation of the linear system, the corresponding linear system is

$$-4x_1 + 6x_2 = 20$$
$$3x_1 + 2x_2 = 46$$

• **EXAMPLE 5-9** _____

Write the linear system corresponding to the tableau

$$\begin{bmatrix} 1 & 0 & | & 5 \\ 0 & 1 & | & 7 \end{bmatrix}$$

Solution

The corresponding linear system is

$$\begin{array}{lll} x_1 + 0x_2 = 5 & \text{or} & x_1 \quad\;\; = 5 \\ 0x_1 + x_2 = 7 & & \quad\;\; x_2 = 7 \end{array}$$

Study the form of the columns to the left of the vertical line in the tableau of Example 5-9. Note that the first entry in column 1 is 1, with the remaining column 1 entry being 0; the second entry in column 2 is 1, with the remaining column 2 entry being 0. When a tableau (or augmented matrix) has the above format, the resulting linear system constitutes its own solution. In other words, the right-hand-side constants of such a tableau constitute the solution to the linear system. Such a tableau is called a **final tableau.** We note that the Gauss-Jordan method for solving linear systems, which we will study in the next section, provides a systematic procedure for changing the tableau corresponding to a linear system to an equivalent final tableau. The concept of a final tableau is so important that we summarize it in the box below.

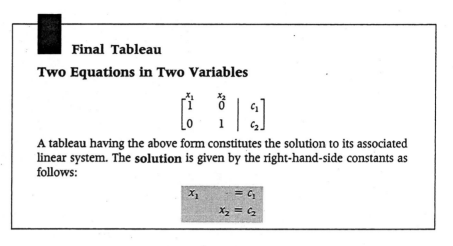

Final Tableau

Two Equations in Two Variables

$$\begin{bmatrix} \overset{x_1}{1} & \overset{x_2}{0} & \Big| & c_1 \\ 0 & 1 & \Big| & c_2 \end{bmatrix}$$

A tableau having the above form constitutes the solution to its associated linear system. The **solution** is given by the right-hand-side constants as follows:

$$x_1 \qquad = c_1$$
$$x_2 = c_2$$

We now consider an applied problem that results in a linear system of three equations in three variables.

PROBLEM

Production Planning

A company makes videocassette recorders (VCRs), stereos, and televisions. To do this requires amounts of labor and raw materials. Specifically, each VCR requires 2 person-hours of time in the assembly department, 1 person-hour in the finishing and inspection department, and 4 units of a part identified as XBH104. Each stereo requires 3 person-hours in assembly, 2 person-hours in finishing and inspection, and 1 unit of part XBH104. Each television requires 5 person-hours in assembly, 1 person-hour in finishing and inspection, and 3 units of part XBH104. For the coming day, the company will have available 780 person-hours in the assembly department, 320 person-hours in the finishing and inspection department, and 500 units of part XBH104. How many of each item should the company make during the coming day if it is to operate at full capacity?

SOLUTION

We apply our problem-solving procedure to solve this problem.

Step 1 *Identify the unknowns. Use letters to denote these quantities.*
We must determine the number of VCRs, stereos, and televisions to make during the coming day. Thus, we let

- x = the number of VCRs to be made
- y = the number of stereos to be made
- z = the number of televisions to be made

Step 2 *Organize the given information, and write the equations that express any relationships existing among the unknowns.*
The information is organized in the following table.

	VCRs	Stereos	Televisions	Limited resources
Assembly	2	3	5	780 person-hours
Finishing and Inspection	1	2	1	320 person-hours
Part XBH104	4	1	3	500 parts

We now write the labor and raw material requirements as equations. First, we consider the assembly department. Since each VCR requires 2 person-hours in assembly, each stereo requires 3 person-hours, and each television requires 5 person-hours, then the expression

$$\underbrace{2(\# \text{ VCRs})}_{\substack{\text{\# of person-hours} \\ \text{to assemble VCRs}}} + \underbrace{3(\# \text{ stereos})}_{\substack{\text{\# of person-hours} \\ \text{to assemble stereos}}} + \underbrace{5(\# \text{ televisions})}_{\substack{\text{\# of person-hours} \\ \text{to assemble televisions}}}$$

represents the number of person-hours of assembly department time used to make all three products. Since 780 person-hours of assembly time must be used, we set the above expression equal to 780 to give the equation

$$2(\# \text{ VCRs}) + 3(\# \text{ stereos}) + 5(\# \text{ televisions}) = 780$$

Since $x = \#$ VCRs, $y = \#$ stereos, and $z = \#$ televisions, the above becomes

$$2x + 3y + 5z = 780$$

Analogously, for the finishing and inspection department, the equation is

$$1(\# \text{ VCRs}) + 2(\# \text{ stereos}) + 1(\# \text{ televisions}) = \# \text{ person-hours}$$

or

$$x + 2y + z = 320$$

Note that this equation implies that the 320 person-hours available in the finishing and inspection department will be used. Finally, the requirement that 500 units of Part XBH104 be used is expressed by the equation

$$4(\# \text{ VCRs}) + 1(\# \text{ stereos}) + 3(\# \text{ televisions}) = \# \text{ parts}$$

or

$$4x + y + 3z = 500$$

Thus, we seek values of x, y, and z that simultaneously satisfy the three equations

$$2x + 3y + 5z = 780$$
$$x + 2y + z = 320$$
$$4x + y + 3z = 500$$

Note that each equation is of the form

$$a_1x + a_2y + a_3z = b$$

where a_1, a_2, a_3, and b are real number constants. Such an equation is a **linear equation in three variables.** Later we will give a more formal definition of a linear equation in n variables. These three equations constitute a **system** of three linear equations in three variables.

Step 3 *Solve the linear system of step 2.*

A **solution** to a linear system of three equations in three variables is a sequence of numbers x, y, and z that, when substituted into each equation, results in a true statement. In other words, the values of x, y, and z must satisfy all three equations. The solution may be written as the ordered triple (x, y, z). In the homework exercises for Section 5-3, we will present this linear system for solution by the Gauss-Jordan method. Now we give a more formal definition of a linear equation in n variables.

An equation of the form

$$a_1x_1 + a_2x_2 + \ldots + a_nx_n = b$$

where a_1, a_2, . . . , a_n, and b are real number constants, is a **linear equation in n variables.** The variables x_1, x_2, . . . , x_n are often written as letters, x, y, z, t, w, . . . , etc.

• EXAMPLE 5-10

Write the tableau (or augmented matrix) corresponding to the linear system for the above production planning problem.

Solution

Using the same concepts as for linear systems of two equations in two variables, we obtain

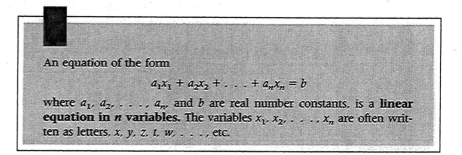

• EXAMPLE 5-11

Write the linear system corresponding to the tableau

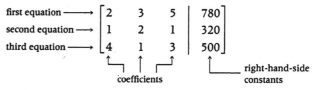

Solution

Remembering that each row of the tableau represents an equation of the linear system, the corresponding linear system is

$$\begin{array}{rcr} x_1 + 0x_2 + 0x_3 &=& -3 \\ 0x_1 + x_2 + 0x_3 &=& 2 \\ 0x_1 + 0x_2 + x_3 &=& 5 \end{array} \quad \text{or} \quad \begin{array}{rcr} x_1 &=& -3 \\ x_2 &=& 2 \\ x_3 &=& 5 \end{array}$$

Study the form of the columns to the left of the vertical line in the tableau of Example 5-11. Note that the first entry in column 1 is 1, with the remaining entries in column 1 being 0s, the second entry in column 2 is 1, with the remaining entries in column 2 being 0s, and the third entry in column 3 is 1, with the remaining entries in column 3 being 0s. When a tableau has the above format, the resulting linear system constitutes its own solution. In other words, the constants to the right of the vertical line of such a tableau constitute the solution to the linear system. Such a tableau is called a **final tableau.** This is such an important concept that we summarize it in the box below.

SUMMARY

Final Tableau

The final tableau for a linear system consisting of n equations in n variables is given below.

$$\begin{array}{cccc} x_1 & x_2 & x_3 & \quad x_n \end{array}$$
$$\left[\begin{array}{ccccc|c} 1 & 0 & 0 & \ldots & 0 & c_1 \\ 0 & 1 & 0 & \ldots & 0 & c_2 \\ 0 & 0 & 1 & \ldots & 0 & c_3 \\ \vdots & \vdots & \vdots & & \vdots & \vdots \\ 0 & 0 & 0 & & 1 & c_n \end{array}\right]$$

The **solution** to the linear system is given by the right-hand-side constants as follows:

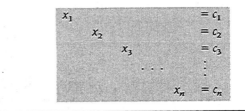

$$\begin{array}{rcl} x_1 & & = c_1 \\ x_2 & & = c_2 \\ x_3 & & = c_3 \\ & \cdots & \vdots \\ & x_n & = c_n \end{array}$$

We conclude this section with more applications that result in linear systems.

Application

A Transportation Problem

A company makes lawn tractors at two plants. The tractors must be transported from the two plants to two retail outlets, as is illustrated in Table 5-1. The plants are called supply points, and the retail outlets are called demand points. Studying Table 5-1, note that plants 1 and 2 have production capacities of 900 and 500 lawn tractors, respectively. Retail outlets 1 and 2 have demand requirements of 600 and 800 lawn tractors, respectively.

PROBLEM

If each plant is to operate at full capacity, how many lawn tractors should be shipped from each plant to each retail outlet in order to ensure that the retail outlets' demand requirements are met?

SOLUTION

Looking at Table 5-1, we let

- x_1 = number of lawn tractors shipped from plant 1 to retail outlet 1
- x_2 = number of lawn tractors shipped from plant 1 to retail outlet 2
- x_3 = number of lawn tractors shipped from plant 2 to retail outlet 1
- x_4 = number of lawn tractors shipped from plant 2 to retail outlet 2

Since plant 1 is to operate at full capacity, then

$$\underbrace{x_1 + x_2}_{} = 900$$

↑────────── number shipped from plant 1

Since plant 2 is to operate at full capacity, then

$$\underbrace{x_3 + x_4}_{} = 500$$

↑────────── number shipped from plant 2

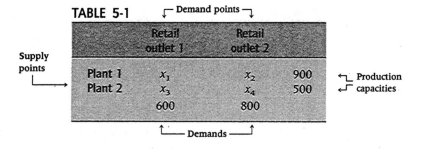

TABLE 5-1 ⌐ Demand points ¬

Supply points	Retail outlet 1	Retail outlet 2	
Plant 1	x_1	x_2	900
Plant 2	x_3	x_4	500
	600	800	

↖ Production capacities

└── Demands ──┘

The demand requirement of retail outlet 1 indicates that

$$\underbrace{x_1 + x_3}_{} = 600$$

└──────── number shipped to retail outlet 1

The demand requirement of retail outlet 2 indicates that

$$\underbrace{x_2 + x_4}_{} = 800$$

└──────── number shipped to retail outlet 2

Thus, our problem is formulated below.

$$
\begin{aligned}
x_1 + x_2 \qquad\qquad &= 900 \\
x_3 + x_4 &= 500 \\
x_1 \qquad + x_3 \qquad &= 600 \\
x_2 \qquad + x_4 &= 800
\end{aligned}
$$

where x_1, x_2, x_3, and $x_4 \geq 0$. Note that this linear system consists of four equations in four variables. We write its tableau below.

$$
\begin{bmatrix}
1 & 1 & 0 & 0 & | & 900 \\
0 & 0 & 1 & 1 & | & 500 \\
1 & 0 & 1 & 0 & | & 600 \\
0 & 1 & 0 & 1 & | & 800
\end{bmatrix}
$$

Investment: Portfolio Allocation

An investment company has $400,000 to be allocated for investment among three types of mutual funds: stock, bond, and money market. The projected annual rate of return and risk level for each of three types of funds are given below

Projected annual rate of return

Stock fund	Bond fund	Money market fund
20%	16%	8%

Risk level

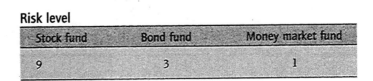

Stock fund	Bond fund	Money market fund
9	3	1

PROBLEM

If the investor wants a projected average annual rate of return of at least 15.5% and a risk level of at most 5, how much should be invested in each type of fund in order to meet these requirements exactly?

SOLUTION

Let

- x_1 = number of dollars invested in the stock fund
- x_2 = number of dollars invested in the bond fund
- x_3 = number of dollars invested in the money market fund

Constraint 1. Total amount invested.
Since $400,000 is to be invested, then

$$x_1 + x_2 + x_3 = 400,000$$

Constraint 2. Average annual rate of return.

$$\text{average annual rate of return} = \frac{\text{dollars of interest earned in 1 year}}{\text{total number of dollars invested}}$$

Since x_1, x_2, and x_3 dollars are to be invested at 20%, 16%, and 8%, respectively, then

$$\text{average annual rate of return} = \frac{\overbrace{0.20x_1 + 0.16x_2 + 0.08x_3}^{\substack{\text{dollars of interest} \\ \text{earned in 1 year}}}}{\underbrace{x_1 + x_2 + x_3}_{\substack{\text{total number of} \\ \text{dollars invested}}}}$$

Since constraint 1 indicates that $x_1 + x_2 + x_3 = 400,000$, and since the average annual rate of return is to be 15.5%, we rewrite the above equation as

$$\frac{0.20x_1 + 0.16x_2 + 0.08x_3}{400,000} = 0.155$$

Multiplying both sides by 400,000 gives the constraint

$$0.20x_1 + 0.16x_2 + 0.08x_3 = 62,000$$

Constraint 3. Average risk level.
If x_1 dollars are invested at a risk level of 9, x_2 dollars are invested at a risk level of 3, and x_3 dollars are invested at a risk level of 1, then

$$\text{average risk level} = \frac{\overbrace{9x_1 + 3x_2 + 1x_3}^{\substack{\text{total risk weighted by number of} \\ \text{dollars invested at each risk level}}}}{\underbrace{x_1 + x_2 + x_3}_{\text{total dollars invested}}}$$

Since $x_1 + x_2 + x_3 = 400,000$ from constraint 1, and since the average risk level is to be 5, then we rewrite the above as

$$\frac{9x_1 + 3x_2 + 1x_3}{400,000} = 5$$

Multiplying both sides by 400,000 gives the constraint

$$9x_1 + 3x_2 + x_3 = 2{,}000{,}000$$

Thus, our problem is formulated as the linear system

$$
\begin{aligned}
x_1 + \quad x_2 + \quad x_3 &= 400{,}000 \\
0.20x_1 + 0.16x_2 + 0.08x_3 &= 62{,}000 \\
9x_1 + \quad 3x_2 + \quad x_3 &= 2{,}000{,}000
\end{aligned}
$$

We write its tableau below.

$$
\begin{bmatrix}
1 & 1 & 1 & 400{,}000 \\
0.20 & 0.16 & 0.08 & 62{,}000 \\
9 & 3 & 1 & 2{,}000{,}000
\end{bmatrix}
$$

Exercises 5-2

Write the tableau corresponding to each of the following linear systems. Do not solve.

1. $2x + 7y = 9$
  $-x + 4y = 15$

2. $-4x + 3y = 19$
  $8x - 2y = 14$

3. $3x_1 \quad = -1$
  $4x_1 + 3x_2 = 7$

4. $x_1 + x_2 = 9$
  $x_2 = 3$

5. $x_1 + 2x_2 + 5x_3 = 6$
  $2x_1 - 3x_2 - 8x_3 = 4$
  $-x_1 + 4x_2 + 5x_3 = 9$

6. $4x_1 + 8x_2 - x_3 = 10$
  $x_1 + \quad x_2 \quad = 9$
  $2x_1 \quad + x_3 = 6$

7. $5x_1 - 7x_2 \quad = 4$
  $3x_2 \quad = 9$
  $x_1 \quad + x_3 = 15$

8. $2x_1 \quad = 10$
  $3x_2 + x_3 = 6$
  $x_3 = 5$

Write the linear system corresponding to each of the following tableaus.

9. $\begin{bmatrix} 4 & 8 & 5 \\ -2 & 6 & 0 \end{bmatrix}$

10. $\begin{bmatrix} 3 & -1 & 2 \\ 5 & -2 & 6 \end{bmatrix}$

11. $\begin{bmatrix} -1 & 1 & 2 & 3 \\ 4 & 0 & -1 & 5 \\ 2 & 1 & -1 & 6 \end{bmatrix}$

12. $\begin{bmatrix} 1 & 0 & -1 & 9 \\ 2 & 4 & 3 & 1 \\ 0 & 0 & 1 & 4 \end{bmatrix}$

13. $\begin{bmatrix} 1 & 0 & 1 & 2 \\ 0 & 1 & 0 & 3 \\ 0 & 0 & 1 & 5 \end{bmatrix}$

14. $\begin{bmatrix} 1 & 0 & 0 & 8 \\ 0 & 1 & 0 & 2 \\ 0 & 0 & 1 & 7 \end{bmatrix}$

Indicate which of the following is a final tableau. For those that are final tableaus, state the solution.

15. $\begin{bmatrix} 1 & 0 & 5 \\ 1 & -1 & 6 \end{bmatrix}$

16. $\begin{bmatrix} 1 & 0 & 4 \\ 0 & 1 & -6 \end{bmatrix}$

17. $\begin{bmatrix} 1 & 0 & 8 \\ 0 & 1 & 3 \end{bmatrix}$

18. $\begin{bmatrix} 0 & 1 & 4 \\ 1 & 0 & 3 \end{bmatrix}$

19. $\begin{bmatrix} 1 & 0 & 0 & 2 \\ 0 & 1 & 0 & -4 \\ 0 & 0 & 1 & 5 \end{bmatrix}$

20. $\begin{bmatrix} -1 & 0 & 0 & 3 \\ 0 & 0 & 1 & 2 \\ 0 & 1 & 0 & -1 \end{bmatrix}$

21. $\begin{bmatrix} 1 & 0 & 0 & 3 \\ 0 & -1 & 0 & 2 \\ 0 & 0 & 1 & 4 \end{bmatrix}$

22. $\begin{bmatrix} 1 & 0 & 0 & 4 \\ 0 & 1 & 0 & -2 \\ 0 & 0 & 1 & 2 \end{bmatrix}$

Applications

23. *Production planning.* A textile company manufactures three types of sweaters: conservative, sporty, and practical. The table below gives the time requirements in person-hours) for a dozen of each type of sweater in the various departments.

	Conservative	Sporty	Practical
Cutting department	5	2	3
Sewing department	3	2	4
Inspection department	1	2	1

If the cutting, sewing, and inspection departments have available 660, 480, and 220 hours, respectively, then how many dozen of each type of sweater should be manufactured? Write the linear system for this problem. Do not solve the linear system.

24. *Investment: Portfolio allocation.* An investor has $600,000 to be allocated among three types of mutual funds: stock, bond, and money market. The projected annual rates of return and risk levels for these three types of funds are given below.

Projected annual rate of return

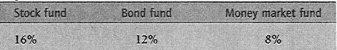

Stock fund	Bond fund	Money market fund
16%	12%	8%

Risk level

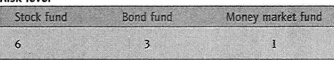

Stock fund	Bond fund	Money market fund
6	3	1

If the investor wants a projected average annual rate of return of at least 13% and a risk level of at most 4, how much should be invested in each type of fund in order to meet these requirements exactly? Write the linear system for this problem. Do not solve.

25. *Transportation problem.* A company makes roll-top desks at two plants. The desks must be transported from the two plants to two retail outlets, as is illustrated in Table 5-2. The production capacities of the plants and demand requirements of the retail outlets are given in Table 5-2.

TABLE 5-2

	Retail outlet 1	Retail outlet 2		
Plant 1	x_1	x_2	300	⌐ Production
Plant 2	x_3	x_4	200	⌐ capacities
	150	350		

└── Demand ──┘

If each plant is to operate at full capacity, how many desks should be shipped from each plant to each retail outlet in order to ensure that the retail outlets' demand requirements are met exactly? Write the linear system for this problem. Do not solve.

26. *Nutrition.* A diet is to consist of three types of foods: A, B, and C. The diet is to provide at least 3100 milligrams of protein, at least 2050 milligrams of iron, and at least 2800 milligrams of calcium. The following table gives the amounts of the above nutrients contained per unit of each type food.

Milligrams per unit of food type

	Food A	Food B	Food C
Protein	8	2	10
Iron	2	7	4
Calcium	6	4	8

If the nutritional requirements are to be met exactly, how many units of each type of food should be included in the diet? Write the linear system for this problem. Do not solve.

27. *Investment: Portfolio allocation.* An investor has $2,000,000 to be allocated among three types of investments: real estate, stocks, and bonds. The projected annual rate of return and risk level for each of the three investments are given below

Projected annual rate of return

Real Estate	Stocks	Bonds
12%	9%	8%

Risk level

Real Estate	Stocks	Bonds
4	6	3

If the investor wants a projected average annual rate of return of at least 11% and a risk level of at most 5, how much should be invested in each type of investment in order to meet these requirements exactly? Write the linear system for this problem. Do not solve.

5-3 • GAUSS-JORDAN METHOD OF SOLVING LINEAR SYSTEMS

In Section 5-2, we learned how to write a linear system in tableau form. We also encountered problems that, when formulated algebraically, resulted in linear systems of sizes larger than two equations in two variables. In this section, we present a method for efficiently solving linear systems of any size. This method is called the **Gauss-Jordan method**. Before proceeding, we restate three possibilities that exist for a solution to a linear system.

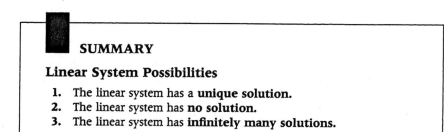

SUMMARY

Linear System Possibilities

1. The linear system has a **unique solution.**
2. The linear system has **no solution.**
3. The linear system has **infinitely many solutions.**

In Section 5-1, we provided graphical insight into each of the above possibilities for linear systems consisting of two equations in two variables. For linear systems of three equations in three variables, we note that each equation represents a plane in three-dimensional space. Figure 5-7 illustrates some of the possible relationships among three planes. Specifically, the three planes in Figure 5-7(a) intersect at a single point. This illustrates a linear system that has a unique solution. If the letters x, y, and z denote the

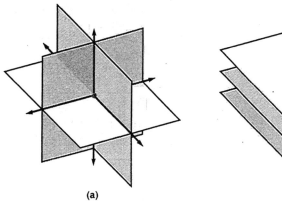

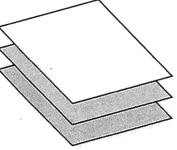

(a)

Unique solution
Planes intersect at a single point

(b)

No solution
Parallel planes

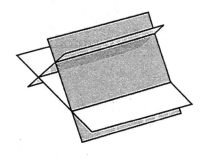

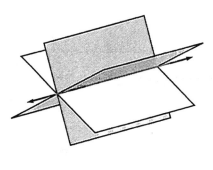

(c)

No solution
There is no point where all
three planes intersect

(d)

Infinitely many solutions
The three planes intersect in a straight line

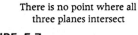

FIGURE 5-7

variables of the linear system, then the intersection point of all three planes is denoted by the ordered triple (x, y, z) that satisfies all three equations. Observe that the planes of Figure 5-7(b) are parallel and, therefore, do not intersect. This illustrates a linear system that has no solution. Figure 5-7(c) illustrates three planes that do not intersect at a single point. This also illustrates a linear system that has no solution. Finally, Figure 5-7(d) illustrates three planes that intersect in a straight line. Each point on the straight line constitutes a solution to the linear system. Since there are infinitely many points on a straight line, there are infinitely many solutions to the respective linear system.

Row Operations

We now consider the Gauss-Jordan method for solving linear systems. As we mentioned in Section 5-2, this method consists of replacing an original linear system by a succession of equivalent linear systems (which have the same solution as the original linear system), the last of which is made up of equations that yield the solution values of the variables. An equivalent linear system is obtained by applying any of the following row operations to any equation (i.e., row) of a linear system. Note that we use the terms *row* and *equation* interchangeably.

SUMMARY

Three Fundamental Row Operations

1. Interchange two rows (equations).
2. Multiply a row (equation) by a nonzero constant.
3. Add a multiple of a row (equation) to another row (equation).

TABLE 5-3

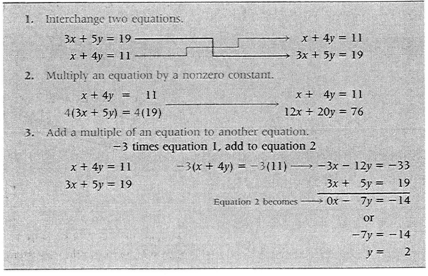

1. Interchange two equations.

$$3x + 5y = 19 \qquad \longrightarrow \qquad x + 4y = 11$$
$$x + 4y = 11 \qquad \longrightarrow \qquad 3x + 5y = 19$$

2. Multiply an equation by a nonzero constant.

$$x + 4y = 11 \qquad\qquad\qquad x + 4y = 11$$
$$4(3x + 5y) = 4(19) \qquad\longrightarrow\qquad 12x + 20y = 76$$

3. Add a multiple of an equation to another equation.
   -3 times equation 1, add to equation 2

$$x + 4y = 11 \qquad -3(x + 4y) = -3(11) \longrightarrow -3x - 12y = -33$$
$$3x + 5y = 19 \qquad\qquad\qquad\qquad\qquad\qquad 3x + 5y = 19$$

$$\text{Equation 2 becomes} \longrightarrow 0x - 7y = -14$$
$$\text{or}$$
$$-7y = -14$$
$$y = 2$$

Note that the above row operations are only formal restatements of some operations that were used to solve linear systems in Section 5-1. For example, if we interchange two equations—say, the first and second equations—of a linear system, we write the first equation second and the second equation first, as is illustrated in Table 5-3. The resulting linear system has the same solution as the original and is thus equivalent. Regarding the second row operation, if we multiply an equation by a nonzero constant (see Table 5-3), the resulting equation is equivalent to the original. We applied this property when using the elimination method of Section 5-1. Finally, we also used the third row operation in Section 5-1 when we multiplied an equation by a nonzero constant to get a variable whose coefficients were additive inverses and then added the two equations to eliminate the variable. This is also illustrated in Table 5-3.

Solving Linear Systems by the Gauss-Jordan Method

We now illustrate the use of row operations to solve linear systems by the Gauss-Jordan method. We begin by considering the linear system

$$2x_1 + 3x_2 = 9$$
$$x_1 + 4x_2 = 17$$

Notation

Note that we are using x_1 and x_2 in place of x and y. Since either choice is acceptable, we will sometimes use $x_1, x_2, x_3, \ldots$ as variables and sometimes $x, y, z, \ldots$.

After making certain that the x_1- and x_2-terms and the right-hand-side constants are arranged in their separate columns, then, as was discussed in Section 5-2, we write a tableau consisting of the coefficients of x_1 and x_2 and the right-hand-side constants, as shown below.

Initial Tableau

$$\begin{bmatrix} 2 & 3 & | & 9 \\ 1 & 4 & | & 17 \end{bmatrix}$$

Since the above tableau is associated with the original linear system to be solved, it is called the **initial tableau.**

Now we must use row operations to obtain an equivalent final tableau having the form below.

Final Tableau

$$\begin{bmatrix} 1 & 0 & | & c_1 \\ 0 & 1 & | & c_2 \end{bmatrix}$$

As was discussed in Section 5-2, the constants c_1 and c_2 represent the solution values to the linear system. We proceed as follows.

Step 1   We must change column 1 of the initial tableau to $\begin{bmatrix} 1 \\ 0 \end{bmatrix}$, the first column of the final tableau. We do this by changing the first coefficient of column 1 to 1 and then changing the remaining coefficient of column 1 to 0.

We change the first coefficient of column 1 to 1 by interchanging rows 1 and 2. This is written in shorthand form as R1 ↔ R2. The double arrow indicates that row 1 becomes row 2 and vice versa. This is illustrated below.

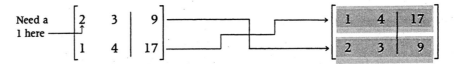

We note that the following row operation could have been used to accomplish the above goal.

Multiply Row 1 by 1/2

or, in other words, [(1/2)R1 → R1]

Note: The notation [(1/2)R1 → R1] means that row 1 is replaced with (1/2)R1.

Since this row operatifon would have given fractions for some row 1 entries, we use the previous row operation, R1 ↔ R2. We do not always have a choice of row operations to accomplish a desired goal.

Now we must change the remaining entry of column 1 to 0. We change the 2 of column 1 to 0 by the row operation

−2 times Row 1, add the result to Row 2

or, in other words, [(−2)R1 + R2 → R2]

Note: The notation [(−2)R1 + R2 → R2] means that row 2 is replaced with (−2)R1 + R2. This is illustrated below. The row operation computations are shown in the grey shaded area.

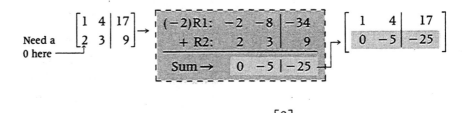

Step 2   Now we must change column 2 to $\begin{bmatrix} 0 \\ 1 \end{bmatrix}$, the second column of the final tableau. We do this by changing the second coefficient of column 2 to 1 and then changing the remaining coefficient of column 2 to 0.

We first change the −5 of column 2 to 1 by the row operation

Multiply Row 2 by −1/5

or, in other words, [(−1/5)R2 → R2]

This is illustrated below. The row operation computations are shown in the grey shaded area.

Now we must change the remaining entry, 4, of column 2 to 0. We do this by using the row operation

$$-4 \text{ times Row 2, add the result to Row 1}$$
$$\text{or, in other words, } [(-4)R2 + R1 \rightarrow R1]$$

This is illustrated below. The row operation computations are shown in the grey shaded area.

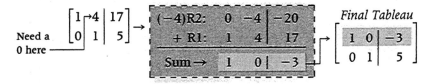

The final tableau indicates the solution $x_1 = -3$ and $x_2 = 5$. We check this result below.

$$2x_1 + 3x_2 = 9 \qquad\qquad x_1 + 4x_2 = 17$$
$$2(-3) + 3(5) \overset{?}{=} 9 \qquad (-3) + 4(5) \overset{?}{=} 17$$
$$9 \overset{\checkmark}{=} 9 \qquad\qquad\qquad 17 \overset{\checkmark}{=} 17$$

We now present an overall summary, followed by a step-by-step summary, of the Gauss-Jordan method.

OVERALL SUMMARY

Gauss-Jordan Method

Consider the linear system

$$a_{11}x_1 + a_{12}x_2 + \ldots + a_{1n}x_n = b_1$$
$$a_{21}x_1 + a_{22}x_2 + \ldots + a_{2n}x_n = b_2$$
$$\vdots \qquad\quad \vdots \qquad\qquad\quad \vdots \qquad\quad \vdots$$
$$a_{n1}x_1 + a_{n2}x_2 + \ldots + a_{nn}x_n = b_n$$

where the double subscript (i, j) of a_{ij} denotes the location of a_{ij} within the tableau. Specifically, the double subscript (i, j) of the coefficient a_{ij} indicates that a_{ij} is located in row i and column j of the tableau. Thus, a_{23} is located in row 2 and column 3, a_{31} is located in row 3 and column 1, etc.

continues

OVERALL SUMMARY—*Continued*

To solve such a linear system by the Gauss-Jordan method, we begin with the initial tableau (shown below)

Initial Tableau

$$\begin{bmatrix} a_{11} & a_{12} & \cdots\cdots & a_{1n} & b_1 \\ a_{21} & a_{22} & \cdots\cdots & a_{2n} & b_2 \\ \vdots & \vdots & & \vdots & \vdots \\ a_{n1} & a_{n2} & \cdots\cdots & a_{nn} & b_n \end{bmatrix}$$

and use row operations to obtain the final tableau (shown below)

Final Tableau

$$\begin{bmatrix} 1 & 0 & \cdots\cdots & 0 & c_1 \\ 0 & 1 & \cdots\cdots & 0 & c_2 \\ \vdots & \vdots & & \vdots & \vdots \\ 0 & 0 & \cdots\cdots & 1 & c_n \end{bmatrix}$$

where $x_1 = c_1, x_2 = c_2, \ldots, x_n = c_n$ is the solution to the linear system. If we cannot obtain the final tableau, then the linear system has either no solutions or infinitely many solutions.

▉ STEP-BY-STEP SUMMARY

Gauss-Jordan Method

Step 1 Change column 1 of the initial tableau to $\begin{bmatrix} 1 \\ 0 \\ \vdots \\ 0 \end{bmatrix}$ by changing the first coefficient of column 1 to 1 and then changing the remaining coefficients of column 1 to 0s. The 1 is usually obtained by using the row operation "Multiply a row by a nonzero constant." Sometimes the row operation "Interchange two rows" is helpful here, as we saw in the illustrative example of this section. The 0s are usually obtained by using the row operation "Add a multiple of a row to another row."

When this step is completed, the tableau will look like the one shown below.

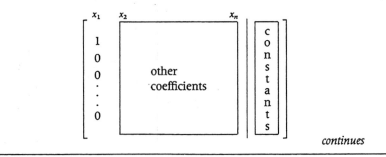

continues

STEP-BY-STEP SUMMARY—*Continued*

$$\begin{bmatrix} 0 \\ 1 \\ 0 \\ \cdot \\ \cdot \\ \cdot \\ 0 \end{bmatrix}$$

Step 2 Change column 2 of the resulting tableau to $\begin{bmatrix} 0 \\ 1 \\ 0 \\ \cdot \\ \cdot \\ \cdot \\ 0 \end{bmatrix}$ by changing
the second coefficient of column 2 to 1 and then changing the remaining
coefficients of column 2 to 0s. Again, the 1 is usually obtained by using
the row operation "Multiply a row by a nonzero constant," and the 0s
are usually obtained by using the row operation "Add a multiple of a
row to another row."

When this step is completed, the tableau will look like the following:

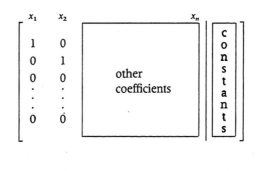

$$\begin{bmatrix} 0 \\ \cdot \\ \cdot \\ \cdot \\ 0 \\ 1 \end{bmatrix}$$

Step n Change column n of the previous tableau to $\begin{bmatrix} 0 \\ \cdot \\ \cdot \\ \cdot \\ 0 \\ 1 \end{bmatrix}$ by changing
the nth coefficient of column n to 1 and then changing the remaining co-
efficients to 0s. Again, the 1 is usually obtained by using the row operation "Multiply a row by a nonzero constant," and the 0s are usually obtained by using the row operation "Add a multiple of a row to another
row."

When this step is completed, the tableau will look like the final tableau shown below.

Final Tableau

$$\begin{array}{ccccc} x_1 & x_2 & x_3 & & x_n \\ \begin{bmatrix} 1 & 0 & 0 & \cdots\cdots\cdots 0 & c_1 \\ 0 & 1 & 0 & \cdots\cdots\cdots 0 & c_2 \\ 0 & 0 & 1 & \cdots\cdots\cdots 0 & c_3 \\ \cdot & \cdot & \cdot & & \cdot \\ \cdot & \cdot & \cdot & & \cdot \\ \cdot & \cdot & \cdot & & \cdot \\ 0 & 0 & 0 & \cdots\cdots\cdots 1 & c_n \end{bmatrix} \end{array}$$

The following examples further illustrate the Gauss-Jordan method.

• **EXAMPLE 5-12** _____

Solve the following linear system by the Gauss-Jordan method.

$$x_1 + 2x_2 - x_3 = 4$$
$$x_1 + x_2 - 2x_3 = 2$$
$$x_1 + 2x_2 + 3x_3 = 8$$

Solution

We first write the initial tableau

Initial Tableau

$$\begin{bmatrix} 1 & 2 & -1 & 4 \\ 1 & 1 & -2 & 2 \\ 1 & 2 & 3 & 8 \end{bmatrix}$$

and then we use row operations, as outlined in the step-by-step summary of the Gauss-Jordan method on pages 274-275.

Step 1   *Change column 1 of the initial tableau to* $\begin{bmatrix} 1 \\ 0 \\ 0 \end{bmatrix}$.

We already have a 1 for the first element of column 1. We need a 0 for the second element in column 1. This is obtained by the row operation

-1 times Row 1, add the result to Row 2

or, in other words, $[(-1)R1 + R2 \rightarrow R2]$

This is illustrated below. The row operation computations are shown in the grey shaded area.

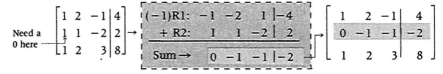

We now need a 0 for the third element of column 1. This is obtained by the row operation

-1 times Row 1, add the result to Row 3

or, in other words, $[(-1)R1 + R3 \rightarrow R3]$

This is illustrated below.

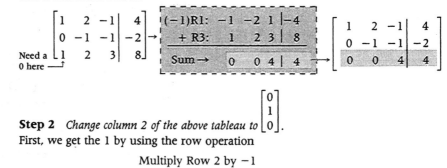

Step 2   *Change column 2 of the above tableau to* $\begin{bmatrix} 0 \\ 1 \\ 0 \end{bmatrix}$.

First, we get the 1 by using the row operation

Multiply Row 2 by -1

or, in other words, $[(-1)R2 \rightarrow R2]$

This is illustrated below. The row operation computations are shown in the grey shaded area.

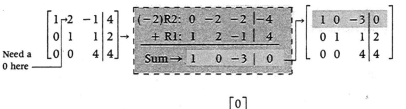

Now we need a 0 for the first element of column 2. We use the row operation

$$-2 \text{ times Row 2, add the result to Row 1}$$

or, in other words, $[(-2)R2 + R1 \rightarrow R1]$

This is illustrated below. The row operation computations are shown in the grey shaded area.

Step 3 *Change column 3 of the above tableau to* $\begin{bmatrix} 0 \\ 0 \\ 1 \end{bmatrix}$.
First we get the 1 by the row operation

$$\text{Multiply Row 3 by } 1/4$$

or, in other words, $[(1/4)R3 \rightarrow R3]$

This is illustrated below. The row operation computations are shown in the grey shaded area.

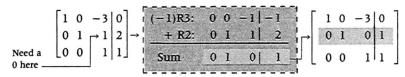

Now we need a 0 for the second entry in column 3. This is obtained by using the row operation

$$-1 \text{ times Row 3, add the result to Row 2}$$

or, in other words, $[(-1)R3 + R2 \rightarrow R2]$

This is illustrated below. The row operation computations are shown in the grey shaded area.

$$
\begin{bmatrix} 1 & 0 & -3 & | & 0 \\ 0 & 1 & 1 & | & 2 \\ 0 & 0 & 1 & | & 1 \end{bmatrix}
\rightarrow
\begin{array}{l} (-1)R3: \quad 0 \quad 0 \quad -1 \quad | \quad -1 \\ + R2: \quad\; 0 \quad 1 \quad\;\; 1 \quad | \quad\;\; 2 \\ \hline Sum \quad\quad 0 \quad 1 \quad\;\; 0 \quad | \quad\;\; 1 \end{array}
\rightarrow
\begin{bmatrix} 1 & 0 & -3 & | & 0 \\ 0 & 1 & 0 & | & 1 \\ 0 & 0 & 1 & | & 1 \end{bmatrix}
$$

Now we need a 0 for the first entry in column 3. We use the row operation

$$3 \text{ times Row 3, add the result to Row 1}$$

or, in other words, $[(3)R3 + R1 \rightarrow R1]$

This is illustrated below. The row operation computations are shown in the grey shaded area.

$$
\begin{bmatrix} 1 & 0 & -3 & | & 0 \\ 0 & 1 & 0 & | & 1 \\ 0 & 0 & 1 & | & 1 \end{bmatrix}
\rightarrow
\begin{array}{ll}
(3)R3: & 0\ \ 0\ \ \ \ 3\ |\ 3 \\
+\ R1: & 1\ \ 0\ -3\ |\ 0 \\
\hline
\text{Sum} \rightarrow & 1\ \ 0\ \ \ \ 0\ |\ 3
\end{array}
\rightarrow
\begin{bmatrix} 1 & 0 & 0 & | & 3 \\ 0 & 1 & 0 & | & 1 \\ 0 & 0 & 1 & | & 1 \end{bmatrix}
$$

Final Tableau

Need a 0 here

The final tableau indicates the solution $x_1 = 3, x_2 = 1, x_3 = 1$, or the ordered triple $(3, 1, 1)$. We leave it to the reader to check this solution.

• EXAMPLE 5-13

Use the Gauss-Jordan method of row operation to solve the linear system

$$x_1 + 2x_2 = 3$$
$$2x_1 + 4x_2 = 8$$

Solution

We first write the initial tableau

Initial Tableau

$$\begin{bmatrix} 1 & 2 & | & 3 \\ 2 & 4 & | & 8 \end{bmatrix}$$

and then use row operations as outlined in the summary on pages 274-275.

Step 1   *Change column 1 to* $\begin{bmatrix} 1 \\ 0 \end{bmatrix}$.

Since we already have a 1 for the first element of column 1, we proceed to change the remaining entry of column 1 to 0 by using the row operation

-2 times Row 1, add the result to Row 2

or, in other words, $[(-2)R1 + R2 \rightarrow R2]$

The resulting tableau is

$$\begin{bmatrix} 1 & 2 & | & 3 \\ 0 & 0 & | & 2 \end{bmatrix}$$

Notice that the second row of the above tableau gives the equation

$$0x_1 + 0x_2 = 2 \quad \text{or} \quad 0 = 2$$

This is an untrue statement (an *inconsistency*) and, hence, an indication that the system has *no solution*. Thus, we proceed no further.

• EXAMPLE 5-14

Use the Gauss-Jordan method to solve

$$x_1 + 2x_2 + x_3 = 3$$
$$2x_1 - 3x_2 - 2x_3 = 5$$
$$2x_1 + 4x_2 + 2x_3 = 6$$

Solution

We first write the initial tableau

Initial Tableau

$$\begin{bmatrix} 1 & 2 & 1 & | & 3 \\ 2 & -3 & -2 & | & 5 \\ 2 & 4 & 2 & | & 6 \end{bmatrix}$$

and then use row operations as outlined in the summary on pages 274-275.

Step 1 *Change column 1 to* $\begin{bmatrix} 1 \\ 0 \\ 0 \end{bmatrix}$.

We already have a 1 for the first coefficient of column 1. We need 0s for the remaining coefficients of column 1. These are obtained by the following two row operations:

- $[(-2)R1 + R2 \rightarrow R2]$ gives us a 0 for the second entry in Column 1.
- $[(-2)R1 + R3 \rightarrow R3]$ gives us a 0 for the third element of Column 1.

The resulting tableau appears below.

$$\begin{bmatrix} 1 & 2 & 1 & 3 \\ 0 & -7 & -4 & -1 \\ 0 & 0 & 0 & 0 \end{bmatrix}$$

Note that since all the entries in row 3 are 0s, it will not be possible to get a 1 for the third element in row 3. If we write the linear system for the above tableau, we get

$$x_1 + 2x_2 + x_3 = 3$$
$$-7x_2 - 4x_3 = -1$$
$$0x_1 + 0x_2 + 0x_3 = 0$$

Observe that the third equation is $0 = 0$, which indicates that the original linear system is equivalent to a system with one less equation.

We continue our attempt to obtain the final tableau and, thus, proceed to step 2.

Step 2 *Change column 2 of the above tableau to* $\begin{bmatrix} 0 \\ 1 \\ 0 \end{bmatrix}$.

We get the 1 by the row operation $[(-1/7)R2 \rightarrow R2]$. The resulting tableau is

$$\begin{bmatrix} 1 & 2 & 1 & 3 \\ 0 & 1 & 4/7 & 1/7 \\ 0 & 0 & 0 & 0 \end{bmatrix}$$

Now, we need a 0 for the first entry in column 2. Using the row operation $[(-2)R2 + R1 \rightarrow R1]$ gets us the 0. The resulting tableau is

$$\begin{bmatrix} 1 & 0 & -1/7 & 19/7 \\ 0 & 1 & 4/7 & 1/7 \\ 0 & 0 & 0 & 0 \end{bmatrix}$$

Step 3 *Change column 3 to* $\begin{bmatrix} 0 \\ 0 \\ 1 \end{bmatrix}$.

However, since row 3 consists of all 0s, this is impossible. Thus, the preceding tableau is the final tableau. Writing the equations corresponding to this final tableau, we have

$$x_1 - \frac{1}{7}x_3 = \frac{19}{7}$$
$$x_2 + \frac{4}{7}x_3 = \frac{1}{7}$$

Note that the third equation, $0 = 0$, is deleted since it is satisfied by all ordered triples (x_1, x_2, x_3). Thus, the original linear system consisting of three equations in three variables is now reduced to two equations in three variables.

Infinitely Many Solutions

In general, when the final tableau of a linear system has more variables than equations, the linear system has infinitely many solutions. For such situations, we classify the variables into two groups:

1. The variables corresponding to the final tableau columns are called **basic variables.**
2. The remaining variables are called **nonbasic variables.**

These are illustrated below for the above problem.

Final Tableau
Columns

basic variables   nonbasic variable
↓   ↓   ↓
x_1 x_2 x_3

$$\begin{bmatrix} 1 & 0 & -1/7 & \bigm| & 19/7 \\ 0 & 1 & 4/7 & \bigm| & 1/7 \\ 0 & 0 & 0 & \bigm| & 0 \end{bmatrix}$$

The infinitely many solutions to a linear system are expressed by solving for the basic variables in terms of the nonbasic variables.

Thus, for the above problem, we solve for x_1 and x_2 in terms of x_3, as is illustrated below.

$$x_1 = \frac{1}{7}x_3 + \frac{19}{7}$$

$$x_2 = -\frac{4}{7}x_3 + \frac{1}{7}$$

Now we let $\boxed{x_3 = t}$, where t denotes any real number; then the *infinitely*

many solutions to the linear system are written as

$$x_1 = \frac{1}{7}t + \frac{19}{7}$$

$$x_2 = -\frac{4}{7}t + \frac{1}{7}$$

$$x_3 = t$$

If $t = 0$, then a solution to the linear system is given by

$$x_1 = \frac{1}{7}(0) + \frac{19}{7} = \frac{19}{7}$$

$$x_2 = -\frac{4}{7}(0) + \frac{1}{7} = \frac{1}{7}$$

$$x_3 = 0$$

If $t = 2$, then a solution is given by

$$x_1 = \frac{1}{7}(2) + \frac{19}{7} = 3$$

$$x_2 = -\frac{4}{7}(2) + \frac{1}{7} = -1$$

$$x_3 = 2$$

SUMMARY

Three Possibilities Exist for Linear Systems with n Equations in n Unknowns

1. *Unique solution.* A linear system has a unique solution if its final tableau has the form below.

$$
\begin{array}{cccc}
x_1 & x_2 & & x_n \\
\end{array}
\left[\begin{array}{cccc|c}
1 & 0 & \cdots\cdots & 0 & c_1 \\
0 & 1 & \cdots\cdots & 0 & c_2 \\
\vdots & \vdots & & \vdots & \vdots \\
0 & 0 & \cdots\cdots & 1 & c_n
\end{array}\right]
$$

Solution:

$$x_1 = c_1, x_2 = c_2, \ldots, x_n = c_n$$

Example:

$$
\left[\begin{array}{ccc|c}
1 & 0 & 0 & 5 \\
0 & 1 & 0 & 3 \\
0 & 0 & 1 & 7
\end{array}\right]
$$

Solution:

$$x_1 = 5, x_2 = 3, x_3 = 7$$

2. *No solution.* If a tableau contains an inconsistency, then there is no solution to the linear system. Recall that an inconsistency appears as a row with 0 entries to the left of the vertical line and a nonzero right-hand-side constant, as illustrated in the tableau below.

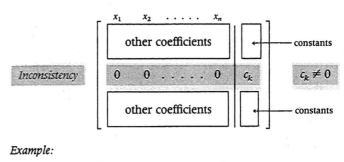

Example:

$$
\begin{array}{c}
\\
\textit{Inconsistency} \\
\\
\end{array}
\left[\begin{array}{ccc|c}
1 & 3 & 1 & 6 \\
0 & 0 & 0 & 8 \\
0 & 1 & 8 & 4
\end{array}\right]
$$

3. *Infinitely many solutions.* If the final tableau has more variables than equations, then there are infinitely many solutions. We then classify the variables as either **basic** or **nonbasic** variables, as illustrated below.

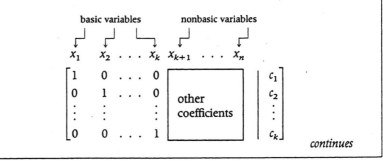

continues

SUMMARY—*Continued*

Then we **solve** for the basic variables in terms of the nonbasic variables.

Example:

basic variables   nonbasic variable

$$\begin{array}{ccc} x_1 & x_2 & x_3 \end{array}$$

$$\begin{bmatrix} 1 & 0 & -2 & | & 5 \\ 0 & 1 & 3 & | & 4 \end{bmatrix} \quad \begin{array}{l} x_1 \;\;\;\;\; - 2x_3 = 5 \\ \;\;\;\;\; x_2 + 3x_3 = 4 \end{array} \;\; \text{or} \;\; \begin{array}{l} x_1 = \;\;\; 2x_3 + 5 \\ x_2 = -3x_3 + 4 \end{array}$$

Example:

basic variables   nonbasic variables

$$\begin{array}{cccc} x_1 & x_2 & x_3 & x_4 \end{array}$$

$$\begin{bmatrix} 1 & 0 & -4 & 3 & | & 8 \\ 0 & 1 & 2 & -7 & | & 9 \end{bmatrix}$$

$$\begin{array}{l} x_1 \;\;\;\;\; - 4x_3 + 3x_4 = 8 \\ \;\;\;\; x_2 + 2x_3 - 7x_4 = 9 \end{array} \;\; \text{or} \;\; \begin{array}{l} x_1 = \;\;\; 4x_3 - 3x_4 + 8 \\ x_2 = -2x_3 + 7x_4 + 9 \end{array}$$

• **EXAMPLE 5-15**

Using the Gauss-Jordan method, solve the linear system

$$\begin{array}{rcrcrcrcr} x_1 & + & 2x_2 & & & + & x_4 & = & 5 \\ & & x_2 & + & & & 2x_4 & = & 6 \\ 2x_1 & + & 4x_2 & + & x_3 & + & x_4 & = & -5 \end{array}$$

Solution

We write the initial tableau.

$$\begin{bmatrix} 1 & 2 & 0 & 1 & | & 5 \\ 0 & 1 & 0 & 2 & | & 6 \\ 2 & 4 & 1 & 1 & | & -5 \end{bmatrix}$$

Since we have more variables than equations, we use row operations to try to obtain an equivalent tableau of the form

$$\begin{array}{cccc} x_1 & x_2 & x_3 & x_4 \end{array}$$
$$\begin{bmatrix} 1 & 0 & 0 & t_1 & | & c_1 \\ 0 & 1 & 0 & t_2 & | & c_2 \\ 0 & 0 & 1 & t_3 & | & c_3 \end{bmatrix}$$

with x_4 as a nonbasic variable. This means that we should use row operations to try to change as many columns as possible to

$$\begin{bmatrix} 1 \\ 0 \\ 0 \end{bmatrix}, \begin{bmatrix} 0 \\ 1 \\ 0 \end{bmatrix}, \ldots$$

Using the row operation $[(-2)R1 + R3 \rightarrow R3]$, followed by $[(-2)R2 + R1 \rightarrow R1]$, we transform the initial tableau into the final tableau below.

Final Tableau

basic variables   nonbasic variable

$$
\begin{array}{cccc}
x_1 & x_2 & x_3 & x_4 \\
\end{array}
$$

$$
\left[\begin{array}{ccc|c}
1 & 0 & 0 & -3 \\
0 & 1 & 0 & 2 \\
0 & 0 & 1 & -1
\end{array}\right.
\left|\begin{array}{r}
-7 \\
6 \\
-15
\end{array}\right]
$$

Writing the equations corresponding to this tableau, we have

$$
\begin{aligned}
x_1 \qquad\qquad - 3x_4 &= -7 \\
x_2 \qquad + 2x_4 &= 6 \\
x_3 - x_4 &= -15
\end{aligned}
$$

Solving for the basic variables, x_1, x_2, x_3, in terms of the nonbasic variable, x_4, gives

$$
\begin{aligned}
x_1 &= 3x_4 - 7 \\
x_2 &= -2x_4 + 6 \\
x_3 &= x_4 - 15
\end{aligned}
$$

If we let $x_4 = t$, where t denotes any real number, then there are *infinitely many solutions* that are expressed as

$$
\begin{aligned}
x_1 &= 3t - 7 \\
x_2 &= -2t + 6 \\
x_3 &= t - 15 \\
x_4 &= t
\end{aligned}
$$

Thus, if $t = 0$, a solution is

$$
\begin{aligned}
x_1 &= 3(0) - 7 = -7 \\
x_2 &= -2(0) + 6 = 6 \\
x_3 &= 0 - 15 = -15 \\
x_4 &= 0
\end{aligned}
$$

If $t = 4$, a solution is

$$
\begin{aligned}
x_1 &= 3(4) - 7 = 5 \\
x_2 &= -2(4) + 6 = -2 \\
x_3 &= 4 - 15 = -11 \\
x_4 &= 4
\end{aligned}
$$

Application

A Transportation Problem

We now solve the transportation problem presented at the end of Section 5-2. Recall that we had to determine how many lawn tractors should be shipped from each plant (assuming each plant is operating at full capacity) to each retail outlet in order to ensure that the reail outlets' demand requirements are met exactly as indicated in Table 5-4 on page 284.

Recall that this problem yielded the linear system below.

Plant 1	$x_1 + x_2$	$= 900$
Plant 2	$x_3 + x_4 = 500$	
Retail outlet 1	$x_1 + x_3$ $= 600$	
Retail outlet 2	$x_2 + x_4 = 800$	

$$
\begin{aligned}
x_1 + x_2 \qquad\qquad &= 900 \\
x_3 + x_4 &= 500 \\
x_1 \qquad + x_3 \qquad &= 600 \\
x_2 \qquad + x_4 &= 800
\end{aligned}
$$

TABLE 5-4

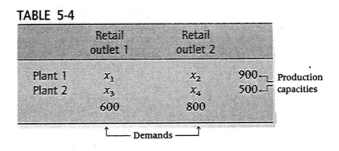

	Retail outlet 1	Retail outlet 2		
Plant 1	x_1	x_2	900	Production
Plant 2	x_3	x_4	500	capacities
	600	800		

└── Demands ──┘

We now proceed to solve the linear system by writing the initial tableau below.

Initial Tableau

$$
\begin{array}{cccc}
x_1 & x_2 & x_3 & x_4 \\
\end{array}
$$

$$
\begin{bmatrix}
1 & 1 & 0 & 0 & 900 \\
0 & 0 & 1 & 1 & 500 \\
1 & 0 & 1 & 0 & 600 \\
0 & 1 & 0 & 1 & 800
\end{bmatrix}
$$

Using the row operations $[(-1)R1 + R3 \rightarrow R3]$, $[R2 \leftrightarrow R4]$, $[(1)R2 + R3 \rightarrow R3]$, $[(-1)R2 + R1 \rightarrow R1]$, and $[(-1)R3 + R4 \rightarrow R4]$ in the order given, we obtain the final tableau.

Final Tableau

basic variables   nonbasic variable

↓   ↓   ↓   ↲

$$
\begin{array}{cccc}
x_1 & x_2 & x_3 & x_4 \\
\end{array}
$$

$$
\begin{bmatrix}
1 & 0 & 0 & -1 & 100 \\
0 & 1 & 0 & 1 & 800 \\
0 & 0 & 1 & 1 & 500 \\
0 & 0 & 0 & 0 & 0
\end{bmatrix}
$$

Solving for the basic variables in terms of the nonbasic variable, we express the *infinitely many solutions* as

$$
\begin{aligned}
x_1 &= x_4 + 100 \\
x_2 &= -x_4 + 800 \\
x_3 &= -x_4 + 500
\end{aligned}
$$

or, letting $x_4 = t$,

$$
\begin{aligned}
x_1 &= t + 100 \\
x_2 &= -t + 800 \\
x_3 &= -t + 500 \\
x_4 &= t
\end{aligned}
$$

Since x_1, x_2, x_3, and $x_4 \geq 0$, then the following inequalities hold:

$t + 100 \geq 0$	$-t + 800 \geq 0$	$-t + 500 \geq 0$	$t \geq 0$
$t \geq -100$	$-t \geq -800$	$-t \geq -500$	
	$t \leq 800$	$t \leq 500$	

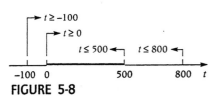

FIGURE 5-8

We have solved each of the above inequalities. The solutions appear in the color screens. Since t must satisfy all of the above results in the color screens, we graph these results in Figure 5-8 and shade the most restrictive range for t in color. Thus, t must satisfy the inequality $0 \leq t \leq 500$, as indicated in Figure 5-8.

Thus, if $t = 300$, then a solution to our problem is $x_1 = 300 + 100 = 400$, $x_2 = -300 + 800 = 500$, $x_3 = -300 + 500 = 200$, and $x_4 = 300$. Looking at Table 5-4, this means that $x_1 = 400$ lawn tractors should be shipped from plant 1 to retail outlet 1, $x_2 = 500$ lawn tractors should be shipped from plant 1 to retail outlet 2, $x_3 = 200$ lawn tractors should be shipped from plant 2 to retail outlet 1, and $x_4 = 300$ lawn tractors should be shipped from plant 2 to retail outlet 2. We should keep in mind that this is only one of infinitely many possible solutions; others can be obtained by choosing values of t such that $0 \leq t \leq 500$.

More Equations Than Variables

Sometimes we encounter a linear system with more equations than variables. The following linear system is such an example:

$$x_1 - x_2 = 1$$
$$4x_1 - x_2 = 7$$
$$3x_1 - x_2 = 5$$

Note that each equation has a straight line as its graph. Thus, the three lines might intersect at a common point, in which case there would be a unique solution; the three lines might be parallel, in which case there would be no solution; the three lines might intersect at different points, in which case there would be no solution; two of the three lines might be the same, so that the intersection with the third line would yield a unique solution; etc.

We will attempt to solve the preceding linear system by the Gauss-Jordan method of row operations. Writing the initial tableau, we have

$$\begin{bmatrix} 1 & -1 & | & 1 \\ 4 & -1 & | & 7 \\ 3 & -1 & | & 5 \end{bmatrix}$$

Since there are more equations than variables, we must use row operations to try to change as many columns as possible to

$$\begin{bmatrix} 1 \\ 0 \\ 0 \end{bmatrix}, \begin{bmatrix} 0 \\ 1 \\ 0 \end{bmatrix}, \ldots$$

Thus, we try to obtain a final tableau with the left-hand side as shown below.

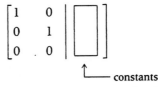

constants

Using row operations, we transform the initial tableau into the final tableau.

$$\begin{bmatrix} 1 & 0 & | & 2 \\ 0 & 1 & | & 1 \\ 0 & 0 & | & 0 \end{bmatrix}$$

Converting this tableau into equation form, we have

$$x_1 = 2$$
$$x_2 = 1$$

Note that the third row is converted into the equation $(0x_1 + 0x_2 = 0$. Since this equation is satisfied by all ordered pairs (x_1, x_2), we delete it from the system. Thus, our linear system has the unique solution $x_1 = 2$ and $x_2 = 1$, or the ordered pair $(2, 1)$.

• **EXAMPLE 5-16** _____

Using the Gauss-Jordan method, solve

$$x_1 - x_2 = 4$$
$$2x_1 + 3x_2 = 8$$
$$5x_1 + x_2 = 7$$

Solution

We write the initial tableau.

$$\begin{bmatrix} 1 & -1 & | & 4 \\ 2 & 3 & | & 8 \\ 5 & 1 & | & 7 \end{bmatrix}$$

Using row operations, we transform the initial tableau into

$$\begin{bmatrix} 1 & 0 & | & 4 \\ 0 & 1 & | & 0 \\ 0 & 0 & | & -13 \end{bmatrix}$$

Note that the third row results in the equation $0x_1 + 0x_2 = -13$, or $0 = -13$, an *inconsistency*. Hence, the system has *no solution*.

• **EXAMPLE 5-17** _____

Using the Gauss-Jordan method, solve

$$x_1 + 2x_2 + x_3 = -3$$
$$2x_1 + 2x_2 + 4x_3 = 2$$
$$x_1 + x_2 + 2x_3 = 1$$
$$-4x_1 - 4x_2 - 8x_3 = -4$$

Solution

We write the initial tableau.

$$\begin{bmatrix} 1 & 2 & 1 & -3 \\ 2 & 2 & 4 & 2 \\ 1 & 1 & 2 & 1 \\ -4 & -4 & -8 & -4 \end{bmatrix}$$

Using row operations, we transform the initial tableau into

$$\begin{bmatrix} 1 & 0 & 3 & 5 \\ 0 & 1 & -1 & -4 \\ 0 & 0 & 0 & 0 \\ 0 & 0 & 0 & 0 \end{bmatrix}$$

Note that each of the last two rows consists of the identity $0 = 0$. Since this identity is satisfied by all ordered triples (x_1, x_2, x_3), we delete the last two rows. The corresponding linear system becomes

$$\begin{aligned} x_1 \quad + 3x_3 &= 5 \\ x_2 - x_3 &= -4 \end{aligned}$$

Solving for x_1 and x_2 in terms of x_3, we obtain

$$\begin{aligned} x_1 &= -3x_3 + 5 \\ x_2 &= x_3 - 4 \end{aligned}$$

Letting $x_3 = t$, the *infinitely many solutions* are expressed as

$$\begin{aligned} x_1 &= -3t + 5 \\ x_2 &= t - 4 \\ x_3 &= t \end{aligned}$$

If $t = 2$, a solution is

$$\begin{aligned} x_1 &= -3(2) + 5 = -1 \\ x_2 &= 2 - 4 = -2 \\ x_3 &= 2 \end{aligned}$$

Exercises 5-3

Perform the indicated row operation on each tableau below.

1. $\begin{bmatrix} 1 & 2 & 4 \\ -2 & 3 & -5 \end{bmatrix} \xrightarrow{(2)R1 + R2 \to R2}$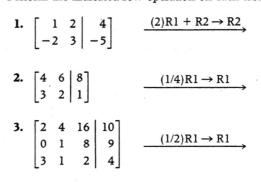

2. $\begin{bmatrix} 4 & 6 & 8 \\ 3 & 2 & 1 \end{bmatrix} \xrightarrow{(1/4)R1 \to R1}$

3. $\begin{bmatrix} 2 & 4 & 16 & 10 \\ 0 & 1 & 8 & 9 \\ 3 & 1 & 2 & 4 \end{bmatrix} \xrightarrow{(1/2)R1 \to R1}$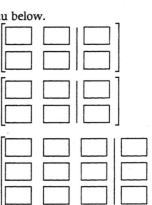

4. $\begin{bmatrix} 1 & 0 & 8 & | & 9 \\ 0 & 1 & 2 & | & 1 \\ 0 & 5 & 3 & | & 8 \end{bmatrix}$ $\xrightarrow{(-5)R2 + R3 \rightarrow R3}$

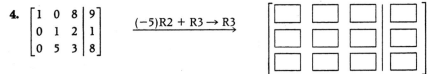

Perform the indicated row operations successively on the tableaus below.

5. $\begin{bmatrix} 1 & 0 & 3 & | & 2 \\ 2 & -1 & 2 & | & 4 \\ -3 & 1 & -1 & | & 5 \end{bmatrix}$ $\xrightarrow[(3)R1 + R3 \rightarrow R3]{(-2)R1 + R2 \rightarrow R2}$

6. $\begin{bmatrix} 1 & 3 & 1 & | & 2 \\ 0 & 1 & -2 & | & 4 \\ 0 & -4 & 6 & | & 5 \end{bmatrix}$ $\xrightarrow[(4)R2 + R3 \rightarrow R3]{(-3)R2 + R1 \rightarrow R1}$

7. $\begin{bmatrix} 1 & 0 & -3 & | & -1 \\ 0 & 1 & 4 & | & -2 \\ 0 & 0 & 1 & | & 3 \end{bmatrix}$ $\xrightarrow[(3)R3 + R1 \rightarrow R1]{(-4)R3 + R2 \rightarrow R2}$

8. $\begin{bmatrix} 1 & 0 & -2 & | & 3 \\ 0 & 1 & 5 & | & -1 \\ 0 & 0 & 1 & | & 4 \end{bmatrix}$ $\xrightarrow[(2)R3 + R1 \rightarrow R1]{(-5)R3 + R2 \rightarrow R2}$

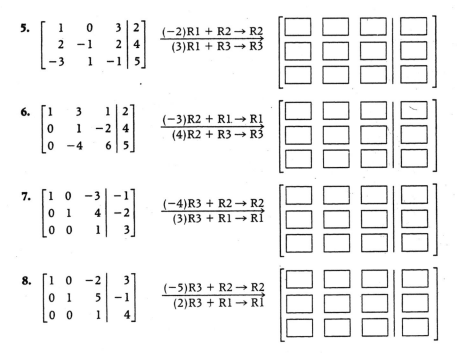

Solve each of the following linear systems by using the Gauss-Jordan method of row operations.

9. $2x - 3y = 6$
$x - 7y = 25$

10. $2x_1 + 3x_2 = 3$
$12x_1 - 15x_2 = -4$

11. $2x + 3y - 5z = -13$
$-x + 2y + 3z = -7$
$3x - 4y - 7z = 15$

12. $x_1 + 3x_2 + x_3 = -3$
$2x_1 + 9x_2 + 2x_3 = -5$
$5x_1 + 48x_2 + 7x_3 = -16$

13. $2x + y + 3z = 11$
$4x + 3y - 2z = -1$
$6x + 5y - 4z = -4$

14. $x_1 + x_2 - 5x_3 = -3$
$2x_1 + x_2 + 10x_3 = 2$
$3x_1 + 2x_2 + 25x_3 = 3$

15. $x_1 + 10x_2 = 34$
$3x_1 + 2x_2 = 18$

16. $2x - y = -7$
$-x + 2y = 8$

17. $5x_1 + 7x_2 + x_3 = 1$
$3x_1 + 2x_2 + 3x_3 = 8$
$2x_1 + 3x_2 + 5x_3 = 19$

18. $3x + 7y + 2z = 2$
$4x + 3y + 3z = 8$
$x + 2y + 4z = -9$

19. $x_1 + 2x_2 + x_3 = 4$
$2x_1 + x_2 - x_3 = -4$
$3x_1 + x_2 + x_3 = 1$

20. $x_1 + x_2 - x_3 = -4$
$-x_1 + x_2 - 2x_3 = 3$
$2x_1 - x_2 - x_3 = 7$

21. $-x_1 + x_2 - x_3 = -6$
$x_1 + 3x_2 + x_3 = 10$
$-2x_1 + x_2 = 6$

22. $x_1 + x_2 + x_3 = -1$
$-x_1 + x_2 = -3$
$x_2 + x_3 = -3$

23. $x_1 - x_2 - x_3 = -4$
$x_1 - 4x_2 \quad\quad = -14$
$\quad\quad x_2 + 2x_3 = 1$

24. $x_1 - x_2 - 2x_3 = 3$
$-x_1 + 2x_2 + x_3 = -6$
$-x_1 + x_2 + 3x_3 = -2$

Solve the following linear systems by using the Gauss-Jordan method of row operations.

25. $x_1 + 2x_2 + x_3 - x_4 = 9$
$\quad\quad x_2 - x_3 + 2x_4 = -3$
$4x_1 \quad\quad + 5x_3 + 3x_4 = 16$
$\quad\quad\quad\quad 2x_3 + 52x_4 = -46$

26. $x_1 + 2x_2 - x_3 + x_4 = -7$
$2x_1 + x_2 + x_3 + 2x_4 = 1$
$-3x_1 - x_2 + x_3 - x_4 = 3$
$x_1 \quad\quad\quad\quad + 2x_4 = -1$

Some of the following linear systems have no solution, and some have infinitely many solutions. Try to solve each by the Gauss-Jordan method of row operations. If the system has no solution, then state so. If the system has infinitely many solutions, express them in terms of t.

27. $3x - 5y = 8$
$-6x + 10y = 30$

28. $2x_1 + 3x_2 = 7$
$-x_1 - 1.5x_2 = -4.5$

29. $8x_1 - 2x_2 = 10$
$-4x_1 + x_2 = -5$

30. $4x_1 - x_2 = 9$
$-12x_1 + 3x_2 = 36$

31. $x_1 - 2x_2 + x_3 = 3$
$3x_1 - 7x_2 + 2x_3 = 4$
$-2x_1 + 4x_2 - 2x_3 = 8$

32. $x_1 + 4x_2 + x_3 = 6$
$2x_1 + 9x_2 + 2x_3 = 8$
$3x_1 + 12x_2 + 3x_3 = 18$

33. $x_1 + x_2 + x_3 = 4$
$x_1 + 2x_2 + 3x_3 = 2$
$2x_1 + 4x_2 + 6x_3 = 5$

34. $x_1 - 2x_2 - 2x_3 = 4$
$-2x_1 + 4x_2 + 4x_3 = -8$
$x_1 + 3x_2 + 2x_3 = 4$

Using the Gauss-Jordan method, solve or attempt to solve each of the following linear systems. If the system has no solutions, then state so. If the system has infinitely many solutions, express them in terms of t.

35. $x_1 + 2x_2 + x_3 = 4$
$2x_1 + x_2 + 5x_3 = 6$

36. $x_1 - 3x_2 + x_3 = 6$
$-2x_1 + 6x_2 - 2x_3 = 9$

37. $x_1 + 2x_2 + x_3 \quad\quad = 4$
$-x_1 - x_2 \quad\quad + x_4 = 5$
$3x_1 + 6x_2 + x_3 + x_4 = 6$

38. $x_1 + 2x_2 + x_3 + x_4 = 5$
$x_1 + 3x_2 + 2x_3 + x_4 = 6$
$2x_1 + 5x_2 + 2x_3 + x_4 = 8$

39. $2x_1 + x_2 + x_3 - x_4 = 6$
$x_1 + x_2 + x_3 - x_4 = 8$
$-2x_1 - x_2 - x_3 + x_4 = 9$

40. $x_1 + x_2 - x_3 + x_4 = 8$
$-x_1 + 2x_2 + 2x_3 + x_4 = -4$

41. $x_1 + 2x_2 - x_3 - x_4 = 5$
$2x_1 + 5x_2 + x_3 - 2x_4 = 8$

42. $x_1 + 2x_2 - x_3 = 5$
$-x_1 + 4x_2 - 11x_3 = 13$

Using the Gauss-Jordan method, solve or attempt to solve each of the following linear systems. If the system has a unique solution, then state the solution. If the system has no solutions, then state so. If the system has infinitely many solutions, express them in terms of t.

43. $x_1 + x_2 = 1$
$2x_1 + x_2 = 4$
$4x_1 + 2x_2 = 8$

44. $x_1 + 2x_2 = 3$
$2x_1 - x_2 = 1$
$2x_1 + x_2 = 4$

45. $x_1 + 3x_2 = 4$
$2x_1 + 6x_2 = 8$
$-3x_1 - 9x_2 = -12$

46. $x_1 + x_2 = 4$
$2x_1 + 3x_2 = 1$
$x_1 - x_2 = 8$

47.
$$2x_1 + x_2 + 3x_3 = 11$$
$$6x_1 + 5x_2 - 4x_3 = -4$$
$$4x_1 + 3x_2 - 2x_3 = -1$$
$$-6x_1 - 5x_2 + 4x_3 = 4$$

48.
$$x_1 + x_2 + 2x_3 = 4$$
$$2x_1 + 3x_2 + x_3 = 8$$
$$2x_1 + 2x_2 + 4x_3 = 8$$
$$-x_1 - x_2 - 2x_3 = -4$$

Applications

49. *Production planning.* Reread the production planning problem beginning on page 259 in Section 5-2. Recall that this problem, when formulated, yielded the linear system

$$2x + 3y + 5z = 780$$
$$x + 2y + z = 320$$
$$4x + y + 3z = 500$$

Solve this linear system and interpret the result.

50. *Investment: Portfolio allocation.* Reread the portfolio allocation problem beginning on page 264 in Section 5-2. Recall that this problem, when formulated, yielded the linear system

$$x_1 + x_2 + x_3 = 400,000$$
$$0.20x_1 + 0.16x_2 + 0.08x_3 = 62,000$$
$$9x_1 + 3x_2 + x_3 = 2,000,000$$

Solve this linear system and interpret the result.

51. *Production planning.* Solve the linear system in Exercise 23 on page 267 at the end of Section 5-2. Interpret the result.

52. *Investment: Portfolio allocation.* Solve the linear system in Exercise 24 on page 267 at the end of Section 5-2. Interpret the result.

53. *Transportation problem.* Solve the linear system in Exercise 25 on page 267 at the end of Section 5-2. Interpret the result.

54. *Production planning.* A company makes three products: A, B, and C. Each product must pass through departments 1 and 2. The time requirements (in person-hours) for a unit of each product in each department are given below.

	Products			Total time (person-hours) available per department
	A	B	C	
Department 1	2	1	1	80
Department 2	1	2	1	100

If each department is to operate at full capacity, how many units of each product should be produced? Write and solve the linear system for this problem. Interpret the result.

55. *Transportation problem.* A company makes industrial air compressors at two plants. The air compressors must be transported from the two plants to two distribution centers, as is illustrated below.

	Distribution center 1	Distribution center 2		
Plant 1	x_1	x_2	500	Production
Plant 2	x_3	x_4	300	capacities
	600	200		

└———— Demands ————┘

The production capacity of each plant and the demand of each distribution center are given above. If each plant is to operate at full capacity, how many air compressors should be shipped from each plant to each distribution center to ensure that the distribution centers' demands are met exactly? Write and solve the linear system for this problem. Interpret the result.

56. *Marketing research: Survey planning.* A marketing research firm is planning a survey of households that are cross-classified with regard to whether or not the household has children versus whether the interview is to take place during the day or evening, as indicated in the table below.

Household	Day	Evening	
Children	x_1	x_2	300 ↰ Total
No children	x_3	x_4	200 ↲ households
	100	400	

Total households

Note that

x_1 = number of households that have children and are to be interviewed during the day

x_2 = number of households that have children and are to be interviewed during the evening

x_3 = number of households that have no children and are to be interviewed during the day

x_4 = number of households that have no children and are to be interviewed during the evening

How many of each type of household should be interviewed in order to ensure that all the households are interviewed? Write and solve the linear system for this problem. Interpret the result.

57. *Blending problem.* A company has developed a new gasoline additive for automobiles. The additive is a blend of three liquid ingredients: A, B, and C. The company's immediate production plans are to make 100,000 gallons of this additive. The cost per gallon for each ingredient is given in the table below.

Cost per gallon

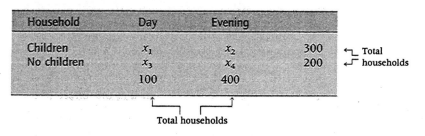

Ingredient A	Ingredient B	Ingredient C
$2	$4	$8

The company wants to ensure that the total cost of 100,000 gallons of this additive does not exceed $600,000 (or, in other words, $6 per gallon). How many gallons of each ingredient should be blended to make 100,000 gallons of additive if the total cost requirement is to be met exactly and if the 100,000-gallon blend is to have an amount of ingredient C that is 5.5 times the amount of ingredient A? Write and solve the linear system for this problem. Interpret the result.

58. *Product mix.* A company uses three types of raw materials to make three products: A, B, and C. The table below indicates the amount of each raw material required for a unit of each product.

Raw material requirements

	Product A	Product B	Product C	Total amounts of raw materials available (pounds)
Raw Material 1	1	2	1	800
Raw Material 2	2	1	5	1300
Raw Material 3	1	2	0	700

How many units of each product should be produced if the raw material supplies are to be exhausted? Wrote and solve the linear system for this problem. Interpret the result.

59. *Nutrition.* A diet consisting of various amounts of three types of foods A, B, and C—must provide minimal amounts of each of three nutrients as indicated below. The table below gives the number of milligrams of each nutrient contained in one ounce of each type of food. Also given are the minimal nutritional requirements for the respective nutrients.

Milligrams of nutrient per ounce of food

Nutrient	Food A	Food B	Food C	Minimal nutritional requirements (milligrams)
Calcium	20	20	40	1800
Iron	10	20	10	800
Vitamin B	20	10	10	700

How many ounces of each type of food should be included in the diet if the minimal nutritional requirements are to be met exactly?

5-4   • MATRICES

In the previous section, we have used tableaus or rectangular arrays to express linear systems. We have learned that a rectangular array of numbers is called a **matrix.** In this section, we will see more uses of rectangular arrays of numbers, or matrices.

We begin with a furniture manufacturer that makes three models—A, B, and C—of dining room sets and kitchen sets. During a given week, the company makes 30 model A, 20 model B, and 45 model C dining room sets. Also, during the same week, the company makes 40 model A, 35 model B, and 60 model C kitchen sets.

We wish to organize this information so that it can be efficiently displayed. The table below is one such display.

	Model A	Model B	Model C
Dining Room Sets	30	20	45
Kitchen Sets	40	35	60

The rectangular array of numbers

$$\begin{bmatrix} 30 & 20 & 45 \\ 40 & 35 & 60 \end{bmatrix}$$

is called a matrix. We now formalize this concept.

A **matrix** is a rectangular array of numbers. Each number is called an **element** of the matrix. Specifically.

$$\begin{array}{c} & \text{col 1} \quad \text{col 2} \quad \text{col 3} \\ \text{row 1} \rightarrow \\ \text{row 2} \rightarrow \end{array} \begin{bmatrix} 3 & 1 & 2 \\ 8 & 0 & -5 \end{bmatrix}$$

is a matrix with two rows and three columns. Thus, it is of **dimension** 2×3, read "two by three." In general, a matrix with m rows and n columns is of dimension $m \times n$. The following are matrices of various dimensions:

$$\begin{bmatrix} 3 \\ 4 \\ 2 \end{bmatrix} \qquad [2 \quad 4 \quad -7] \qquad \begin{bmatrix} 4 & 5 \\ 6 & -1 \end{bmatrix}$$

dimension   dimension   dimension
3×1 1×3 2×2

A matrix of only one column is called a **column matrix.** The matrix

$$\begin{bmatrix} 3 \\ -1 \end{bmatrix}$$

is an example of a column matrix. A matrix of only one row is called a **row matrix.** The matrix

$$[5 \quad 0 \quad -1 \quad 7]$$

is an example of a row matrix. A matrix with as many rows as columns is called a **square matrix.** The matrix

$$\begin{bmatrix} 3 & 4 \\ 6 & 0 \end{bmatrix}$$

is an example of a square matrix.

As we have already seen, matrices provide useful ways of presenting data. As a specific example, we consider the following product-mix problem.

• EXAMPLE 5-18

A company makes three types—A, B, and C—of table saws. The time requirement for each type of table saw in each of three departments is given in the 3×3 matrix.

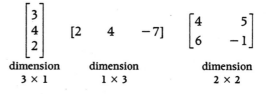

Type A Type B Type C
$$\begin{bmatrix} 2 & 3 & 4 \\ 3 & 5 & 2 \\ 6 & 3 & 5 \end{bmatrix}$$ Department I
Department II
Department III

Assuming that the time requirements are given in hours, state how many hours each type of table saw requires in each department.

Solution

Studying this matrix, note that each type A table saw requires 2 hours in department I, 3 hours in department II, and 6 hours in department III. Each type B table saw requires 3 hours in department I, 5 hours in department II, and 3 hours in department III. And each type C table saw requires 4 hours in department I, 2 hours in department II, and 5 hours in department III.

Matrix Notation

Matrices are usually denoted by capital letters. Thus, the matrix

$$B = \begin{bmatrix} 5 & 3 & 1 \\ 8 & 0 & 2 \end{bmatrix}$$

may be referred to by the letter B.

It is sometimes necessary to refer to a general matrix of a given dimension. For example, a general matrix A of dimension 2×3 is

$$A = \begin{bmatrix} a_{11} & a_{12} & a_{13} \\ a_{21} & a_{22} & a_{23} \end{bmatrix}$$

Note that the individual elements of the matrix A are denoted by a_{ij}, where i denotes the row in which the element is located and j denotes the column. Thus, a_{11} denotes the element located in the first row and first column, a_{12} denotes the element in the first row and second column, ..., and a_{23} denotes the element in the second row and third column. In general, a matrix A of dimension $m \times n$ is denoted by

$$A = \begin{bmatrix} a_{11} & a_{12} & \cdots \cdots & a_{1n} \\ a_{21} & a_{22} & \cdots \cdots & a_{2n} \\ \vdots & \vdots & & \vdots \\ a_{m1} & a_{m2} & \cdots \cdots & a_{mn} \end{bmatrix}$$

Equality of Matrices

Two matrices are **equal** if they are of the same dimension and if their corresponding elements are equal. Thus, if

$$A = \begin{bmatrix} 4 & 3 \\ -2 & 1 \end{bmatrix} \quad \text{and} \quad B = \begin{bmatrix} 8/2 & 3 \\ -2 & 6/6 \end{bmatrix}$$

then $A = B$. However, if $C = [1 \quad 6]$ and $D = [6 \quad 1]$, then $C \neq D$ since corresponding elements are not equal.

Adding and Subtracting Matrices

If two or more matrices are of the same dimension, then they may be *added*. The **sum** of two or more matrices is a matrix where each element is the sum of the corresponding elements of the individual matrices. Similar statements hold for subtraction of matrices. Thus, if

$$A = \begin{bmatrix} 1 & 0 & -5 \\ 8 & -2 & 9 \end{bmatrix} \quad \text{and} \quad B = \begin{bmatrix} 4 & 2 & 3 \\ 5 & 1 & 7 \end{bmatrix}$$

then

$$A + B = \begin{bmatrix} 1+4 & 0+2 & -5+3 \\ 8+5 & -2+1 & 9+7 \end{bmatrix} = \begin{bmatrix} 5 & 2 & -2 \\ 13 & -1 & 16 \end{bmatrix}$$

$$A - B = \begin{bmatrix} 1-4 & 0-2 & -5-3 \\ 8-5 & -2-1 & 9-7 \end{bmatrix} = \begin{bmatrix} -3 & -2 & -8 \\ 3 & -3 & 2 \end{bmatrix}$$

• EXAMPLE 5-19

Matrix N shows the number of dryers shipped from two plants, P_1 and P_2, to three warehouses, W_1, W_2, and W_3, during the month of November.

$$N = \begin{array}{c} \\ P_1 \\ P_2 \end{array} \begin{array}{ccc} W_1 & W_2 & W_3 \\ \begin{bmatrix} 100 & 50 & 70 \\ 300 & 20 & 80 \end{bmatrix} \end{array}$$

Matrix D shows the corresponding shipments made during December.

$$D = \begin{array}{c} \\ P_1 \\ P_2 \end{array} \begin{array}{ccc} W_1 & W_2 & W_3 \\ \begin{bmatrix} 200 & 150 & 80 \\ 400 & 90 & 100 \end{bmatrix} \end{array}$$

Find the matrix showing the combined shipment for both months.

Solution

Here,

$$N + D = \begin{bmatrix} 100+200 & 50+150 & 70+80 \\ 300+400 & 20+90 & 80+100 \end{bmatrix}$$

$$= \begin{bmatrix} 300 & 200 & 150 \\ 700 & 110 & 180 \end{bmatrix}$$

Multiplying a Matrix by a Number

If a matrix A is multiplied by a number k, then the resulting matrix, kA, is determined by multiplying each element of matrix A by k. Specifically, if

$$A = \begin{bmatrix} 6 & 5 \\ 1 & 7 \end{bmatrix}$$

then

$$2A = \begin{bmatrix} 2 \cdot 6 & 2 \cdot 5 \\ 2 \cdot 1 & 2 \cdot 7 \end{bmatrix} = \begin{bmatrix} 12 & 10 \\ 2 & 14 \end{bmatrix}$$

Observe that

$$A + A = \begin{bmatrix} 6 & 5 \\ 1 & 7 \end{bmatrix} + \begin{bmatrix} 6 & 5 \\ 1 & 7 \end{bmatrix} = \begin{bmatrix} 12 & 10 \\ 2 & 14 \end{bmatrix} = 2A$$

• EXAMPLE 5-20 Cost Allocation. _____

The matrix below gives monthly utility costs for each of three plants operated by a company.

$$C = \begin{array}{ccc} \text{Plant 1} & \text{Plant 2} & \text{Plant 3} \\ \begin{bmatrix} \$9000 & \$8000 & \$10,000 \\ \$9800 & \$8900 & \$11,600 \\ \$7600 & \$7900 & \$9800 \end{bmatrix} & \begin{array}{l} \text{January} \\ \text{February} \\ \text{March} \end{array} \end{array}$$

If 40% of utility costs are attributed to electricity, determine the electricity cost for each plant for each of the above months.

Solution

Electricity costs are given by the matrix

$$0.40C = \begin{bmatrix} (0.40)(\$9000) & (0.40)(\$8000) & (0.40)(\$10,000) \\ (0.40)(\$9800) & (0.40)(\$8900) & (0.40)(\$11,600) \\ (0.40)(\$7600) & (0.40)(\$7900) & (0.40)(\$9800) \end{bmatrix}$$

$$= \begin{array}{ccc} \text{Plant 1} & \text{Plant 2} & \text{Plant 3} \\ \begin{bmatrix} \$3600 & \$3200 & \$4000 \\ \$3920 & \$3560 & \$4640 \\ \$3040 & \$3160 & \$3920 \end{bmatrix} & \begin{array}{l} \text{January} \\ \text{February} \\ \text{March} \end{array} \end{array}$$

Exercises 5-4

State the dimension of each of the following matrices.

1. $\begin{bmatrix} 4 & 3 & -1 \\ 8 & 2 & 6 \end{bmatrix}$

2. $\begin{bmatrix} 6 & 8 \\ 5 & -4 \\ 2 & 0 \end{bmatrix}$

3. $\begin{bmatrix} 8 & 4 & 0 \\ 1 & 1 & 0 \\ 2 & 2 & 0 \end{bmatrix}$

4. $\begin{bmatrix} 8 & 4 \\ 6 & -10 \end{bmatrix}$

5. $\begin{bmatrix} 4 & -1 & 6 \end{bmatrix}$

6. $\begin{bmatrix} 7 \\ -1 \end{bmatrix}$

7. $\begin{bmatrix} 5 \\ 0 \\ -1 \\ 4 \end{bmatrix}$

8. $\begin{bmatrix} 3 & 0 & -1 & 5 \end{bmatrix}$

Identify each of the following as either a row matrix or a column matrix.

9. $\begin{bmatrix} 4 & 3 & 0 \end{bmatrix}$

10. $\begin{bmatrix} 7 & -1 \end{bmatrix}$

11. $\begin{bmatrix} 8 \\ 4 \end{bmatrix}$

12. $\begin{bmatrix} 9 \\ 2 \\ 0 \end{bmatrix}$

Which of the following are square matrices?

13. $\begin{bmatrix} 3 & 6 & 1 \\ 8 & 2 & 0 \end{bmatrix}$

14. $\begin{bmatrix} 4 & 3 \\ 2 & 0 \end{bmatrix}$

15.
$$\begin{bmatrix} 8 & 1 & 0 \\ 4 & 3 & 0 \\ 8 & 2 & 1 \end{bmatrix}$$

16.
$$\begin{bmatrix} 8 & 6 & 1 & 0 \\ 2 & 3 & 0 & 0 \end{bmatrix}$$

For Exercises 17-20, indicate whether the statement is true or false.

17. If
$$A = \begin{bmatrix} 5 & 3 & 6 \\ 8 & 2 & 1 \end{bmatrix} \quad \text{and} \quad B = \begin{bmatrix} 10/2 & 12/4 & 6 \\ 8 & 14/7 & 9/9 \end{bmatrix}$$
then $A = B$.

18. If
$$C = \begin{bmatrix} 5 & 6 \\ 8 & 4 \end{bmatrix} \quad \text{and} \quad D = \begin{bmatrix} 5 & 6 & 0 \\ 8 & 4 & 0 \end{bmatrix}$$
then $C = D$.

19. If
$$E = \begin{bmatrix} 4 & 8 \\ 6 & 2 \end{bmatrix} \quad \text{and} \quad F = \begin{bmatrix} 8 & 4 \\ 6 & 2 \end{bmatrix}$$
then $E = F$.

20. If
$$H = \begin{bmatrix} 4 & 1 \\ 6 & -2 \end{bmatrix} \quad \text{and} \quad K = \begin{bmatrix} 4 & 8/8 \\ 6 & -2 \end{bmatrix}$$
then $H = K$.

21. Let
$$A = \begin{bmatrix} x \\ y \end{bmatrix} \quad \text{and} \quad B = \begin{bmatrix} 4 \\ -1 \end{bmatrix}$$
Given that $A = B$, what are the values of x and y?

22. Let
$$C = \begin{bmatrix} x_1 \\ x_2 \\ x_3 \end{bmatrix} \quad \text{and} \quad D = \begin{bmatrix} 1 \\ 0 \\ -3 \end{bmatrix}$$
Given that $C = D$, what are the values of x_1, x_2, and x_3?

23. Let
$$H = \begin{bmatrix} x & y \\ z & w \end{bmatrix} \quad \text{and} \quad K = \begin{bmatrix} 1 & -4 \\ 5 & -7 \end{bmatrix}$$
Given that $H = K$, what are the values of x, y, z, and w?

Compute each of the following if
$$A = \begin{bmatrix} 3 & 1 & 2 \\ -1 & 5 & -2 \end{bmatrix} \quad B = \begin{bmatrix} 0 & 4 & 1 \\ 2 & -5 & 3 \end{bmatrix} \quad C = \begin{bmatrix} 4 & 3 & 0 \\ -2 & 5 & -1 \end{bmatrix}$$

24. $A + B$	**25.** $A - B$	**26.** $B - A$
27. $A + C$	**28.** $A - C$	**29.** $C - A$
30. $B + C$	**31.** $B - C$	**32.** $C - B$
33. $A + B + C$	**34.** $A + B - C$	**35.** $A + C - B$
36. $2A$	**37.** $3B$	**38.** $5C$
39. $-3A$	**40.** $-6B$	**41.** $-2C$
42. $C + 2A$	**43.** $A - 3B$	**44.** $B + 5C$
45. $B - 3A$	**46.** $A - 6B + 5C$	**47.** $A + B - 2C$

If $A = [3 \quad -4 \quad 1]$ and $B = [2 \quad 0 \quad -3]$, compute each of the following:

48. $A + B$ **49.** $A - B$ **50.** $B - A$

51. $3A$ **52.** $-2B$ **53.** $A - 2B$

54. $B + 3A$ **55.** $B - 3A$ **56.** $A + 2B$

If $C = \begin{bmatrix} 8 \\ 2 \end{bmatrix}$ and $D = \begin{bmatrix} -7 \\ 1 \end{bmatrix}$, compute each of the following:

57. $C + D$ **58.** $C - D$ **59.** $D - C$

60. $5C$ **61.** $-3D$ **62.** $C - 3D$

63. $5C + D$ **64.** $D - 5C$ **65.** $C + 3D$

Perform the indicated operations.

66. $\begin{bmatrix} 4 & 3 \\ -1 & 2 \end{bmatrix} + \begin{bmatrix} -8 & 0 \\ 2 & 5 \end{bmatrix}$ **67.** $\begin{bmatrix} 1 & -1 \\ 2 & 0 \end{bmatrix} + \begin{bmatrix} -2 & -4 \\ 3 & 9 \end{bmatrix}$

68. $\begin{bmatrix} 8 & 3 & -1 \\ 1 & 0 & 2 \end{bmatrix} - \begin{bmatrix} -1 & 1 & 2 \\ 0 & -2 & -4 \end{bmatrix}$

69. $\begin{bmatrix} -1 & 2 \\ 4 & -3 \\ 0 & -1 \end{bmatrix} - \begin{bmatrix} 4 & -3 \\ 1 & 2 \\ -2 & 6 \end{bmatrix}$

70. $2\begin{bmatrix} 1 & 4 \\ 2 & 1 \end{bmatrix} + \begin{bmatrix} 1 & 0 \\ -1 & 3 \end{bmatrix}$ **71.** $\begin{bmatrix} 4 & 2 \\ -1 & 10 \end{bmatrix} - 3\begin{bmatrix} 1 & -2 \\ 2 & -4 \end{bmatrix}$

72. $-3\begin{bmatrix} -1 & 6 \\ -2 & -1 \end{bmatrix} + 2\begin{bmatrix} 0 & 4 \\ -2 & 1 \end{bmatrix}$ **73.** $2\begin{bmatrix} 10 & 5 \\ 2 & 4 \end{bmatrix} - 3\begin{bmatrix} -1 & -2 \\ 1 & 4 \end{bmatrix}$

74. Let $X = \begin{bmatrix} x_1 \\ x_2 \end{bmatrix}$ and $B = \begin{bmatrix} 6 \\ 15 \end{bmatrix}$. Given that $3X = B$, find X.

75. Let $X = \begin{bmatrix} x_1 \\ x_2 \\ x_3 \end{bmatrix}$ and $C = \begin{bmatrix} 15 \\ 20 \\ 30 \end{bmatrix}$. Given that $5X = C$, find X.

76. If $A = \begin{bmatrix} 4 & 1 \\ 3 & 2 \end{bmatrix}$ and $B = \begin{bmatrix} -1 & 5 \\ 6 & 4 \end{bmatrix}$, verify that $A + B = B + A$.

77. If Z is a matrix whose elements are all zeros, then given that

$$X = \begin{bmatrix} a & b \\ c & d \end{bmatrix}$$

verify the following:
a) $X - X = Z$
b) $X + Z = X$

78. If $A = \begin{bmatrix} 2 & -5 \\ 3 & 1 \end{bmatrix}$, $B = \begin{bmatrix} 2 & 1 \\ 5 & 0 \end{bmatrix}$, and $C = \begin{bmatrix} 2 & -6 \\ 7 & 1 \end{bmatrix}$, verify the following:
a) $A + B = B + A$ (commutative property of addition)
b) $A + (B + C) = (A + B) + C$ (associative property of addition)

Applications

79. *Sales tabulations*. Matrix J shows the number of sofas shipped from two plants, P_1 and P_2, to four warehouses, W_1, W_2, W_3, and W_4, during the month of July.

$$J = \begin{array}{c} \\ P_1 \\ P_2 \end{array} \begin{array}{cccc} W_1 & W_2 & W_3 & W_4 \\ \begin{bmatrix} 200 & 50 & 70 & 100 \\ 300 & 50 & 10 & 0 \end{bmatrix} \end{array}$$

Matrix A shows the corresponding shipments made during August.

$$A = \begin{array}{c} \\ P_1 \\ P_2 \end{array} \begin{array}{cccc} W_1 & W_2 & W_3 & W_4 \\ \begin{bmatrix} 100 & 30 & 10 & 50 \\ 70 & 400 & 200 & 80 \end{bmatrix} \end{array}$$

Find the matrix showing the combined shipment for both months.

80. *Cost analysis.* Larry Merrick operates three fruit stores: S_1, S_2, and S_3. Each store stocks apples, oranges, grapes, and pears. Larry does his buying on Monday, Wednesday, and Friday. Matrix M shows the amounts spent by Larry on each item for each store on Monday.

$$M = \begin{array}{cccc} S_1 & S_2 & S_3 & \\ \begin{bmatrix} \$200 & \$500 & \$300 \\ \$100 & \$400 & \$210 \\ \$500 & \$280 & \$\ 80 \\ \$150 & \$350 & \$250 \end{bmatrix} & \begin{array}{l} \text{apples} \\ \text{oranges} \\ \text{grapes} \\ \text{pears} \end{array} \end{array}$$

Matrices W and F show the corresponding expenditures for Wednesday and Friday, respectively.

$$W = \begin{array}{cccc} S_1 & S_2 & S_3 & \\ \begin{bmatrix} \$150 & \$\ 80 & \$100 \\ \$250 & \$300 & \$150 \\ \$\ 70 & \$\ 50 & \$\ 90 \\ \$120 & \$215 & \$160 \end{bmatrix} & \begin{array}{l} \text{apples} \\ \text{oranges} \\ \text{grapes} \\ \text{pears} \end{array} \end{array}$$

$$F = \begin{array}{cccc} S_1 & S_2 & S_3 & \\ \begin{bmatrix} \$209 & \$180 & \$120 \\ \$310 & \$140 & \$230 \\ \$\ 80 & \$\ 75 & \$\ 55 \\ \$\ 95 & \$\ 90 & \$170 \end{bmatrix} & \begin{array}{l} \text{apples} \\ \text{oranges} \\ \text{grapes} \\ \text{pears} \end{array} \end{array}$$

a) Find the matrix showing the combined purchases for Monday and Wednesday.

b) Find the matrix showing the combined purchases for Wednesday and Friday.

c) Find the matrix showing the combined purchases for Monday, Wednesday, and Friday.

81. *Production.* During a given day, a company made 30 type A, 40 type B, and 60 type C scarves. During the same day, the company also made 25 matching type A, 40 matching type B, and 50 matching type C mittens. Organize this information in a 2×3 matrix.

82. The time requirements (in hours) of a unit of each of three products in each of three departments are given in the matrix below.

	Product 1	Product 2	Product 3
Department 1	5	2	4
Department 2	1	8	3
Department 3	2	1	5

State the number of hours each product requires in each department.

83. *Data.* The weights (in pounds) of six people before taking a weight reduction program were 350, 249, 260, 195, 275, and 295. The weights of these same people after the weight reduction program are 345, 200, 220, 140, 200, and 230, respectively. Summarize this information in a 6×2 matrix.

84. *Commission.* The matrix below gives the total sales of each of three real estate agents at a given agency for the first 3 months of a particular year.

$$
\begin{array}{cccc}
 & \text{Mr. Alton} & \text{Mrs. Smith} & \text{Ms. Harris} \\
S = & \begin{bmatrix} \$160,\!000 & \$250,\!000 & \$190,\!000 \\ \$110,\!000 & \$180,\!000 & \$140,\!000 \\ \$90,\!000 & \$80,\!000 & \$85,\!000 \end{bmatrix} & & \begin{array}{l} \text{January} \\ \text{February} \\ \text{March} \end{array}
\end{array}
$$

If the agency pays its agents a commission of 3% based on sales, then write the matrix that gives the commission for each agent for each month.

5-5   • MULTIPLYING MATRICES

In this section, we will learn how to multiply matrices. To begin, we present an application that demonstrates the need for matrix multiplication.

Application

Sales Revenue

A company produces three products: A, B, and C. The number of units produced and sold of each product during each of two given months appears in the matrix below.

Quantity Sold Matrix

$$
\begin{array}{cccc}
 & \text{Product A} & \text{Product B} & \text{Product C} \\
\begin{array}{c} \text{February} \\ \text{March} \end{array} & \begin{bmatrix} 100 & 300 & 500 \\ 200 & 500 & 400 \end{bmatrix}
\end{array}
$$

The unit selling price for each product is given in the matrix below.

Unit Selling Price Matrix

$$
\begin{array}{cc}
\begin{array}{c} \text{Product A} \\ \text{Product B} \\ \text{Product C} \end{array} & \begin{bmatrix} 45 \\ 50 \\ 80 \end{bmatrix}
\end{array}
$$

We wish to create a matrix that contains the monthly total sales revenue gained from selling all three products. Since sales revenue is the product of quantity sold and unit selling price, we write the quantity sold and unit selling price matrices next to each other, as shown below.

$$
\begin{array}{cc}
\text{Quantity Sold} & \text{Unit Selling} \\
\end{array}
$$

$$
\begin{array}{ccccc}
 & \text{A} & \text{B} & \text{C} & \text{Price} \\
\begin{array}{c} \text{February} \\ \text{March} \end{array} & \begin{bmatrix} 100 & 300 & 500 \\ 200 & 500 & 400 \end{bmatrix} & \cdot & \begin{bmatrix} 45 \\ 50 \\ 80 \end{bmatrix} & \begin{array}{c} \text{A} \\ \text{B} \\ \text{C} \end{array}
\end{array}
$$

To determine February's total sales revenue, we multiply the quantity sold for each product in February by its respective unit selling price and add the products. Thus, we multiply the February entries in the left matrix by the corresponding entries in the right matrix to obtain

$$
\begin{array}{c}
\text{\textit{Quantity Sold}}\\
\begin{array}{ccc}
\text{A} & \text{B} & \text{C}
\end{array}
\end{array}
\quad
\begin{array}{c}
\text{\textit{Unit Selling}}\\
\text{\textit{Price}}
\end{array}
$$

February $\quad [100 \quad 300 \quad 500] \cdot \begin{bmatrix} 45 \\ 50 \\ 80 \end{bmatrix} \begin{matrix} \text{A} \\ \text{B} \\ \text{C} \end{matrix} = 100(45) + 300(50) + 500(80)$

$$= 4500 + 15{,}000 + 40{,}000$$

$$= \$59{,}500 \qquad \text{February sales revenue}$$

Note that we have multiplied the first entry in the row matrix by the first entry in the column matrix, the second entry in the row matrix by the second entry in the column matrix, and the third entry in the row matrix by the third entry in the column matrix, and then added the products. Such a product of a row matrix and a column matrix is called a **dot product.** We will have more to say about this later.

To determine March's total sales revenue, we multiply the March entries of the quantity sold matrix by the corresponding entries of the unit selling price matrix, as shown below.

$$
\begin{array}{c}
\text{\textit{Quantity Sold}}\\
\begin{array}{ccc}
\text{A} & \text{B} & \text{C}
\end{array}
\end{array}
\quad
\begin{array}{c}
\text{\textit{Unit Selling}}\\
\text{\textit{Price}}
\end{array}
$$

March $\quad [200 \quad 500 \quad 400] \cdot \begin{bmatrix} 45 \\ 50 \\ 80 \end{bmatrix} \begin{matrix} \text{A} \\ \text{B} \\ \text{C} \end{matrix} = 200(45) + 500(50) + 400(80)$

$$= 9000 + 25{,}000 + 32{,}000$$

$$= \$66{,}000 \qquad \text{March sales revenue}$$

Again, we note that to compute the total sales revenues for February and March, we computed a special type of product between a row matrix and a column matrix. As mentioned earlier, such a product is called a dot product, which we formally define in the box below.

Dot Product

The dot product between a left row matrix and a right column matrix, each containing the same number of entries, is determined by multiplying the first entry of the row matrix by the first entry of the column matrix, the second entry of the row matrix by the second entry of the column matrix, . . . , and the last entry of the row matrix by the last entry of the column matrix, and then adding the products, as shown below. Note that a dot product results in a real number.

$$[a_1 \quad a_2 \quad . \ . \ a_n] \cdot \begin{bmatrix} b_1 \\ b_2 \\ \vdots \\ b_n \end{bmatrix} = a_1 b_1 + a_2 b_2 + \ . \ . \ . + a_n b_n \qquad \text{A real number}$$

• **EXAMPLE 5-21** ———————————————————————————

Compute the dot product of

$$[2 \quad -1 \quad 0 \quad 3] \quad \text{and} \quad \begin{bmatrix} 4 \\ -5 \\ 1 \\ 8 \end{bmatrix}$$

Solution

The dot product is

$$[2 \quad -1 \quad 0 \quad 3] \begin{bmatrix} 4 \\ -5 \\ 1 \\ 8 \end{bmatrix} = 2(4) + (-1)(-5) + 0(1) + 3(8)$$

$$= 8 + 5 + 0 + 24$$

$$= 37$$

• **EXAMPLE 5-22** ———————————————————————————

A grocery store carries three brands of detergent: Brand X, Brand Y, and Brand Z. The row matrix below represents the number of units of each of these brands sold during the month of June.

	Brand X	Brand Y	Brand Z
Number of units	[100	500	300]

The column matrix below represents the unit selling price of each brand:

$$P = \begin{bmatrix} \$2.00 \\ \$1.00 \\ \$1.50 \end{bmatrix} \begin{matrix} \text{Brand X} \\ \text{Brand Y} \\ \text{Brand Z} \end{matrix}$$

Find the total sales revenue for all these products during the month of June.

Solution

The total sales revenue is given by the dot product of the two matrices, which we compute below. Hence,

$$[100 \quad 500 \quad 300] \begin{bmatrix} \$2.00 \\ \$1.00 \\ \$1.50 \end{bmatrix} = 100(\$2.00) + 500(\$1.00) + 300(\$1.50)$$

$$= \$1150$$

Returning to our sales revenue application on page 300, we will illustrate the use of matrices to organize all of the information of the problem. Specifically, we list the February and March total sales revenues in a column matrix next to the quantity and unit selling price matrices, as shown below.

	Quantity Sold A	B	C	Unit Selling Price		Total Sales Revenue	
February	[100	300	50]	[45	A	[59,500]	February
March	[200	500	400]	50	B	= [66,000]	March
				80	C		

As indicated by the equal sign, the total sales revenue matrix is the product of the quantity sold matrix and the unit selling price matrix.

Product Matrices

We now discuss multiplying matrices in general. If

$$A = \begin{bmatrix} 4 & 3 & 2 \\ 5 & 1 & 6 \end{bmatrix} \quad \text{and} \quad B = \begin{bmatrix} 2 & 4 \\ 1 & 0 \\ -1 & 2 \end{bmatrix}$$

then the product matrix AB is determined by the following procedure.

Step 1 Partition the left matrix, A, into rows and the right matrix, B, into columns, as follows:

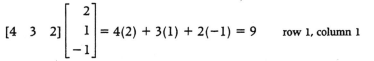

Step 2 Compute the dot product between each row of the left matrix, A, and each column of the right matrix, B. Write these dot products in a matrix such that the dot product between row i of matrix A and column j of matrix B is located in row i and column j of the new matrix. The resulting new matrix is the product matrix AB.

We illustrate this process by computing the product matrix AB. Looking at the rows and columns of step 1 above, we begin by computing the dot product between row 1 of the left matrix (i.e., matrix A) and column 1 of the right matrix (i.e., matrix B), as shown below.

$$[4 \quad 3 \quad 2] \begin{bmatrix} 2 \\ 1 \\ -1 \end{bmatrix} = 4(2) + 3(1) + 2(-1) = 9 \qquad \text{row 1, column 1}$$

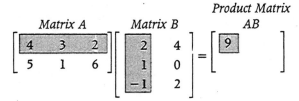

Next we find the dot product between row 1 of the left matrix and column 2 of the right matrix, as shown below.

$$[4 \quad 3 \quad 2] \begin{bmatrix} 4 \\ 0 \\ 2 \end{bmatrix} = 4(4) + 3(0) + 2(2) = 20 \qquad \text{row 1, column 2}$$

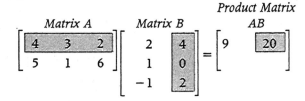

Since we have computed the dot product between row 1 of the left matrix and each of the columns of the right matrix, we now proceed to compute the dot product between row 2 of the left matrix and each column of the right matrix. Thus, we compute the dot product between row 2 and column 1, as shown below.

$$[5 \quad 1 \quad 6]\begin{bmatrix} 2 \\ 1 \\ -1 \end{bmatrix} = 5(2) + 1(1) + 6(-1) = 5 \qquad \text{row 2, column 1}$$

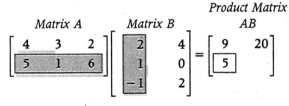

Now we compute the dot product between row 2 of the left matrix and column 2 of the right matrix.

$$[5 \quad 1 \quad 6]\begin{bmatrix} 4 \\ 0 \\ 2 \end{bmatrix} = 5(4) + 1(0) + 6(2) = 32 \qquad \text{row 2, column 2}$$

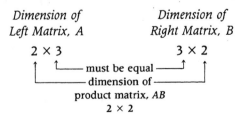

Since we have now computed the dot product between each row of the left matrix and each column of the right matrix, we are finished, and, thus, the product matrix AB is given below.

Product Matrix

$$AB = \begin{bmatrix} 9 & 20 \\ 5 & 32 \end{bmatrix}$$

Observe that the product matrix AB is defined if and only if the number of columns in the left matrix, A, equals the number of rows in the right matrix, B. Note also that the product matrix has the same number of rows as the left matrix, A, and the same number of columns as the right matrix, B. These details are illustrated as follows:

Dimension of   *Dimension of*
Left Matrix, A   *Right Matrix, B*

2×3 3×2

must be equal

dimension of
product matrix, AB
2×2

Dimensions

In general, if A is an $m \times n$ matrix and B is an $n \times k$ matrix, then the product AB is an $m \times k$ matrix, as shown here:

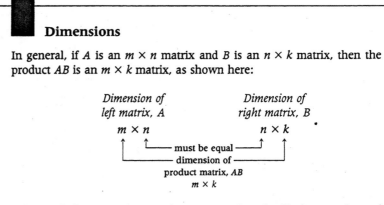

A product matrix can be computed only if the number of columns in the left matrix equals the number of rows in the right matrix.

We now summarize the process of matrix multiplication.

Matrix Multiplication

If A is an $m \times n$ matrix and B is an $n \times k$ matrix, the product matrix, AB, is determined as follows.

Step 1 Partition the left matrix into rows and the right matrix into columns.

$$
\begin{array}{c}
\begin{array}{cccc} \text{col 1} & \text{col 2} & \ldots & \text{col } n \end{array} \quad \begin{array}{ccccc} \text{col 1} & \text{col 2} & \ldots & \text{col } k \end{array}
\end{array}
$$

$$
\begin{array}{c}
\text{row 1} \\ \text{row 2} \\ \\ \text{row } m
\end{array}
\begin{bmatrix}
a_{11} & a_{12} & \ldots & a_{1n} \\
a_{21} & a_{22} & \ldots & a_{2n} \\
\vdots & \vdots & & \vdots \\
a_{m1} & a_{m2} & \ldots & a_{mn}
\end{bmatrix}
\begin{bmatrix}
b_{11} \\ b_{21} \\ \vdots \\ b_{n1}
\end{bmatrix}
\begin{bmatrix}
b_{12} \\ b_{22} \\ \vdots \\ b_{n2}
\end{bmatrix}
\ldots
\begin{bmatrix}
b_{1k} \\ b_{2k} \\ \vdots \\ b_{nk}
\end{bmatrix}
$$

Step 2 Compute the dot product between each row of the left matrix and each column of the right matrix. Write these dot products in a matrix such that the dot product between row i of the left matrix and column j of the right matrix is located in row i and column j of the product matrix. Thus, if c_{ij} denotes the entry in row i and column j of the product matrix, then

$$
c_{ij} = [a_{i1} \quad a_{i2} \quad \ldots \quad a_{in}] \begin{bmatrix} b_{1j} \\ b_{2j} \\ \vdots \\ b_{nj} \end{bmatrix} = a_{i1}b_{1j} + a_{i2}b_{2j} + \ldots + a_{in}b_{nj}
$$

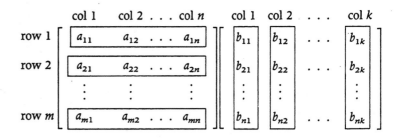

continues

Matrix Multiplication—*Continued*

The following tableaus are color coded to illustrate this process. Begin with row 1 of the left matrix, and compute the dot product between row 1 of the left matrix and each respective column of the right matrix, as shown below.

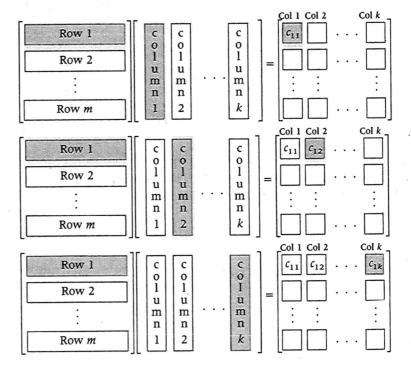

Next compute the dot product between row 2 of the left matrix and each respective column of the right matrix, as shown below.

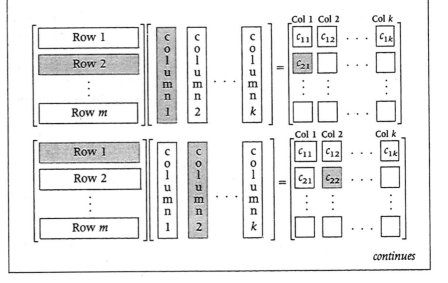

continues

Matrix Multiplication—*Continued*

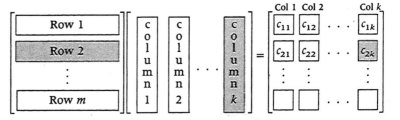

Continuing in this manner, finally, compute the dot product between row m of the left matrix and each respective column of the right matrix, as shown below.

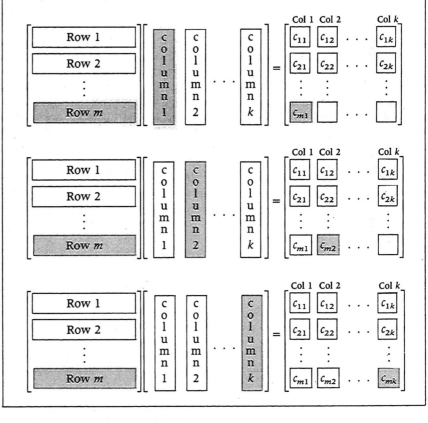

• **EXAMPLE 5-23** _____

Given that

$$F = \begin{bmatrix} 4 & 1 \\ 3 & 5 \\ 0 & 2 \end{bmatrix} \quad \text{and} \quad G = \begin{bmatrix} -3 & 7 \\ 1 & -2 \end{bmatrix}$$

find the product FG.

Solution

Note the following:

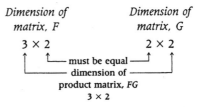

Step 1   Partition the left matrix into rows and the right matrix into columns, as shown below.

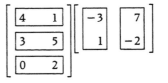

Step 2   Compute the dot product between each row of the left matrix and each column of the right matrix. We begin with row 1 of the left matrix and compute the dot product between row 1 of the left matrix and each respective column of the right matrix, as shown below.

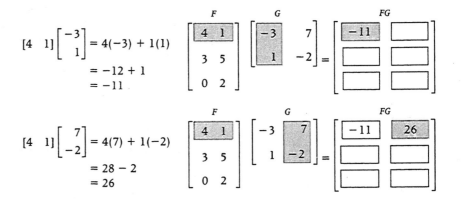

$$[4 \quad 1]\begin{bmatrix} -3 \\ 1 \end{bmatrix} = 4(-3) + 1(1)$$
$$= -12 + 1$$
$$= -11$$

$$[4 \quad 1]\begin{bmatrix} 7 \\ -2 \end{bmatrix} = 4(7) + 1(-2)$$
$$= 28 - 2$$
$$= 26$$

Next we find the dot product between row 2 of the left matrix and each respective column of the right matrix, as shown below.

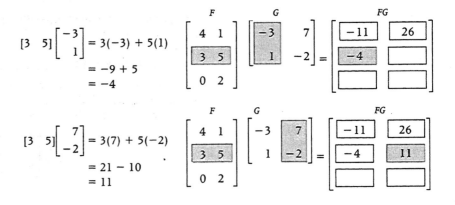

$$[3 \quad 5]\begin{bmatrix} -3 \\ 1 \end{bmatrix} = 3(-3) + 5(1)$$
$$= -9 + 5$$
$$= -4$$

$$[3 \quad 5]\begin{bmatrix} 7 \\ -2 \end{bmatrix} = 3(7) + 5(-2)$$
$$= 21 - 10$$
$$= 11$$

Finally, we find the dot product between row 3 of the left matrix and each respective column of the right matrix, as shown below.

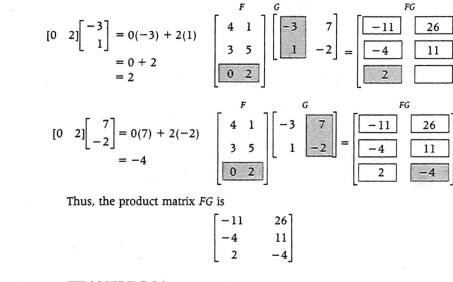

$$[0 \quad 2]\begin{bmatrix} -3 \\ 1 \end{bmatrix} = 0(-3) + 2(1)$$
$$= 0 + 2$$
$$= 2$$

$$[0 \quad 2]\begin{bmatrix} 7 \\ -2 \end{bmatrix} = 0(7) + 2(-2)$$
$$= -4$$

Thus, the product matrix FG is

$$\begin{bmatrix} -11 & 26 \\ -4 & 11 \\ 2 & -4 \end{bmatrix}$$

• EXAMPLE 5-24

The Saf-T-Flo Company manufactures two models of faucets: model A and model B. Each model must pass through department I (Assembly) and department II (Polishing). The unit time requirements (in hours) for each model in each department are given by matrix T:

$$\begin{array}{cc} \text{Model A} & \text{Model B} \end{array}$$
$$T = \begin{bmatrix} 3 & 5 \\ 2 & 1 \end{bmatrix} \begin{array}{l} \text{Department I} \\ \text{Department II} \end{array}$$

The production requirements of each model are given by matrix P.

$$P = \begin{bmatrix} 500 \\ 700 \end{bmatrix} \begin{array}{l} \text{Model A} \\ \text{Model B} \end{array}$$

Find the matrix that expresses the total time requirement for each department.

Solution

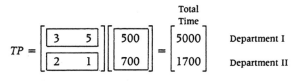

$$TP = \begin{bmatrix} 3 & 5 \\ 2 & 1 \end{bmatrix}\begin{bmatrix} 500 \\ 700 \end{bmatrix} = \begin{bmatrix} 5000 \\ 1700 \end{bmatrix} \begin{array}{l} \text{Department I} \\ \text{Department II} \end{array}$$

Thus, departments I and II need 5000 hours and 1700 hours, respectively, to satisfy production requirements.

• EXAMPLE 5-25

Suppose that the Saf-T-Flo Company of Example 5-24 has two plants: plant X and plant Y. The unit time requirements (in hours) for each model in each department are the same for both plants and are given by matrix T:

$$\begin{array}{cc} \text{Model A} & \text{Model B} \end{array}$$
$$T = \begin{bmatrix} 3 & 5 \\ 2 & 1 \end{bmatrix} \begin{array}{l} \text{Department I} \\ \text{Department II} \end{array}$$

The production requirements of each model in each plant are given by matrix R:

$$R = \begin{matrix} & \text{Plant X} & \text{Plant Y} \\ & \begin{bmatrix} 500 & 800 \\ 700 & 300 \end{bmatrix} & \begin{matrix} \text{Model A} \\ \text{Model B} \end{matrix} \end{matrix}$$

Find the matrix that expresses the total time requirement for each department in each plant.

Solution

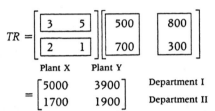

$$= \begin{matrix} & \text{Plant X} & \text{Plant Y} \\ & \begin{bmatrix} 5000 & 3900 \\ 1700 & 1900 \end{bmatrix} & \begin{matrix} \text{Department I} \\ \text{Department II} \end{matrix} \end{matrix}$$

Thus, departments I and II of plant X need 5000 hours and 1700 hours, respectively, to satisfy production requirements. Also, departments I and II of plant Y need 3900 hours and 1900 hours, respectively, to satisfy production requirements.

Linear Systems and Matrix Equations

A linear system such as

$$\begin{aligned} 3x + 5y &= 1 \\ -2x + 7y &= -11 \end{aligned}$$

can be rewritten in matrix form as follows:

$$\begin{bmatrix} 3 & 5 \\ -2 & 7 \end{bmatrix} \begin{bmatrix} x \\ y \end{bmatrix} = \begin{bmatrix} 1 \\ -11 \end{bmatrix}$$

If

$$A = \begin{bmatrix} 3 & 5 \\ -2 & 7 \end{bmatrix} \quad X = \begin{bmatrix} x \\ y \end{bmatrix} \quad B = \begin{bmatrix} 1 \\ -11 \end{bmatrix}$$

then the preceding system may be recast as the matrix equation

$$AX = B$$

To verify that the matrix equation $AX = B$ is equivalent to the original system, we first find the product matrix AX. Hence,

$$AX = \begin{bmatrix} 3 & 5 \\ -2 & 7 \end{bmatrix} \begin{bmatrix} x \\ y \end{bmatrix} = \begin{bmatrix} 3x + 5y \\ -2x + 7y \end{bmatrix}$$

Since

$$AX = B$$

then

$$\begin{bmatrix} 3x + 5y \\ -2x + 7y \end{bmatrix} = \begin{bmatrix} 1 \\ -11 \end{bmatrix}$$

Matrix equality requires that corresponding elements of both matrices be equal. Thus,

$$3x + 5y = 1$$
$$-2x + 7y = -11$$

Observe that these are the equations of our original system.

In general, a **linear system**

$$a_{11}x_1 + a_{12}x_2 + \ldots + a_{1n}x_n = b_1$$
$$a_{21}x_1 + a_{22}x_2 + \ldots + a_{2n}x_n = b_2$$
$$\vdots$$
$$a_{n1}x_1 + a_{n2}x_2 + \ldots + a_{nn}x_n = b_n$$

can be written as the **matrix equation**

$$AX = B$$

as shown below.

$$\begin{bmatrix} a_{11} & a_{12} & \ldots & a_{1n} \\ a_{21} & a_{22} & \ldots & a_{2n} \\ \vdots & \vdots & & \vdots \\ a_{n1} & a_{n2} & \ldots & a_{nn} \end{bmatrix} \begin{bmatrix} x_1 \\ x_2 \\ \vdots \\ x_n \end{bmatrix} = \begin{bmatrix} b_1 \\ b_2 \\ \vdots \\ b_n \end{bmatrix}$$

Observe that matrix X contains the unknowns of the linear system, whereas matrix A contains the coefficients of the unknowns, and matrix B contains the right-hand-side constants of the linear system.

• EXAMPLE 5-26

The following is a linear system consisting of three equations and three variables. Rewrite this linear system in the matrix form $AX = B$.

$$4x_1 - .7x_2 + 3x_3 = 16$$
$$9x_1 + 3x_2 - 6x_3 = 5$$
$$-2x_1 - 5x_2 + 8x_3 = 11$$

Solution

Here, we have

$$\underbrace{\begin{bmatrix} 4 & -7 & 3 \\ 9 & 3 & -6 \\ -2 & -5 & 8 \end{bmatrix} \begin{bmatrix} x_1 \\ x_2 \\ x_3 \end{bmatrix}}_{AX} = \underbrace{\begin{bmatrix} 16 \\ 5 \\ 11 \end{bmatrix}}_{B}$$

Identity Matrices

The number 1 is called the **multiplicative identity** for real numbers because

$$a \cdot 1 = 1 \cdot a = a$$

for all real numbers a. In other words, the product of any real number a and 1 is the real number a. Similarly, an **identity matrix** is a square matrix I such that

$$AI = IA = A$$

where A is a square matrix of the same dimension as I.

The matrix

$$I = \begin{bmatrix} 1 & 0 \\ 0 & 1 \end{bmatrix}$$

is the multiplicative identity for square matrices of dimension 2×2. If

$$A = \begin{bmatrix} 3 & 5 \\ -2 & 7 \end{bmatrix}$$

then observe that

$$AI = A$$

$$\overset{A}{\begin{bmatrix} 3 & 5 \\ -2 & 7 \end{bmatrix}} \overset{I}{\begin{bmatrix} 1 & 0 \\ 0 & 1 \end{bmatrix}} = \overset{A}{\begin{bmatrix} 3 & 5 \\ -2 & 7 \end{bmatrix}}$$

$$IA = A$$

$$\overset{I}{\begin{bmatrix} 1 & 0 \\ 0 & 1 \end{bmatrix}} \overset{A}{\begin{bmatrix} 3 & 5 \\ -2 & 7 \end{bmatrix}} = \overset{A}{\begin{bmatrix} 3 & 5 \\ -2 & 7 \end{bmatrix}}$$

For square matrices of dimension 3×3, the multiplicative identity is

$$I = \begin{bmatrix} 1 & 0 & 0 \\ 0 & 1 & 0 \\ 0 & 0 & 1 \end{bmatrix}$$

In general, the $n \times n$ matrix

$$I = \begin{bmatrix} 1 & 0 & 0 & \ldots & 0 \\ 0 & 1 & 0 & \ldots & 0 \\ 0 & 0 & 1 & \ldots & 0 \\ \vdots & \vdots & \vdots & & \vdots \\ 0 & 0 & 0 & \ldots & 1 \end{bmatrix}$$

is the multiplicative identity for square matrices of dimension $n \times n$.

• **EXAMPLE 5-27** ─────────────────────────

If

$$A = \begin{bmatrix} 1 & -4 & 7 \\ 3 & 2 & -5 \\ -1 & -6 & -8 \end{bmatrix} \quad \text{and} \quad I = \begin{bmatrix} 1 & 0 & 0 \\ 0 & 1 & 0 \\ 0 & 0 & 1 \end{bmatrix}$$

verify that $AI = IA = A$.

Solution

$$AI = \begin{bmatrix} 1 & -4 & 7 \\ 3 & 2 & -5 \\ -1 & -6 & -8 \end{bmatrix} \begin{bmatrix} 1 & 0 & 0 \\ 0 & 1 & 0 \\ 0 & 0 & 1 \end{bmatrix}$$

$$= \begin{bmatrix} 1 & -4 & 7 \\ 3 & 2 & -5 \\ -1 & -6 & -8 \end{bmatrix} = A$$

$$IA = \begin{bmatrix} 1 & 0 & 0 \\ 0 & 1 & 0 \\ 0 & 0 & 1 \end{bmatrix} \begin{bmatrix} 1 & -4 & 7 \\ 3 & 2 & -5 \\ -1 & -6 & -8 \end{bmatrix}$$

$$= \begin{bmatrix} 1 & -4 & 7 \\ 3 & 2 & -5 \\ -1 & -6 & -8 \end{bmatrix} = A$$

Exercises 5-5

Compute the dot product between each pair of matrices.

1. $[1 \quad 2]$ and $\begin{bmatrix} -3 \\ 6 \end{bmatrix}$

2. $[3 \quad -1]$ and $\begin{bmatrix} -2 \\ 7 \end{bmatrix}$

3. $[1 \quad 4 \quad 0 \quad -3]$ and $\begin{bmatrix} 8 \\ -1 \\ 0 \\ 2 \end{bmatrix}$

4. $[-2 \quad 0 \quad 1 \quad -1]$ and $\begin{bmatrix} 1 \\ 2 \\ -1 \\ 4 \end{bmatrix}$.

5. *The following problem appeared on a past Uniform CPA Examination.* Dancy, Inc., is going to begin producing a new chemical cleaner containing alcohol, peroxide, and enzyme. Each quart of the new cleaner will require 1/2 quart of alcohol, 1/6 quart of peroxide, and 1/3 quart of enzyme. The cost per quart is $0.40 for alcohol, $0.60 for peroxide, and $0.20 for enzyme. If the requirements are listed in matrix R

$$R = [1/2 \quad 1/6 \quad 1/3]$$

and their unit costs are listed in matrix C

$$C = \begin{bmatrix} 0.40 \\ 0.60 \\ 0.20 \end{bmatrix}$$

then state and perform the matrix operation to determine the cost of producing 1 quart of cleaner.

For each of the following, determine the dimension of the product matrix *AB*.

6. *A* is a 2 × 2 matrix, and *B* is a 2 × 4 matrix.
7. *A* is a 3 × 4 matrix, and *B* is a 4 × 5 matrix.
8. *A* is a 2 × 5 matrix, and *B* is a 5 × 3 matrix.
9. *A* is a 4 × 2 matrix, and *B* is a 2 × 4 matrix.
10. *A* is a 4 × 4 matrix, and *B* is a 4 × 4 matrix.

For each of the following, determine if it is possible to calculate the product matrix *CD*.

11. *C* is a 2 × 5 matrix, and *D* is a 4 × 2 matrix.
12. *C* is a 3 × 4 matrix, and *D* is a 2 × 5 matrix.
13. *C* is a 2 × 2 matrix, and *D* is a 2 × 2 matrix.

14. C is a 2 × 3 matrix, and D is a 3 × 7 matrix.

15–18. Repeat Exercises 11-14 for the product matrix DC.

Find each of the following matrix products.

19. $\begin{bmatrix} 4 & 3 \\ 2 & 1 \end{bmatrix}\begin{bmatrix} -1 & 1 \\ 5 & -2 \end{bmatrix}$

20. $\begin{bmatrix} 4 & 1 \\ 0 & 2 \end{bmatrix}\begin{bmatrix} 8 & -6 \\ -1 & 4 \end{bmatrix}$

21. $\begin{bmatrix} -1 & 2 \end{bmatrix}\begin{bmatrix} 8 & 3 \\ 1 & 6 \end{bmatrix}$

22. $\begin{bmatrix} 3 & -2 \end{bmatrix}\begin{bmatrix} 2 & 4 \\ -1 & -2 \end{bmatrix}$

23. $\begin{bmatrix} 3 & 4 \\ 2 & 6 \end{bmatrix}\begin{bmatrix} 1 \\ -5 \end{bmatrix}$

24. $\begin{bmatrix} -1 & 2 \\ 0 & 7 \end{bmatrix}\begin{bmatrix} -4 \\ 3 \end{bmatrix}$

25. $\begin{bmatrix} 1 & 2 & -3 \\ -1 & 0 & 2 \\ -2 & 1 & -1 \end{bmatrix}\begin{bmatrix} 2 \\ 4 \\ -4 \end{bmatrix}$

26. $\begin{bmatrix} 2 & 0 & -1 \\ -1 & 3 & -5 \\ 1 & -1 & 2 \end{bmatrix}\begin{bmatrix} -5 \\ 1 \\ -2 \end{bmatrix}$

27. $\begin{bmatrix} 1 & 2 & -3 \\ 0 & -1 & 3 \\ 5 & 0 & -4 \end{bmatrix}\begin{bmatrix} 1 & 3 \\ 2 & 1 \\ -2 & 6 \end{bmatrix}$

28. $\begin{bmatrix} 5 & 4 & -1 \\ -2 & 5 & -3 \\ 1 & 0 & -1 \end{bmatrix}\begin{bmatrix} -2 & 1 \\ 1 & 0 \\ 0 & -3 \end{bmatrix}$

29. $\begin{bmatrix} 4 & 6 \\ 2 & -1 \\ 8 & 0 \end{bmatrix}\begin{bmatrix} 1 & 3 \\ 2 & 4 \end{bmatrix}$

30. $\begin{bmatrix} 8 & 4 \\ -1 & 0 \\ 2 & 1 \end{bmatrix}\begin{bmatrix} 1 & 0 & -1 \\ -2 & 1 & 4 \end{bmatrix}$

31. $\begin{bmatrix} 1 & -4 & 2 \\ 2 & 0 & -1 \\ 3 & 1 & 1 \end{bmatrix}\begin{bmatrix} -2 & 1 & 3 \\ 1 & 2 & -2 \\ 4 & 0 & -1 \end{bmatrix}$

32. $\begin{bmatrix} 2 & 1 & -1 \\ -3 & -1 & 2 \\ 4 & 1 & -2 \end{bmatrix}\begin{bmatrix} 0 & 1 & -1 \\ -2 & 1 & 1 \\ 1 & 4 & -3 \end{bmatrix}$

Given that $A = \begin{bmatrix} 4 & 6 \\ -5 & 2 \end{bmatrix}$ and $B = \begin{bmatrix} 1 & -2 \\ -3 & 4 \end{bmatrix}$

33. Calculate AB.

34. Calculate BA.

35. Does $AB = BA$?

Given that

$$A = \begin{bmatrix} 1 & 3 & 7 \\ 2 & 4 & 0 \\ -1 & 5 & -2 \end{bmatrix} \quad B = \begin{bmatrix} 1 & 5 \\ 3 & 7 \\ -7 & 2 \end{bmatrix} \quad C = \begin{bmatrix} 2 & -1 & 0 & 6 \\ -1 & 4 & 3 & 2 \end{bmatrix} \quad D = \begin{bmatrix} 1 & 0 & -2 \\ 3 & -1 & 1 \end{bmatrix}$$

calculate, if possible, each of the following.

36. AB **37.** BA **38.** BC
39. CB **40.** BD **41.** DB
42. DA **43.** AD **44.** DC

45. $(AB)C$ (*Hint:* Multiply the result of Exercise 36 by C. Remember that C is written to the right of product matrix AB.)

46. $A(BC)$ (*Hint:* Multiply the result of Exercise 38 by A. Remember that A is written to the left of product matrix BC.)

47. Verify that the answers to Exercises 45 and 46 are the same. You have just verified the associative property of matrix multiplication, which states that $A(BC) = (AB)C$ for matrices A, B, and C, where these products exist. This is not a mathematical proof, which is beyond the scope of this book. We will, however, accept this property from now on.

48. Given that

$$A = \begin{bmatrix} 2 & -3 \\ 1 & 4 \end{bmatrix} \quad B = \begin{bmatrix} 2 & 0 \\ -1 & 5 \end{bmatrix} \quad C = \begin{bmatrix} 2 & 7 \\ -1 & -3 \end{bmatrix}$$

verify that

a) $A(BC) = (AB)C$ (associative property of multiplication)

b) $A(B + C) = AB + AC$ (distributive property)

c) $(B + C)A = BA + CA$

We note that the above do not constitute mathematical proofs. However, we will accept these properties from now on.

49. Given that $A = \begin{bmatrix} 4 & 3 \\ 8 & 0 \end{bmatrix}$ and $B = \begin{bmatrix} 7 & -1 \\ -2 & 4 \end{bmatrix}$, verify that $AB \neq BA$. Although this does not constitute a mathematical proof, we will accept this property from now on.

50. If $A^2 = AA$, compute A^2 for each of the following matrices A:

a) $\begin{bmatrix} 2 & 3 \\ -1 & 4 \end{bmatrix}$

b) $\begin{bmatrix} -8 & 0 \\ 1 & 2 \end{bmatrix}$

c) $\begin{bmatrix} 1 & 2 & 1 \\ 4 & -1 & 0 \\ 2 & 0 & 2 \end{bmatrix}$

d) $\begin{bmatrix} -1 & 2 & 3 \\ 5 & -2 & 1 \\ 4 & -4 & 0 \end{bmatrix}$

51. If $A^3 = A^2A$, compute A^3 for each of the matrices of Exercise 50.

52. Compute A^3 for each of the following matrices A:

a) $\begin{bmatrix} 4 & -7 \\ 0 & 1 \end{bmatrix}$

b) $\begin{bmatrix} -2 & -3 \\ 1 & 4 \end{bmatrix}$

c) $\begin{bmatrix} -1 & 0 & 2 \\ -3 & 1 & 1 \\ 2 & -1 & 3 \end{bmatrix}$

d) $\begin{bmatrix} 4 & -1 & -3 \\ 1 & 2 & 1 \\ 0 & 1 & 0 \end{bmatrix}$

53. Using the results of Exercises 50 through 52, define A^n for positive integers n and square matrix A.

Rewrite each of the following linear systems in the matrix form $AX = B$.

54. $\begin{aligned} 2x + 3y &= 7 \\ -4x + 5y &= 9 \end{aligned}$

55. $\begin{aligned} x_1 + 5x_2 &= 6 \\ 4x_1 + 8x_2 &= 11 \end{aligned}$

56. $\begin{aligned} 3x_1 - 7x_2 - 5x_3 &= 11 \\ x_1 + 4x_2 - 2x_3 &= 4 \\ 5x_1 + 9x_2 + 8x_3 &= 16 \end{aligned}$

57. $\begin{aligned} 2x + 3y + z &= 11 \\ x \quad\quad + 2z &= 9 \\ 4y + 5z &= 17 \end{aligned}$

58. $\begin{aligned} 5x - 7y &= 9 \\ -x + 2y &= 1 \end{aligned}$

59. $\begin{aligned} 2x_1 - x_2 &= 6 \\ 3x_1 + 2x_2 &= 9 \end{aligned}$

60. $\begin{aligned} x_1 - 2x_2 + x_3 &= 4 \\ 2x_1 - x_2 \quad\quad &= 8 \\ x_1 \quad\quad + 2x_3 &= 5 \end{aligned}$

61. $\begin{aligned} -x_1 + x_2 - 2x_3 &= 10 \\ 6x_1 \quad\quad + 2x_3 &= 5 \\ x_2 - x_3 &= 9 \end{aligned}$

Write the linear system corresponding to each of the following.

62. $\begin{bmatrix} 2 & 4 \\ -1 & 5 \end{bmatrix} \begin{bmatrix} x \\ y \end{bmatrix} = \begin{bmatrix} 6 \\ -4 \end{bmatrix}$

63. $\begin{bmatrix} 1 & -3 \\ 2 & 4 \end{bmatrix} \begin{bmatrix} x_1 \\ x_2 \end{bmatrix} = \begin{bmatrix} 3 \\ -7 \end{bmatrix}$

64. $\begin{bmatrix} 2 & 1 & 0 \\ 1 & -1 & 3 \\ 3 & 1 & -1 \end{bmatrix} \begin{bmatrix} x_1 \\ x_2 \\ x_3 \end{bmatrix} = \begin{bmatrix} -1 \\ 2 \\ 3 \end{bmatrix}$

65. $\begin{bmatrix} 4 & 1 & -1 \\ 5 & 0 & 2 \\ -2 & 1 & -2 \end{bmatrix} \begin{bmatrix} x_1 \\ x_2 \\ x_3 \end{bmatrix} = \begin{bmatrix} -4 \\ 1 \\ -1 \end{bmatrix}$

66. $\begin{bmatrix} 1 & 0 & -1 \\ 2 & 1 & -3 \\ 5 & -2 & 1 \end{bmatrix} \begin{bmatrix} x_1 \\ x_2 \\ x_3 \end{bmatrix} = \begin{bmatrix} -4 \\ -3 \\ 5 \end{bmatrix}$

67. $\begin{bmatrix} 1 & 4 & -1 \\ 2 & 1 & 0 \\ 4 & 1 & -5 \end{bmatrix} \begin{bmatrix} x_1 \\ x_2 \\ x_3 \end{bmatrix} = \begin{bmatrix} 2 \\ 1 \\ 5 \end{bmatrix}$

68. Given that $A = \begin{bmatrix} 3 & 2 \\ -5 & -6 \end{bmatrix}$ and $I = \begin{bmatrix} 1 & 0 \\ 0 & 1 \end{bmatrix}$, verify that $AI = IA = A$.

69. Given that

$$A = \begin{bmatrix} 4 & 3 & 6 \\ 8 & 2 & 7 \\ -1 & 1 & 4 \end{bmatrix} \quad I = \begin{bmatrix} 1 & 0 & 0 \\ 0 & 1 & 0 \\ 0 & 0 & 1 \end{bmatrix}$$

verify that $AI = IA = A$.

70. Given that $A = \begin{bmatrix} a & b \\ c & d \end{bmatrix}$, where a, b, c, and d are real numbers, and $I = \begin{bmatrix} 1 & 0 \\ 0 & 1 \end{bmatrix}$, verify that $AI = IA = A$.

71. Given that

$$B = \begin{bmatrix} 2 & 3 \\ 7 & 4 \\ 5 & 7 \end{bmatrix} \qquad I = \begin{bmatrix} 1 & 0 \\ 0 & 1 \end{bmatrix}$$

verify that $BI = B$.

72. Given that

$$X = \begin{bmatrix} x_1 \\ x_2 \\ x_3 \end{bmatrix} \qquad A = \begin{bmatrix} 1 & 2 & -1 \\ 4 & 0 & -1 \\ 5 & 1 & 2 \end{bmatrix}$$

verify that $X - AX = (I - A)X$. (*Hint:* Compute the left-hand side and then the right-hand side, and verify that they are equal.)

Applications

73. *Costs.* A company produces three products: A, B, and C. The number of units produced of each product during each of three given months appears in the matrix below.

Production volume

	Product A	Product B	Product C
April	200	500	300
May	400	200	600
June	600	800	900

The variable cost per unit for each product is given in the matrix below.

	Variable cost per unit
Product A	30
Product B	20
Product C	50

Determine the matrix that gives the total variable cost for each of the indicated months.

74. *Production planning.* A company produces two models of a particular product. The time (in hours) required for each model in each of three departments is given in the matrix below.

Department time requirements per unit of model

	Model A	Model B
Department 1	2	3
Department 2	1	2
Department 3	3	4

The projected production volume (in units) for each model for each of the next two months is given in the matrix below.

Projected production volume

	March	April
Model A	6000	8000
Model B	9000	7000

Determine the matrix that gives the projected time requirement for each department for the given months.

75. *Election projection.* A city is divided into four voting districts. Based on a recent survey, the matrix below gives the percentage of each district that plan to vote for a particular party candidate in an upcoming mayoral election.

	District			
	1	2	3	4
Republican	0.30	0.50	0.40	0.10
Democrat	0.60	0.20	0.55	0.86
Independent	0.10	0.30	0.05	0.04

The number of people expected to vote in each district has been projected from past voter turnout. These numbers are given in the matrix below.

	Expected voter turnout
District 1	60,000
District 2	100,000
District 3	70,000
District 4	90,000

Determine the matrix that gives the projected number of votes for the respective party candidates. State the projected winning party.

76. *Data computation.* Matrix operations provide useful methods for performing computations on sets of data. The matrix below gives test grades of four students on each of three exams.

Exam grades

	John	Mary	Pete	Joan
Exam 1	60	80	50	90
Exam 2	90	50	80	70
Exam 3	100	90	70	80

Compute the matrix product

$$[0.20 \quad 0.50 \quad 0.30] \begin{bmatrix} 60 & 80 & 50 & 90 \\ 90 & 50 & 80 & 70 \\ 100 & 90 & 70 & 80 \end{bmatrix}$$

Note that the resulting product matrix gives a weighted average of the exam grades for each student.

a) State the weighted average for each student. How much weight is given to each exam?

b) Give the resulting weighted averages for the weights given by the matrix [0.30 0.10 0.60].

5-6 • INVERSE OF A SQUARE MATRIX

The multiplicative inverse of a real number a is that number $1/a$ that, when multiplied by a, results in the multiplicative identify, 1. Thus,

$$a \cdot \frac{1}{a} = \frac{1}{a} \cdot a = 1 \qquad \text{(for } a \neq 0\text{)}$$

We use the multiplicative inverse of a number to solve linear equations of the form $ax = b$, where $a \neq 0$. Specifically, we solve for x by multiplying both sides by $1/a$.

In the previous section, we learned to write linear systems as matrix equations of the form $AX = B$, where A, X, and B are matrices. Thus, in terms of matrices, solving the linear system means solving for the unknown matrix, X. Just as we solve the linear equation $ax = b$ for x by multiplying both sides by the multiplicative inverse of a, $1/a$, we also solve the matrix equation $AX = B$ for X by multiplying both sides by a matrix called the inverse of matrix A, if it exists. We define the inverse of a matrix as follows.

The **multiplicative inverse** (if it exists) of a square matrix A is that square matrix A^{-1} that, when multiplied by A, results in the identity matrix, I. Thus, for a square matrix A, its inverse (if it exists) is denoted by A^{-1} where A^{-1} is that square matrix that satisfies both conditions

$$AA^{-1} = I \qquad \text{and} \qquad A^{-1}A = I$$

We also note that if, for any given matrix, its inverse exists, then it is unique.

• **EXAMPLE 5-28**

If $A = \begin{bmatrix} 2 & 3 \\ 5 & 4 \end{bmatrix}$, then verifty that $A^{-1} = \begin{bmatrix} -4/7 & 3/7 \\ 5/7 & -2/7 \end{bmatrix}$.

Solution

We must compute the products AA^{-1} and $A^{-1}A$, and then verify that they each yield the identity matrix. Hence,

$$AA^{-1} = \begin{bmatrix} 2 & 3 \\ 5 & 4 \end{bmatrix} \begin{bmatrix} -4/7 & 3/7 \\ 5/7 & -2/7 \end{bmatrix} = \begin{bmatrix} 1 & 0 \\ 0 & 1 \end{bmatrix} = I$$

$$A^{-1}A = \begin{bmatrix} -4/7 & 3/7 \\ 5/7 & -2/7 \end{bmatrix} \begin{bmatrix} 2 & 3 \\ 5 & 4 \end{bmatrix} = \begin{bmatrix} 1 & 0 \\ 0 & 1 \end{bmatrix} = I$$

Thus,

$$AA^{-1} = I = A^{-1}A$$

We note that because of the way matrix multiplication is defined, only square matrices can have inverses.

Computing Matrix Inverses

We now focus on developing a procedure to compute A^{-1}, if it exists, for a square matrix A. We begin with the matrix

$$A = \begin{bmatrix} 2 & 3 \\ 1 & 4 \end{bmatrix}$$

and let

$$A^{-1} = \begin{bmatrix} a & b \\ c & d \end{bmatrix}$$

where a, b, c, and d are unknowns. It is our goal to find values for a, b, c, and d such that

$$AA^{-1} = I$$

or, equivalently,

$$\overset{A}{\begin{bmatrix} 2 & 3 \\ 1 & 4 \end{bmatrix}} \overset{A^{-1}}{\begin{bmatrix} a & b \\ c & d \end{bmatrix}} = \overset{I}{\begin{bmatrix} 1 & 0 \\ 0 & 1 \end{bmatrix}}$$

Multiplying the left-hand side yields

$$\begin{bmatrix} 2a + 3c & 2b + 3d \\ a + 4c & b + 4d \end{bmatrix} = \begin{bmatrix} 1 & 0 \\ 0 & 1 \end{bmatrix}$$

The equality of the above matrices implies that corresponding entries are equal. Hence,

$$2a + 3c = 1 \qquad 2b + 3d = 0$$
$$a + 4c = 0 \qquad b + 4d = 1$$

Observe that the above constitute two linear systems that can be written in tableau form as

$$\overset{a \quad c}{\begin{bmatrix} 2 & 3 & | & 1 \\ 1 & 4 & | & 0 \end{bmatrix}} \qquad \overset{b \quad d}{\begin{bmatrix} 2 & 3 & | & 0 \\ 1 & 4 & | & 1 \end{bmatrix}}$$

Such tableaus, as we learned in Section 5-2, are also called **augmented matrices.**

We can solve each of the above linear systems by the Gauss-Jordan method. Since the matrix to the left of the vertical line is the same (i.e., it is matrix A) for both of the above tableaus, we can combine the right-hand-side columns of both tableaus and write the two tableaus as a single augmented matrix (or tableau), as illustrated below.

$$\overset{A \qquad\quad I}{\begin{bmatrix} 2 & 3 & | & 1 & 0 \\ 1 & 4 & | & 0 & 1 \end{bmatrix}} \qquad \text{denoted } [A \mid I]$$

Since matrix A is to the left of the vertical line and the identity matrix is to its right, such an augmented matrix is denoted as $[A \mid I]$.

When we apply the Gauss-Jordan method to such an augmented matrix $[A \mid I]$, we transform it into an equivalent matrix of the form

$$\begin{bmatrix} 1 & 0 \\ 0 & 1 \end{bmatrix} \begin{array}{|c|} \hline A^{-1} \\ \hline \end{array} \qquad \text{denoted } [I \mid A^{-1}]$$

where A^{-1} appears on the right-hand side. Such a matrix is denoted as $[I \mid A^{-1}]$.

We now apply the Gauss-Jordan method to compute A^{-1}. Remember that this method involves the use of three fundamental row operations, which we repeat:

1. Interchange two rows of a matrix.
2. Multiply a row of a matrix by a nonzero constant.
3. Add a multiple of a row to another row.

Step 1 *Change column 1 of $[A \mid I]$ to* $\begin{bmatrix} 1 \\ 0 \end{bmatrix}$.

We get the 1 first by interchanging Rows 1 and 2 or, in other words, $[R1 \leftrightarrow R2]$. This gives the tableau below.

$$\begin{bmatrix} 1 & 4 & 0 & 1 \\ 2 & 3 & 1 & 0 \end{bmatrix}$$

Now we need a 0 for the second entry in column 1. This is obtained by the row operation

$$-2 \text{ times Row 1, add the result to Row 2,}$$
$$\text{or, in other words, } [(-2)R1 + R2 \rightarrow R2]$$

The resulting tableau is

$$\begin{bmatrix} 1 & 4 & 0 & 1 \\ 0 & -5 & 1 & -2 \end{bmatrix}$$

Step 2 *Change column 2 of the above matrix to* $\begin{bmatrix} 0 \\ 1 \end{bmatrix}$.

We get the 1 first by the row operation

$$\text{Multiply Row 2 by } -1/5,$$
$$\text{or, in other words, } [(-1/5)R2 \rightarrow R2]$$

This gives the tableau

$$\begin{bmatrix} 1 & 4 & 0 & 1 \\ 0 & 1 & -1/5 & 2/5 \end{bmatrix}$$

Now we get a 0 for the first entry in column 2 by the row operation

$$-4 \text{ times row 2, add the result to row 1,}$$
$$\text{or, in other words, } [(-4)R2 + R1 \rightarrow R1]$$

This gives the final tableau

$$\begin{bmatrix} 1 & 0 & \bigm| & 4/5 & -3/5 \\ 0 & 1 & \bigm| & -1/5 & 2/5 \end{bmatrix}$$

Thus,

$$A^{-1} = \begin{bmatrix} 4/5 & -3/5 \\ -1/5 & 2/5 \end{bmatrix}$$

We check our result by noting that

$$AA^{-1} = \begin{bmatrix} 2 & 3 \\ 1 & 4 \end{bmatrix}\begin{bmatrix} 4/5 & -3/5 \\ -1/5 & 2/5 \end{bmatrix} = \begin{bmatrix} 1 & 0 \\ 0 & 1 \end{bmatrix}$$

$$A^{-1}A = \begin{bmatrix} 4/5 & -3/5 \\ -1/5 & 2/5 \end{bmatrix}\begin{bmatrix} 2 & 3 \\ 1 & 4 \end{bmatrix} = \begin{bmatrix} 1 & 0 \\ 0 & 1 \end{bmatrix}$$

To Compute a Matrix Inverse

In general, to find the multiplicative inverse of an $n \times n$ matrix, A, we begin with the initial tableau or augmented matrix, $[A \mid I]$:

$$\begin{bmatrix} a_{11} & a_{12} & \ldots & a_{1n} & \bigm| & 1 & 0 & \ldots & 0 \\ a_{21} & a_{22} & \ldots & a_{2n} & \bigm| & 0 & 1 & \ldots & 0 \\ \vdots & \vdots & & \vdots & \bigm| & \vdots & \vdots & & \vdots \\ a_{n1} & a_{n2} & \ldots & a_{nn} & \bigm| & 0 & 0 & \ldots & 1 \end{bmatrix}$$

and use row operations to obtain the final tableau or augmented matrix, $[I \mid A^{-1}]$:

• **EXAMPLE 5-29**

If

$$A = \begin{bmatrix} 3 & -1 & 1 \\ 2 & 2 & 0 \\ 0 & 1 & 2 \end{bmatrix}$$

compute A^{-1}.

Solution

We write the initial tableau or augmented matrix, $[A \mid I]$.

$$\begin{bmatrix} 3 & -1 & 1 & \bigm| & 1 & 0 & 0 \\ 2 & 2 & 0 & \bigm| & 0 & 1 & 0 \\ 0 & 1 & 2 & \bigm| & 0 & 0 & 1 \end{bmatrix}$$

Step 1 *Change column 1 to* $\begin{bmatrix} 1 \\ 0 \\ 0 \end{bmatrix}$.

We show the transformations from one matrix to the next and the appropriate row operations.

$$\begin{bmatrix} 3 & -1 & 1 & | & 1 & 0 & 0 \\ 2 & 2 & 0 & | & 0 & 1 & 0 \\ 0 & 1 & 2 & | & 0 & 0 & 1 \end{bmatrix} \xrightarrow{(-1)R2 + R1 \to R1} \begin{bmatrix} 1 & -3 & 1 & | & 1 & -1 & 0 \\ 2 & 2 & 0 & | & 0 & 1 & 0 \\ 0 & 1 & 2 & | & 0 & 0 & 1 \end{bmatrix}$$

$$\begin{bmatrix} 1 & -3 & 1 & | & 1 & -1 & 0 \\ 2 & 2 & 0 & | & 0 & 1 & 0 \\ 0 & 1 & 2 & | & 0 & 0 & 1 \end{bmatrix} \xrightarrow{(-2)R1 + R2 \to R2} \begin{bmatrix} 1 & -3 & 1 & | & 1 & -1 & 0 \\ 0 & 8 & -2 & | & -2 & 3 & 0 \\ 0 & 1 & 2 & | & 0 & 0 & 1 \end{bmatrix}$$

Step 2 *Change column 2 to* $\begin{bmatrix} 0 \\ 1 \\ 0 \end{bmatrix}$.

$$\begin{bmatrix} 1 & -3 & 1 & | & 1 & -1 & 0 \\ 0 & 8 & -2 & | & -2 & 3 & 0 \\ 0 & 1 & 2 & | & 0 & 0 & 1 \end{bmatrix} \xrightarrow{(-7)R3 + R2 \to R2} \begin{bmatrix} 1 & -3 & 1 & | & 1 & -1 & 0 \\ 0 & 1 & -16 & | & -2 & 3 & -7 \\ 0 & 1 & 2 & | & 0 & 0 & 1 \end{bmatrix}$$

$$\begin{bmatrix} 1 & -3 & 1 & | & 1 & -1 & 0 \\ 0 & 1 & -16 & | & -2 & 3 & -7 \\ 0 & 1 & 2 & | & 0 & 0 & 1 \end{bmatrix} \xrightarrow[(-1)R2 + R3 \to R3]{(3)R2 + R1 \to R1} \begin{bmatrix} 1 & 0 & -47 & | & -5 & 8 & -21 \\ 0 & 1 & -16 & | & -2 & 3 & -7 \\ 0 & 0 & 18 & | & 2 & -3 & 8 \end{bmatrix}$$

Step 3 *Change column 3 to* $\begin{bmatrix} 0 \\ 0 \\ 1 \end{bmatrix}$.

$$\begin{bmatrix} 1 & 0 & -47 & | & -5 & 8 & -21 \\ 0 & 1 & -16 & | & -2 & 3 & -7 \\ 0 & 0 & 18 & | & 2 & -3 & 8 \end{bmatrix} \xrightarrow{(1/18)R3 \to R3} \begin{bmatrix} 1 & 0 & -47 & | & -5 & 8 & -21 \\ 0 & 1 & -16 & | & -2 & 3 & -7 \\ 0 & 0 & 1 & | & 1/9 & -1/6 & 4/9 \end{bmatrix}$$

$$\begin{bmatrix} 1 & 0 & -47 & | & -5 & 8 & -21 \\ 0 & 1 & -16 & | & -2 & 3 & -16 \\ 0 & 0 & 1 & | & 1/9 & -1/6 & 4/9 \end{bmatrix} \xrightarrow[(47)R3 + R1 \to R1]{(16)R3 + R2 \to R2} \begin{bmatrix} 1 & 0 & 0 & | & 2/9 & 1/6 & -1/9 \\ 0 & 1 & 0 & | & -2/9 & 1/3 & 1/9 \\ 0 & 0 & 1 & | & 1/9 & -1/6 & 4/9 \end{bmatrix}$$

$$\underbrace{\phantom{\begin{matrix} 2/9 & 1/6 & -1/9 \end{matrix}}}_{A^{-1}}$$

We leave it for the reader to check that $AA^{-1} = I = A^{-1}A$.

Matrix Inverse May Not Exist

Not all square matrices have inverses. If, during the process of computing the inverse of a matrix A, a row consisting entirely of 0s appears in the left-hand side of the tableau, then the matrix A has no inverse. To illustrate this case, we will attempt to compute the inverse of matrix A where

Initial Tableau, [A | I]

$$A = \begin{bmatrix} 1 & 2 \\ 4 & 8 \end{bmatrix} \qquad \begin{bmatrix} 1 & 2 & | & 1 & 0 \\ 4 & 8 & | & 0 & 1 \end{bmatrix}$$

Since we already have a 1 in the upper left-hand corner, we multiply row 1 by -4 and add the result to row 2. This gives us a 0 in the lower left-hand corner:

$$\left[\begin{array}{cc|cc} 1 & 2 & 1 & 0 \\ 0 & 0 & -4 & 1 \end{array}\right]$$

Observe that the left-hand side of row 2 consists entirely of 0s, with at least one nonzero right-hand side entry. This type of situation indicates that the matrix A has *no inverse*. Thus, for this example, A^{-1} does not exist.

Exercises 5-6

Determine whether or not the following matrices are inverses of each other.

1. $\begin{bmatrix} 1 & -3/2 \\ 1 & -2 \end{bmatrix}$ and $\begin{bmatrix} 4 & -3 \\ 2 & -2 \end{bmatrix}$

2. $\begin{bmatrix} 4 & 1 \\ 3 & 0 \end{bmatrix}$ and $\begin{bmatrix} 1 & 2 \\ -1 & 4 \end{bmatrix}$

3. $\begin{bmatrix} 7 & -8 \\ 3 & -3 \end{bmatrix}$ and $\begin{bmatrix} -1 & 8/3 \\ -1 & 7/3 \end{bmatrix}$

4. $\begin{bmatrix} 1 & 3 & 0 \\ 0 & 1 & 0 \\ 1 & 2 & 1 \end{bmatrix}$ and $\begin{bmatrix} 1 & -3 & 0 \\ 0 & 1 & 0 \\ 0 & -2 & 1 \end{bmatrix}$

5. $\begin{bmatrix} 5 & 6 \\ 3 & 4 \end{bmatrix}$ and $\begin{bmatrix} 2 & -3 \\ -3/2 & 5/2 \end{bmatrix}$

6. $\begin{bmatrix} 1 & 0 & 0 \\ 0 & 1 & 0 \\ 2 & 3 & 1 \end{bmatrix}$ and $\begin{bmatrix} 1 & 0 & 0 \\ 0 & 1 & 0 \\ -2 & -3 & 1 \end{bmatrix}$

7. $\begin{bmatrix} 1 & 2 \\ 5 & -1 \end{bmatrix}$ and $\begin{bmatrix} 8 & 0 \\ 4 & 1 \end{bmatrix}$

8. $\begin{bmatrix} 1 & 3 & 2 \\ 0 & 1 & 4 \\ 0 & 0 & 1 \end{bmatrix}$ and $\begin{bmatrix} 1 & -3 & 10 \\ 0 & 1 & -4 \\ 0 & 0 & 1 \end{bmatrix}$

9. Given that $A = \begin{bmatrix} 1 & 5 \\ 2 & 11 \end{bmatrix}$,

    a) Compute A^{-1}.
    b) Verify that $AA^{-1} = A^{-1}A = I$.

10. Given that $B = \begin{bmatrix} 1 & 4 & 5 \\ 0 & 1 & 3 \\ 0 & 1 & 4 \end{bmatrix}$,

    a) Compute B^{-1}.
    b) Verify that $BB^{-1} = B^{-1}B = I$.

Find the inverse of each of the following matrices:

11. $\begin{bmatrix} 5 & -1 \\ -3 & 7 \end{bmatrix}$

12. $\begin{bmatrix} 1 & 3 \\ 2 & -4 \end{bmatrix}$

13. $\begin{bmatrix} 0 & 1 \\ 1 & 1 \end{bmatrix}$

14. $\begin{bmatrix} 1 & -1 & 3 \\ 0 & 2 & -4 \\ -2 & 2 & -5 \end{bmatrix}$

15. $\begin{bmatrix} 3 & 2 & 1 \\ 4 & -3 & 2 \\ 2 & 4 & -3 \end{bmatrix}$

16. $\begin{bmatrix} -1 & 1 & -2 \\ -2 & 0 & -4 \\ 6 & 2 & 10 \end{bmatrix}$

17. $\begin{bmatrix} 3 & 4 \\ 2 & -7 \end{bmatrix}$

18. $\begin{bmatrix} 1 & 3 \\ 2 & 4 \end{bmatrix}$

19. $\begin{bmatrix} 2 & 3 \\ 4 & -1 \end{bmatrix}$

20. $\begin{bmatrix} 1 & 1 & 2 \\ 3 & -1 & 3 \\ 2 & -5 & 2 \end{bmatrix}$

21. $\begin{bmatrix} 1 & 2 & 1 \\ 4 & 1 & 0 \\ 0 & 0 & 1 \end{bmatrix}$

22. $\begin{bmatrix} 1 & 2 & 2 \\ 8 & -6 & 2 \\ 8 & 4 & 4 \end{bmatrix}$

23. Given that $K = \begin{bmatrix} 2 & 3 \\ -10 & -15 \end{bmatrix}$, try to find K^{-1}. Does K^{-1} exist?

24. Given that $H = \begin{bmatrix} 1 & 2 & -1 \\ 2 & 4 & 3 \\ -2 & -4 & 2 \end{bmatrix}$, try to find H^{-1}. Does H^{-1} exist?

Find the inverse, if it exists, of each of the following matrices:

25. $\begin{bmatrix} -1 & 1 & 1 & 0 \\ 0 & 0 & 0 & 2 \\ 3 & 3 & 0 & 0 \\ 4 & 2 & 2 & 0 \end{bmatrix}$

26. $\begin{bmatrix} 1 & 2 & 1 & 0 \\ 2 & 2 & 0 & 4 \\ 6 & -3 & 3 & -3 \\ 1 & 1 & 0 & 2 \end{bmatrix}$

5-7 • SOLVING SQUARE LINEAR SYSTEMS BY MATRIX INVERSES

In order to solve the linear equation

$$ax = b \ \text{(where a} \neq 0)$$

for x, we multiply both sides by $1/a$, the multiplicative inverse of a, to obtain

$$\left(\frac{1}{a}\right)ax = \left(\frac{1}{a}\right)b$$

$$x = \left(\frac{1}{a}\right)b$$

Analogously, we may use the multiplicative inverse of a matrix to solve linear systems. Consider the linear system

$$2x_1 + 3x_2 = 9$$
$$5x_1 + 4x_2 = 26$$

Expressing this system in matrix form, $AX = B$, we have

$$\begin{bmatrix} 2 & 3 \\ 5 & 4 \end{bmatrix}\begin{bmatrix} x_1 \\ x_2 \end{bmatrix} = \begin{bmatrix} 9 \\ 26 \end{bmatrix}$$

If we multiply both sides of the matrix equation, $AX = B$, by A^{-1} (assuming that A^{-1} exists), we have

$$A^{-1}(AX) = A^{-1}B$$

Since $A^{-1}(AX) = (A^{-1}A)X$ by the associative property and $A^{-1}A = I$, the left-hand side becomes IX, and the equation reads

$$IX = A^{-1}B$$

Since $IX = X$, we obtain

$$X = A^{-1}B$$

Thus, the solution to a matrix equation $AX = B$ is

$$X = A^{-1}B$$

Returning to our example,

$$\begin{bmatrix} 2 & 3 \\ 5 & 4 \end{bmatrix} \begin{bmatrix} x_1 \\ x_2 \end{bmatrix} = \begin{bmatrix} 9 \\ 26 \end{bmatrix}$$

we must find A^{-1} by beginning with the augmented matrix or initial tableau, $[A \mid I]$,

$$\begin{bmatrix} 2 & 3 & \vline & 1 & 0 \\ 5 & 4 & \vline & 0 & 1 \end{bmatrix}$$

and using row operations to obtain the final tableau, $[I \mid A^{-1}]$,

$$\begin{bmatrix} 1 & 0 & \vline & -4/7 & 3/7 \\ 0 & 1 & \vline & 5/7 & -2/7 \end{bmatrix}$$

Hence,

$$A^{-1} = \begin{bmatrix} -4/7 & 3/7 \\ 5/7 & -2/7 \end{bmatrix}$$

Next we find the product $A^{-1}B$:

$$A^{-1}B = \begin{bmatrix} -4/7 & 3/7 \\ 5/7 & -2/7 \end{bmatrix} \begin{bmatrix} 9 \\ 26 \end{bmatrix} = \begin{bmatrix} 6 \\ -1 \end{bmatrix}$$

Thus, the solution is

$$X = A^{-1}B$$
$$\begin{bmatrix} x_1 \\ x_2 \end{bmatrix} = \begin{bmatrix} 6 \\ -1 \end{bmatrix}$$

Therefore, $(6, -1)$ is the solution to our linear system.

SUMMARY

Using a Matrix Inverse to Solve a Square Linear System

Consider a linear system

$$a_{11}x_1 + a_{12}x_2 + \ldots + a_{1n}x_n = b_1$$
$$a_{21}x_1 + a_{22}x_2 + \ldots + a_{2n}x_n = b_2$$
$$\vdots \qquad \vdots \qquad\qquad \vdots \quad \vdots$$
$$a_{n1}x_1 + a_{n2}x_2 + \ldots + a_{nn}x_n = b_n$$

that, when written as the matrix equation

$$AX = B$$

becomes

$$\begin{bmatrix} a_{11} & a_{12} & \ldots & a_{1n} \\ a_{21} & a_{22} & \ldots & a_{2n} \\ \vdots & \vdots & & \vdots \\ a_{n1} & a_{n2} & \ldots & a_{nn} \end{bmatrix} \begin{bmatrix} x_1 \\ x_2 \\ \vdots \\ x_n \end{bmatrix} = \begin{bmatrix} b_1 \\ b_2 \\ \vdots \\ b_n \end{bmatrix}.$$

 continues

> **SUMMARY**—*Continued*
>
> The **solution** to this linear system is given by the matrix equation
>
> $$X = A^{-1}B$$
>
> where
>
>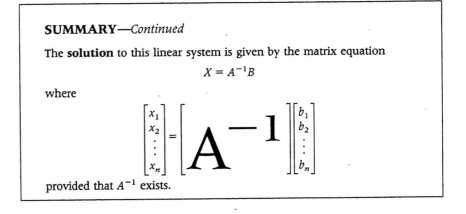
>
> provided that A^{-1} exists.

• **EXAMPLE 5-30** _____

Use the matrix inverse to solve the linear system

$$x_1 + 3x_2 + 3x_3 = 4$$
$$2x_1 + 7x_2 + 7x_3 = 9$$
$$2x_1 + 7x_2 + 6x_3 = 10$$

Solution

Rewriting the linear system in matrix form, $AX = B$, we have

$$\begin{bmatrix} 1 & 3 & 3 \\ 2 & 7 & 7 \\ 2 & 7 & 6 \end{bmatrix}\begin{bmatrix} x_1 \\ x_2 \\ x_3 \end{bmatrix} = \begin{bmatrix} 4 \\ 9 \\ 10 \end{bmatrix}$$

Hence,

$$A = \begin{bmatrix} 1 & 3 & 3 \\ 2 & 7 & 7 \\ 2 & 7 & 6 \end{bmatrix} \quad X = \begin{bmatrix} x_1 \\ x_2 \\ x_3 \end{bmatrix} \quad B = \begin{bmatrix} 4 \\ 9 \\ 10 \end{bmatrix}$$

We must find A^{-1} by beginning with the initial tableau, $[A \mid I]$,

$$\begin{array}{c} A \qquad\qquad\quad I \end{array}$$
$$\left[\begin{array}{ccc|ccc} 1 & 3 & 3 & 1 & 0 & 0 \\ 2 & 7 & 7 & 0 & 1 & 0 \\ 2 & 7 & 6 & 0 & 0 & 1 \end{array}\right]$$

and using row operations to obtain the final tableau, $[I \mid A^{-1}]$,

$$\begin{array}{c} I \qquad\qquad\quad A^{-1} \end{array}$$
$$\left[\begin{array}{ccc|ccc} 1 & 0 & 0 & 7 & -3 & 0 \\ 0 & 1 & 0 & -2 & 0 & 1 \\ 0 & 0 & 1 & 0 & 1 & -1 \end{array}\right]$$

Hence,

$$A^{-1} = \begin{bmatrix} 7 & -3 & 0 \\ -2 & 0 & 1 \\ 0 & 1 & -1 \end{bmatrix}$$

We now find the product $A^{-1}B$.

$$A^{-1}B = \begin{bmatrix} 7 & -3 & 0 \\ -2 & 0 & 1 \\ 0 & 1 & -1 \end{bmatrix} \begin{bmatrix} 4 \\ 9 \\ 10 \end{bmatrix} = \begin{bmatrix} 1 \\ 2 \\ -1 \end{bmatrix}$$

Thus, the solution is

$$X = A^{-1}B$$

$$\begin{bmatrix} x_1 \\ x_2 \\ x_3 \end{bmatrix} = \begin{bmatrix} 1 \\ 2 \\ -1 \end{bmatrix}$$

Therefore, $(1, 2, -1)$ is the solution to our linear system.

The method of solving a square linear system $AX = B$ by using A^{-1} (if A^{-1} exists) is relatively inefficient for large square linear systems unless A^{-1} is known beforehand or can easily be determined by using a computer. However, in this age of "cheap computing," most students have access to a computer. Under these circumstances, this method is advantageous for solving square linear systems $AX = B$, especially when matrix B changes and matrix A does not.

Application

PROBLEM

A company manufactures shoes and slippers. Matrix A gives the time requirements (in hours) for each pair of shoes and slippers in departments I and II.

$$\begin{array}{cc} \text{Shoes} & \text{Slippers} \end{array}$$
$$A = \begin{bmatrix} 3 & 4 \\ 5 & 2 \end{bmatrix} \begin{array}{l} \text{Department I} \\ \text{Department II} \end{array}$$

Matrix B represents the time (in hours) available in each department. All this time must be used.

$$B = \begin{bmatrix} 450 \\ 400 \end{bmatrix} \begin{array}{l} \text{Department I} \\ \text{Department II} \end{array}$$

We must determine how many pairs of shoes and slippers should be produced if the departments operate at full capacity.

SOLUTION

If the numbers of pairs of shoes and pairs of slippers to be manufactured are represented by the matrix

$$X = \begin{bmatrix} x_1 \\ x_2 \end{bmatrix} \begin{array}{l} \text{Pairs of shoes} \\ \text{Pairs of slippers} \end{array}$$

then X satisfies the matrix equation

$$AX = B$$

$$\begin{bmatrix} 3 & 4 \\ 5 & 2 \end{bmatrix} \begin{bmatrix} x_1 \\ x_2 \end{bmatrix} = \begin{bmatrix} 450 \\ 400 \end{bmatrix}$$

Using row operations, it can be determined that

$$A^{-1} = \begin{bmatrix} -1/7 & 2/7 \\ 5/14 & -3/14 \end{bmatrix}$$

Solving for X yields

$$X = A^{-1}B$$

$$\begin{bmatrix} x_1 \\ x_2 \end{bmatrix} = \begin{bmatrix} -1/7 & 2/7 \\ 5/14 & -3/14 \end{bmatrix} \begin{bmatrix} 450 \\ 400 \end{bmatrix} = \begin{bmatrix} 50 \\ 75 \end{bmatrix}$$

Thus, the company should produce

$$x_1 = 50 \text{ pairs of shoes}$$
$$x_2 = 75 \text{ pairs of slippers}$$

The advantage of using A^{-1} to solve this problem becomes apparent when we consider the following change. Suppose matrix B, which represents the time available in each department, changes from

$$\begin{bmatrix} 450 \\ 400 \end{bmatrix} \quad \text{to} \quad \begin{bmatrix} 490 \\ 280 \end{bmatrix}$$

Then, since

$$X = A^{-1} B$$

the new solution X may be determined by multiplying A^{-1} times the new matrix B. Since matrix A is unchanged, it is not necessary to recalculate A^{-1}. For example, if matrix B is changed to

$$B = \begin{bmatrix} 490 \\ 280 \end{bmatrix}$$

then

$$X = A^{-1}B$$

$$\begin{bmatrix} x_1 \\ x_2 \end{bmatrix} = \begin{bmatrix} -1/7 & 2/7 \\ 5/14 & -3/14 \end{bmatrix} \begin{bmatrix} 490 \\ 280 \end{bmatrix} = \begin{bmatrix} 10 \\ 115 \end{bmatrix}$$

Thus, the company should produce

$$x_1 = 10 \text{ pairs of shoes}$$
$$x_2 = 115 \text{ pairs of slippers}$$

Exercises 5-7

Find x_1 and x_2 for each of the following.

1. $\begin{bmatrix} x_1 \\ x_2 \end{bmatrix} = \begin{bmatrix} 2 & 1 \\ -1 & 3 \end{bmatrix} \begin{bmatrix} 5 \\ 2 \end{bmatrix}$

2. $\begin{bmatrix} x_1 \\ x_2 \end{bmatrix} = \begin{bmatrix} -1 & 4 \\ 5 & -2 \end{bmatrix} \begin{bmatrix} -3 \\ 6 \end{bmatrix}$

3. $\begin{bmatrix} x_1 \\ x_2 \end{bmatrix} = \begin{bmatrix} 4 & -1 \\ -1 & 3 \end{bmatrix} \begin{bmatrix} 5 \\ 2 \end{bmatrix}$

4. $\begin{bmatrix} x_1 \\ x_2 \end{bmatrix} = \begin{bmatrix} 3 & 1 \\ -2 & 5 \end{bmatrix} \begin{bmatrix} 4 \\ 3 \end{bmatrix}$

Express each of the following linear systems in matrix form $AX = B$. Then compute A^{-1} and use it to solve the linear system.

5. $x_1 + 2x_2 = 9$
   $-x_1 + 3x_2 = 1$

6. $x_1 + x_2 = 9$
   $2x_1 + 3x_2 = 25$

7. $x_1 \qquad + x_3 = 11$
   $\quad x_2 + 4x_3 = 39$
   $2x_1 + 3x_2 + x_3 = 22$

8. $x_1 + x_2 + 5x = 21$
   $\quad x_2 + 3x_3 = 15$
   $3x_1 + 3x_2 + 16x_3 = 67$

9. $x_1 + x_2 + x_3 = 3$
   $x_1 + 2x_2 + 3x_3 = 10$
   $\quad x_2 + 4x_3 = 17$

10. $x_1 - x_2 + x_3 = 8$
    $x_1 \qquad + 4x_3 = 19$
    $\quad x_2 + 2x_3 = 7$

11. $x_1 + x_2 \qquad = 3$
    $\quad x_2 + 3x_3 = -7$
    $4x_1 + 6x_2 + 7x_3 = -5$

12. $x_1 + x_2 - 2x_3 = -4$
    $x_1 + 2x_2 + 3x_3 = 7$
    $\quad 2x_2 + 12x_3 = 26$

13. $2x - 3y = 6$
    $x - 7y = 25$

14. $4x_1 - 5x_2 = -2$
    $3x_1 + 2x_2 = -13$

15. $2x + 3y - 5z = -13$
    $-x + 2y + 3z = -7$
    $3x - 4y - 7z = 15$

16. $2x_1 - 3x_2 + 4x_3 = 8$
    $3x_1 + x_2 - 2x_3 = 11$
    $5x_1 - 2x_2 + 3x_3 = 10$

17. $5x_1 + 7x_2 + x_3 = 1$
    $3x_1 + 2x_2 + 3x_3 = 8$
    $2x_1 + 3x_2 + 5x_3 = 19$

18. $3x + 7y + 2z = 2$
    $4x + 3y + 3z = 8$
    $x + 2y + 4z = -9$

19. $4x_1 + x_2 = 8$
    $6x_1 - 2x_2 = -9$

20. $(1/2)x + 5y = 17$
    $3x + 2y = 18$

21. $2x + y + 3z = 11$
    $4x + 3y - 2z = -1$
    $6x + 5y - 4z = -4$

22. $x_1 + x_2 - 5x_3 = -3$
    $2x_1 + x_2 + 10x_3 = 2$
    $3x_1 + 2x_2 + 25x_3 = 3$

23. Express the following linear system in matrix form, $AX = B$. Then compute A^{-1} and use it to solve the linear system.

$$x_1 \quad + x_3 - x_4 = -2$$
$$x_2 - x_3 + 2x_4 = 12$$
$$4x_1 \quad + 5x_3 - 3x_4 = 2$$
$$2x_3 + 3x_4 = 27$$

24. Express the following linear system in matrix form, $AX = B$. Then compute A^{-1} and use it to solve the linear system.

$$x_1 + 2x_2 - x_3 + x_4 = -7$$
$$2x_1 + x_2 + x_3 + 2x_4 = 1$$
$$-3x_1 - x_2 + x_3 - x_4 = 3$$
$$x_1 \qquad + 2x_4 = -1$$

25. *Nutrition.* A diet must provide exactly 1200 milligrams of protein and 1000 milligrams of iron. These nutrients will be obtained by eating meat and spinach.

Each pound of meat contains 500 milligrams of protein and 100 milligrams of iron. Each pound of spinach contains 200 milligrams of protein and 800 milligrams of iron.

a) If matrix A lists the number of milligrams of protein and iron obtained from a pound of meat and from a pound of spinach, respectively, then fill in the elements of matrix A.

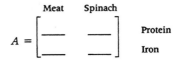

b) If matrix B lists the amounts required of protein and iron, respectively, then fill in the elements of matrix B.

c) If $X = \begin{bmatrix} x_1 \\ x_2 \end{bmatrix}$, where x_1 and x_2 represent the number of pounds of meat and spinach, respectively, that should be eaten in order to provide the proper amounts of protein and iron, then write the matrix equation relating A, X, and B.

d) Solve the matrix equation of part c for X and interpret the answer.

e) Repeat parts c and d for $B = \begin{bmatrix} 2300 \\ 3500 \end{bmatrix}$.

26. *Production scheduling.* A company manufactures three products: A, B, and C. Each product must pass through three machines: I, II, and III. Each unit of product A requires 3 hours on I, 2 hours on II, and 4 hours on III. Each unit of product B requires 2 hours on I, 4 hours on II, and 6 hours on III. Each unit of product C requires 3 hours on I, 5 hours on II, and 7 hours on III.

a) If matrix T shows the time requirements of each product on each machine, then fill in the elements of matrix T:

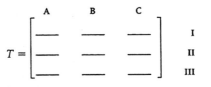

b) If machines I, II, and III have available 150, 240, and 360 hours, respectively, then express this information in matrix B:

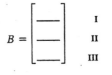

c) If $X = \begin{bmatrix} x_1 \\ x_2 \\ x_3 \end{bmatrix}$, where x_1, x_2, and x_3 represent the numbers of units of products A, B, and C, respectively, produced, then write the matrix equation relating T, X, and B.

d) Solve the matrix equation of part c and interpret the answer.

e) Repeat parts c and d for $B = \begin{bmatrix} 170 \\ 250 \\ 390 \end{bmatrix}$.

27. *Resource allocation.* A company produces two products—XB17 and XB18—for the automotive industry. The matrix below gives the compositions (%) of two raw materials—RM1 and RM2—in each product.

Products

		XB17	XB18
Raw materials	RM1	1	3
	RM2	2	0.5

If 220 units of RM1 and 330 units of RM2 are available next month, how many units of each product can be produced if all available raw materials are to be used?
a) Set up the linear system for this problem.
b) Write the linear system as the matrix equation $AX = B$.
c) Determine A^{-1}.
d) Use A^{-1} to solve the linear system.
e) Suppose next month's availability of RM1 and RM2 is changed to 440 and 110 units, respectively. How many units of each product can be produced if all available raw materials must be used?

28. A company produces dipthelene and triptilene. The matrix below gives the amounts (in liters) of the raw materials zolene and ptolene needed to produce 1 liter of each product.

Products

		Dipthelene	Triptilene
Raw materials	Zolene	2	1
	Ptolene	4	3

The raw materials are highly volatile and must be used immediately. If there are 700 liters of zolene and 2000 liters of ptolene on hand, determine how many liters of each product should be produced.
a) Set up the linear system for this problem.
b) Write the linear system as the matrix equation $AX = B$.
c) Determine A^{-1}.
d) Use A^{-1} to solve the linear system.
e) Suppose additional amounts of 100 liters of zolene and 100 liters of ptolene have just arrived. Determine how many liters of each product should now be produced.

29. *Investment analysis.* An investor has $100,000 to invest. A portion will be invested at 7% and the remainder at 9%. If an annual income of $8500 is desired, determine the amount that should be invested at each rate.
a) Set up the linear system for this problem.
b) Write the linear system as the matrix equation $AX = B$.
c) Determine A^{-1}.
d) Use A^{-1} to solve the linear system.
e) Recalculate your answers to part d if the amount invested changes to $200,000 and the desired annual income changes to $15,000.

5-8 • LEONTIEF'S INPUT-OUTPUT MODEL

Nobel prize winner Wassily Leontief developed a model to study the interdependence among industries of an economy. Since the model assumes that some of the output of an industry is needed as input in other industries of the economy, it is termed **Leontief's input-output model.** The model, which is invaluable to economic planning and development, provides a method for solving the following problem.

SUMMARY

Input-Output Problem

An economy consists of n industries. Some of the output of a given industry is needed by other industries in the economy. This is called **internal demand.** The remainder of such output is needed by industries outside the economy. This is called **final** (or **external**) **demand.** What quantity of output should each of the n industries produce in order to satisfy the total demand for its output? Total demand is the sum of internal demand and final (or external) demand.

As an illustrative example, we consider a simplified economy that produces three commodities: C_1, C_2, and C_3. Production of 1 unit of C_1 requires 0 units of C_1, 1/2 unit of C_2, and 1/4 unit of C_3. This is summarized by the column vector below.

Producing of 1 unit of C_1 requires

$$\begin{bmatrix} 0 \\ 1/2 \\ 1/4 \end{bmatrix} \begin{matrix} \text{unit of } C_1 \\ \text{unit of } C_2 \\ \text{unit of } C_3 \end{matrix}$$

The column vectors giving production requirements for C_2 and C_3 are as follows:

Producing of 1 unit of C_2 requires

$$\begin{bmatrix} 1/6 \\ 0 \\ 1/3 \end{bmatrix} \begin{matrix} \text{unit of } C_1 \\ \text{unit of } C_2 \\ \text{unit of } C_3 \end{matrix}$$

Producing of 1 unit of C_3 requires

$$\begin{bmatrix} 1/2 \\ 1/8 \\ 0 \end{bmatrix} \begin{matrix} \text{unit of } C_1 \\ \text{unit of } C_2 \\ \text{unit of } C_3 \end{matrix}$$

If we write the second column vector alongside the first, and the third alongside the second, we obtain the matrix

$$
\begin{array}{c}
\textit{To produce 1 unit of} \\
\begin{array}{ccc}
C_1 & C_2 & C_3
\end{array}
\end{array}
$$

$$
A = \begin{bmatrix} 0 & 1/6 & 1/2 \\ 1/2 & 0 & 1/8 \\ 1/4 & 1/3 & 0 \end{bmatrix}
\begin{array}{l}
\textit{requires} \\
\text{unit of } C_1 \\
\text{unit of } C_2 \\
\text{unit of } C_3
\end{array}
$$

Matrix A is called the **technological** or **input-output** matrix of the economy. The technological matrix of an economy shows the interdependence of its industries or commodities.

Since we wish to determine the number of units of each commodity to be produced, we let

$$x_1 = \text{number of units of } C_1 \text{ produced}$$
$$x_2 = \text{number of units of } C_2 \text{ produced}$$
$$x_3 = \text{number of units of } C_3 \text{ produced}$$

and define matrix X as

$$
X = \begin{bmatrix} x_1 \\ x_2 \\ x_3 \end{bmatrix}
$$

Since matrix X gives the number of units produced of each commodity, it is called the **production** or **total output matrix.**

The final (or external) demand for each commodity (or industry) is given by

$$d_1 = \text{final (or external) demand for } C_1$$
$$d_2 = \text{final (or external) demand for } C_2$$
$$d_3 = \text{final (or external) demand for } C_3$$

Thus, we define the final (or external) demand matrix D as

$$
D = \begin{bmatrix} d_1 \\ d_2 \\ d_3 \end{bmatrix}
$$

The product matrix AX gives the internal demands for the respective commodities, as illustrated below.

$$
AX = \begin{bmatrix} 0 & 1/6 & 1/2 \\ 1/2 & 0 & 1/8 \\ 1/4 & 1/3 & 0 \end{bmatrix}\begin{bmatrix} x_1 \\ x_2 \\ x_3 \end{bmatrix}
$$

$$
= \begin{bmatrix} 0x_1 + \dfrac{1}{6}x_2 + \dfrac{1}{2}x_3 \\[2mm] \dfrac{1}{2}x_1 + 0x_2 + \dfrac{1}{8}x_3 \\[2mm] \dfrac{1}{4}x_1 + \dfrac{1}{3}x_2 + 0x_3 \end{bmatrix}
\begin{array}{l}
\leftarrow \text{number of units of } C_1 \\ \quad\text{consumed internally} \\
\leftarrow \text{number of units of } C_2 \\ \quad\text{consumed internally} \\
\leftarrow \text{number of units of } C_3 \\ \quad\text{consumed internally}
\end{array}
$$

To verify the interpretation of matrix AX, we analyze its first entry below:

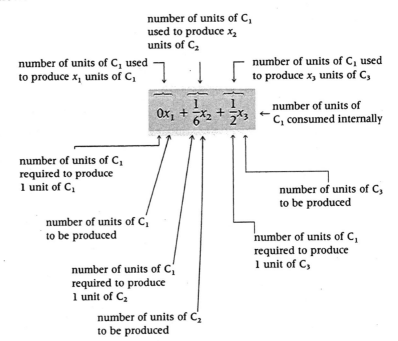

The remaining entries of matrix AX are interpreted analogously. Since

$$\text{total output} = \text{internal demand} + \text{final (or external) demand}$$

we have the corresponding matrix equation

$$X = AX + DZ$$

The basic goal of input-output analysis is to determine the total output or production, X, necessary for a given final (or external) demand, D. Thus, the preceding matrix equation must be solved for X. Hence,

$$X = AX + D$$
$$X - AX = D$$
$$(I - A)X = D \qquad \text{(See Exercise 72, Section 5-5)}$$
$$X = (I - A)^{-1}D$$

assuming $(I - A)^{-1}$ exists.

Returning to our example,

$$I - A = \begin{bmatrix} 1 & 0 & 0 \\ 0 & 1 & 0 \\ 0 & 0 & 1 \end{bmatrix} - \begin{bmatrix} 0 & 1/6 & 1/2 \\ 1/2 & 0 & 1/8 \\ 1/4 & 1/3 & 0 \end{bmatrix} = \begin{bmatrix} 1 & -1/6 & -1/2 \\ -1/2 & 1 & -1/8 \\ -1/4 & -1/3 & 1 \end{bmatrix}$$

Using row operations, it is determined that

$$(I - A)^{-1} = \begin{bmatrix} \dfrac{184}{127} & \dfrac{64}{127} & \dfrac{100}{127} \\[2mm] \dfrac{102}{127} & \dfrac{168}{127} & \dfrac{72}{127} \\[2mm] \dfrac{80}{127} & \dfrac{72}{127} & \dfrac{176}{127} \end{bmatrix}$$

Suppose a final (or external) demand of

$$D = \begin{bmatrix} 254 \\ 127 \\ 381 \end{bmatrix} \quad \begin{matrix} \text{units of } C_1 \\ \text{units of } C_2 \\ \text{units of } C_3 \end{matrix}$$

is desired. Then a total output of

$$X = (I - A)^{-1}D$$

$$= \begin{bmatrix} \dfrac{184}{127} & \dfrac{64}{127} & \dfrac{100}{127} \\[2mm] \dfrac{102}{127} & \dfrac{168}{127} & \dfrac{72}{127} \\[2mm] \dfrac{80}{127} & \dfrac{72}{127} & \dfrac{176}{127} \end{bmatrix} \begin{bmatrix} 254 \\ 127 \\ 381 \end{bmatrix}$$

$$= \begin{bmatrix} 732 \\ 588 \\ 760 \end{bmatrix} \quad \begin{matrix} \text{units of } C_1 \\ \text{units of } C_2 \\ \text{units of } C_3 \end{matrix}$$

is required.

Since our discussion of Leontief's input-output model has assumed the existence of a final (or external) demand, it is called **Leontief's open model.** In other words, an open model assumes that the production of the n industries of an economy is not all consumed internally. An input-output model that assumes all of the production of the n industries of an economy is consumed internally is called a **closed model.**

In a closed model, the final (or external) demand matrix, D, is a matrix of 0s, so that the matrix equation

$$X = AX + D$$

becomes

$$X = AX + 0$$

where 0 denotes a column matrix consisting of n 0s. Solving for X yields.

$$X - AX = 0$$

$$\text{or}$$

$$(I - A)X = 0$$

The above equation has infinitely many solutions if $(I - A)^{-1}$ does not exist. If $(I - A)^{-1}$ does not exist, the infinitely many solutions are expressed parametrically. Of course, if $(I - A)^{-1}$ does exist, the solution matrix X consists of a column of 0s.

SUMMARY

Input-Output Problem

Given a technological matrix A, a total output matrix X, and an external demand matrix D, the following matrix equation holds:

$$\underset{\text{output}}{\underset{\text{Total}}{}} \quad \underset{\text{demand}}{\underset{\text{Internal}}{}} \quad \underset{\text{demand}}{\underset{\text{External}}{}}$$

$$X = AX + D$$

The goal of input-output analysis is to determine the total output matrix, X, necessary for a given external demand matrix, D. The **solution** is given by

$$X = (I - A)^{-1}D$$

assuming $(I - A)^{-1}$ exists.

Exercises 5-8

1. A primitive economy has only two commodities: oil and coal. Production of 1 barrel of oil requires 1/2 ton of coal. Production of 1 ton of coal requires 1/4 barrel of oil.
   a) If A is the technological matrix of this economy, then fill in the elements of A:

   Requirements for

   1 barrel of oil   1 ton of coal

   $$A = \begin{bmatrix} \underline{\quad} & \underline{\quad} \\ \underline{\quad} & \underline{\quad} \end{bmatrix} \begin{matrix} \text{Oil} \\ \text{Coal} \end{matrix}$$

   b) If matrix D gives the desired final (or external) demands

   $$D = \begin{bmatrix} 210 \\ 490 \end{bmatrix} \begin{matrix} \text{Barrels of oil} \\ \text{Tons of coal} \end{matrix}$$

   then determine the required total output for each commodity.

2. An economy has three commodities: C_1, C_2, and C_3. Production of 1 unit of C_1 requires ¼ unit of C_2. Production of 1 unit of C_2 requires ½ unit of C_1 and 1/3 unit of C_3. Production of 1 unit of C_3 requires 1/4 unit of C_1 and 1/2 unit of C_2.
   a) Write the technological matrix for this economy.
   b) If matrix D gives the desired final (or external) demands

   $$D = \begin{bmatrix} 231 \\ 462 \\ 924 \end{bmatrix} \begin{matrix} \text{units of } C_1 \\ \text{units of } C_2 \\ \text{units of } C_3 \end{matrix}$$

   then determine the required total output for each commodity.

3. Given the technological matrix A and the final (or external) demand matrix D for some economy, determine the total output matrix X.

   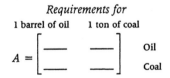

   $$A = \begin{bmatrix} 0.1 & 0.2 \\ 0.3 & 0.1 \end{bmatrix} \qquad D = \begin{bmatrix} 30 \\ 20 \end{bmatrix}$$

4. Given the technological matrix A and the final (or external) demand matrix D for some economy, determine the total output matrix X.

$$A = \begin{bmatrix} 0.1 & 0.4 \\ 0.2 & 0.3 \end{bmatrix} \quad D = \begin{bmatrix} 800 \\ 1000 \end{bmatrix}$$

5. Given the technological matrix A and the final (or external) demand matrix D for some economy, determine the total output matrix X.

$$A = \begin{bmatrix} 0.3 & 0.1 & 0.2 \\ 0.2 & 0.1 & 0.1 \\ 0.2 & 0.1 & 0.1 \end{bmatrix} \quad D = \begin{bmatrix} 50 \\ 30 \\ 90 \end{bmatrix}$$

6. Given the technological matrix A and the final (or external) demand matrix D for some economy, determine the total output matrix X.

$$A = \begin{bmatrix} 0.1 & 0.2 & 0.2 \\ 0.2 & 0.1 & 0.2 \\ 0.2 & 0.2 & 0.1 \end{bmatrix} \quad D = \begin{bmatrix} 100 \\ 200 \\ 180 \end{bmatrix}$$

7. Assume that we have calculated the total output that each of two industries should produce in order to satisfy total demand and that

$$(I - A)^{-1} = \begin{bmatrix} 1.4 & 0.8 \\ 1.1 & 0.9 \end{bmatrix}$$

However, suppose that the final (or external) demands have changed subsequent to our calculation of total output. The matrix ΔD gives the change in final (or external) demand for each industry.

$$\Delta D = \begin{bmatrix} -2 \\ 6 \end{bmatrix} \begin{matrix} \leftarrow \text{change in final demand for industry 1} \\ \leftarrow \text{change in final demand for industry 2} \end{matrix}$$

Determine the change in total output needed to meet the changes in the final demands.

Hint: Replace the matrix equation

$$X = (I - A)^{-1}D$$

with

$$\Delta X = (I - A)^{-1}\Delta D$$

where

$$\Delta X = \begin{bmatrix} \Delta x_1 \\ \Delta x_2 \end{bmatrix} \begin{matrix} \leftarrow \text{change in total output for industry 1} \\ \leftarrow \text{change in total output for industry 2} \end{matrix}$$

8. Repeat Exercise 7 for

$$\Delta D = \begin{bmatrix} 10 \\ -1 \end{bmatrix}$$

9. Repeat Exercise 7 for

$$(I - A)^{-1} = \begin{bmatrix} 2.3 & 1.5 \\ 0.9 & 1.2 \end{bmatrix} \quad \Delta D = \begin{bmatrix} 4 \\ -1 \end{bmatrix}$$

EXTRA DIVIDENDS

• *Oil Refinery Scheduling—Merco Oil Refinery*

The Merco Oil Refinery owns three oil wells. Oil from the well in Saudi Arabia is refined into 0.2 million barrels of regular gasoline, 0.1 million barrels of unleaded gasoline, and 0.3 million barrels of kerosene each day. Oil from the well in Kuwait is refined into 0.3 million barrels of regular gasoline, 0.2 million barrels of unleaded gasoline, and 0.1 million barrels of kerosene each day. Oil from the well in Egypt is refined into 0.4 million barrels of regular gasoline, 0.1 million barrels of unleaded gasoline, and 0.4 million barrels of kerosene each day. The company needs to produce 19 million barrels of regular gasoline, 10 million barrels of unleaded gasoline, and 20 million barrels of kerosene to meet demand requirements. Assuming that adequate lead time for transportation assures a continual flow, how many days should each well be operated in order to meet the demand requirements?

Exercises

1. Complete the following table, which summarizes the preceding information:

	Well in Saudi Arabia	Well in Kuwait	Well in Egypt	Demand requirements
Regular	(___)	(___)	(___)	(___)
Unleaded	(___)	(___)	(___)	(___)
Kerosene	(___)	(___)	(___)	(___)

2. Define each decision variable, and write the linear system of equations for this problem.
3. Write the linear system in matrix form, $AX = B$.
4. Determine A^{-1} and solve the linear system.
5. Suppose the demand requirements are changed to 20 million barrels of regular gasoline, 10 million barrels of unleaded gasoline, and 15 million barrels of kerosene. How many days should each well be operated in order to meet the demand requirements?

CHAPTER 5 HIGHLIGHTS

• Concepts

Your ability to answer the following questions is one indicator of the depth of your mastery of this chapter's important concepts. Note that the questions are grouped under various topic headings. For any question that you cannot answer, refer to the appropriate section of the chapter indicated by the topic heading. Pay particular attention to the summary boxes within a section.

5-1 LINEAR SYSTEMS (TWO EQUATIONS IN TWO VARIABLES)

1. Graphically, each equation of a linear system in two variables constitutes a(n)

_____ _____.

2. The solution to a linear system in two variables is the _____ _____ of the straight lines.

3. If a linear system of two equations in two variables has no solution, this means that the straight lines are _____.

4. If a linear system of two equations in two variables has infinitely many solutions, this means that the straight lines _____.

5. Name two methods that are most efficient for solving linear systems of two equations in two variables.

6. Briefly state the three steps of the problem-solving procedure given in this section.

5-2   LINEAR SYSTEMS; TABLEAUS; PROBLEM FORMULATION

7. Write the format of the final tableau for a linear system consisting of
   a) Two equations in two variables
   b) Three equations in three variables

8. Write the general form of a linear equation in
   a) Two variables   b) Three variables   c) n variables

5-3   GAUSS-JORDAN METHOD OF SOLVING LINEAR SYSTEMS

9. State the three fundamental row operations.

10. Write the format of the final tableau for a linear system of n equations in n unknowns. If this tableau is not obtainable by row operations, then the linear system has either _____ _____ or _____ _____ _____.

11. Write a tableau that contains an inconsistency.

12. If a final tableau has more _____ than _____, this indicates that there are infinitely many solutions. The infinitely many solutions are expressed by solving for the _____ variables in terms of the _____ variables.

5-4   MATRICES

13. A matrix is a(n) _____ array of numbers.

14. State the conditions for matrices to be equal.

15. In order for matrices to be added or subtracted, they must be of the _____ _____.

16. How do you multiply a matrix by a number.

5-5   MULTIPLYING MATRICES

17. If A is an $m \times n$ matrix and B is an $n \times r$ matrix, then the product, AB, is a(n) _____ matrix.

18. State the condition that allows the computation of a product of two matrices.

19. Write the 3×3, 4×4, and 5×5 identity matrices.

5-6   INVERSE OF A SQUARE MATRIX

20. Define the inverse of a square matrix.

21. Do all square matrices have inverses?

22. If the inverse of a square matrix exists, is it unique?

5-7   SOLVING SQUARE LINEAR SYSTEMS BY MATRIX INVERSES

23. To solve the linear equation $ax = b$, where $a \neq 0$, we use the _____ _____ of the number a. To solve the matrix equation $AX = B$ for X, we use _____, provided it exists.

24. The solution to a matrix equation $AX = B$ is $X =$ _____, provided that _____ exists.

5-8 LEONTIEF'S INPUT-OUTPUT MODEL

25. Given an economy consisting of n industries, the output of a given industry that is needed by other industries in the economy is called _____ _____ . The remainder of such output, needed by industries outside the economy, is called _____ _____.

26. Given the matrix equation $X = AX + D$, interpret
a) X b) AX c) D

27. For Question 26, the goal of input-output analysis is to determine matrix _____. This matrix is given by the matrix equation _____ , provided that _____ exists.

REVIEW EXERCISES

• *Method of Elimination*

Solve Exercises 1–6 by the method of elimination.

1. $x + 2y = 2$
$3x - 5y = 17$

2. $2x + 3y = 18$
$6x + y = 22$

3. $3x - 5y = 8$
$-6x + 10y = 12$

4. $-5x + 2y = 2$
$x + 3y = 20$

5. $\dfrac{x}{4} + \dfrac{y}{3} = 6$
$\dfrac{x}{2} - \dfrac{y}{5} = -1$

6. $\dfrac{x}{3} - \dfrac{y}{5} = 3$
$\dfrac{x}{4} + y = 8$

• *Method of Substitution*

Solve Exercises 7 and 8 by the method of substitution.

7. $3x + y = 48$
$y = 5x$

8. $2x + 5y = 27$
$x = 2y$

• *Linear System Possibilities*

For Exercises 9 and 10,
a) Try to solve the linear system.
b) Verify that the linear system has infinitely many solutions by converting each equation into slope-intercept form.
c) State three solutions to the linear system.

9. $5x - 2y = 20$
$-15x + 6y = -60$

10. $-6x - 2y = 4$
$y = -3x - 2$

11. Draw a graph of a linear system (two equations in two variables) that has a unique solution.

12. Draw a graph of a linear system (two equations in two variables) that has no solution.

13. Draw a graph of a linear system (two equations in two variables) that has infinitely many solutions.

• *Gauss-Jordan Method of Row Operations*

Solve Exercises 14–21 by the Gauss-Jordan method of row operations.

14.
$$x + y + 2z = 9$$
$$2x - y + 3z = 12$$
$$3x + 2y + z = 11$$

15.
$$2x_1 + x_2 + 5x_3 = 27$$
$$x_1 + x_3 = 8$$
$$-x_1 + x_2 = -7$$

16.
$$x_1 + 3x_2 + x_3 = 10$$
$$5x_1 + 16x_2 + 9x_3 = 54$$

17.
$$2x_1 + x_2 - x_3 = 8$$
$$-6x_1 - 3x_2 + 3x_3 = 15$$

18.
$$x_1 + x_2 = 3$$
$$2x_1 + x_2 = 1$$
$$4x_1 - x_2 = -13$$

19.
$$x_1 - x_2 = 7$$
$$2x_1 + 3x_2 = 13$$
$$x_1 + x_2 = 6$$

20.
$$3x_1 + 4x_2 - 2x_3 = 10$$
$$x_1 - 2x_2 + x_3 = 2$$
$$2x_1 - 6x_2 + 3x_3 = 7$$

21.
$$x_1 - x_2 + 2x_3 = 5$$
$$-2x_1 + 3x_2 = -2$$
$$-x_1 + x_3 = 4$$

For the tableaus in Exercises 22–27, state the solution to the linear system if a unique solution exists. If there is no solution, state so. If there are infinitely many solutions, express them in terms of t.

22.
$$\begin{bmatrix} 1 & 0 & 0 & | & 5 \\ 0 & 1 & 0 & | & -2 \\ 0 & 0 & 1 & | & 6 \end{bmatrix}$$

23.
$$\begin{bmatrix} 1 & 0 & 4 & | & 3 \\ 0 & 1 & 0 & | & 5 \\ 0 & 0 & 0 & | & 4 \end{bmatrix}$$

24.
$$\begin{bmatrix} 1 & 0 & 2 & | & 7 \\ 0 & 1 & -1 & | & 8 \\ 0 & 0 & 0 & | & 0 \end{bmatrix}$$

25.
$$\begin{bmatrix} 1 & 0 & | & -3 \\ 0 & 1 & | & 4 \\ 0 & 0 & | & 6 \end{bmatrix}$$

26.
$$\begin{bmatrix} 1 & 0 & -2 & | & 3 \\ 0 & 1 & 6 & | & 4 \end{bmatrix}$$

27.
$$\begin{bmatrix} 1 & 0 & 0 & | & 9 \\ 0 & 1 & 0 & | & -3 \\ 0 & 0 & 0 & | & 0 \end{bmatrix}$$

• *Matrices*

If

$$A = \begin{bmatrix} 3 & 4 \\ 1 & -2 \\ 0 & 1 \end{bmatrix} \quad B = \begin{bmatrix} -2 & 3 \\ 1 & -1 \\ 1 & 2 \end{bmatrix} \quad C = \begin{bmatrix} 1 & 2 & 1 \\ 2 & 1 & 0 \end{bmatrix}$$

compute

28. $A + B$ **29.** $A - B$ **30.** $B - A$ **31.** $A - 3B$
32. AC **33.** CA **34.** BC **35.** $(BC)A$

• *Matrix Inverse*

For Exercises 36 and 37
a) Find the inverse
b) Verify that your result is correct

36.
$$\begin{bmatrix} 1 & -2 & 1 \\ 2 & -5 & 0 \\ 0 & 0 & 1 \end{bmatrix}$$

37.
$$\begin{bmatrix} 1 & 2 & 2 \\ 3 & 7 & 1 \\ 0 & 1 & 0 \end{bmatrix}$$

Express the linear systems of Exercises 38–41 in matrix form, $AX = B$. Then compute A^{-1} and use it to solve the linear system.

38.
$$x + 2y = 2$$
$$3x - 5y = 17$$

39.
$$2x + 3y = 18$$
$$6x + y = 22$$

40.
$$
\begin{aligned}
x + y + 2z &= 9 \\
2x - y + 3z &= 12 \\
3x + 2y + z &= 11
\end{aligned}
$$

41.
$$
\begin{aligned}
2x_1 + x_2 + 5x_3 &= 27 \\
x_1 + x_3 &= 8 \\
-x_1 + x_2 &= -7
\end{aligned}
$$

Applications

Formulate each of Exercises 42-45 as a linear system, and solve the linear system.

42. *Investment.* An investor has $20,000 to invest in bonds and stocks. For the coming year, bonds and stocks are expected to yield 8% and 10%, respectively. For tax purposes, the investor wants to earn $1900 during the year from the $20,000 invested. How much should be invested in bonds and how much in stocks?

43. *Mixture.* An alloy containing 30% silver is to be mixed with an alloy containing 80% silver to produce 100 pounds of an alloy containing 70% silver. Determine the amount of each alloy needed.

44. *Production planning.* The time requirements (in person-hours) per unit of product for each of three products in each of three departments are given below.

	Product A	Product B	Product C
Department 1	2	1	3
Department 2	1	2	1
Department 3	2	2	1

Departments 1, 2, and 3 have available 80, 80, and 60 person-hours, respectively. How many units of each product should be produced if all available person-hours are to be used?

45. *Transportation problem.* A firm produces desks at two plants. The desks must be transported from the two plants to two distribution centers, as is illustrated below.

	Distribution center 1	Distribution center 2	
Plant 1	x_1	x_2	800 ⟵⌐ Production
Plant 2	x_3	x_4	500 ⟵⌐ capacities
	700	600	

⟵——— Demands ———⟶

The production capacity of each plant and the demand of each distribution center are given above. If each plant is to operate at full capacity, how many desks should be shipped from each plant to each distribution center to ensure that the distribution centers' demands are met exactly?

46. *Costs.* A firm produces three products: A, B, and C. The number of units produced of each product during each of three given months appears in the matrix below.

Production volume

	Product A	Product B	Product C
June	300	400	200
July	500	600	800
August	400	300	500

The variable cost per unit for each product is given in the matrix below.

	Variable cost per unit
Product A	50
Product B	70
Product C	60

Determine the matrix that gives the total variable cost for each of the indicated months.

47. *Leontief's input-output model.* Given the technological matrix A and the final (or external) demand matrix D for some economy,
   a) Interpret each entry of the technological matrix
   b) Interpret each entry of the final demand matrix
   c) Determine the total output matrix X and interpret the result

$$A = \begin{bmatrix} 0.4 & 0.2 & 0.3 \\ 0.2 & 0.4 & 0.3 \\ 0.3 & 0.3 & 0.4 \end{bmatrix} \quad D = \begin{bmatrix} 200 \\ 500 \\ 400 \end{bmatrix}$$

6

LINEAR PROGRAMMING: THE GRAPHICAL METHOD

Introductory Application

Linear Programming: Product Mix

Williams Motors, which sells both American cars and imports, is planning its order for the next quarter. Current demand indicates that at least 240, but at most 450 cars should be ordered and that the number of imports ordered should be at least twice the number of American cars ordered. On the average, each American car costs the dealer $9000, and each foreign car costs $12,000. Budgetary and financing constraints limit next quarter's outlay for cars to $5,700,000. If Williams Motors makes an average profit of $600 per American car and $400 per foreign car, determine how many of each type should be ordered for the next quarter in order to maximize profits.

In this chapter, we will develop a procedure for formulating and solving such problems. This problem is solved in Example 6-7.

6-1 • LINEAR INEQUALITIES IN TWO VARIABLES

B. J. Wheels, Inc., makes two models of bicycles: model X and model Y. During any workday, the paint shop at B. J. Wheels has 24 person-hours available for these two models. Each model X bicycle uses 2 person-hours of paint shop time, and each model Y uses 3 person-hours of paint shop time. If, during a given day, the paint shop paints x model X and y model Y bicycles, then the number of person-hours of paint shop time used on these two models is given by the expression

$$2x + 3y$$

Since there are 24 person-hours available daily, then the above expression cannot exceed 24. Hence,

$$2x + 3y \leq 24$$

Note that the inequality $\leq$ implies that not all of the 24 person-hours have to be used.

A statement such as

$$2x + 3y \leq 24$$

is a **linear inequality in two variables.** If the inequality sign ($\leq$) is replaced by the equal sign ($=$), then the above linear inequality becomes the linear equation (equality)

$$2x + 3y = 24$$

Since we have already studied linear equations in Chapter 1, we will define linear inequalities in two variables in terms of linear equations.

SUMMARY

Linear Inequalities in Two Variables

If the equal sign ($=$) of a linear equation in two variables is replaced by an inequality sign ($<$, $>$, $\leq$, $\geq$), the resulting expression is a linear inequality in two variables.

Thus, the statements

$$2x + 3y < 24$$
$$2x + 3y \geq 24$$
$$y \leq 5x - 7$$
$$x > 3y + 4$$

are examples of linear inequalities in two variables. In this section, we discuss the graphing of linear inequalities in two variables.

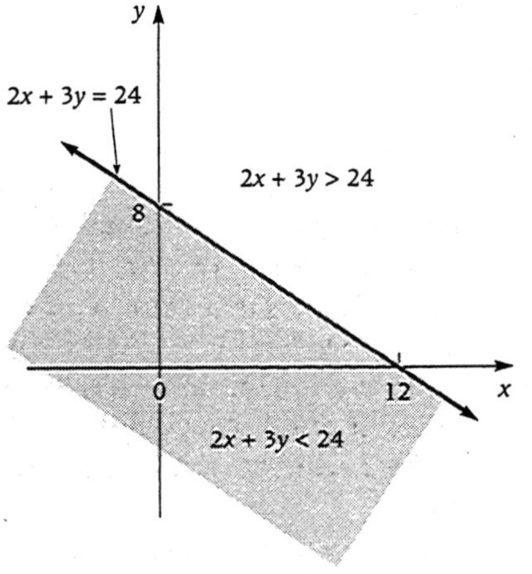

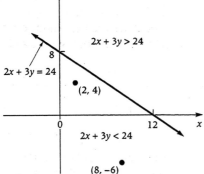

FIGURE 6-1

To graph a linear inequality such as

$$2x + 3y \leq 24$$

we should observe that the corresponding straight line, $2x + 3y = 24$, divides the plane into two regions (see Figure 6-1). One region consists of all points satisfying the inequality $2x + 3y < 24$, whereas the other consists of all points satisfying the inequality $2x + 3y > 24$.

Observing Figure 6-1, note that points *below* the straight line satisfy the linear inequality $2x + 3y < 24$. This can be verified by arbitrarily selecting a few points (x, y) from this region and substituting their coordinates into the inequality $2x + 3y < 24$ (see Figure 6-2). Points lying *above* the straight line satisfy the linear inequality $2x + 3y > 24$. This can be verified by selecting a few points (x, y) from this area above the straight line and substituting their coordinates into the inequality $2x + 3y > 24$ (see Figure 6-3 on page 349). Thus, all points (x, y) satisfying the inequality $2x + 3y \leq 24$ are located either *on or below* the straight line $2x + 3y = 24$ (see Figure 6-4 on page 349). For such points with positive x- and y-coordinates, the x- and y-coordinates represent the various combinations of numbers of model X and model Y bicycles that can be serviced by the paint shop during a given workday.

In general, when graphing linear inequalities, we should first sketch the corresponding straight line and then determine whether the points satisfying the inequality lie above or below that straight line. This is such an important procedure that we restate it in the box below.

■ To Graph Linear Inequalities

First, graph the corresponding straight line and then determine whether the points (x, y) satisfying the inequality lie **above** or **below** the straight line.

We now illustrate this graphing procedure. As an example, we will graph the linear inequality discussed in this section,

$$2x + 3y \leq 24$$

Since we have already illustrated its graph, let us pretend we have not seen Figure 6-1.

We first find the y-intercept of the corresponding straight line by setting $x = 0$ and solving for y. Hence,

$$2(0) + 3y \leq 24$$
$$3y \leq 24$$
$$y \leq 8$$

Thus, the y-intercept is $(0, 8)$. The inequality $y \leq 8$ indicates that all points $(0, y)$ satisfying the inequality lie on the y-axis *at or below* $y = 8$. This result is graphed as an arrow pointing below the marker at $y = 8$ on the y-axis in Figure 6-5 on page 350.

2x + 3y < 24

    $(2, 4)$: $2(2) + 3(4) < 24$
                     $16 < 24$

    $(8, -6)$: $2(8) + 3(-6) < 24$
                      $-2 < 24$

FIGURE 6-2

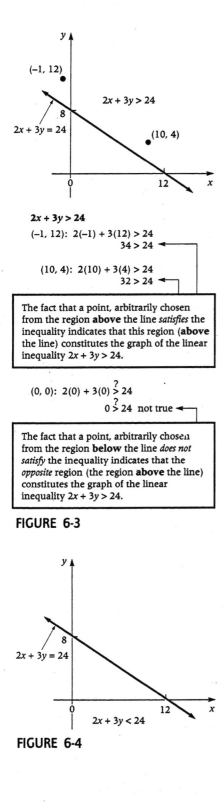

$2x + 3y > 24$

(-1, 12): $2(-1) + 3(12) > 24$

$34 > 24$

(10, 4): $2(10) + 3(4) > 24$

$32 > 24$

The fact that a point, arbitrarily chosen from the region **above** the line *satisfies* the inequality indicates that this region (**above** the line) constitutes the graph of the linear inequality $2x + 3y > 24$.

(0, 0): $2(0) + 3(0) \overset{?}{>} 24$

$0 \overset{?}{>} 24$ not true

The fact that a point, arbitrarily chosen from the region **below** the line *does not satisfy* the inequality indicates that the *opposite* region (the region **above** the line) constitutes the graph of the linear inequality $2x + 3y > 24$.

FIGURE 6-3

FIGURE 6-4

Now we find the *x*-intercept by setting $y = 0$ and solving for *x*. Hence,

$$2x + 3(0) \leq 24$$
$$2x \leq 24$$
$$x \leq 12$$

Thus, the *x*-intercept is (12, 0). The inequality $x \leq 12$ indicates that all points (*x*, 0) satisfying the inequality lie on the *x*-axis *at or to the left of* $x = 12$. This result is graphed as an arrow pointing to the left of the marker at $x = 12$ on the *x*-axis in Figure 6-5. Connecting the intercepts of Figure 6-5, we obtain the straight line $2x + 3y = 24$, along with the region represented by the inequality $2x + 3y < 24$ (see Figure 6-6 on page 350). Observe that the direction of the arrows indicates whether the associated region is either above or below the straight line.

As we can see in Figure 6-6, the region corresponding to $2x + 3y < 24$ lies below the line $2x + 3y = 24$. We indicate this by *shading the region **not** associated with $2x + 3y < 24$* and leaving the region corresponding to $2x + 3y < 24$ in white. Although this seems contrary to what one would expect, the reason for this procedure will become apparent later in this section. We will repeat this procedure throughout this chapter, so we restate it in the box below. Since most of the inequalities that we will graph will contain either $\leq$ or $\geq$ inequality signs, we will state the procedure only for these inequality signs. However, we will include a remark regarding $<$ and $>$ inequality signs.

To Graph Linear Inequalities

Shade the Region to Be Discarded

1. *Find the y-intercept.* Set $x = 0$ and solve for *y*. This gives a linear inequality of the form $y \leq c$ or $y \geq c$, where *c* is a constant. Mark the *y*-intercept and draw an arrow indicating whether the points (0, *y*) lie above or below the *y*-intercept.

2. *Find the x-intercept.* Set $y = 0$ and solve for *x*. This gives an inequality of the form $x \leq c$ or $x \geq c$, where *c* is a constant. Mark the *x*-intercept and draw an arrow indicating whether the points (*x*, 0) lie to the right of or to the left of the *x*-intercept.

3. *Shade the region to be discarded.* Draw a straight line through the intercepts determined in steps 1 and 2. The direction of the arrows (from steps 1 and 2) on the *x*- and *y*-axes indicates the location of the region corresponding to the linear inequality being graphed. Shade the region not associated with the linear inequality. In other words, *shade the region to be discarded.* Thus, the region corresponding to the linear inequality remains in white. Its **boundary** is the straight line previously drawn.

Remark:

a) If a linear inequality contains either $<$ or $>$ inequality signs, its *boundary is **not** included* in its graph and is therefore drawn as a *dotted line.*

b) If a linear inequality contains either $\leq$ or $\geq$ inequality signs, its *boundary **is** included* in its graph and is therefore drawn as a *solid line.*

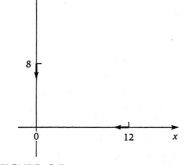

FIGURE 6-5

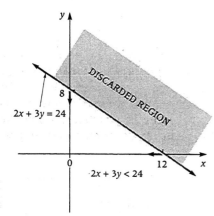

FIGURE 6-6

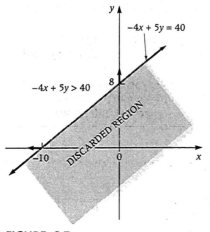

FIGURE 6-7

• **EXAMPLE 6-1** _____

Graph $-4x + 5y \geq 40$.

Solution

First, we find the y-intercept by setting $x = 0$ and using the rules of inequalities to solve for y. Hence,

$$-4(0) + 5y \geq 40$$
$$5y \geq 40$$
$$y \geq 8$$

Thus, the y-intercept is $(0, 8)$. The inequality $y \geq 8$ is graphed in Figure 6-7 as an arrow pointing above the marker at $y = 8$ on the y-axis.

Next, we find the x-intercept by setting $y = 0$ and solving for x. Hence,

$$-4x + 5(0) \geq 40$$
$$-4x \geq 40$$
$$x \leq -10$$

Reverse the direction of an inequality when multiplying or dividing both sides by a negative number.

Remember that we reverse the direction of an inequality when we multiply or divide both sides by a negative number. Thus, the x-intercept is $(-10, 0)$. The inequality $x \leq -10$ is graphed in Figure 6-7 as an arrow pointing to the left of the marker at $x = -10$ on the x-axis.

We draw a straight line through the intercepts. The arrows at the intercepts $x = -10$ and $y = 8$ point to the region associated with $-4x + 5y > 40$. As we can see in Figure 6-7, the arrows point to the region *above* the line $-4x + 5y = 40$. Since we shade the region to be discarded, the region corresponding to $-4x + 5y > 40$ remains in white. Thus, the white region plus the straight line $-4x + 5y = 40$ constitutes the graph of $-4x + 5y \geq 40$.

_____   •

Systems of Linear Inequalities

If we graph a set of points (x, y) satisfying *more than one* linear inequality, we are graphing a **system of linear inequalities.** Specifically, the graph of the system

$$3x + 5y \geq 30$$
$$4x - y \leq 17$$

consists of the set of points (x, y) satisfying *both* inequalities.

To graph a system of two linear inequalities, we graph each inequality on the same axis system and then determine the region common to both. Every point (x, y) in the common region will, of course, satisfy both inequalities. The preceding system of linear inequalities is graphed in Figures 6-8 and 6-9 on page 351.

First, we graph $3x + 5y \geq 30$. Setting $x = 0$ gives $5y \geq 30$, or $y \geq 6$. This is graphed in Figure 6-8 as an arrow pointing above the marker at $y = 6$ on the y-axis. Setting $y = 0$ gives $3x \geq 30$, or $x \geq 10$. This is graphed in Figure 6-8 as an arrow pointing to the right of the marker at $x = 10$ on the x-axis. We draw a straight line through the intercepts. The arrows at the intercepts $x = 10$ and $y = 6$ point to the region associated with $3x + 5y > 30$. Since we *shade the region to be discarded,* the remaining white region of Figure 6-8 is associated with $3x + 5y > 30$. Thus, the white re-

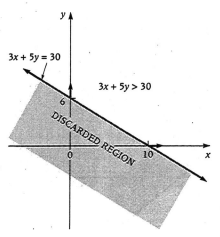

3x + 5y = 30

3x + 5y > 30

DISCARDED REGION

FIGURE 6-8

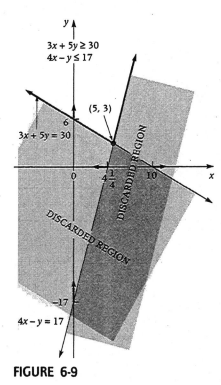

3x + 5y ≥ 30
4x − y ≤ 17

(5, 3)

3x + 5y = 30

DISCARDED REGION

DISCARDED REGION

−17

4x − y = 17

FIGURE 6-9

gion plus the straight line $3x + 5y = 30$ constitutes the graph of $3x + 5y \geq 30$.

Next, we graph $4x - y \leq 17$. Setting $x = 0$ gives $-y \leq 17$, or $y \geq -17$. Remember that we reverse the direction of an inequality when we multiply or divide both sides by a negative number. This is graphed in Figure 6-9 as an arrow pointing above the number $y = -17$ on the y-axis. Setting $y = 0$ gives $4x \leq 17$, or $x \leq 4\frac{1}{4}$. This is graphed in Figure 6-9 as an arrow pointing to the left of the number $x = 4\frac{1}{4}$ on the x-axis. We draw a straight line through the intercepts. The arrows at the intercepts $y = -17$ and $x = 4\frac{1}{4}$ point to the region associated with $4x - y < 17$. We shade the region to be discarded. The *remaining white region and its boundary* in Figure 6-9 comprise the graph of our system of linear inequalities. Observe that this region is *not bounded* on all sides. Thus, it is called an **unbounded region.** Unbounded regions will be discussed in greater detail in Section 6-3.

Vertex Points

The *corner points* on the boundary of a region such as that of Figure 6-9 are called **vertex points.** Observe that the region of Figure 6-9 contains only one vertex point (5, 3). Since this vertex point is the intersection of the straight lines $3x + 5y = 30$ and $4x - y = 17$, its coordinates are determined by solving the associated linear system of equations, using the methods discussed in Chapter 5. Vertex points will take on special importance in the next section of this chapter.

To Graph a System of Linear Inequalities

Graph each inequality on the same set of axes. For each inequality, shade the region to be discarded. The remaining region, the unshaded (white) region, if it exists, constitutes the region associated with the system.

1. If all of the linear inequalities are of the ≤ or ≥ type, then the *boundary* of the white region *is included* in the region associated with the system.

2. If any linear inequality is of the < or > type, then the portion of the *boundary* (of the white region) corresponding to such an inequality is *not included* in the region associated with the system.

• **EXAMPLE 6-2** _____

Graph the system

$$4x + 5y \leq 40$$
$$3x - 2y \leq 24$$
$$x \geq 0$$
$$y \geq 0$$

Solution

The system is graphed in Figures 6-10 through 6-13. The region common to all of the inequalities appears in Figure 6-13 on page 353.

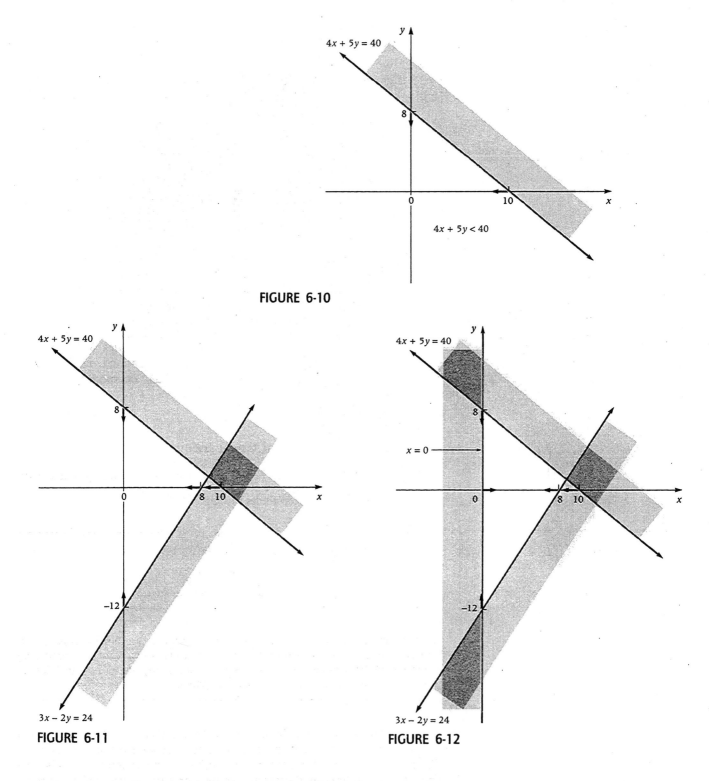

FIGURE 6-10

FIGURE 6-11

FIGURE 6-12

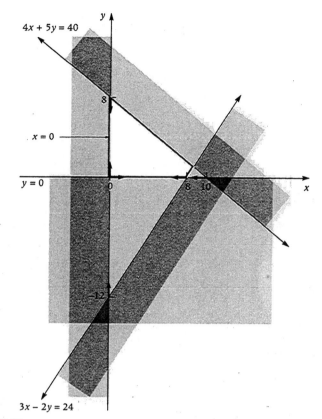

FIGURE 6-13

Note that the inclusion of both inequalities $x \geq 0$ and $y \geq 0$ results in a region that is located within the first quadrant.

• **EXAMPLE 6-3** —————————————————————————————

Graph the system

$$2x + 5y \leq 20$$
$$2x + 5y \geq 30$$

Solution

Both inequalities are graphed on the same set of axes in Figure 6-14 on page 354. Since the shaded region represents the region to be discarded, there is no remaining white region. This means that there are no points satisfying both inequalities. In other words, there are **no solutions** to the system.

—————————————————————————————————————— •

Throughout this and the next chapter, we will be using the symbols $\leq$ and $\geq$ to write inequalities that express relationships between quantities. Since it is important to use inequality symbols correctly to express relationships that are often stated verbally, we include a summary of phrases associated with each respective inequality symbol.

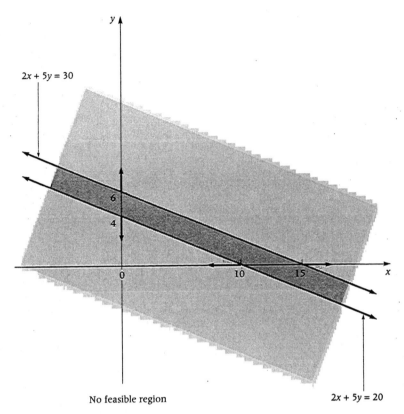

FIGURE 6-14

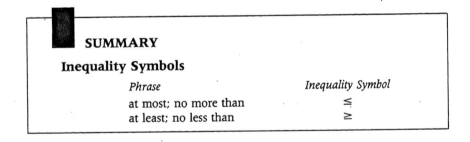

SUMMARY

Inequality Symbols

Phrase	*Inequality Symbol*
at most; no more than	≤
at least; no less than	≥

Application

• **EXAMPLE 6-4   Product Mix.**

A company makes bicycles and motorbikes, each of which must pass through departments I and II. Department I (Assembly) has at most 450 hours, and department II (Inspection) has at most 400 hours available for both products. Each bicycle requires 3 hours of time in department I and 5 hours of time in department II. Each motorbike requires 4 hours of time in department I and 2 hours of time in department II. How many bicycles and motorbikes can be made in order to satisfy departmental time constraints?

Solution

We apply our problem-solving procedure (see Section 5-1).

Step 1 *Identify the unknowns. Use letters to denote these quantities.*
We let

$$x = \text{number of bicycles to be made}$$
$$y = \text{number of motorbikes to be made}$$

Step 2 *Organize the given information, and write the equations (or inequalities) that express any relationships among the unknowns.*
The given information is listed in the table below.

	x bicycles	y motorbikes	Resource capacity
Department I	3 hours/bicycle	4 hours/motorbike	At most 450 hours available
Department II	5 hours/bicycle	2 hours/motorbike	At most 400 hours available

The departmental time constraints are expressed by the inequalities

Department I	$3x + 4y \leq 450$	
Department II	$5x + 2y \leq 400$	
	$x \geq 0$	Cannot have a negative number of bicycles
	$y \geq 0$	Cannot have a negative number of motorbikes

Step 3 *Solve the equations (or inequalities) of step 2.*
We must graph the region corresponding to the system of linear inequalities of step 2. This region is graphed in Figures 6-15 through 6-18. Any point (x, y) in the

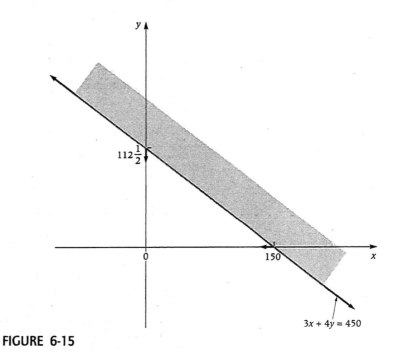

FIGURE 6-15

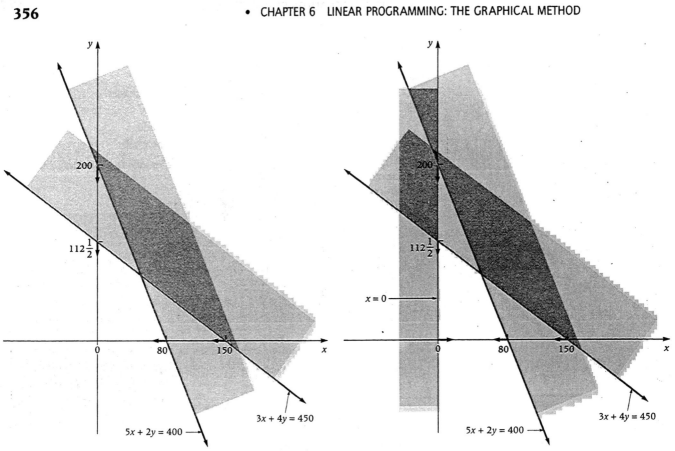

FIGURE 6-16

FIGURE 6-17

white region of Figure 6-18 will satisfy the departmental time constraints. In other words, if, for any point (x, y) of the white region of Figure 6-18 on page 357, x bicycles and y motorbikes are made, then the departmental time constraints represented by the linear inequalities will be satisfied.

Also, observe in Figure 6-18 that we have labeled the vertex points with their ordered pairs. Note that the *vertex point (50, 75)* was determined by solving the linear system

$$3x + 4y = 450$$
$$5x + 2y = 400$$

• EXAMPLE 6-5   Product Mix Continued. _____

Suppose the company of Example 6-4 receives an order for 10 bicycles and marketing studies indicate that no more than 90 motorbikes should be made. Indicate how these additional restrictions change the graph of Figure 6-18.

Solution

The order for 10 bicycles means that at least 10 bicycles should be produced. This results in the additional inequality

$$x \geq 10$$

That no more than 90 motorbikes should be made results in the additional inequality

$$y \leq 90$$

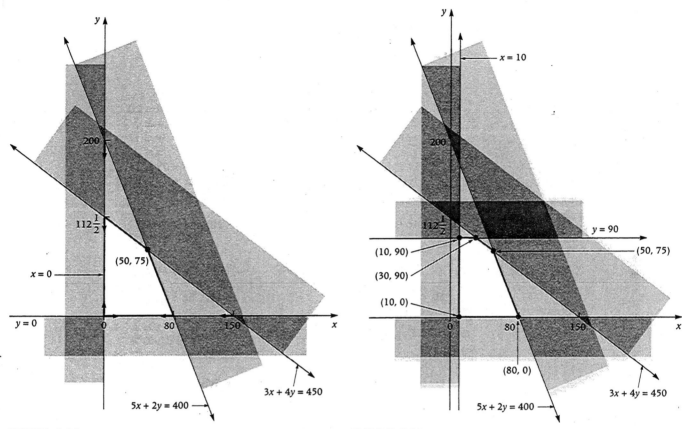

FIGURE 6-18

FIGURE 6-19

Thus, we must graph the region corresponding to the system of linear inequalities

$$3x + 4y \le 450$$
$$5x + 2y \le 400$$
$$x \ge 10$$
$$y \ge 0$$
$$y \le 90$$

These two inequalities can be combined to read $0 \le y \le 90$.

The resulting graph is given in Figure 6-19. Comparing the graph of Figure 6-19 with that of Figure 6-18, observe that the inequality $x \ge 10$ restricts the solution region to the right of the vertical line $x = 10$, while the inequality $y \le 90$ restricts the solution region below the horizontal line $y = 90$. Note that the *vertex point (30, 90)* was determined by solving the linear system

$$3x + 4y = 450$$
$$y = 90$$

Exercises 6-1

Graph each of the following inequalities.

1. $4x + 5y \ge 40$ **2.** $-3x + 2y \le 12$
3. $x - y \ge 5$ **4.** $-2x - 4y \ge 16$

5. $2x + y \leq 12$ **6.** $3x - y \leq 15$

7. $x + 3y < 4$ **8.** $-2x + y > 8$

9. $9x - 2y \geq 36$ **10.** $7x - 3y \leq -21$

11. $-4x - 7y \geq -28$ **12.** $x + y < 7$

Graph each of the following systems.

13. $3x + 9y \geq 27$
$2x - 3y \leq 12$

14. $2x + 5y \leq 20$
$x \geq 0$

15. $-3x + 2y \geq -12$
$y \geq -6$

16. $4x - 3y \leq 12$
$x \leq 2$

17. $3x + 4y \leq 48$
$5x + 3y \leq 30$
$x \geq 0$
$y \geq 0$

18. $2x + 7y \geq 28$
$2x + y \geq 8$
$x \geq 0$
$y \geq 0$

19. $6x + 7y \leq 42$
$3x + 5y \leq 25$
$x \geq 0$
$y \geq 0$

20. $6x + 7y \leq 42$
$3x + 5y \leq 25$
$x - y \leq 6$
$x \geq 0$
$y \geq 0$

21. $5x + 2y \geq 30$
$3x + 4y \geq 24$
$x + y \geq 7.6$
$x \geq 0$
$y \geq 0$

22. $3x + y \leq 30$
$2x + 3y \leq 24$
$x \geq 1$
$0 \leq y \leq 7$

Try to graph each of the following systems. What are the results?

23. $3x + 4y \leq 12$
$3x + 4y \geq 24$

24. $x + y \leq 5$
$x - y \geq 5$
$y \geq 1$

25. Model X requires 5 hours in the assembly department, while model Y requires 7 hours in this department. If the assembly department has at most 105 hours available for these two products, write the linear inequality that expresses the relationship between the number of units of each model produced. Graph the inequality.

26. An investor invests x amount of dollars at 8% and y dollars at 9% in order to maintain income of at least $60,000. Write the linear inequality that expresses the relationship between the amounts invested at the different rates. Graph the inequality.

27. Each gadget requires 4 hours in the cutting department, while each widget requires 5 hours in the same department. If the cutting department has at most 80 hours available, write the linear inequality that expresses the relationship between the number of gadgets and widgets produced. Graph the inequality.

28. Each pound of food A contains 500 milligrams of vitamin C, while each pound of food B contains 300 milligrams of vitamin C. A diet consisting of both foods A and B must yield at least 15,000 milligrams of vitamin C. Write the linear inequality that expresses the relationship between the amounts of both foods. Graph the inequality.

29. *Product mix.* A company makes two types of truck tires: type A and type B. Each lot of type A tires requires 2 hours in department 1 and 1 hour in department 2. Each lot of type B tires requires 5 hours in department 1 and 2 hours in department 2. If departments 1 and 2 have available at most 250 and 120 hours, respectively, how many lots of type A and type B tires can be made in order that departmental time constraints are satisfied?

a) Write the corresponding system of linear inequalities.

b) Graph the region.

c) Determine the vertex points.

30. *Investments.* An investor has at most $1,000,000 to allocate among stocks and bonds. Stocks are expected to yield 10% and bonds 8%. How should the amount invested be allocated if the investor wishes to earn at least $85,000?

a) Write the system of linear inequalities.

b) Graph the region.

c) Determine the vertex points.

31. *Marketing research survey.* It costs $30 to survey a family in city 1, while it costs $40 to survey a family in city 2. The maximum amount budgeted for the complete survey is $12,000. At least 100 city 1 families and 120 city 2 families must be surveyed. How many families should be surveyed from each city?

a) Write the system of linear inequalities.

b) Graph the region.

c) Determine the vertex points.

32. *Agriculture.* A farmer has available 2000 acres for the planting of two crops: A and B. Each acre planted with crop A will generate sales revenue of $4000, while each acre planted with crop B will generate sales revenue of $5000. Total sales revenue of at least $9,000,000 is required. If at least 500 acres of crop A and at least 500 acres of crop B must be planted, how many acres of each crop should be planted?

a) Write the system of linear inequalities.

b) Graph the region.

c) Determine the vertex points.

33. *Land use planning.* A parcel of 1,000,000 acres is available for development in a given country. According to an authoritative report, x acres are to be zoned A-2, which means a lot size of 2 acres, and y acres are to be zoned A-3, which means a lot size of 3 acres. At least 480,000 lots are required. There must be at least 200,000 acres zoned A-2 and at least 60,000 acres zoned A-3.

a) Write the system of linear inequalities that shows the possible values of x and y.

b) Graph the region.

c) Determine the vertex points.

6-2 • LINEAR PROGRAMMING

A common problem of most businesses is the optimal allocation of limited resources among competing activities. Linear programming is a method for solving such problems. Historically, linear programming was developed to solve resource allocation problems of the U.S. Air Force during World War II. Much of the development of linear programming is credited to George B. Dantzig, who gave a general formulation of a linear programming problem and a method of solving it. This method is called the simplex method and is discussed in Chapter 7. In this chapter, we will discuss the graphical method for solving linear programming problems.

In this and subsequent sections of this chapter, we will be engaged in the process of formulating and solving linear programming problems. Such problems are special types of word problems that include an overall goal of either maximizing or minimizing some quantity, which can be written as a linear algebraic expression. In order that we have a systematic procedure for approaching such problems, we will present a linear programming problem-solving procedure while solving the following problem. We note that a substantial portion of this process has already been explained in Section 6-1.

PROBLEM

Production Planning

A company that manufactures sneakers and walking shoes must decide how many pairs of each to make during the next week. The company makes profits of $20 on each pair of sneakers and $16 on each pair of walking shoes. Both products are manufactured in the sewing department, which has a limited labor capacity of 480 person-hours for the next week. Each pair of sneakers uses 1 person-hour, and each pair of walking shoes uses 2 person-hours in this department. Another critical constraint, which affects the number of sneakers and walking shoes produced, is imposed by a limited availability of a raw material—XBSL504—which is used in the manufacture of both products. Specifically, each pair of sneakers requires 3 units of XBSL504, and each pair of walking shoes requires 4 units of this raw material. The company has only 1080 units of XBSL504 available during the next week. Finally, one of the company's major outlets has placed an order for 60 pairs of sneakers and 30 pairs of walking shoes. These must be made during the next week. How many pairs of sneakers and walking shoes should the company plan to make next week in order to maximize total profit?

SOLUTION

Step 1 *Identify the quantity to be either maximized or minimized and the related unknowns.*
These unknowns are called **decision variables.** Use letters to denote these quantities. Write an equation for the quantity to be either maximized or minimized.

We seek to maximize total profit. We must determine the number of pairs of sneakers and walking shoes to make next week in order that total profit is maximized. Thus, we let

$$P = \text{total profit for next week}$$
$$x = \text{number of pairs of sneakers}$$
$$y = \text{number of pairs of walking shoes}$$

Then the **objective function** is given by

$$P = 20x + 16y$$

and the objective is to maximize P.

Step 2 *Organize the given information, and write the linear inequalities that express any relationships existing among the unknowns.*

Decision variables

	x sneakers	y walking shoes	Resource capacity
Unit profits	$20/pair	$16/pair	
Sewing department	1 person-hour/pair	2 person-hours/pair	At most 480
Raw material XBSL504	3 units/pair	4 units/pair	At most 1080

Also,

- At least 60 pairs of sneakers must be produced.
- At least 30 pairs of walking shoes must be produced.

Algebraic Formulation

The constraints of the problem yield linear inequalities as derived below.

Sewing Department: Since it takes 1 person-hour to make 1 pair of sneakers, it takes x person-hours to make x pairs of sneakers. Since it takes 3 person-hours to make 1 pair of walking shoes, it takes $3y$ person-hours to make y pairs of walking shoes. Thus, it takes

$$1x + 3y$$

hours to make x pairs of sneakers and y pairs of walking shoes. Since the sewing department has at most 480 person-hours available next week, then

$$x + 3y \le 480$$

Raw Material XBSL504: Since each pair of sneakers uses 3 units and each pair of walking shoes uses 4 units of XBSL504, then the total number of units of XBSL504 used by x pairs of sneakers and y pairs of walking shoes is given by the expression

$$3x + 4y$$

Since there will be at most 1080 units of XBSL504 available next week, then

$$3x + 4y \le 1080$$

Demand Requirements: The fact that at least 60 pairs of sneakers must be made next week in order to satisfy demand requirements yields the inequality

$$x \ge 60$$

Also, the fact that at least 30 pairs of walking shoes must be made next week in order to satisfy demand requirements yields the inequality

$$y \geq 30$$

The complete formulation of this problem appears below.

$$\text{Maximize } P = 20x + 16y \qquad \text{Objective function}$$

$$\text{subject to} \quad \begin{aligned} x + 2y &\leq 480 \\ 3x + 4y &\leq 1080 \\ x &\geq 60 \\ y &\geq 30 \end{aligned} \right\} \quad \text{Constraints}$$

Step 3 *Determine the values of* x *and* y *that satisfy the constraints and also maximize the value of the objective function.*

Note that the constraints constitute a system of linear inequalities. If a region corresponding to this system of linear inequalities exists, its graph will reveal a set of points (x, y) that satisfy the constraints of the problem. Figures 6-20 through 6-23 on pages 362-364 illustrate the process of graphing the system of linear inequalities. Remember that, for each figure, the shaded region constitutes the region to be discarded; the white region and its boundary comprise the set of points that satisfy the respective linear inequalities.

Observe that Figure 6-23 reveals the region associated with the constraints of the problem. Since this region consists of a set of points (x, y) that satisfy all the constraints of the problem, it is called the **feasible region.** The coordinates of any point (x, y) of the feasible region constitute a feasible solution to our linear programming problem. In other words, if we choose any point (x, y) of the feasible region and manufacture x pairs of sneakers and y pairs of walking shoes, then this product mix is a feasible solution to the problem. Remember that *feasible* means that all the constraints of the problem are satisfied.

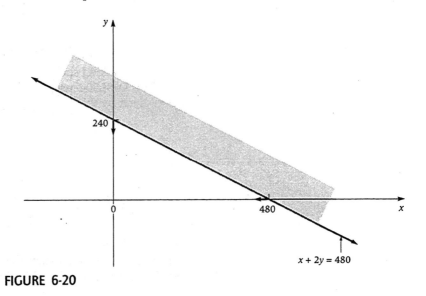

FIGURE 6-20

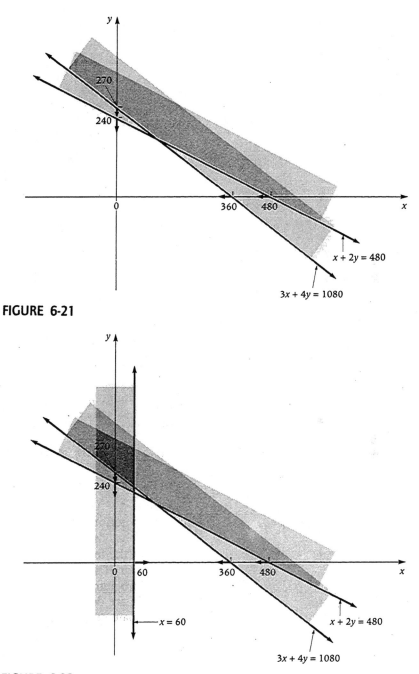

FIGURE 6-21

FIGURE 6-22

Optimal Solution

We must now determine which points (x, y) of the feasible region, if substituted into the objective function, yield a maximum value for P. At first glance, it would appear that we must substitute each point (x, y) of the feasible region into the objective function. But, since the feasible region

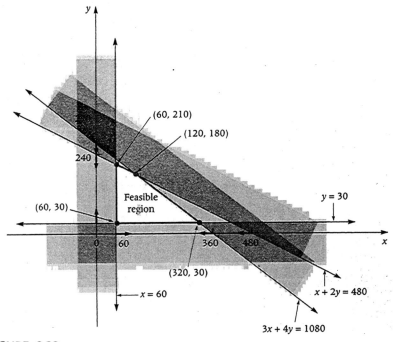

FIGURE 6-23

consists of infinitely many points, this is impossible. However, in the next section of this chapter, we will show the following.

An optimal value of an objective function, if it exists, will occur at one or more of the vertex points or on the boundary of the feasible region.

The feasible region, with its vertex points, is displayed in Figure 6-24. Remember that the vertex points are the corner points located on the boundary of the feasible region. Since each vertex point is an intersection point of a pair of straight lines that correspond to respective constraints of the linear programming problem, then the x- and y-coordinates of each vertex point are determined by solving the linear system associated with each such pair of intersecting straight lines. We state below the linear systems to be solved in order to determine the coordinates of the indicated vertex points.

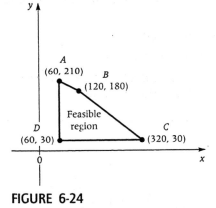

FIGURE 6-24

Vertex Point A	Vertex Point B	Vertex Point C
Linear system:	Linear system:	Linear system:
$x + 2y = 480$	$x + 2y = 480$	$3x + 4y = 1080$
$x = 60$	$3x + 4y = 1080$	$y = 30$
Solution:	Solution:	Solution:
$(60, 210)$	$(120, 180)$	$(320, 30)$

To find the optimal solution, we substitute the coordinates of each vertex point into the objective function to determine which point (or points) yields the maximum profit. Hence,

Maximize $P = 20x + 16y$ Objective function

Vertex Points

(60, 30)	$P = 20(60) + 16(30) = \$1680$
(60, 210)	$P = 20(60) + 16(210) = \$4560$
(120, 180)	$P = 20(120) + 16(180) = \$5280$
(320, 30)	$P = 20(320) + 16(30) = \$6880$ Maximum profit

Observe that the vertex point (320, 30) yields the maximum profit of \$6880. Therefore, the optimal solution to the linear programming problem is

$x = 320$ pairs of sneakers

$y = 30$ pairs of walking shoes

Maximum profit $P = \$6880$

Step 4 *Investigate the implications of the optimal solution.*

This involves substituting the optimal solution values into each constraint inequality.

Sewing Department Constraint:

$$x + 2y \leq 480$$
$$320 + 2(30) \leq 480$$
$$380 \leq 480$$

The left-hand-side value, 380, indicates the actual number of person-hours used in the sewing department to make 320 sneakers and 30 walking shoes. The right-hand-side value, 480, indicates the number of person-hours available in the sewing department. Since the left-hand-side value is less than the right-hand-side value, this indicates that not all of the available 480 person-hours are needed. The unused person-hours are determined by subtracting the left-hand-side value (LHS) from the right-hand-side value (RHS) to obtain

$$\text{RHS} - \text{LHS} = 480 - 380$$
$$= 100 \text{ person-hours}$$

This difference is called **slack** and represents unused capacity in a $\leq$ constraint. We formalize this concept in the box below.

SUMMARY

Slack

$\leq$ **Constraint.**   The difference between the right-hand-side (RHS) and left-hand-side (LHS) values of a $\leq$ constraint is called **slack** and represents *unused capacity* for that constraint.

$$\text{Slack} = \text{RHS} - \text{LHS}$$

continues

SUMMARY—*Continued*

If slack = 0 for a constraint, this implies that all of the available capacity or resource of that constraint is being utilized by the optimal solution to the linear programming problem. Such a constraint is called a **binding** constraint.

Raw Material Constraint:

$$3x + 4y \leq 1080$$
$$3(320) + 4(30) \leq 1080$$
$$1080 \leq 1080$$

Since LHS = RHS for this constraint, then slack = 0. Thus, all 1080 units of raw material XBSL504 are being used to make the optimal product mix of sneakers and walking shoes. Thus, this constraint is said to be *binding*, as noted in the box above.

Minimal Sneaker Requirement:

$$x \geq 60$$
$$320 \geq 60$$

The left-hand-side value gives the actual number of pairs of sneakers made. The right-hand-side value indicates the minimum number of pairs of sneakers required. Since the left-hand-side value exceeds the right-hand-side value, there is a **surplus** of sneakers with respect to the minimal requirement. The amount of surplus is determined below.

$$\text{Surplus} = \text{LHS} - \text{RHS}$$
$$= 320 - 60 = 260 \text{ sneakers}$$

We formally present the concept of surplus in the following summary box.

SUMMARY

Surplus

≥ Constraint. The difference between the left-hand-side (LHS) and right-hand-side (RHS) values of a ≥ constraint is called **surplus** and represents the amount by which the minimal requirement of the right-hand side is being exceeded.

$$\text{Surplus} = \text{LHS} - \text{RHS}$$

If surplus = 0 for a constraint, this implies that the minimal requirement of the constraint is being met exactly, but not exceeded. Such a constraint is also called a **binding** constraint.

Minimal Walking Shoe Requirement:

$$y \geq 30$$
$$30 \geq 30$$

Since the left-hand side equals the right-hand side, the minimal walking shoe requirement is being met exactly. In other words, there is no surplus. This constraint is said to be *binding*, as noted in the box above.

Now that we have illustrated the complete process of formulating and solving a linear programming problem, we summarize the linear programming problem-solving procedure in the box below. This is followed by a summary of step 3 of the linear programming problem-solving procedure.

To Solve a Linear Programming Problem

Step 1 Identify the quantity to be optimized and the related decision variables. Write an equation for the quantity to be either maximized or minimized. This equation is called the **objective function.**

Step 2 Write the algebraic formulation for the problem. Organize the given information, and write the linear inequalities that express any relationships existing among the decision variables. These inequalities constitute the constraints of the problem and are usually based on limited resources.

Step 3 Determine an optimal solution, if it exists. Solve the algebraic formulation. In other words, find values of the decision variables that satisfy the inequalities (i.e., constraints) of the problem and optimize the value of the objective function. These decision variable values constitute an optimal solution to the linear programming problem.

Step 4 Investigate the implications of an optimal solution with regard to the constraints. Of course, this assumes that an optimal solution exists.

To Determine an Optimal Solution

A linear programming problem, when formulated algebraically, consists of a linear objective function and a set of linear inequality constraints.

1. First, graph the region corresponding to the system of linear inequality constraints. Since this region, if it exists, consists of a set of points (x, y) that satisfy all the constraints of the problem, it is called the **feasible region.**
2. Second, determine the coordinates of the corner points located on the boundary of the feasible region. Such corner points are called **vertex points.**
3. Finally, substitute the coordinates of each vertex point into the objective function. The vertex point(s) giving the optimal value of the objective function yield(s) the optimal solution to the linear programming problem.

That this procedure produces an optimal solution, if one exists, is due to the result stated below.

Fundamental Theorem of Linear Programming. An optimal solution, if one exists, to a linear programming problem will occur at one or more of the vertex points or on the boundary of the feasible region.

The above result, along with related concepts, will be explained in greater detail in the next section of this chapter.

We now consider, in Example 6-6, a linear programming problem that involves minimizing the value of an objective function.

• EXAMPLE 6-6 Nutritional Requirements. ⎯⎯⎯⎯⎯⎯

A diet is to include at least 140 milligrams of vitamin A and at least 145 milligrams of vitamin B. These requirements are to be obtained from two types of foods: type I, which contains 10 milligrams of vitamin A and 20 milligrams of vitamin B per pound; and type II, which contains 30 milligrams of vitamin A and 15 milligrams of vitamin B per pound. If type I and type II foods cost $2 and $8 per pound, respectively, how many pounds of each type should be purchased to satisfy the requirements at *minimum cost?*

Solution

Step 1 *Identify the quantity to be optimized and the related decision variables.*
We must determine the number of pounds of type I and type II foods to buy in order that total cost is minimized. Thus, we let

$$C = \text{total food cost}$$
$$x = \text{number of pounds of type I food to be bought}$$
$$y = \text{number of pounds of type II food to be bought}$$

The objective function is given by

$$C = 2x + 8y$$

and the objective is to minimize C.

Step 2 *Organize the given information, and write the linear inequalities that express any relationships existing among the decision variables.*

Decision variables

	x type I	y type II	Requirement
Unit cost	$2/pound	$8/pound	
Vitamin A	10 milligrams/pound	30 milligrams/pound	At least 140 milligrams
Vitamin B	20 milligrams/pound	15 milligrams/pound	At least 145 milligrams

Our problem is written algebraically as

$$\text{Minimize} \quad C = 2x + 8y$$
$$\text{subject to} \quad 10x + 30y \geq 140$$
$$20x + 15y \geq 145$$
$$x \geq 0$$
$$y \geq 0$$

Note that the first two constraints contain the inequality symbol $\geq$ since 140 milligrams and 145 milligrams are *minimal* requirements of vitamins A and B, respectively.

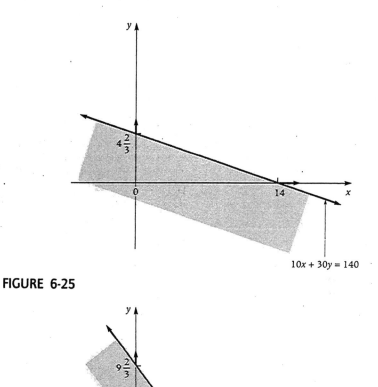

FIGURE 6-25

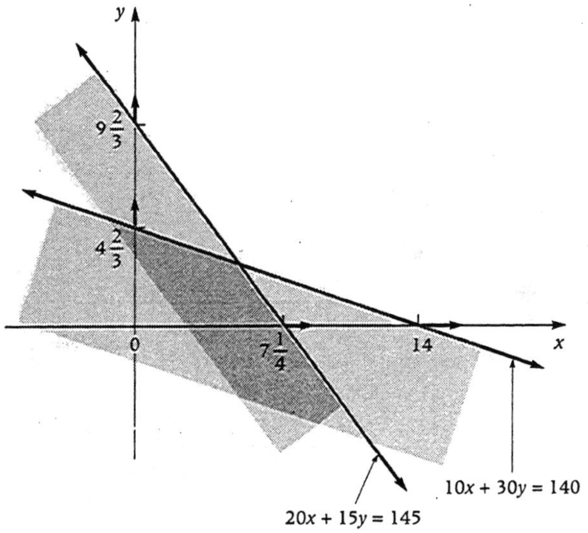

FIGURE 6-26

Step 3 *Determine the optimal solution.*
The feasible region is determined by graphing the linear inequality constraints (see Figure 6-25 through 6-28, pages 369-370). The vertex points are $(0, 9\frac{2}{3})$, $(5, 3)$, and $(14, 0)$. Note that $(5, 3)$ was determined by solving the linear system of equations

$$10x + 30y = 140$$
$$20x + 15y = 145$$

We now substitute the coordinates of each vertex point into the objective function $C = 2x + 8y$ to determine which yields the minimum cost. Hence,

$(0, 9\frac{2}{3})$ $C = 2(0) + 8\left(\dfrac{29}{3}\right) = \$77.33$

$(5, 3)$ $C = 2(5) + 8(3) = \$34.00$

$(14, 0)$ $C = 2(14) + 8(0) = \$28.00$ Minimum cost

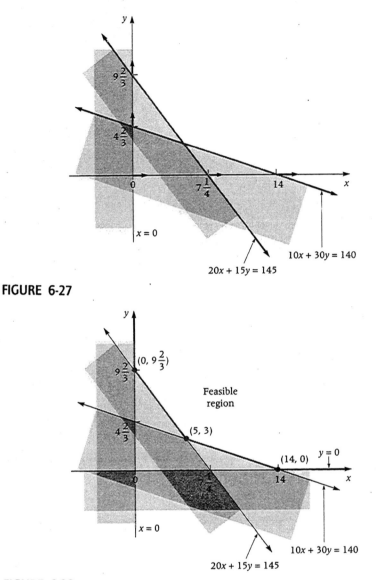

FIGURE 6-27

FIGURE 6-28

Since the vertex point (14, 0) yields the minimum cost of $28, then the optimal solution is

$x = 14$ pounds of type I food should be bought

$y = 0$ pounds of type II food should be bought

Step 4 *Investigate the implications of the optimal solution.*
Substituting the optimal solution values into each constraint gives the following.
  Vitamin A Constraint:

$$10x + 30y \geq 140$$
$$10(14) + 30(0) \geq 140$$
$$140 \geq 140$$

Since LHS = RHS, *surplus = 0*, and, therefore, the minimal vitamin A requirement is being met exactly. This constraint is binding.

Vitamin B Constraint:

$$20x + 15y \geq 145$$
$$20(14) + 15(0) \geq 145$$
$$280 \geq 145$$

Note that LHS > RHS. Thus,

$$\text{surplus} = \text{LHS} - \text{RHS}$$
$$= 280 - 145 = 135 \text{ milligrams of vitamin B}$$

and, therefore, the minimal vitamin B requirement is being exceeded by 135 milligrams.

We conclude this section with the following problem.

• EXAMPLE 6-7   Product Mix.

Williams Motors, which sells both American cars and imports, is planning its order for the next quarter. Current demand indicates that at least 240, but at most 450 cars should be ordered and that the number of imports ordered should be at least twice the number of American cars ordered. On the average, each American car costs the dealer $9000, and each foreign car costs $12,000. Budgetary and financing constraints limit next quarter's outlay for cars to $5,700,000. If Williams Motors makes an average profit of $600 per American car and $400 per foreign car, determine how many of each type should be ordered for next quarter.

Solution

Step 1 *Identify the quantity to be optimized and the related decision variables.*
We must determine the number of American and foreign cars to be ordered so that the total profit is maximized. Thus, we let

$$P = \text{total profit}$$
$$x = \text{number of American cars to be ordered}$$
$$y = \text{number of foreign cars to be ordered}$$

The objective function is given by

$$P = 600x + 400y$$

and the objective is to maximize P.

Step 2 *Organize the given information, and write the linear inequalities that express any relationships existing among the decision variables.*
The constraints are formulated as follows. Since at least 240, but at most 450 cars must be ordered, this is formulated as the two constraints

$$x + y \geq 240$$
$$x + y \leq 450$$

Since the number of imports ordered should be at least twice the number of American cars ordered, this is written algebraically as the constraint

$$y \geq 2x$$
$$\text{or} \qquad \text{Add } -2x \text{ to each side.}$$
$$-2x + y \geq 0$$

The budgetary constraint limiting the total outlay to $5,700,000 is written as

$$9000x + 12,000y \leq 5,700,000$$

Thus, the problem is formulated as

$$\text{Maximize } P = 600x + 400y$$

subject to the constraints

$$x + y \geq 240$$
$$x + y \leq 450$$
$$-2x + y \geq 0$$
$$9000x + 12,000y \leq 5,700,000$$
$$x \geq 0$$
$$y \geq 0$$

Step 3 *Determine the optimal solution.*

The constraints are graphed in Figure 6-29, and the region of feasible solutions is unshaded.

The vertex points are (0, 240), (0, 450), (150, 300), and (80, 160). The vertex point (150, 300) was determined by solving the linear system

$$x + y = 450$$
$$-2x + y = 0$$

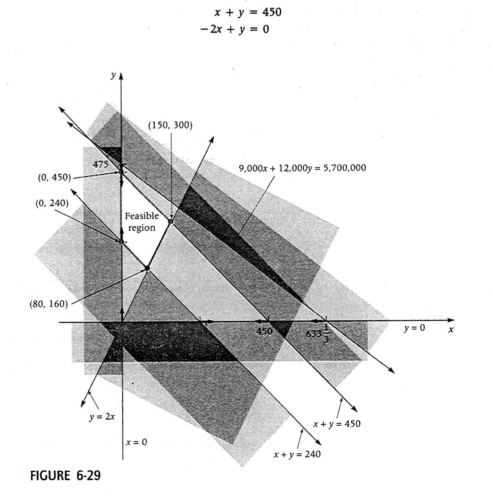

FIGURE 6-29

The vertex point (80, 160) was determined by solving the linear system

$$x + y = 240$$
$$-2x + y = 0$$

We now substitute the coordinates of each vertex point into the objective function $P = 600x + 400y$ to determine which yields the maximum profit. Hence,

(0, 240)	$P = 600(0) + 400(240) = \$96,000$
(0, 450)	$P = 600(0) + 400(450) = \$180,000$
(150, 300)	$P = 600(150) + 400(300) = \$210,000$ Maximum profit
(80, 160)	$P = 600(80) + 400(160) = \$112,000$

Note that the vertex point (150, 300) gives the maximum profit of $210,000. Thus, the optimal solution is

$$x = 150 \text{ American cars should be ordered}$$
$$y = 300 \text{ foreign cars should be ordered}$$

Step 4   *Investigate the implications of the optimal solution.*

Substituting the optimal solution values into each constraint gives the following.

$$\text{Number of cars} \rightarrow \quad x + y \geq 240$$
$$150 + 300 \geq 240$$
$$450 \geq 240$$
$$\text{Surplus} = \text{LHS} - \text{RHS}$$
$$= 450 - 240 = 210 \text{ cars}$$

Thus, the requirement that at least 240 cars be produced is exceeded by 210 cars.

$$\text{Number of cars} \rightarrow \quad x + y \leq 450$$
$$150 + 300 \leq 450$$
$$450 \leq 450$$
$$\text{Slack} = \text{RHS} - \text{LHS}$$
$$= 450 - 450 = 0$$

The requirement that no more than 450 cars be produced is being met exactly. In other words, the constraint is binding.

$$\text{Number of foreign cars} \rightarrow \quad y \geq 2x \quad \leftarrow \text{Number of American cars}$$
$$300 \geq 2(150)$$
$$300 \geq 300$$
$$\text{Surplus} = \text{LHS} - \text{RHS}$$
$$= 300 - 300 = 0$$

The requirement that the number of foreign cars ordered be at least twice the number of American cars ordered is being met exactly. In other words, the constraint is binding.

Budgetary Constraint:

$$9000x + 12,000y \leq 5,700,000$$
$$9000(150) + 12,000(300) \leq 5,700,000$$
$$4,950,000 \leq 5,700,000$$
$$\text{slack} = \text{RHS} - \text{LHS}$$
$$= 5,700,000 - 4,950,000$$
$$= \$750,000$$

Thus, of the $5,700,000 available for the purchase of cars, $750,000 remains unspent.

Exercises 6-2

For each feasible region and objective function, determine the optimal solutions.

1. Maximize $z = 4x + 7y$
   (see Figure 6-30).
2. Minimize $z = 2x + 5y$
   (see Figure 6-31).
3. Minimize $z = 0.70x + 0.40y$
   (see Figure 6-32).
4. Maximize $z = 5x + 9y$
   (see Figure 6-33).
5. Maximize $z = 0.80x + 0.30y$
   (see Figure 6-34).
6. Minimize $z = 3x + 10y$
   (see Figure 6-35).

Solve each of the following linear programing problems.

7. Maximize $P = 5x + 4y$
   subject to $3x + 4y \le 24$
   $2x + y \le 14$
   $x, y \ge 0$
8. Maximize $P = 2x + 7y$
   subject to $x + y \le 10$
   $2x + y \le 18$
   $x, y \ge 0$

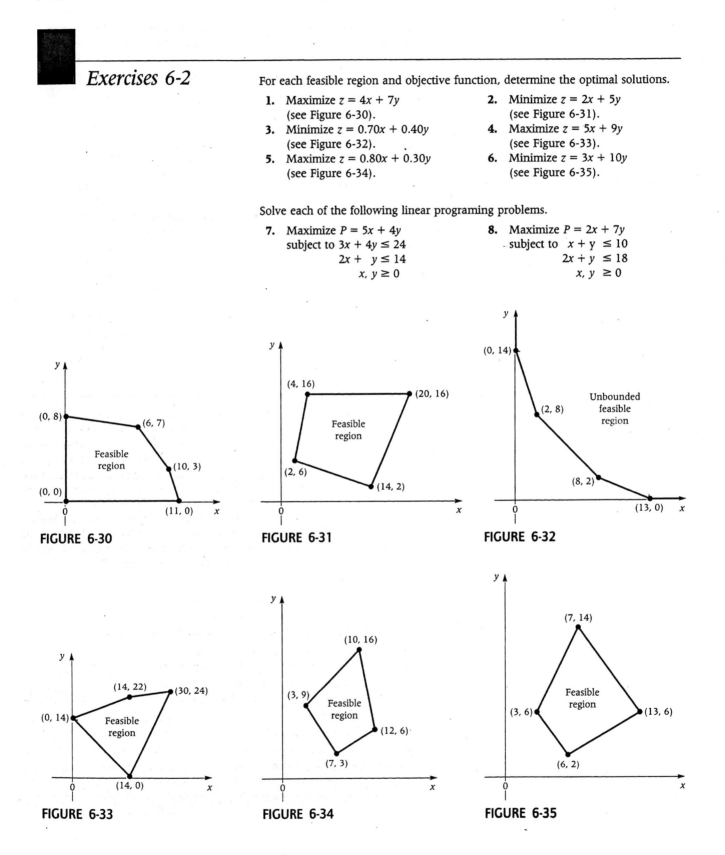

FIGURE 6-30

FIGURE 6-31

FIGURE 6-32

FIGURE 6-33

FIGURE 6-34

FIGURE 6-35

9. Minimize $C = 4x + 9y$
   subject to $x + y \geq 12$
   $3x + 2y \geq 30$
   $x, y \geq 0$

10. Minimize $C = 8x + 6y$
    subject to $4x + 5y \geq 40$
    $2x + y \geq 18$
    $x, y \geq 0$

11. Maximize $z = 10x + 30y$
    subject to $3x + 5y \leq 30$
    $2x + 4y \leq 22$
    $x, y \geq 0$

12. Maximize $z = 30x + 20y$
    subject to $5x + 7y \leq 70$
    $3x + 2y \leq 30$
    $x, y \geq 0$

13. Minimize $z = 20x + 40y$
    subject to $x + y \geq 10$
    $3x + 4y \geq 36$
    $x + y \leq 40$
    $x, y \geq 0$

14. Minimize $z = 30x + 50y$
    subject to $2x + y \geq 20$
    $x + y \geq 12$
    $x + y \leq 30$
    $x, y \geq 0$

15. Maximize $z = 3x + 5y$
    subject to $2x + y \leq 30$
    $x - 2y \leq 10$
    $x \geq 4$
    $y \geq 1$

16. Maximize $z = 2x + 3y$
    subject to $3x + y \leq 30$
    $2x - y \leq 16$
    $x \geq 2$
    $y \geq 1$

17. Maximize $z = 20x + 30y$
    subject to $x + 4y \leq 20$
    $2x - y \leq 30$
    $-x + y \leq 4$
    $x, y \geq 0$

18. Maximize $z = 40x + 100y$
    subject to $2x + 5y \leq 40$
    $-x + 3y \leq 18$
    $x + y \geq 6$
    $x \geq 0$
    $y \geq 2$

Applications

19. *Production planning.* A company manufactures two types of jackets: casual and formal. The company makes profits of $30 per casual jacket and $50 per formal jacket. Both types of jackets must pass through the cutting department, which has available 960 person-hours during the next week, and the sewing department, which has available 400 person-hours during the next week. Each casual jacket requires 2 person-hours in the cutting department and 1 person-hour in the sewing department. Each formal jacket requires 3 person-hours in the cutting department and 1 person-hour in the sewing department. Additionally, there is an order for 150 casual jackets and 50 formal jackets, which must be made next week. How many of each type of jacket should be made next week in order to maximize total profit and satisfy the above constraints?

a) Fill in the blanks below.

Step 1 $x = $ _____
                    $y = $ _____

Objective function: Maximize ____ = ____$x + $ ____y

Step 2   ┌── Decision Variables ──┐

	casual	formal	
Unit profits	____	____	
Cutting department	____ person-hours per jacket	____ person-hours per jacket	At most ____
Sewing department	____ person-hours per jacket	____ person-hours per jacket	At most ____

Also,
- At least _____ casual jackets must be produced.
- At least _____ formal jackets must be produced.

Constraints:

Cutting department _____ .

Sewing department _____

$x \geq$ _____

$y \geq$ _____

Step 3   Solve the algebraic formulation of steps 1 and 2.

Step 4   Investigate the implications of the optimal solution.

Cutting department   slack = _____

Sewing department   slack = _____

Constraint: $x \geq 150$ surplus = _____

Constraint: $y \geq 50$ surplus = _____

b)   How many person-hours are used in the cutting department?

c)   How many person-hours are used in the sewing department?

20. *Investment: Portfolio allocation.* An investor has at most $20,000 to be allocated for investment in conservative and aggressive mutual funds. The projected annual rate of return for each mutual fund is given below along with its risk level.

Projected annual rate of return

Conservative mutual fund	Aggressive mutual fund
18%	22%

Risk level

Conservative mutual fund	Aggressive mutual fund
2	6

If the investor wants an average risk level of no more than 3, then how much should be invested in each mutual fund in order to maximize the total projected annual return?

Fill in the blanks below.

Step 1 x = number of dollars invested in the conservative mutual fund

$y =$ _____

Objective function: Maximize _____ = _____ $x +$ _____ y

Step 2   Constraints:
- Total amount invested $\leq 20,000$

_____ + _____ $\leq 20,000$
- Average risk level ≤ 3

If x dollars are invested at a risk level of 2 and y dollars are invested at a risk level of 6, then the average risk level is given by

$$\frac{2x + 6y}{x + y}$$

Since the average risk level must be no more than 3, this gives the constraint

$$\frac{2x + 6y}{x + y} \leq 3$$

Multiplying both sides by $x + y$ (where $x + y > 0$) gives

$$2x + 6y \leq 3(\underline{\quad} + \underline{\quad})$$

Using the distributive law and then subtracting $3x$ and $3y$ from both sides results in

$$\underline{\quad}x + \underline{\quad}y \leq 0$$

Also, the non-negativity restrictions result in

$$x \geq \underline{\quad}$$
$$y \geq \underline{\quad}$$

Step 3   Solve the algebraic formulation of steps 1 and 2.

Step 4   Investigate the implications of the optimal solution.

Constraint 1:   Total amount invested = ____

Slack = ____

Constraint 2:   State the average risk level for the optimal solution.

Slack = ____

21. *Investment: Portfolio allocation.* Repeat Exercise 20 under the additional constraints that at least $6000 must be invested in the conservative mutual fund and at most $4000 must be invested in the aggressive mutual fund.

22. *Media selection.* A company executive must determine the optimal mix of radio and TV ads to purchase for next month. Each radio ad costs $1500, and each TV ad costs $2000. There must be a combined total of at least 1200 ads. Also, each radio ad is expected to reach 1000 families, and each TV ad is expected to reach 1500 families. It is required that at least 1,500,000 families be reached.
    a) How many of each type of ad should be purchased for next month in order to minimize the total cost?
    b) What is the minimum total cost?
    c) Determine the surplus for each constraint.
    d) How many families will be reached?
    e) How many ads will be bought?

23. Repeat Exercise 22 under the assumption that each radio ad costs $1200 and each TV ad costs $2000.

24. *Product mix.* A company manufactures motorcycles and mopeds, each of which must pass through two machines: machine 1 and machine 2. Each motorcycle requires 2 hours on machine 1 and 5 hours on machine 2. Each moped requires 3 hours on machine 1 and 1 hour on machine 2. Machines 1 and 2 have available 90 hours and 160 hours, respectively, for these two products.
    a) If the company makes a profit of $120 on each motorcycle and $60 on each moped, how many of each should be produced in order to maximize total profit and satisfy the constraints of the problem? Determine the amount of slack for each constraint.
    b) If the company makes only $30 on each motorcycle and $90 on each moped, how many of each should be produced in order to maximize total profit and satisfy the constraints of the problem? Determine the amount of slack for each constraint.

25. *Nutrition.* A diet must provide at least 1200 milligrams of protein and at least 1000 milligrams of iron. These nutrients are to be obtained from eating meat and spinach. Each pound of meat contains 500 milligrams of protein and 100 milligrams of iron. Each pound of spinach contains 200 milligrams of protein and 800 milligrams of iron. If meat and spinach cost $3.00 and $1.50 per pound, respectively, how many pounds of each should be eaten in order to minimize total cost and satisfy the constraints of the problem? Determine the amount of surplus for each constraint.

26. *Product mix.* A manufacturer produces two models of televisions—T140 and T240—each of which must pass through two departments, D1 and D2. Each unit of T140 requires 3 hours in D1 and 4 hours in D2. Each unit of T240 requires 6 hours in D1 and 4 hours in D2. Departments D1 and D2 each have 60 hours available. If the manufacturer makes a profit of $10 per unit on T140 and $30 per unit on T240, then
    a) How many units of each should be made in order to maximize total profit and satisfy the constraints of the problem?
    b) What is the maximum profit?
    c) Determine the amount of slack in each constraint.
    d) How many hours are used in each department?

27. *Agriculture.* A farmer owns a 100-acre farm and wants to plant a combination of two crops: A and B. Crop A requires 60 person-hours of labor per acre, and crop B requires 80 person-hours of labor per acre. The farmer has 6600 person-hours of labor available.
    a) If the farmer makes a profit of $400 per acre on crop A and $500 per acre on crop B, how many acres of each crop should be planted in order to maximize total profit and satisfy the constraints of the problem?
    b) What is the maximum profit?
    c) Determine the amount of slack in each constraint.
    d) How many acres are planted?
    e) How many person-hours of labor are used?

28. Repeat Exercise 27 under the assumption that the farmer makes a profit of $500 per acre on each crop.

29. *Fuel allocation.* A factory uses two types of fuel—F10 and F20—for heating and other purposes. At least 3800 gallons of fuel are needed each day. Some byproducts are produced by the burning of the fuel. Each gallon of F10 leaves a residue of 0.02 pound of ash and 0.06 pound of soot. Each gallon of F20 leaves a residue of 0.05 pound of ash and 0.01 pound of soot. The factory needs at least 120 pounds of ash and at least 136 pounds of soot. If F10 and F20 cost $1.50 and $1.10 per gallon, respectively, then
    a) How many gallons of each type should be purchased in order to minimize total cost and satisfy the constraints of the problem?
    b) What is the minimum cost?
    c) Determine the amount of surplus for each constraint.
    d) How many gallons of fuel are bought daily?
    e) How many pounds of ash are produced daily?
    f) How many pounds of soot are produced daily?

30. *The following problem appeared on a past Uniform CPA Examination.* A company markets two products: Alpha and Gamma. The marginal contributions per gallon are $5 for Alpha and $4 for Gamma. Both products consist of two ingredients: D and K. Alpha contains 80% D and 20% K, while the proportions of the same ingredients in Gamma are 40% and 60%, respectively. The current inventory is 16,000 gallons of D and 6000 gallons of K. The only com-

pany producing D and K is on strike and will neither deliver nor produce them in the foreseeable future.

a) The company wishes to know how many gallons of Alpha and Gamma it should produce with its present stock of raw materials in order to maximize its total revenue.

b) What is the maximum total revenue?

c) Determine the amount of slack for each constraint.

d) How many gallons of D are used?

e) How many gallons of K are used?

31. *The following problem appeared on a past Uniform CPA Examination.* Patsy, Inc., manufactures two products: X and Y. Each product must be processed in each of three departments: machining, assembling, and finishing. The hours needed to produce 1 unit of product per department and the maximum possible hours per department are as follows:

| | Production hours per unit | | Maximum capacity |
Department	X	Y	(in hours)
Machining	2	1	420
Assembling	2	2	500
Finishing	2	3	600

In addition, $X \geq 50$ and $Y \geq 50$. The objective function is to maximize profits, where profit = $4X + $2Y. Given the objective and constraints,

a) What is the most profitable number of units of X and Y to manufacture?

b) What is the maximum profit?

c) Determine the slack or surplus for each constraint.

d) How many hours are used in the machining department?

e) How many hours are used in the assembling department?

f) How many hours are used in the finishing department?

32. A pharmaceutical company plans to manufacture two new drugs: diopthelene and gramamine. Each case of diopthelene requires 3 hours of processing time and 1 hour of curing time per week. Each case of gramamine requires 5 hours of processing time and 5 hours of curing time per week. The company's time schedule allows 55 hours of processing time and 45 hours of curing time weekly for the two drugs. Additionally, the company must produce no more than 10 cases of diopthelene and no more than 9 cases of gramamine each week. If the company makes a profit of $400 on each case of diopthelene and $500 on each case of gramamine, then

a) How many cases of each should be produced in order to maximize total profit and satisfy the constraints of the problem?

b) What is the maximum profit?

c) Determine the amount of slack for each constraint.

d) How many hours of processing time are required in total?

e) How many hours of curing time are required in total?

33. *Marketing strategy.* A company markets its product to wholesale and retail outlets with unit profits of $90 and $120, respectively. The company's limited sales force allows for a total marketing effort of at most 17,280 hours for the next month. A past analysis of marketing efforts has revealed that each unit sold to wholesale outlets requires 2.4 hours of sales effort, while each unit

sold to retail outlets requires 3.6 hours of sales effort. If next month's production plans call for at most 5600 units of this product, then

a) How many should be distributed to each outlet?
b) What is the maximum profit?
c) Determine the amount of slack for each constraint.
d) How many units of this product will be produced next month?
e) How many hours of marketing effort are expended?

34. Repeat Exercise 33 with the added restriction that the number of wholesale outlets must be less than or equal to 4 times the number of retail outlets.

35. Repeat Exercise 33 with the added restriction that the number of wholesale outlets must be at least 4 times the number of retail outlets.

6-3 • FUNDAMENTAL THEOREM OF LINEAR PROGRAMMING

Having solved linear programming problems in the previous section, we now show why an optimal value of an objective function, if it exists, will occur at one or more of the vertex points or on the boundary of the feasible region. Using the introductory linear programming problem of Section 6-2 as an example, we again illustrate the graph of its region of feasible solutions (see Figure 6-36). Observe that the objective function

$$P = 20x + 16y$$

with its maximum value, $P = 6800$, also appears on the graph as

$$6800 = 20x + 16y$$

Note that it passes through the optimal solution, (320, 30).

Now suppose we substitute some other point of the feasible region into the objective function $P = 20x + 16y$. Choosing (70, 40), we obtain

$$P = 20(70) + 16(40) = \$2040$$

Note that $P = \$2040$ is less than the maximum value, $P = \$6800$. If we include the graph of the objective function $2040 = 20x + 16y$ with the graph of Figure 6-36, we obtain the graph of Figure 6-37. Observe that the graph of the objective function $2040 = 20x + 16y$ is parallel to the graph of the objective function $6800 = 20x + 16y$, but is located closer to the origin.

In general, if we consider the objective function $P = 20x + 16y$ and solve the equation for y to obtain the slope-intercept form

$$y = \frac{-5}{4}x + \frac{P}{16}$$

we note that $P/16$ is the y-intercept of the objective function, as is indicated in Figure 6-37. Studying the graph of the objective function $P = 20x + 16y$ in Figure 6-37, note that P takes on its maximum value over the feasible region at the vertex point (320, 30).

We note that the graph of the objective function must always pass through at least one point of the feasible region. Otherwise, the constraints of the linear programming problem would not be satisfied.

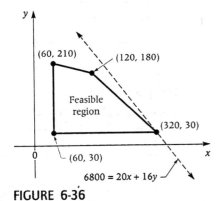

FIGURE 6-36

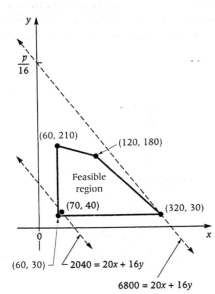

FIGURE 6-37

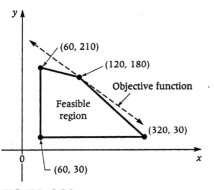

FIGURE 6-38

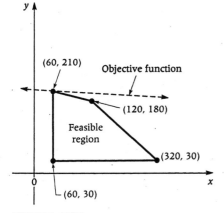

FIGURE 6-39

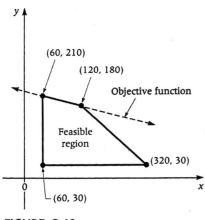

FIGURE 6-40

Note also that if the unit profits were changed so that the slope of the objective function decreased substantially in absolute value, then the vertex point (120, 180) would yield the maximum value of P (see Figure 6-38). If the unit profits were changed so that the slope of the objective function further decreased in absolute value, then the vertex point (60, 210) would yield the maximum value of P (see Figure 6-39).

In addition, if the slope of the objective function equaled the slope of one of the constraints, then more than one vertex point would yield an optimal solution (see Figure 6-40). In fact, both vertex points and all points on the straight line between them yield optimal values for P. Thus, in the present example, the vertex points (60, 210) and (120, 180) and all points on the straight line between them yield optimal values of P (see Figure 6-40).

Also, if our goal were to minimize the value of the objective function, then the vertex point (60, 30) would yield an optimal solution, as shown in Figure 6-41.

The discussions in the previous paragraphs have demonstrated what we have already stated in the shaded box on page 367. Since the importance of this statement should not be underestimated, we restate it below.

SUMMARY

Fundamental Theorem of Linear Programming

An optimal value of an objective function, if it exists, will occur at one or more of the vertex points or on the boundary of the region of feasible solutions.

We now consider Example 6-6 of Section 6-2, a linear programming problem that involves minimizing the value of an objective function. Its feasible region is given in Figure 6-42. Observing the graph of Figure 6-42, note that the feasible region is **unbounded.** That is, it is not completely enclosed by its boundary lines. If our goal were to maximize the value of the objective function $C = 2x + 8y$, as indicated in Figure 6-43 on page 382,

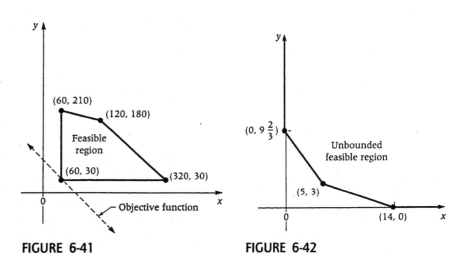

FIGURE 6-41   **FIGURE 6-42**

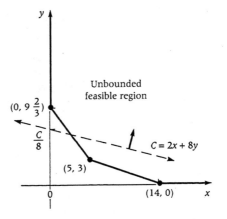

FIGURE 6-43

then there would be no optimal solution to this problem since the value of C increases indefinitely as the objective function moves in the direction of the arrow. However, since our goal in Example 6-6 was to minimize the value of C, then we observe that the vertex point (14, 0) yields the optimal solution to the linear programming problem.

Thus, we can understand that the following statements are true for linear programming problems.

1. If a feasible region is *bounded,* then there is always an optimal solution to the associated linear programming problem. Such an optimal solution will occur at one or more vertex points or on the boundary interval between two vertex points.
2. If a feasible region is *unbounded,* then there may or may not be an optimal solution to the associated linear programming problem.

The following box contains a complete summary of different situations that can be encountered when solving linear programming problems.

■ SUMMARY

Linear Programming

When solving a linear programming problem, one of the following situations will occur:

1. An **optimal solution** exists at a *single vertex point.*
2. There is **more than one optimal solution.** This situation occurs when the objective function line is parallel to a constraint line. Thus, optimal solutions exist at two vertex points and on the connecting boundary interval.
3. There is **no optimal solution** because a *feasible region does not exist.*
4. There is **no optimal solution** because the *feasible region is unbounded,* and, therefore, a best solution does not exist because there is always a better solution. We note, however, that unbounded feasible regions may or may not yield optimal solutions. This depends on the graph of the unbounded feasible region and the optimal direction of movement of the graph of the objective function.

Exercises 6-3

Each of the following graphs illustrates a feasible region and an objective function (labeled *z*) for a linear programming problem. Each objective function (*z*) has an arrow that indicates its direction of optimal movement. For each of the following, state the optimal solution(s) or identify whichever linear programming situation occurs.

1.

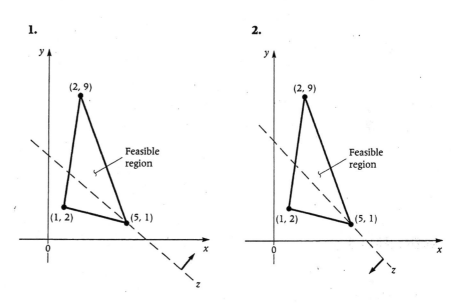

2.

3.

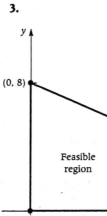

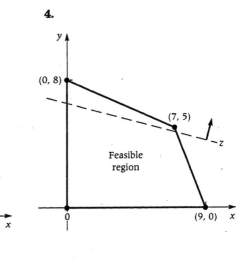

4.

5.

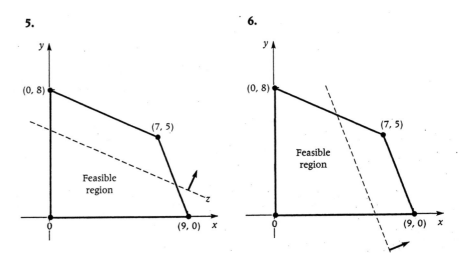

6.

7.

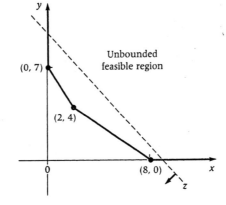

8.

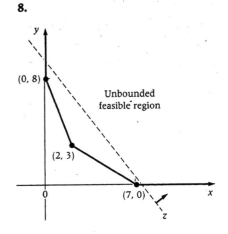

9.

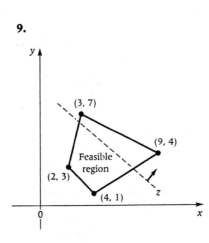

10.

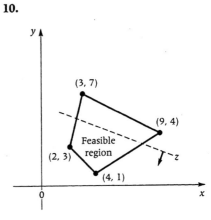

11.

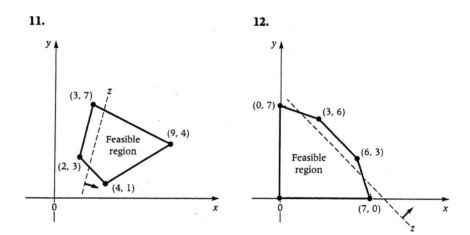

12.

13.

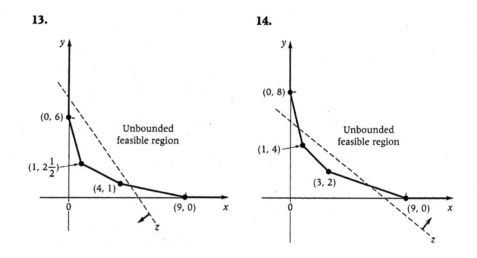

14.

Which linear programming situation occurs for each of the problems below?

15. Maximize $z = 3x + 5y$
  subject to $x + y \leq 5$
  $\qquad\quad x + y \geq 7$
  $\qquad\qquad\quad x \geq 0$
  $\qquad\qquad\quad y \geq 0$

16. Maximize $z = 5x + 2y$
  subject to $7x + 5y \leq 35$
  $\qquad\quad x + \ y \geq 8$
  $\qquad\qquad\quad x \geq 0$
  $\qquad\qquad\quad y \geq 0$

17. Minimize $z = 12x + 15y$
  subject to $3x + 2y \leq 48$
  $\qquad\qquad\quad x \geq 4$
  $\qquad\quad 0 \leq y \leq 20$

18. Minimize $z = 10x + 4y$
  subject to $5x + 2y \geq 60$
  $\qquad\qquad\quad x \geq 4$
  $\qquad\qquad\quad y \geq 6$

19. Maximize $z = 10x + 20y$
  subject to $3x + 4y \geq 60$
  $\qquad\qquad\quad x \geq 4$
  $\qquad\qquad\quad y \geq 3$

CHAPTER 6 HIGHLIGHTS

• Concepts

Your ability to answer the following questions is one indicator of the depth of your mastery of this chapter's important concepts. Note that the questions are grouped under various topic headings. For any question that you cannot answer, refer to the appropriate section of the chapter indicated by the topic heading. Pay particular attention to the summary boxes within a section.

6-1 LINEAR INEQUALITIES IN TWO VARIABLES

1. Write the general form of a linear inequality in two variables.
2. Give the procedure to graph a linear inequality.
3. Give the procedure to graph a system of linear inequalities.

6-2 LINEAR PROGRAMMING

4. State the four steps of the linear programming problem-solving procedure.
5. Give the graphical procedure for determining the optimal solution to a linear programming problem.
6. Give the formula for slack and interpret the result.
7. To what type of constraint is slack relevant?
8. If, for a particular constraint, slack = 0, the constraint is called a(n)

   _____. Interpret this result.
9. Give the formula for surplus and interpret the result.
10. To what type of constraint is surplus relevant?
11. If, for a particular constraint, surplus = 0, the constraint is called a(n)

    _____. Interpret this result.

6-3 FUNDAMENTAL THEOREM OF LINEAR PROGRAMMING

12. State the fundamental theorem of linear programming.
13. If a feasible region is bounded, does an optimal solution exist for the corresponding linear programming problem?
14. If a feasible region is unbounded, what possibilities exist regarding an optimal solution for the corresponding linear programming problem?
15. If an objective function line is parallel to a constraint line, what does this imply with regard to an optimal solution?
16. What is the cause of an unbounded solution?
17. If a feasible region does not exist for a linear programming problem, what does this imply with regard to an optimal solution?

REVIEW EXERCISES

• Graphing Linear Inequalities

Graph each of the following.

1. $3x + 2y \leq 24$
2. $-2x + 5y \leq 40$
3. $5x + 4y \geq 40$
4. $3x - 7y \geq 42$

• Graphing Systems of Linear Inequalities

Graph each linear system.

5. $x + y \leq 12$
    $8x + 4y \leq 64$

7. $2x + 3y \leq 12$
    $6x + 5y \leq 30$
    $x \geq 0$
    $y \geq 0$

6. $-5x + 2y \geq 20$
    $y \geq 5$

8. $x + y \geq 20$
    $y \geq x$
    $x \geq 0$
    $y \geq 12$

• Linear Programming

Solve each of the following.

9. Maximize $z = 2x + 5y$
    subject to $2x + y \leq 40$
    $3x + y \leq 48$
    $x, y \geq 0$

11. Minimize $z = 5x + 2y$
    subject to $x + y \geq 20$
    $x + 3y \geq 30$
    $x, y \geq 0$

10. Maximize $z = 6x + 4y$
    subject to $2x + 3y \leq 30$
    $x \geq 3$
    $y \geq 2$

12. Minimize $z = 4x + 5y$
    subject to $4x + 3y \geq 24$
    $x \leq 5$
    $y \leq 6$
    $x, y \geq 0$

Applications

Exercises 13-15 are adapted from problems that appeared on past Uniform CPA Examinations.

a) Formulate the linear programming problem.
b) Solve.
c) Investigate the implications of the optimal solution.

13. The Sanch Company plans to expand its sales force by opening several new branch offices. Sanch has $5,200,000 in capital available for new branch offices. Sanch will consider opening only two types of branches: 10-person branches (type A) and 5-person branches (type B). Expected initial cash outlays are $650,000 for a type A branch and $335,000 for a type B branch. Expected annual cash inflow, net of income taxes, is $46,000 for a type A branch and $18,000 for a type B branch. Sanch will hire no more than 100 employees for the new branch offices. How many of each type should be opened?

14. Repeat Exercise 13 under the added constraint that Sanch will not open more than 10 branch offices.

15. The raw material requirements for a unit of each of two products are given below.

	Product A	Product B
Raw material 1	3	4
Raw material 2	7	2
Unit profit	$10	$4

If 300 units of raw material 1 and 400 units of raw material 2 are available, how many units of each product should be produced?

16. *Investment: Portfolio allocation.* An investor has at least $30,000 to be allocated for investment in bond and stock mutual funds. The projected annual rate of return for each mutual fund is given below, along with its risk level.

Projected annual rate of return

Bond fund	Stock fund
15%	20%

Risk level

Bond fund	Stock fund
3	5

If the investor wants an annual rate of return of at least 16%, how much should be invested in each fund in order to minimize the total risk?

• Fundamental Theorem of Linear Programming

Draw a graph of a feasible region and an objective function that illustrates each of the following.

17. An optimal solution exists at a single vertex point.
18. There is more than one optimal solution.
19. There is no optimal solution because a feasible solution does not exist.
20. There is no optimal solution because the feasible region is unbounded.

Appendix B
Special Topics

- ## DERIVATION OF THE QUADRATIC FORMULA

On page 79 of·Section 2-2, we stated the quadratic formula for solutions, if any exist, to quadratic equations of the form

$$ax^2 + bx + c = 0 \qquad (a \neq 0)$$

The quadratic formula is derived by beginning with the above equation and dividing both sides by a to obtain

$$x^2 + \frac{b}{a}x + \frac{c}{a} = 0$$

Subtracting c/a from both sides gives

$$x^2 + \frac{b}{a}x = -\frac{c}{a}$$

Adding $(b/2a)^2$ or, equivalently, $b^2/4a^2$ to both sides gives a perfect square for the left-hand side as given below.

$$x^2 + \frac{b}{a}x + \left(\frac{b}{2a}\right)^2 = \frac{b^2}{4a^2} - \frac{c}{a}$$

The left-hand side can be expressed in factored form as indicated below

$$\left(x + \frac{b}{2a}\right)^2 = \frac{b^2}{4a^2} - \frac{c}{a}\left(\frac{4a}{4a}\right)$$

and the (c/a) term is multiplied by $4a/4a$ to give a common denominator. Combining the right-hand-side terms gives

$$\left(x + \frac{b}{2a}\right)^2 = \frac{b^2 - 4ac}{4a^2}$$

Solving the resulting formula for x, we begin by taking the square root of each side to obtain

$$x + \frac{b}{2a} = \pm \sqrt{\frac{b^2 - 4ac}{4a^2}}$$

Using a property of square roots on the right-hand side, the above becomes

$$x + \frac{b}{2a} = \pm \frac{\sqrt{b^2 - 4ac}}{\sqrt{4a^2}}$$

$$= \pm \frac{\sqrt{b^2 - 4ac}}{2a}$$

Adding $-b/2a$ to both sides results in

$$x = -\frac{b}{2a} \pm \frac{\sqrt{b^2 - 4ac}}{2a}$$

$$= \frac{-b \pm \sqrt{b^2 - 4ac}}{2a}$$

Note that

1. There is one real solution if $b^2 - 4ac = 0$. That solution is $-b/2a$.
2. There are no real solutions if $b^2 - 4ac < 0$. This is because the square root of a negative number does not exist.
3. There are two real solutions if $b^2 - 4ac > 0$:

$$x = \frac{-b + \sqrt{b^2 - 4ac}}{2a} \qquad x = \frac{-b - \sqrt{b^2 - 4ac}}{2a}$$

• DISTANCE; THE EQUATION OF A CIRCLE

Sometimes we must find the distance between two points on the rectangular coordinate system. The distance between the two points, (x_1, y_1) and (x_2, y_2), in Figure B-1 is denoted by d. Observe that the vertical dis-

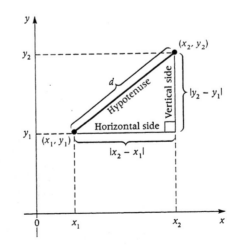

FIGURE B-1

tance between the two points is $|y_2 - y_1|$ and the horizontal distance between the two points is $|x_2 - x_1|$. Also, the vertical distance, $|y_2 - y_1|$, is the length of the vertical side of the right triangle, and the horizontal distance, $|x_2 - x_1|$, the length of the horizontal side of the right triangle. The length of the hypotenuse is the distance, d, between the two points, (x_1, y_1) and (x_2, y_2). According to the Pythagorean theorem,

$$d^2 = (\text{horizontal distance})^2 + (\text{vertical distance})^2$$
$$= |x_2 - x_1|^2 + |y_2 - y_1|^2$$
$$= (x_2 - x_1)^2 + (y_2 - y_1)^2$$

Hence,

$$d = \sqrt{(x_2 - x_1)^2 + (y_2 - y_1)^2} \qquad \text{Distance Formula}$$

Since this formula gives the distance between two points, (x_1, y_1) and (x_2, y_2), in the plane, it is called the **distance formula.**

• EXAMPLE B-1

Find the distance between $(1, -2)$ and $(4, 5)$ in Figure B-2.

Solution

Let $(x_1, y_1) = (1, -2)$ and $(x_2, y_2) = (4, 5)$. Then the distance, d, between the points is

$$d = \sqrt{(x_2 - x_1)^2 + (y_2 - y_1)^2}$$
$$= \sqrt{(4 - 1)^2 + [5 - (-2)]^2}$$
$$= \sqrt{3^2 + 7^2}$$
$$= \sqrt{58} \approx 7.62$$

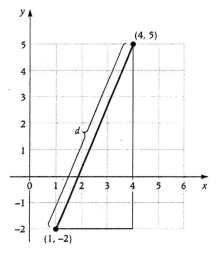

FIGURE B-2

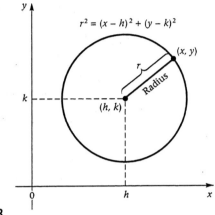

FIGURE B-3

Consider the circle of radius, r, with center at (h, k), as shown in Figure B-3. The circle consists of all points (x, y) that are at distance r from (h, k). Using the distance formula, the distance between a point (x, y) on the circle and the center, (h, k), is given by

$$r = \sqrt{(x - h)^2 + (y - k)^2}$$

Squaring both sides, we have the equation of a circle of radius r and center at (h, k).

$$r^2 = (x - h)^2 + (y - k)^2 \qquad \text{Equation of a circle}$$

Thus, any point (x, y) on the circle satisfies this equation.

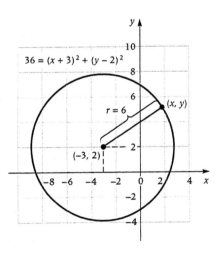

FIGURE B-4

• **EXAMPLE B-2** _____

Find the equation of a circle of radius 6 with center at $(-3, 2)$.

Solution

The equation of a circle of radius r and center (h, k) is $r^2 = (x - h)^2 + (y - k)^2$. Since $(h, k) = (-3, 2)$ and $r = 6$, this equation becomes $6^2 = [x - (-3)]^2 + (y - 2)^2$. Thus, the equation of the circle is $36 = (x + 3)^2 + (y - 2)^2$. The circle appears in Figure B-4 on page A-10.

Exercises

Find the distance between the following points.

1. $(4, 6)$ and $(7, 10)$ 2. $(-1, 2)$ and $(8, 5)$
3. $(3, 0)$ and $(4, 2)$ 4. $(-2, 8)$ and $(-1, -3)$
5. $(5, 3)$ and $(5, 7)$ 6. $(1, 4)$ and $(8, 4)$
7. $(8, 2)$ and $(6, 9)$ 8. $(-6, 2)$ and $(-6, -5)$
9. Find y so that the distance between the origin and the point $(4, y)$ is 6.
10. Find x so that the distance between the origin and the point $(x, 3)$ is 4.
11. Find y so that the distance between $(3, 1)$ and $(7, y)$ is 5.

Find the equation of each of the following circles.

12. Center at $(4, 6)$ and radius is 8
13. Center at $(-2, 5)$ and radius is 3
14. Center at $(4, 0)$ and radius is 6
15. Center at $(0, 3)$ and radius is 5

Graph each of the following:

16. $(x - 2)^2 + (y - 5)^2 = 81$ 17. $x^2 + y^2 = 36$
18. $(x + 9)^2 + (y - 1)^2 = 64$ 19. $x^2 + (y - 1)^2 = 25$

Answers

1. $d = \sqrt{(7 - 4)^2 + (10 - 6)^2} = \sqrt{3^2 + 4^2} = \sqrt{25} = 5$
2. $d = \sqrt{[8 - (-1)]^2 + (5 - 2)^2} = \sqrt{9^2 + 3^2} = \sqrt{90} \approx 9.49$
3. $d = \sqrt{(4 - 3)^2 + (2 - 0)^2} = \sqrt{1^2 + 2^2} = \sqrt{5} \approx 2.24$
4. $d = \sqrt{[-1 - (-2)]^2 + (-3 - 8)^2} = \sqrt{1^2 + (-11)^2} = \sqrt{122} \approx 11.05$
5. $d = \sqrt{(5 - 5)^2 + (7 - 3)^2} = \sqrt{0^2 + 4^2} = \sqrt{16} = 4$
6. $d = \sqrt{(8 - 1)^2 + (4 - 4)^2} = \sqrt{7^2 + 0^2} = \sqrt{49} = 7$
7. $d = \sqrt{(6 - 8)^2 + (9 - 2)^2} = \sqrt{(-2)^2 + 7^2} = \sqrt{53} \approx 7.28$
8. $d = \sqrt{[-6 - (-6)]^2 + (-5 - 2)^2} = \sqrt{0^2 + (-7)^2} = \sqrt{49} = 7$
9. $6 = \sqrt{(4 - 0)^2 + (y - 0)^2} = \sqrt{4^2 + y^2} = \sqrt{16 + y^2}$, so $36 = 6^2 = (\sqrt{16 + y^2})^2 = 16 + y^2$. Therefore, $y^2 = 36 - 16 = 20$, and so $y = \pm\sqrt{20} \approx \pm 4.47$.
10. $4 = \sqrt{(x - 0)^2 + (3 - 0)^2} = \sqrt{x^2 + 3^2} = \sqrt{x^2 + 9}$, so $16 = 4^2 = (\sqrt{x^2 + 9})^2 = x^2 + 9$. Therefore, $x^2 = 16 - 9 = 7$, and so $x = \pm\sqrt{7} \approx \pm 2.65$.
11. $5 = \sqrt{(7 - 3)^2 + (y - 1)^2} = \sqrt{4^2 + (y - 1)^2} = \sqrt{16 + (y - 1)^2}$, so $25 = 5^2 = [\sqrt{16 + (y - 1)^2}]^2 = 16 + (y - 1)^2$. Therefore, $(y - 1)^2 = 25 - 16 = 9$, and so $y - 1 = \pm 3$. Thus, $y = 3 + 1 = 4$, or $y = -3 + 1 = -2$.
12. $(x - 4)^2 + (y - 6)^2 = 8^2$, or $(x - 4)^2 + (y - 6)^2 = 64$
13. $[x - (-2)]^2 + (y - 5)^2 = 3^2$, or $(x + 2)^2 + (y - 5)^2 = 9$

14. $(x - 4)^2 + (y - 0)^2 = 6^2$, or $(x - 4)^2 + y^2 = 36$
15. $(x - 0)^2 + (y - 3)^2 = 5^2$, or $x^2 + (y - 3)^2 = 25$
16. $(x - 2)^2 + (y - 5)^2 = 81$

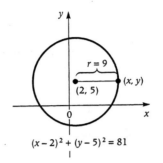

17. $x^2 + y^2 = 36$

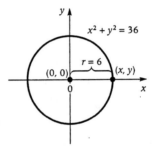

18. $(x + 9)^2 + (y - 1)^2 = 64$

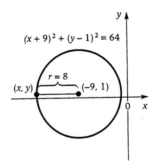

19. $x^2 + (y - 1)^2 = 25$

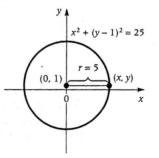

• DETERMINANTS

A **determinant** is a number associated with a square matrix. Given a 2×2 matrix

$$A = \begin{bmatrix} a_{11} & a_{12} \\ a_{21} & a_{22} \end{bmatrix}$$

its determinant is denoted by either of the following:

$$|A| \qquad \begin{vmatrix} a_{11} & a_{12} \\ a_{21} & a_{22} \end{vmatrix}$$

The determinant of A is defined as follows:

$$|A| = \begin{vmatrix} a_{11} & a_{12} \\ a_{21} & a_{22} \end{vmatrix} = a_{11}a_{22} - a_{12}a_{21}$$

Thus, if

$$A = \begin{bmatrix} 4 & 3 \\ 8 & 7 \end{bmatrix}$$

its determinant is

$$|A| = \begin{vmatrix} 4 & 3 \\ 8 & 7 \end{vmatrix} = (4)(7) = (3)(8) = 4$$

• EXAMPLE B-3 _____

Find $\begin{vmatrix} -8 & 5 \\ 4 & 6 \end{vmatrix}$.

Solution

$$\begin{vmatrix} -8 & 5 \\ 4 & 6 \end{vmatrix} = (-8)(6) - (5)(4) = -68$$

• EXAMPLE B-4 _____

If

$$A = \begin{bmatrix} -4 & 3 \\ -2 & -1 \end{bmatrix}$$

find the determinant of A.

Solution

$$|A| = (-4)(-1) - (3)(-2) = 10$$

Finding the determinant of a square matrix of a dimension greater than 2×2 is more complicated than in the 2×2 case. In order to find the determinant of a square matrix of dimension greater than 2×2, we must understand the following concept.

> ### Minor of an Element
>
> Each element a_{ij} of a square matrix of dimension $n \times n$ has an associated square matrix of dimension $(n - 1) \times (n - 1)$, which is determined by blocking out the row and column of element a_{ij}. The determinant of the associated $(n - 1) \times (n - 1)$ matrix is called the **minor** of element a_{ij}.

For example, consider the general 3×3 matrix

$$A = \begin{bmatrix} a_{11} & a_{12} & a_{13} \\ a_{21} & a_{22} & a_{23} \\ a_{31} & a_{32} & a_{33} \end{bmatrix}$$

To find the minor of element a_{12}, we block out the row and column of a_{12} as shown here.

$$\begin{bmatrix} a_{11} & a_{12} & a_{13} \\ a_{21} & a_{22} & a_{23} \\ a_{31} & a_{32} & a_{33} \end{bmatrix}$$

The remaining 2×2 matrix is

$$\begin{bmatrix} a_{21} & a_{23} \\ a_{31} & a_{33} \end{bmatrix}$$

Its determinant

$$\begin{vmatrix} a_{21} & a_{23} \\ a_{31} & a_{33} \end{vmatrix} = a_{21}a_{33} - a_{23}a_{31}$$

is the *minor of a_{12}*.

• EXAMPLE B-5

Find the minor of -2 (located in row 2 and column 2) of matrix B.

$$B = \begin{bmatrix} 1 & 0 & 5 \\ 4 & -2 & -3 \\ 6 & -1 & 8 \end{bmatrix}$$

Solution

We first block out the row and column of -2 as shown below.

The remaining 2×2 matrix is

$$\begin{bmatrix} 1 & 5 \\ 6 & 8 \end{bmatrix}$$

Its determinant,

$$\begin{vmatrix} 1 & 5 \\ 6 & 8 \end{vmatrix} = (1)(8) - (5)(6) = -22$$

is the minor of -2.

Now that we know how to find the minor of an element a_{ij} of a square matrix, we must also understand the following concept.

Cofactor of an Element

Each element a_{ij} of a square matrix has an associated number called the **cofactor** of a_{ij}. The cofactor of an element a_{ij} is determined by the following procedure:

Step 1   Find the *minor* of element a_{ij}.
Step 2   Multiply the minor by $(-1)^{i+j}$, where i is the row number of element a_{ij} and j is the column number of a_{ij}.

We illustrate by finding the cofactor of an element of the matrix

$$M = \begin{bmatrix} 2 & -3 & 3 \\ -6 & 2 & -4 \\ 7 & 2 & -5 \end{bmatrix}$$

Let's find the cofactor of -6, which is located in row 2 and column 1 of matrix M. We first find the *minor of* -6 by blocking out its row and column as shown here

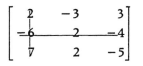

and then finding the determinant of the resulting matrix. Hence,

$$\begin{vmatrix} -3 & 3 \\ 2 & -5 \end{vmatrix} = (-3)(-5) - (3)(2) = 9$$

is the minor of -6. Multiplying 9, the minor of -6, by

$$(-1)^{i+j}$$

where i is the row number of -6 and j is its column number, gives

$$(-1)^{2+1}(9) = -1(9) = -9$$

Thus, -9 is the cofactor of -6.

The minor and cofactor of each element of column 3 of matrix M are given in Table B-1.

TABLE B-1

Element	Minor	Cofactor
Element 3 located in row 1 and column 3 of M	$\begin{vmatrix} -6 & 2 \\ 7 & 2 \end{vmatrix} = -26$	$(-1)^{1+3}(-26) = -26$
Element -4 located in row 2 and column 3 of M	$\begin{vmatrix} 2 & -3 \\ 7 & 2 \end{vmatrix} = 25$	$(-1)^{2+3}(25) = -25$
Element -5 located in row 3 and column 3 of M	$\begin{vmatrix} 2 & -3 \\ -6 & 2 \end{vmatrix} = -14$	$(-1)^{3+3}(-14) = -14$

Now that we know how to determine the cofactor of an element of a square matrix, we are ready to learn how to find the determinant of a square matrix of dimension higher than 2×2. The procedure is as follows.

To Find the Determinant of an $n \times n$ Matrix ($n > 2$)

Step 1   Choose either a row or a column of the original matrix.

Step 2   Multiply each element of this chosen row (or column) by its respective cofactor.

Step 3   Add the products obtained in step 2. The result is the determinant of the matrix.

• EXAMPLE B-6

Find the determinant of matrix M where

$$M = \begin{bmatrix} 2 & -3 & 3 \\ -6 & 2 & -4 \\ 7 & 2 & -5 \end{bmatrix}$$

Solution

Since the cofactors of the elements in column 3 are given in Table B-1 of this section, we choose column 3 of matrix M. Multiplying each element in column 3 by its respective cofactor and adding the products gives

$$\begin{aligned} |M| &= 3(-26) + (-4)(-25) + (-5)(-14) \\ &= -78 + 100 + 70 \\ &= 92 \end{aligned}$$

• EXAMPLE B-7

Find the determinant of matrix M of the previous example by choosing row 2.

Solution

The cofactors of -6, 2, and -4 are -9, -31, and -25, respectively. Multiplying each element of row 2 by its respective cofactor and adding the products gives

$$|M| = (-6)(-9) + 2(-31) + (-4)(-25)$$
$$= 54 - 62 + 100$$
$$= 92$$

Note that $|M| = 92$ regardless of the row or column with which we choose to find the determinant of M.

In general, the determinant of a given square matrix is the same number regardless of the row or column chosen.

• **EXAMPLE B-8**

Find $|A|$ if

$$A = \begin{bmatrix} 1 & 0 & -1 & 4 \\ 0 & 3 & 2 & -4 \\ 2 & 0 & -1 & 0 \\ 5 & 0 & 0 & 0 \end{bmatrix}$$

Solution

Choosing column 2, we determine the cofactor of 3 to be

$$(-1)^{2+2} \begin{vmatrix} 1 & -1 & 4 \\ 2 & -1 & 0 \\ 5 & 0 & 0 \end{vmatrix}$$

We need not determine the cofactors of the 0s since the product of a 0 and its cofactor is 0. We determine that

$$\begin{vmatrix} 1 & -1 & 4 \\ 2 & -1 & 0 \\ 5 & 0 & 0 \end{vmatrix} = 20$$

and, thus, the cofactor of 3 is

$$(-1)^{2+2}(20) = 20$$

Hence,

$$|A| = 3(20) = 60$$

Exercises

1. Find $|D|$ if

$$D = \begin{bmatrix} 2 & -1 & 3 \\ 3 & 2 & -4 \\ 4 & 2 & -5 \end{bmatrix}$$

2. Find $|C|$ if

$$C = \begin{bmatrix} 5 & 3 & 2 \\ 8 & -1 & 4 \\ 1 & 2 & -3 \end{bmatrix}$$

3. Find $|H|$ if

$$H = \begin{bmatrix} 5 & 0 & 4 \\ 3 & 2 & -1 \\ -8 & -5 & 7 \end{bmatrix}$$

4. Find $|K|$ if

$$K = \begin{bmatrix} 0 & -1 & 5 \\ 2 & -3 & -4 \\ 0 & 4 & 7 \end{bmatrix}$$

5. Find $|N|$ if

$$N = \begin{bmatrix} 4 & 0 & 3 & 1 \\ -1 & 0 & 2 & -3 \\ 3 & 5 & 1 & -2 \\ -4 & 0 & -3 & 1 \end{bmatrix}$$

Answers

1. $|D| = -9$
2. $|C| = 93$
3. $|H| = 49$
4. $|K| = 54$
5. $|N| = -110$

Appendix C
Tables

TABLE 1   Common logarithms

x	0	1	2	3	4	5	6	7	8	9
1.0	0.0000	0.0043	0.0086	0.0128	0.0170	0.0212	0.0253	0.0294	0.0334	0.0374
1.1	0.0414	0.0453	0.0492	0.0531	0.0569	0.0607	0.0645	0.0682	0.0719	0.0755
1.2	0.0792	0.0828	0.0864	0.0899	0.0934	0.0969	0.1004	0.1038	0.1072	0.1106
1.3	0.1139	0.1173	0.1206	0.1239	0.1271	0.1303	0.1335	0.1367	0.1399	0.1430
1.4	0.1461	0.1492	0.1523	0.1553	0.1584	0.1614	0.1644	0.1673	0.1703	0.1732
1.5	0.1761	0.1790	0.1818	0.1847	0.1875	0.1903	0.1931	0.1959	0.1987	0.2014
1.6	0.2041	0.2068	0.2095	0.2122	0.2148	0.2175	0.2201	0.2227	0.2253	0.2279
1.7	0.2304	0.2330	0.2355	0.2380	0.2405	0.2430	0.2455	0.2480	0.2504	0.2529
1.8	0.2553	0.2577	0.2601	0.2625	0.2648	0.2672	0.2695	0.2718	0.2742	0.2765
1.9	0.2788	0.2810	0.2833	0.2856	0.2878	0.2900	0.2923	0.2945	0.2967	0.2989
2.0	0.3010	0.3032	0.3054	0.3075	0.3096	0.3118	0.3139	0.3160	0.3181	0.3201
2.1	0.3222	0.3243	0.3263	0.3284	0.3304	0.3324	0.3345	0.3365	0.3385	0.3404
2.2	0.3424	0.3444	0.3464	0.3483	0.3502	0.3522	0.3541	0.3560	0.3579	0.3598
2.3	0.3617	0.3636	0.3655	0.3674	0.3692	0.3711	0.3729	0.3747	0.3766	0.3784
2.4	0.3802	0.3820	0.3838	0.3856	0.3874	0.3892	0.3909	0.3927	0.3945	0.3962
2.5	0.3979	0.3997	0.4014	0.4031	0.4048	0.4065	0.4082	0.4099	0.4116	0.4133
2.6	0.4150	0.4166	0.4183	0.4200	0.4216	0.4232	0.4249	0.4265	0.4281	0.4298
2.7	0.4314	0.4330	0.4346	0.4362	0.4378	0.4393	0.4409	0.4425	0.4440	0.4456
2.8	0.4472	0.4487	0.4502	0.4518	0.4533	0.4548	0.4564	0.4579	0.4594	0.4609
2.9	0.4624	0.4639	0.4654	0.4669	0.4683	0.4698	0.4713	0.4728	0.4742	0.4757
3.0	0.4771	0.4786	0.4800	0.4814	0.4829	0.4843	0.4857	0.4871	0.4886	0.4900
3.1	0.4914	0.4928	0.4942	0.4955	0.4969	0.4983	0.4997	0.5011	0.5024	0.5038
3.2	0.5052	0.5065	0.5079	0.5092	0.5105	0.5119	0.5132	0.5145	0.5159	0.5172
3.3	0.5185	0.5198	0.5211	0.5224	0.5237	0.5250	0.5263	0.5276	0.5289	0.5302
3.4	0.5315	0.5328	0.5340	0.5353	0.5366	0.5378	0.5391	0.5403	0.5416	0.5428
3.5	0.5441	0.5453	0.5465	0.5478	0.5490	0.5502	0.5515	0.5527	0.5539	0.5551
3.6	0.5563	0.5575	0.5587	0.5599	0.5611	0.5623	0.5635	0.5647	0.5658	0.5670
3.7	0.5682	0.5694	0.5705	0.5717	0.5729	0.5740	0.5752	0.5763	0.5775	0.5786
3.8	0.5798	0.5809	0.5821	0.5832	0.5843	0.5855	0.5866	0.5877	0.5888	0.5899
3.9	0.5911	0.5922	0.5933	0.5944	0.5955	0.5966	0.5977	0.5988	0.5999	0.6010
4.0	0.6021	0.6031	0.6042	0.6053	0.6064	0.6075	0.6085	0.6096	0.6107	0.6117
4.1	0.6128	0.6138	0.6149	0.6160	0.6170	0.6180	0.6191	0.6201	0.6212	0.6222
4.2	0.6232	0.6243	0.6253	0.6263	0.6274	0.6284	0.6294	0.6304	0.6314	0.6325

continues

TABLE 1 Common logarithms *(continued)*

x	0	1	2	3	4	5	6	7	8	9
4.3	0.6335	0.6345	0.6355	0.6365	0.6375	0.6385	0.6395	0.6405	0.6415	0.6425
4.4	0.6435	0.6444	0.6454	0.6464	0.6474	0.6484	0.6493	0.6503	0.6513	0.6522
4.5	0.6532	0.6542	0.6551	0.6561	0.6571	0.6580	0.6590	0.6599	0.6609	0.6618
4.6	0.6628	0.6637	0.6646	0.6656	0.6665	0.6675	0.6684	0.6693	0.6702	0.6712
4.7	0.6721	0.6730	0.6739	0.6749	0.6758	0.6767	0.6776	0.6785	0.6794	0.6803
4.8	0.6812	0.6821	0.6830	0.6839	0.6848	0.6857	0.6866	0.6875	0.6884	0.6893
4.9	0.6902	0.6911	0.6920	0.6928	0.6937	0.6946	0.6955	0.6964	0.6972	0.6981
5.0	0.6990	0.6998	0.7007	0.7016	0.7024	0.7033	0.7042	0.7050	0.7059	0.7067
5.1	0.7076	0.7084	0.7093	0.7101	0.7110	0.7118	0.7126	0.7135	0.7143	0.7152
5.2	0.7160	0.7168	0.7177	0.7185	0.7193	7.7202	0.7210	0.7218	0.7226	0.7235
5.3	0.7243	0.7251	0.7259	0.7267	0.7275	0.7284	0.7292	0.7300	0.7308	0.7316
5.4	0.7324	0.7332	0.7340	0.7348	0.7356	0.7364	0.7372	0.7380	0.7388	0.7396
5.5	0.7404	0.7412	0.7419	0.7427	0.7435	0.7443	0.7451	0.7459	0.7466	0.7474
5.6	0.7482	0.7490	0.7497	0.7505	0.7513	0.7520	0.7528	0.7536	0.7543	0.7551
5.7	0.7559	0.7566	0.7574	0.7582	0.7589	0.7597	0.7604	0.7612	0.7619	0.7627
5.8	0.7634	0.7642	0.7649	0.7657	0.7664	0.7672	0.7679	0.7686	0.7694	0.7701
5.9	0.7709	0.7716	0.7723	0.7731	0.7738	0.7745	0.7752	0.7760	0.7767	0.7774
6.0	0.7782	0.7789	0.7796	0.7803	0.7810	0.7818	0.7825	0.7832	0.7839	0.7846
6.1	0.7853	0.7860	0.7868	0.7875	0.7882	0.7889	0.7896	0.7903	0.7910	0.7917
6.2	0.7924	0.7931	0.7938	0.7945	0.7952	0.7959	0.7966	0.7973	0.7980	0.7987
6.3	0.7993	0.8000	0.8007	0.8014	0.8021	0.8028	0.8035	0.8041	0.8048	0.8055
6.4	0.8062	0.8069	0.8075	0.8082	0.8089	0.8096	0.8102	0.8109	0.8116	0.8122
6.5	0.8129	0.8136	0.8142	0.8149	0.8156	0.8162	0.8169	0.8176	0.8182	0.8189
6.6	0.8195	0.8202	0.8209	0.8215	0.8222	0.8228	0.8235	0.8241	0.8248	0.8254
6.7	0.8261	0.8267	0.8274	0.8280	0.8287	0.8293	0.8299	0.8306	0.8312	0.8319
6.8	0.8325	0.8331	0.8338	0.8344	0.8351	0.8357	0.8363	0.8370	0.8376	0.8382
6.9	0.8388	0.8395	0.8401	0.8407	0.8414	0.8420	0.8426	0.8432	0.8439	0.8445
7.0	0.8451	0.8457	0.8463	0.8470	0.8476	0.8482	0.8488	0.8494	0.8500	0.8506
7.1	0.8513	0.8519	0.8525	0.8531	0.8537	0.8543	0.8549	0.8555	0.8561	0.8567
7.2	0.8573	0.8579	0.8585	0.8591	0.8597	0.8603	0.8609	0.8615	0.8621	0.8627
7.3	0.8633	0.8639	0.8645	0.8651	0.8657	0.8663	0.8669	0.8675	0.8681	0.8686
7.4	0.8692	0.8698	0.8704	0.8710	0.8716	0.8722	0.8727	0.8733	0.8739	0.8745
7.5	0.8751	0.8756	0.8762	0.8768	0.8774	0.8779	0.8785	0.8791	0.8797	0.8802
7.6	0.8808	0.8814	0.8820	0.8825	0.8831	0.8837	0.8842	0.8848	0.8854	0.8859
7.7	0.8865	0.8871	0.8876	0.8882	0.8887	0.8893	0.8899	0.8904	0.8910	0.8915
7.8	0.8921	0.8927	0.8932	0.8938	0.8943	0.8949	0.8954	0.8960	0.8965	0.8971
7.9	0.8976	0.8982	0.8987	0.8993	0.8998	0.9004	0.9009	0.9015	0.9020	0.9025
8.0	0.9031	0.9036	0.9042	0.9047	0.9053	0.9058	0.9063	0.9069	0.9074	0.9079
8.1	0.9085	0.9090	0.9096	0.9101	0.9106	0.9112	0.9117	0.9122	0.9128	0.9133
8.2	0.9138	0.9143	0.9149	0.9154	0.9159	0.9165	0.9170	0.9175	0.9180	0.9186
8.3	0.9191	0.9196	0.9201	0.9206	0.9212	0.9217	0.9222	0.9227	0.9232	0.9238
8.4	0.9243	0.9248	0.9253	0.9258	0.9263	0.9269	0.9274	0.9279	0.9284	0.9289
8.5	0.9294	0.9299	0.9304	0.9309	0.9315	0.9320	0.9325	0.9330	0.9335	0.9340
8.6	0.9345	0.9350	0.9355	0.9360	0.9365	0.9370	0.9375	0.9380	0.9385	0.9390
8.7	0.9395	0.9400	0.9405	0.9410	0.9415	0.9420	0.9425	0.9430	0.9435	0.9440
8.8	0.9445	0.9450	0.9455	0.9460	0.9465	0.9469	0.9474	0.9479	0.9484	0.9489
8.9	0.9494	0.9499	0.9504	0.9509	0.9513	0.9518	0.9523	0.9528	0.9533	0.9538
9.0	0.9542	0.9547	0.9552	0.9557	0.9562	0.9566	0.9571	0.9576	0.9581	0.9586
9.1	0.9590	0.9595	0.9600	0.9605	0.9609	0.9614	0.9619	0.9624	0.9628	0.9633

continues

TABLE 1   Common logarithms *(continued)*

x	0	1	2	3	4	5	6	7	8	9
9.2	0.9638	0.9643	0.9647	0.9652	0.9657	0.9661	0.9666	0.9671	0.9675	0.9680
9.3	0.9685	0.9689	0.9694	0.9699	0.9703	0.9708	0.9713	0.9717	0.9722	0.9727
9.4	0.9731	0.9736	0.9741	0.9745	0.9750	0.9754	0.9759	0.9764	0.9768	0.9773
9.5	0.9777	0.9782	0.9786	0.9791	0.9795	0.9800	0.9805	0.9809	0.9814	0.9818
9.6	0.9823	0.9827	0.9832	0.9836	0.9841	0.9845	0.9850	0.9854	0.9859	0.9863
9.7	0.9868	0.9872	0.9877	0.9881	0.9886	0.9890	0.9894	0.9899	0.9903	0.9908
9.8	0.9912	0.9917	0.9921	0.9926	0.9930	0.9934	0.9939	0.9943	0.9948	0.9952
9.9	0.9956	0.9961	0.9965	0.9969	0.9974	0.9978	0.9983	0.9987	0.9991	0.9996

TABLE 2   Natural logarithms

x	ln x	x	ln x	x	ln x
0.1	−2.302585	3.5	1.252763	6.9	1.931521
0.2	−1.609438	3.6	1.280934	7.0	1.945910
0.3	−1.203973	3.7	1.308333	7.1	1.960095
0.4	−0.916291	3.8	1.335001	7.2	1.974081
0.5	−0.693147	3.9	1.360977	7.3	1.987874
0.6	−0.510826	4.0	1.386294	7.4	2.001480
0.7	−0.356675	4.1	1.410987	7.5	2.014903
0.8	−0.223144	4.2	1.435085	7.6	2.028148
0.9	−0.105361	4.3	1.458615	7.7	2.041220
1.0	0.000000	4.4	1.481605	7.8	2.054124
1.1	0.095310	4.5	1.504077	7.9	2.066863
1.2	0.182322	4.6	1.526056	8.0	2.079442
1.3	0.262364	4.7	1.547563	8.1	2.091864
1.4	0.336472	4.8	1.568616	8.2	2.104134
1.5	0.405465	4.9	1.589235	8.3	2.116256
1.6	0.470004	5.0	1.609438	8.4	2.128232
1.7	0.530628	5.1	1.629241	8.5	2.140066
1.8	0.587787	5.2	1.648659	8.6	2.151762
1.9	0.641854	5.3	1.667707	8.7	2.163323
2.0	0.693147	5.4	1.686399	8.8	2.174752
2.1	0.741937	5.5	1.704748	8.9	2.186051
2.2	0.788457	5.6	1.722767	9.0	2.197225
2.3	0.832909	5.7	1.740466	9.1	2.208274
2.4	0.875469	5.8	1.757858	9.2	2.219203
2.5	0.916291	5.9	1.774952	9.3	2.230014
2.6	0.955511	6.0	1.791759	9.4	2.240710
2.7	0.993252	6.1	1.808289	9.5	2.251292
2.8	1.029619	6.2	1.824549	9.6	2.261763
2.9	1.064711	6.3	1.840550	9.7	2.272126
3.0	1.098612	6.4	1.856298	9.8	2.282382
3.1	1.131402	6.5	1.871802	9.9	2.292535
3.2	1.163151	6.6	1.887070	10.0	2.302585
3.3	1.193922	6.7	1.902108	11.0	2.397895
3.4	1.223775	6.8	1.916923	12.0	2.484907

continues

TABLE 2 Natural logarithms *(continued)*

x	ln x	x	ln x	x	ln x
13.0	2.564949	25.0	3.218876	65.0	4.174387
14.0	2.639057	30.0	3.401197	70.0	4.248495
15.0	2.708050	35.0	3.555348	75.0	4.317488
16.0	2.772589	40.0	3.688879	80.0	4.382027
17.0	2.833213	45.0	3.806662	85.0	4.442651
18.0	2.890372	50.0	3.912023	90.0	4.499810
19.0	2.944439	55.0	4.007333	95.0	4.553877
20.0	2.995732	60.0	4.094345	100.0	4.605170

TABLE 3 Exponential functions

x	e^x	e^{-x}	x	e^x	e^{-x}
0.00	1.000000	1.000000	1.40	4.055200	0.246597
0.01	1.010050	0.990050	1.50	4.481689	0.223130
0.02	1.020201	0.980199	1.60	4.953032	0.201897
0.03	1.030455	0.970446	1.70	5.473947	0.182684
0.04	1.040811	0.960789	1.80	6.049647	0.165299
0.05	1.051271	0.951229	1.90	6.685894	0.149569
0.06	1.061837	0.941765	2.00	7.389056	0.135335
0.07	1.072508	0.932394	2.10	8.166170	0.122456
0.08	1.083287	0.923116	2.20	9.025013	0.110803
0.09	1.094174	0.913931	2.30	9.974182	0.100259
0.10	1.105171	0.904837	2.40	11.023176	0.090718
0.11	1.116278	0.895834	2.50	12.182494	0.082085
0.12	1.127497	0.886920	2.60	13.463738	0.074274
0.13	1.138828	0.878095	2.70	14.879732	0.067206
0.14	1.150274	0.869358	2.80	16.444647	0.060810
0.15	1.161834	0.860708	2.90	18.174145	0.055023
0.16	1.173511	0.852144	3.00	20.085537	0.049787
0.17	1.185305	0.843665	3.50	33.115452	0.030197
0.18	1.197217	0.835270	4.00	54.598150	0.018316
0.19	1.209250	0.826959	4.50	90.017131	0.011109
0.20	1.221403	0.818731	5.00	148.413159	0.006738
0.30	1.349859	0.740818	5.50	244.691932	0.004087
0.40	1.491825	0.670320	6.00	403.428793	0.002479
0.50	1.648721	0.606531	6.50	665.141633	0.001503
0.60	1.822119	0.548812	7.00	1096.633158	0.000912
0.70	2.013753	0.496585	7.50	1808.042414	0.000553
0.80	2.225541	0.449329	8.00	2980.957987	0.000335
0.90	2.459603	0.406570	8.50	4914.768840	0.000203
1.00	2.718282	0.367879	9.00	8103.083928	0.000123
1.10	3.004166	0.332871	9.50	13359.726830	0.000075
1.20	3.320117	0.301194	10.00	22026.465795	0.000045
1.30	3.669297	0.272532			

TABLE 4 Compound amount $(1 + i)^n$

n	½%	¾%	1%	1¼%	1½%	1¾%	2%
1	1.005000	1.007500	1.010000	1.012500	1.015000	1.017500	1.020000
2	1.010025	1.015056	1.020100	1.025156	1.030225	1.035306	1.040400
3	1.015075	1.022669	1.030301	1.037971	1.045678	1.053424	1.061208
4	1.020151	1.030339	1.040604	1.050945	1.061364	1.071859	1.082432
5	1.025251	1.038067	1.051010	1.064082	1.077284	1.090617	1.104081
6	1.030378	1.045852	1.061520	1.077383	1.093443	1.109702	1.126162
7	1.035529	1.053696	1.072135	1.090850	1.109845	1.129122	1.148686
8	1.040707	1.061599	1.082857	1.104486	1.126493	1.148882	1.171659
9	1.045911	1.069561	1.093685	1.118292	1.143390	1.168987	1.195093
10	1.051140	1.077583	1.104622	1.132271	1.160541	1.189444	1.218994
11	1.056396	1.085664	1.115668	1.146424	1.177949	1.210260	1.243374
12	1.061678	1.093807	1.126825	1.160755	1.195618	1.231439	1.268242
13	1.066986	1.102010	1.138093	1.175264	1.213552	1.252990	1.293607
14	1.072321	1.110276	1.149474	1.189955	1.231756	1.274917	1.319479
15	1.077683	1.118603	1.160969	1.204829	1.250232	1.297228	1.345868
16	1.083071	1.126992	1.172579	1.219890	1.268986	1.319929	1.372786
17	1.088487	1.135445	1.184304	1.235138	1.288020	1.343028	1.400241
18	1.093929	1.143960	1.196147	1.250577	1.307341	1.366531	1.428246
19	1.099399	1.152540	1.208109	1.266210	1.326951	1.390445	1.456811
20	1.104896	1.161184	1.220190	1.282037	1.346855	1.414778	1.485947
21	1.110420	1.169893	1.232392	1.298063	1.367058	1.439537	1.515666
22	1.115972	1.178667	1.244716	1.314288	1.387564	1.464729	1.545980
23	1.121552	1.187507	1.257163	1.330717	1.408377	1.490361	1.576899
24	1.127160	1.196414	1.269735	1.347351	1.429503	1.516443	1.608437
25	1.132796	1.205387	1.282432	1.364193	1.450945	1.542981	1.640606
26	1.138460	1.214427	1.295256	1.381245	1.472710	1.569983	1.673418
27	1.144152	1.223535	1.308209	1.398511	1.494800	1.597457	1.706886
28	1.149873	1.232712	1.321291	1.415992	1.517222	1.625413	1.741024
29	1.155622	1.241957	1.334504	1.433692	1.539981	1.653858	1.775845
30	1.161400	1.251272	1.347849	1.451613	1.563080	1.682800	1.811362
31	1.167207	1.260656	1.361327	1.469759	1.586526	1.712249	1.847589
32	1.173043	1.270111	1.374941	1.488131	1.610324	1.742213	1.884541
33	1.178908	1.279637	1.388690	1.506732	1.634479	1.772702	1.922231
34	1.184803	1.289234	1.402577	1.525566	1.658996	1.803725	1.960676
35	1.190727	1.298904	1.416603	1.544636	1.683881	1.835290	1.999890
36	1.196681	1.308645	1.430769	1.563944	1.709140	1.867407	2.039887
37	1.202664	1.318460	1.445076	1.583493	1.734777	1.900087	2.080685
38	1.208677	1.328349	1.459527	1.603287	1.760798	1.933338	2.122299
39	1.214721	1.338311	1.474123	1.623328	1.787210	1.967172	2.164745
40	1.220794	1.348349	1.488864	1.643619	1.814018	2.001597	2.208040
41	1.226898	1.358461	1.503752	1.664165	1.841229	2.036625	2.252200
42	1.233033	1.368650	1.518790	1.684967	1.868847	2.072266	2.297244
43	1.239198	1.378915	1.533978	1.706029	1.896880	2.108531	2.343189
44	1.245394	1.389256	1.549318	1.727354	1.925333	2.145430	2.390053
45	1.251621	1.399676	1.564811	1.748946	1.954213	2.182975	2.437854
46	1.257879	1.410173	1.580459	1.770808	1.983526	2.221177	2.486611
47	1.264168	1.420750	1.596263	1.792943	2.013279	2.260048	2.536344
48	1.270489	1.431405	1.612226	1.815355	2.043478	2.299599	2.587070
49	1.276842	1.442141	1.628348	1.838047	2.074130	2.339842	2.638812

continues

TABLE 4 Compound amount $(1 + i)^n$ (continued)

n	½%	¾%	1%	1¼%	1½%	1¾%	2%
50	1.283226	1.452957	1.644632	1.861022	2.105242	2.380789	2.691588
51	1.289642	1.463854	1.661078	1.884285	2.136821	2.422453	2.745420
52	1.296090	1.474833	1.677689	1.907839	2.168873	2.464846	2.800328
53	1.302571	1.485894	1.694466	1.931687	2.201406	2.507980	2.856335
54	1.309083	1.497038	1.711410	1.955833	2.234428	2.551870	2.913461
55	1.315629	1.508266	1.728525	1.980281	2.267944	2.596528	2.971731
56	1.322207	1.519578	1.745810	2.005034	2.301963	2.641967	3.031165
57	1.328818	1.530975	1.763268	2.030097	2.336493	2.688202	3.091789
58	1.335462	1.542457	1.780901	2.055473	2.371540	2.735245	3.153624
59	1.342139	1.554026	1.798710	2.081167	2.407113	2.783112	3.216697
60	1.348850	1.565681	1.816697	2.107181	2.443220	2.831816	3.281031
61	1.355594	1.577424	1.834864	2.133521	2.479868	2.881373	3.346651
62	1.362372	1.589254	1.853212	2.160190	2.517066	2.931797	3.413584
63	1.369184	1.601174	1.871744	2.187193	2.554822	2.983104	3.481856
64	1.376030	1.613183	1.890462	2.214532	2.593144	3.035308	3.551493
65	1.382910	1.625281	1.909366	2.242214	2.632042	3.088426	3.622523
66	1.389825	1.637471	1.928460	2.270242	2.671522	3.142473	3.694974
67	1.396774	1.649752	1.947745	2.298620	2.711595	3.197466	3.768873
68	1.403758	1.662125	1.967222	2.327353	2.752269	3.253422	3.844251
69	1.410777	1.674591	1.986894	2.356444	2.793553	3.310357	3.921136
70	1.417831	1.687151	2.006763	2.385900	2.835456	3.368288	3.999558
71	1.424920	1.699804	2.026831	2.415724	2.877988	3.427233	4.079549
72	1.432044	1.712553	2.047099	2.445920	2.921158	3.487210	4.161140
73	1.439204	1.725397	2.067570	2.476494	2.964975	3.548236	4.244363
74	1.446401	1.738337	2.088246	2.507450	3.009450	3.610330	4.329250
75	1.453633	1.751375	2.109128	2.538794	3.054592	3.673511	4.415835
76	1.460901	1.764510	2.130220	2.570529	3.100411	3.737797	4.504152
77	1.468205	1.777744	2.151522	2.602660	3.146917	3.803209	4.594235
78	1.475546	1.791077	2.173037	2.635193	3.194120	3.869765	4.686120
79	1.482924	1.804510	2.194768	2.668133	3.242032	3.937486	4.779842
80	1.490339	1.818044	2.216715	2.701485	3.290663	4.006392	4.875439
81	1.497790	1.831679	2.238882	2.735254	3.340023	4.076504	4.972948
82	1.505279	1.845417	2.261271	2.769444	3.390123	4.147843	5.072407
83	1.512806	1.859258	2.283884	2.804062	3.440975	4.220430	5.173855
84	1.520370	1.873202	2.306723	2.839113	3.492590	4.294287	5.277332
85	1.527971	1.887251	2.329790	2.874602	3.544978	4.369437	5.382879
86	1.535611	1.901405	2.353088	2.910534	3.598153	4.445903	5.490536
87	1.543289	1.915666	2.376619	2.946916	3.652125	4.523706	5.600347
88	1.551006	1.930033	2.400385	2.983753	3.706907	4.602871	5.712354
89	1.558761	1.944509	2.424389	3.021049	3.762511	4.683421	5.826601
90	1.566555	1.959092	2.448633	3.058813	3.818949	4.765381	5.943133
91	1.574387	1.973786	2.473119	3.097048	3.876233	4.848775	6.061996
92	1.582259	1.988589	2.497850	3.135761	3.934376	4.933629	6.183236
93	1.590171	2.003503	2.522829	3.174958	3.993392	5.019967	6.306900
94	1.598122	2.018530	2.548057	3.214645	4.053293	5.107816	6.433038
95	1.606112	2.033669	2.573538	3.254828	4.114092	5.197203	6.561699
96	1.614143	2.048921	2.599273	3.295513	4.175804	5.288154	6.692933
97	1.622213	2.064288	2.625266	3.336707	4.238441	5.380697	6.826792
98	1.630324	2.079770	2.651518	3.378416	4.302017	5.474859	6.963328
99	1.638476	2.095369	2.678033	3.420646	4.366547	5.570669	7.102594
100	1.646668	2.111084	2.704814	3.463404	4.432046	5.668156	7.244646

TABLE 4   Compound amount $(1 + i)^n$

n	3%	4%	5%	6%	7%	8%	9%
1	1.030000	1.040000	1.050000	1.060000	1.070000	1.080000	1.090000
2	1.060900	1.081600	1.102500	1.123600	1.144900	1.166400	1.188100
3	1.092727	1.124864	1.157625	1.191016	1.225043	1.259712	1.295029
4	1.125509	1.169859	1.215506	1.262477	1.310796	1.360489	1.411582
5	1.159274	1.216653	1.276282	1.338226	1.402552	1.469328	1.538624
6	1.194052	1.265319	1.340096	1.418519	1.500730	1.586874	1.677100
7	1.229874	1.315932	1.407100	1.503630	1.605781	1.713824	1.828039
8	1.266770	1.368569	1.477455	1.593848	1.718186	1.850930	1.992563
9	1.304773	1.423312	1.551328	1.689479	1.838459	1.999005	2.171893
10	1.343916	1.480244	1.628895	1.790848	1.967151	2.158925	2.367364
11	1.384234	1.539454	1.710339	1.898299	2.104852	2.331639	2.580426
12	1.425761	1.601032	1.795856	2.012196	2.252192	2.518170	2.812665
13	1.468534	1.665074	1.885649	2.132928	2.409845	2.719624	3.065805
14	1.512590	1.731676	1.979932	2.260904	2.578534	2.937194	3.341727
15	1.557967	1.800944	2.078928	2.396558	2.759032	3.172169	3.642482
16	1.604706	1.872981	2.182875	2.540352	2.952164	3.425943	3.970306
17	1.652848	1.947900	2.292018	2.692773	3.158815	3.700018	4.327633
18	1.702433	2.025817	2.406619	2.854339	3.379932	3.996019	4.717120
19	1.753506	2.106849	2.526950	3.025600	3.616528	4.315701	5.141661
20	1.806111	2.191123	2.653298	3.207135	3.869684	4.660957	5.604411
21	1.860295	2.278768	2.785963	3.399564	4.140562	5.033834	6.108808
22	1.916103	2.369919	2.925261	3.603537	4.430402	5.436540	6.658600
23	1.973587	2.464716	3.071524	3.819750	4.740530	5.871464	7.257874
24	2.032794	2.563304	3.225100	4.048935	5.072367	6.341181	7.911083
25	2.093778	2.665836	3.386355	4.291871	5.427433	6.848475	8.623081
26	2.156591	2.772470	3.555673	4.549383	5.807353	7.396353	9.399158
27	2.221289	2.883369	3.733456	4.822346	6.213868	7.988061	10.245082
28	2.287928	2.998703	3.920129	5.111687	6.648838	8.627106	11.167140
29	2.356566	3.118651	4.116136	5.418388	7.114257	9.317275	12.172182
30	2.427262	3.243398	4.321942	5.743491	7.612255	10.062657	13.267678
31	2.500080	3.373133	4.538039	6.088101	8.145113	10.867669	14.461770
32	2.575083	3.508059	4.764941	6.453387	8.715271	11.737083	15.763329
33	2.652335	3.648381	5.003189	6.840590	9.325340	12.676050	17.182028
34	2.731905	3.794316	5.253348	7.251025	9.978114	13.690134	18.728411
35	2.813862	3.946089	5.516015	7.686087	10.676581	14.785344	20.413968
36	2.898278	4.103933	5.791816	8.147252	11.423942	15.968172	22.251225
37	2.985227	4.268090	6.081407	8.636087	12.223618	17.245626	24.253835
38	3.074783	4.438813	6.385477	9.154252	13.079271	18.625276	26.436680
39	3.167027	4.616366	6.704751	9.703507	13.994820	20.115298	28.815982
40	3.262038	4.801021	7.039989	10.285718	14.974458	21.724521	31.409420
41	3.359899	4.993061	7.391988	10.902861	16.022670	23.462483	34.236268
42	3.460696	5.192784	7.761588	11.557033	17.144257	25.339482	37.317532
43	3.564517	5.400495	8.149667	12.250455	18.344355	27.366640	40.676110
44	3.671452	5.616515	8.557150	12.985482	19.628460	29.555972	44.336960
45	3.781596	5.841176	8.985008	13.764611	21.002452	31.920449	48.327286
46	3.895044	6.074823	9.434258	14.590487	22.472623	34.474085	52.676742
47	4.011895	6.317816	9.905971	15.465917	24.045707	37.232012	57.417649
48	4.132252	6.570528	10.401270	16.393872	25.728907	40.210573	62.585237
49	4.256219	6.833349	10.921333	17.377504	27.529930	43.427419	68.217908

continues

TABLE 4 Compound amount $(1 + i)^n$ (continued)

n	3%	4%	5%	6%	7%	8%	9%
50	4.383906	7.106683	11.467400	18.420154	29.457025	46.901613	74.357520
51	4.515423	7.390951	12.040770	19.525364	31.519017	50.653742	81.049697
52	4.650886	7.686589	12.642808	20.696885	33.725348	54.706041	88.344170
53	4.790412	7.994052	13.274949	21.938698	36.086122	59.082524	96.295145
54	4.934125	8.313814	13.938696	23.255020	38.612151	63.809126	104.961708
55	5.082149	8.646367	14.635631	24.650322	41.315001	68.913856	114.408262
56	5.234613	8.992222	15.367412	26.129341	44.207052	74.426965	124.705005
57	5.391651	9.351910	16.135783	27.697101	47.301545	80.381122	135.928456
58	5.553401	9.725987	16.942572	29.358927	50.612653	86.811612	148.162017
59	5.720003	10.115026	17.789701	31.120463	54.155539	93.756540	161.496598
60	5.891603	10.519627	18.679186	32.987691	57.946427	101.257064	176.031292
61	6.068351	10.940413	19.613145	34.966952	62.002677	109.357629	191.874108
62	6.250402	11.378029	20.593802	37.064969	66.342864	118.106239	209.142778
63	6.437914	11.833150	21.623493	39.288868	70.986865	127.554738	227.965628
64	6.631051	12.306476	22.704667	41.646200	75.955945	137.759117	248.482535
65	6.829983	12.798735	23.839901	44.144972	81.272861	148.779847	270.845963
66	7.034882	13.310685	25.031896	46.793670	86.961962	160.682234	295.222099
67	7.245929	13.843112	26.283490	49.601290	93.049299	173.536813	321.792088
68	7.463307	14.396836	27.597665	52.577368	99.562750	187.419758	350.753376
69	7.687206	14.972710	28.977548	55.732010	106.532142	202.413339	382.321180
70	7.917822	15.571618	30.426426	59.075930	113.989392	218.606406	416.730086
71	8.155357	16.194483	31.947747	62.620486	121.968650	236.094918	454.235794
72	8.400017	16.842262	33.545134	66.377715	130.506455	254.982512	495.117015
73	8.652018	17.515953	35.222391	70.360378	139.641907	275.381113	539.677547
74	8.911578	18.216591	36.983510	74.582001	149.416840	297.411602	588.248526
75	9.178926	18.945255	38.832686	79.056921	159.876019	321.204530	641.190893
76	9.454293	19.703065	40.774320	83.800336	171.067341	346.900892	698.898074
77	9.737922	20.491187	42.813036	88.828356	183.042055	374.652964	761.798900
78	10.030060	21.310835	44.953688	94.158058	195.854998	404.625201	830.360801
79	10.330962	22.163268	47.201372	99.807541	209.564848	436.995217	905.093274
80	10.640891	23.049799	49.561441	105.795993	224.234388	471.954834	986.551668
81	10.960117	23.971791	52.039513	112.143753	239.930795	509.711221	1075.341318
82	11.288921	24.930663	54.641489	118.872378	256.725950	550.488119	1172.122037
83	11.627588	25.927889	57.373563	126.004721	274.696767	594.527168	1277.613020
84	11.976416	26.965005	60.242241	133.565004	293.925541	642.089342	1392.598192
85	12.335709	28.043605	63.254353	141.578904	314.500328	693.456489	1517.932029
86	12.705780	29.165349	66.417071	150.073639	336.515351	748.933008	1654.545912
87	13.086953	30.331963	69.737925	159.078057	360.071426	808.847649	1803.455044
88	13.479562	31.545242	73.224821	168.622741	385.276426	873.555461	1965.765998
89	13.883949	32.807051	76.886062	178.740105	412.245776	943.439897	2142.684938
90	14.300467	34.119333	80.730365	189.464511	441.102980	1018.915089	2335.526582
91	14.729481	35.484107	84.766883	200.832382	471.980188	1100.428296	2545.723975
92	15.171366	36.903471	89.005227	212.882325	505.018802	1188.462560	2774.839132
93	15.626507	38.379610	93.455489	225.655264	540.370118	1283.539565	3024.574654
94	16.095302	39.914794	98.128263	239.194580	578.196026	1386.222730	3296.786373
95	16.578161	41.511386	103.034676	253.546255	618.669748	1497.120549	3593.497147
96	17.075506	43.171841	108.186410	268.759030	661.976630	1616.890192	3916.911890
97	17.587771	44.898715	113.595731	284.884572	708.314994	1746.241408	4269.433960
98	18.115404	46.694664	119.275517	301.977646	757.897044	1885.940720	4653.683016
99	18.658866	48.562450	125.239293	320.096305	810.949837	2036.815978	5072.514488
100	19.218632	50.504948	131.501258	339.302084	867.716326	2199.761256	5529.040792

TABLE 4 Compound amount $(1 + i)^n$

n	10%	11%	12%	13%	14%	15%	16%
1	1.100000	1.110000	1.120000	1.130000	1.140000	1.150000	1.16000
2	1.210000	1.232100	1.254400	1.276900	1.299600	1.322500	1.34560
3	1.331000	1.367631	1.404928	1.442897	1.481544	1.520875	1.56090
4	1.464100	1.518070	1.573519	1.630474	1.688960	1.749006	1.81064
5	1.610510	1.685058	1.762342	1.842435	1.925415	2.011357	2.10034
6	1.771561	1.870415	1.973823	2.081952	2.194973	2.313061	2.43640
7	1.948717	2.076160	2.210681	2.352605	2.502269	2.660020	2.82622
8	2.143589	2.304538	2.475963	2.658444	2.852586	3.059023	3.27841
9	2.357948	2.558037	2.773079	3.004042	3.251949	3.517876	3.80296
10	2.593742	2.839421	3.105848	3.394567	3.707221	4.045558	4.41144
11	2.853117	3.151757	3.478550	3.835861	4.226232	4.652391	5.11726
12	3.138428	3.498451	3.895976	4.334523	4.817905	5.350250	5.93603
13	3.452271	3.883280	4.363493	4.898011	5.492411	6.152788	6.88579
14	3.797498	4.310441	4.887112	5.534753	6.261349	7.075706	7.98752
15	4.177248	4.784589	5.473566	6.254270	7.137938	8.137062	9.26552
16	4.594973	5.310894	6.130394	7.067326	8.137249	9.357621	10.74800
17	5.054470	5.895093	6.866041	7.986078	9.276464	10.761264	12.46768
18	5.559917	6.543553	7.689966	9.024268	10.575169	12.375454	14.46251
19	6.115909	7.263344	8.612762	10.197423	12.055693	14.231772	16.77652
20	6.727500	8.062312	9.646293	11.523088	13.743490	16.366537	19.46076
21	7.400250	8.949166	10.803848	13.021089	15.667578	18.821518	22.57448
22	8.140275	9.933574	12.100310	14.713831	17.861039	21.644746	26.18640
23	8.954302	11.026267	13.552347	16.626629	20.361585	24.891458	30.37622
24	9.849733	12.239157	15.178629	18.788091	23.212207	28.625176	35.23642
25	10.834706	13.585464	17.000064	21.230542	26.461916	32.918953	40.87424
26	11.918177	15.079865	19.040072	23.990513	30.166584	37.856796	47.41412
27	13.109994	16.738650	21.324881	27.109279	34.389906	43.535315	55.00038
28	14.420994	18.579901	23.883866	30.633486	39.204493	50.065612	63.80044
29	15.863093	20.623691	26.749930	34.615839	44.693122	57.575454	74.00851
30	17.449402	22.892297	29.959922	39.115898	50.950159	66.211772	85.84988
31	19.194342	25.410449	33.555113	44.200965	58.083181	76.143538	99.58586
32	21.113777	28.205599	37.581726	49.947090	66.214826	87.565068	115.51959
33	23.225154	31.308214	42.091533	56.440212	75.484902	100.699829	134.00273
34	25.547670	34.752118	47.142517	63.777439	86.052788	115.804803	155.44317
35	28.102437	38.574851	52.799620	72.068506	98.100178	133.175523	180.31407
36	30.912681	42.818085	59.135574	81.437412	111.834203	153.151852	209.16432
37	34.003949	47.528074	66.231843	92.024276	127.490992	176.124630	242.63062
38	37.404343	52.756162	74.179664	103.987432	145.339731	202.543324	281.45151
39	41.144778	58.559340	83.081224	117.505798	165.687293	232.924823	326.48376
40	45.259256	65.000867	93.050970	132.781552	188.883514	267.863546	378.72116
41	49.785181	72.150963	104.217087	150.043153	215.327206	308.043078	439.31654
42	54.763699	80.087569	116.723137	169.548763	245.473015	354.249540	509.60719
43	60.240069	88.897201	130.729914	191.590103	279.839237	407.386971	591.14434
44	66.264076	98.675893	146.417503	216.496816	319.016730	468.495017	685.72744
45	72.890484	109.530242	163.987604	244.641402	363.679072	538.769269	795.44383
46	80.179532	121.578568	183.666116	276.444784	414.594142	619.584659	922.71484
47	88.197485	134.952211	205.706050	312.382606	472.637322	712.522358	1070.34921
48	97.017234	149.796954	230.390776	352.992345	538.806547	819.400712	1241.60509
49	106.718957	166.274619	258.037669	398.881350	614.239464	942.310819	1440.26190
50	117.390853	184.564827	289.002190	450.735925	700.232988	1083.657442	1670.70380

A-28 • APPENDIXES

TABLE 5 Present value $(1 + i)^{-n}$

n	½%	¾%	1%	1¼%	1½%	1¾%	2%
1	0.995025	0.992556	0.990099	0.987654	0.985222	0.982801	0.980392
2	0.990075	0.985167	0.980296	0.975461	0.970662	0.965898	0.961169
3	0.985149	0.977833	0.970590	0.963418	0.956317	0.949285	0.942322
4	0.980248	0.970554	0.960980	0.951524	0.942184	0.932959	0.923845
5	0.975371	0.963329	0.951466	0.939777	0.928260	0.916913	0.905731
6	0.970518	0.956158	0.942045	0.928175	0.914542	0.901143	0.887971
7	0.965690	0.949040	0.932718	0.916716	0.901027	0.885644	0.870560
8	0.960885	0.941975	0.923483	0.905398	0.887711	0.870412	0.853490
9	0.956105	0.934963	0.914340	0.894221	0.874592	0.855441	0.836755
10	0.951348	0.928003	0.905287	0.883181	0.861667	0.840729	0.820348
11	0.946615	0.921095	0.896324	0.872277	0.848933	0.826269	0.804263
12	0.941905	0.914238	0.887449	0.861509	0.836387	0.812058	0.788493
13	0.937219	0.907432	0.878663	0.850873	0.824027	0.798091	0.773033
14	0.932556	0.900677	0.869963	0.840368	0.811849	0.784365	0.757875
15	0.927917	0.893973	0.861349	0.829993	0.799852	0.770875	0.743015
16	0.923300	0.887318	0.852821	0.819746	0.788031	0.757616	0.728446
17	0.918707	0.880712	0.844377	0.809626	0.776385	0.744586	0.714163
18	0.914136	0.874156	0.836017	0.799631	0.764912	0.731780	0.700159
19	0.909588	0.867649	0.827740	0.789759	0.753607	0.719194	0.686431
20	0.905063	0.861190	0.819544	0.780009	0.742470	0.706825	0.672971
21	0.900560	0.854779	0.811430	0.770379	0.731498	0.694668	0.659776
22	0.896080	0.848416	0.803396	0.760868	0.720688	0.682720	0.646839
23	0.891622	0.842100	0.795442	0.751475	0.710037	0.670978	0.634156
24	0.887186	0.835831	0.787566	0.742197	0.699544	0.659438	0.621721
25	0.882772	0.829609	0.779768	0.733034	0.689206	0.648096	0.609531
26	0.878380	0.823434	0.772048	0.723984	0.679021	0.636950	0.597579
27	0.874010	0.817304	0.764404	0.715046	0.668986	0.625995	0.585862
28	0.869662	0.811220	0.756836	0.706219	0.659099	0.615228	0.574375
29	0.865335	0.805181	0.749342	0.697500	0.649359	0.604647	0.563112
30	0.861030	0.799187	0.741923	0.688889	0.639762	0.594248	0.552071
31	0.856746	0.793238	0.734577	0.680384	0.630308	0.584027	0.541246
32	0.852484	0.787333	0.727304	0.671984	0.620993	0.573982	0.530633
33	0.848242	0.781472	0.720103	0.663688	0.611816	0.564111	0.520229
34	0.844022	0.775654	0.712973	0.655494	0.602774	0.554408	0.510028
35	0.839823	0.769880	0.705914	0.647402	0.593866	0.544873	0.500028
36	0.835645	0.764149	0.698925	0.639409	0.585090	0.535502	0.490223
37	0.831487	0.758461	0.692005	0.631515	0.576443	0.526292	0.480611
38	0.827351	0.752814	0.685153	0.623719	0.567924	0.517240	0.471187
39	0.823235	0.747210	0.678370	0.616019	0.559531	0.508344	0.461948
40	0.819139	0.741648	0.671653	0.608413	0.551262	0.499601	0.452890
41	0.815064	0.736127	0.665003	0.600902	0.543116	0.491008	0.444010
42	0.811009	0.730647	0.658419	0.593484	0.535089	0.482563	0.435304
43	0.806974	0.725208	0.651900	0.586157	0.527182	0.474264	0.426769
44	0.802959	0.719810	0.645445	0.578920	0.519391	0.466107	0.418401
45	0.798964	0.714451	0.639055	0.571773	0.511715	0.458090	0.410197
46	0.794989	0.709133	0.632728	0.564714	0.504153	0.450212	0.402154
47	0.791034	0.703854	0.626463	0.557742	0.496702	0.442469	0.394268
48	0.787098	0.698614	0.620260	0.550856	0.489362	0.434858	0.386538
49	0.783128	0.693414	0.614199	0.544056	0.482130	0.427379	0.378958
50	0.779286	0.688252	0.608039	0.537339	0.475005	0.420029	0.371528

continues

TABLE 5 Present value $(1 + i)^{-n}$ (continued)

n	½%	¾%	1%	1¼%	1½%	1¾%	2%
51	0.775409	0.683128	0.602019	0.530705	0.467985	0.412805	0.364243
52	0.771551	0.678043	0.596058	0.524153	0.461069	0.405705	0.357101
53	0.767713	0.672995	0.590156	0.517682	0.454255	0.398727	0.350099
54	0.763893	0.667986	0.584313	0.511291	0.447542	0.391869	0.343234
55	0.760093	0.663013	0.578528	0.504979	0.440928	0.385130	0.336504
56	0.756311	0.658077	0.572800	0.498745	0.434412	0.378506	0.329906
57	0.752548	0.653178	0.567129	0.492587	0.427992	0.371996	0.323437
58	0.748804	0.648316	0.561514	0.486506	0.421667	0.365598	0.317095
59	0.745079	0.643490	0.555954	0.480500	0.415435	0.359310	0.310878
60	0.741372	0.638700	0.550450	0.474568	0.409296	0.353130	0.304782
61	0.737684	0.633945	0.545000	0.468709	0.403247	0.347057	0.298806
62	0.734014	0.629226	0.539604	0.462922	0.397288	0.341088	0.292947
63	0.730362	0.624542	0.534261	0.457207	0.391417	0.335221	0.287203
64	0.726728	0.619893	0.528971	0.451563	0.385632	0.329456	0.281572
65	0.723113	0.615278	0.523734	0.445988	0.379933	0.323790	0.276051
66	0.719515	0.610698	0.518548	0.440482	0.374318	0.318221	0.270638
67	0.715935	0.606152	0.513414	0.435044	0.368787	0.312748	0.265331
68	0.712374	0.601639	0.508331	0.429673	0.363337	0.307369	0.260129
69	0.708829	0.597161	0.503298	0.424368	0.357967	0.302082	0.255028
70	0.705303	0.592715	0.498315	0.419129	0.352677	0.296887	0.250028
71	0.701794	0.588303	0.493381	0.413955	0.347465	0.291781	0.245125
72	0.698302	0.583924	0.488496	0.408844	0.342330	0.286762	0.240319
73	0.694828	0.579577	0.483659	0.403797	0.337271	0.281830	0.235607
74	0.691371	0.575262	0.478871	0.398811	0.332287	0.276983	0.230987
75	0.687932	0.570980	0.474129	0.393888	0.327376	0.272219	0.226458
76	0.684509	0.566730	0.469435	0.389025	0.322538	0.267537	0.222017
77	0.681104	0.562511	0.464787	0.384222	0.317771	0.262936	0.217664
78	0.677715	0.558323	0.460185	0.379479	0.313075	0.258414	0.213396
79	0.674343	0.554167	0.455629	0.374794	0.308448	0.253969	0.209212
80	0.670988	0.550042	0.451118	0.370167	0.303890	0.249601	0.205110
81	0.667650	0.545947	0.446651	0.365597	0.299399	0.245308	0.201088
82	0.664329	0.541883	0.442229	0.361083	0.294975	0.241089	0.197145
83	0.661023	0.537849	0.437851	0.356625	0.290615	0.236943	0.193279
84	0.657735	0.533845	0.433515	0.352223	0.286321	0.232868	0.189490
85	0.654462	0.529871	0.429223	0.347874	0.282089	0.228862	0.185774
86	0.651206	0.525927	0.424974	0.343580	0.277920	0.224926	0.182132
87	0.647967	0.522012	0.420766	0.339338	0.273813	0.221058	0.178560
88	0.644743	0.518126	0.416600	0.335148	0.269767	0.217256	0.175059
89	0.641535	0.514269	0.412475	0.331011	0.265780	0.213519	0.171627
90	0.638344	0.510440	0.408391	0.326924	0.261852	0.209847	0.168261
91	0.635168	0.506641	0.404348	0.322888	0.257982	0.206238	0.164962
92	0.632008	0.502869	0.400344	0.318902	0.254170	0.202691	0.161728
93	0.628863	0.499126	0.396380	0.314965	0.250414	0.199204	0.158556
94	0.625735	0.495410	0.392456	0.311076	0.246713	0.195778	0.155448
95	0.622622	0.491722	0.388570	0.307236	0.243067	0.192411	0.152400
96	0.619524	0.488062	0.384723	0.303443	0.239475	0.189102	0.149411
97	0.616442	0.484428	0.380914	0.299697	0.235936	0.185850	0.146482
98	0.613375	0.480822	0.377142	0.295997	0.232449	0.182653	0.143609
99	0.610323	0.477243	0.373408	0.292342	0.229014	0.179512	0.140794
100	0.607287	0.473690	0.369711	0.288733	0.225629	0.176424	0.138033

TABLE 5 Present value $(1 + i)^{-n}$

n	3%	4%	5%	6%	7%	8%	9%
1	0.970874	0.961538	0.952381	0.943396	0.934579	0.925926	0.917431
2	0.942596	0.924556	0.907029	0.889996	0.873439	0.857339	0.841680
3	0.915142	0.888996	0.863838	0.839619	0.816298	0.793832	0.772183
4	0.888487	0.854804	0.822702	0.792094	0.762895	0.735030	0.708425
5	0.862609	0.821927	0.783526	0.747258	0.712986	0.680583	0.649931
6	0.837484	0.790315	0.746215	0.704961	0.666342	0.630170	0.596267
7	0.813092	0.759918	0.710681	0.665057	0.622750	0.583490	0.547034
8	0.789409	0.730690	0.676839	0.627412	0.582009	0.540269	0.501866
9	0.766417	0.702587	0.644609	0.591898	0.543934	0.500249	0.460428
10	0.744094	0.675564	0.613913	0.558395	0.508349	0.463193	0.422411
11	0.722421	0.649581	0.584679	0.526788	0.475093	0.428883	0.387533
12	0.701380	0.624597	0.556837	0.496969	0.444012	0.397114	0.355535
13	0.680951	0.600574	0.530321	0.468839	0.414964	0.367698	0.326179
14	0.661118	0.577475	0.505068	0.442301	0.387817	0.340461	0.299246
15	0.641862	0.555265	0.481017	0.417265	0.362446	0.315242	0.274538
16	0.623167	0.533908	0.458112	0.393646	0.338735	0.291890	0.251870
17	0.605016	0.513373	0.436297	0.371364	0.316574	0.270269	0.231073
18	0.587395	0.493628	0.415521	0.350344	0.295864	0.250249	0.211994
19	0.570286	0.474642	0.395734	0.330513	0.276508	0.231712	0.194490
20	0.553676	0.456387	0.376889	0.311805	0.258419	0.214548	0.178431
21	0.537549	0.438834	0.358942	0.294155	0.241513	0.198656	0.163698
22	0.521893	0.421955	0.341850	0.277505	0.225713	0.183941	0.150182
23	0.506692	0.405726	0.325571	0.261797	0.210947	0.170315	0.137781
24	0.491934	0.390121	0.310068	0.246979	0.197147	0.157699	0.126405
25	0.477606	0.375117	0.295303	0.232999	0.184249	0.146018	0.115968
26	0.463695	0.360689	0.281241	0.219810	0.172195	0.135202	0.106393
27	0.450189	0.346817	0.267848	0.207368	0.160930	0.125187	0.097608
28	0.437077	0.333477	0.255094	0.195630	0.150402	0.115914	0.089548
29	0.424346	0.320651	0.242946	0.184557	0.140563	0.107328	0.082155
30	0.411987	0.308319	0.231377	0.174110	0.131367	0.099377	0.075371
31	0.399987	0.296460	0.220359	0.164255	0.122773	0.092016	0.069148
32	0.388337	0.285058	0.209866	0.154957	0.114741	0.085200	0.063438
33	0.377026	0.274094	0.199873	0.146186	0.107235	0.078889	0.058200
34	0.366045	0.263552	0.190355	0.137912	0.100219	0.073045	0.053395
35	0.355383	0.253415	0.181290	0.130105	0.093663	0.067635	0.048986
36	0.345032	0.243669	0.172657	0.122741	0.087535	0.062625	0.044941
37	0.334983	0.234297	0.164436	0.115793	0.081809	0.057986	0.041231
38	0.325226	0.225285	0.156605	0.109239	0.076457	0.053690	0.037826
39	0.315754	0.216621	0.149148	0.103056	0.071455	0.049713	0.034703
40	0.306557	0.208289	0.142046	0.097222	0.066780	0.046031	0.031838
41	0.297628	0.200278	0.135282	0.091719	0.062412	0.042621	0.029209
42	0.288959	0.192575	0.128840	0.086527	0.058329	0.039464	0.026797
43	0.280543	0.185168	0.122704	0.081630	0.054513	0.036541	0.024584
44	0.272372	0.178046	0.116861	0.077009	0.050946	0.033834	0.022555
45	0.264439	0.171198	0.111297	0.072650	0.047613	0.031328	0.020692
46	0.256737	0.164614	0.105997	0.068538	0.044499	0.029007	0.018984
47	0.249259	0.158283	0.100949	0.064658	0.041587	0.026859	0.017416
48	0.241999	0.152195	0.096142	0.060998	0.038867	0.024869	0.015978
49	0.234950	0.146341	0.091564	0.057546	0.036324	0.023027	0.014659
50	0.228107	0.140713	0.087204	0.054288	0.033948	0.021321	0.013449

continues

TABLE 5 Present value $(1 + i)^{-n}$ (continued)

n	3%	4%	5%	6%	7%	8%	9%
51	0.221463	0.135301	0.083051	0.051215	0.031727	0.019742	0.012338
52	0.215013	0.130097	0.079096	0.048316	0.029651	0.018280	0.011319
53	0.208750	0.125093	0.075330	0.045582	0.027711	0.016925	0.010385
54	0.202670	0.120282	0.071743	0.043001	0.025899	0.015672	0.009527
55	0.196767	0.115656	0.068326	0.040567	0.024204	0.014511	0.008741
56	0.191036	0.111207	0.065073	0.038271	0.022621	0.013436	0.008019
57	0.185472	0.106930	0.061974	0.036105	0.021141	0.012441	0.007357
58	0.180070	0.102817	0.059023	0.034061	0.019758	0.011519	0.006749
59	0.174825	0.098863	0.056212	0.032133	0.018465	0.010666	0.006192
60	0.169733	0.095060	0.053536	0.030314	0.017257	0.009876	0.005681
61	0.164789	0.091404	0.050986	0.028598	0.016128	0.009144	0.005212
62	0.159990	0.087889	0.048558	0.026980	0.015073	0.008467	0.004781
63	0.155330	0.084508	0.046246	0.025453	0.014087	0.007840	0.004387
64	0.150806	0.081258	0.044044	0.024012	0.013166	0.007259	0.004024
65	0.146413	0.078133	0.041946	0.022653	0.012304	0.006721	0.003692
66	0.142149	0.075128	0.039949	0.021370	0.011499	0.006223	0.003387
67	0.138009	0.072238	0.038047	0.020161	0.010747	0.005762	0.003108
68	0.133989	0.069460	0.036235	0.019020	0.010044	0.005336	0.002851
69	0.130086	0.066788	0.034509	0.017943	0.009387	0.004940	0.002616
70	0.126297	0.064219	0.032866	0.016927	0.008773	0.004574	0.002400
71	0.122619	0.061749	0.031301	0.015969	0.008199	0.004236	0.002201
72	0.119047	0.059374	0.029811	0.015065	0.007662	0.003922	0.002020
73	0.115580	0.057091	0.028391	0.014213	0.007161	0.003631	0.001853
74	0.112214	0.054895	0.027039	0.013408	0.006693	0.003362	0.001700
75	0.108945	0.052784	0.025752	0.012649	0.006255	0.003113	0.001560
76	0.105772	0.050754	0.024525	0.011933	0.005846	0.002883	0.001431
77	0.102691	0.048801	0.023357	0.011258	0.005463	0.002669	0.001313
78	0.099700	0.046924	0.022245	0.010620	0.005106	0.002471	0.001204
79	0.096796	0.045120	0.021186	0.010019	0.004772	0.002288	0.001105
80	0.093977	0.043384	0.020177	0.009452	0.004460	0.002119	0.001014
81	0.091240	0.041716	0.019216	0.008917	0.004168	0.001962	0.000930
82	0.088582	0.040111	0.018301	0.008412	0.003895	0.001817	0.000853
83	0.086002	0.038569	0.017430	0.007936	0.003640	0.001682	0.000783
84	0.083497	0.037085	0.016600	0.007487	0.003402	0.001557	0.000718
85	0.081065	0.035659	0.015809	0.007063	0.003180	0.001442	0.000659
86	0.078704	0.034287	0.015056	0.006663	0.002972	0.001335	0.000604
87	0.076412	0.032969	0.014339	0.006286	0.002777	0.001236	0.000554
88	0.074186	0.031701	0.013657	0.005930	0.002596	0.001145	0.000509
89	0.072026	0.030481	0.013006	0.005595	0.002426	0.001060	0.000467
90	0.069928	0.029309	0.012387	0.005278	0.002267	0.000981	0.000428
91	0.067891	0.028182	0.011797	0.004979	0.002119	0.000909	0.000393
92	0.065914	0.027098	0.011235	0.004697	0.001980	0.000841	0.000360
93	0.063994	0.026056	0.010700	0.004432	0.001851	0.000779	0.000331
94	0.062130	0.025053	0.010191	0.004181	0.001730	0.000721	0.000303
95	0.060320	0.024090	0.009705	0.003944	0.001616	0.000668	0.000278
96	0.058563	0.023163	0.009243	0.003721	0.001511	0.000618	0.000255
97	0.056858	0.022272	0.008803	0.003510	0.001412	0.000573	0.000234
98	0.055202	0.021416	0.008384	0.003312	0.001319	0.000530	0.000215
99	0.053594	0.020592	0.007985	0.003124	0.001233	0.000491	0.000197
100	0.052033	0.019800	0.007604	0.002947	0.001152	0.000455	0.000181

TABLE 5 Present value $(1 + i)^{-n}$

n	10%	11%	12%	13%	14%	15%	16%
1	0.909091	0.900901	0.892857	0.884956	0.877193	0.869565	0.862069
2	0.826446	0.811622	0.797194	0.783147	0.769468	0.756144	0.743163
3	0.751315	0.731191	0.711780	0.693050	0.674972	0.657516	0.640658
4	0.683013	0.658731	0.635518	0.613319	0.592080	0.571753	0.552291
5	0.620921	0.593451	0.567427	0.542760	0.519369	0.497177	0.476113
6	0.564474	0.534641	0.506631	0.480319	0.455587	0.432328	0.410442
7	0.513158	0.481658	0.452349	0.425061	0.399637	0.375937	0.353830
8	0.466507	0.433926	0.403883	0.376160	0.350559	0.326902	0.305025
9	0.424098	0.390925	0.360610	0.332885	0.307508	0.284262	0.262953
10	0.385543	0.352184	0.321973	0.294588	0.269744	0.247185	0.226684
11	0.350494	0.317283	0.287476	0.260698	0.236617	0.214943	0.195417
12	0.318631	0.285841	0.256675	0.230706	0.207559	0.186907	0.168463
13	0.289664	0.257514	0.229174	0.204165	0.182069	0.162528	0.145227
14	0.263331	0.231995	0.204620	0.180677	0.159710	0.141329	0.125195
15	0.239392	0.209004	0.182696	0.159891	0.140096	0.122894	0.107927
16	0.217629	0.188292	0.163122	0.141496	0.122892	0.106865	0.093041
17	0.197845	0.169633	0.145644	0.125218	0.107800	0.092926	0.080207
18	0.179859	0.152822	0.130040	0.110812	0.094561	0.080805	0.069144
19	0.163508	0.137678	0.116107	0.098064	0.082948	0.070265	0.059607
20	0.148644	0.124034	0.103667	0.086782	0.072762	0.061100	0.051385
21	0.135131	0.111742	0.092560	0.076798	0.063826	0.053131	0.044298
22	0.122846	0.100669	0.082643	0.067963	0.055988	0.046201	0.038188
23	0.111678	0.090693	0.073788	0.060144	0.049112	0.040174	0.032920
24	0.101526	0.081705	0.065882	0.053225	0.043081	0.034934	0.028380
25	0.092296	0.073608	0.058823	0.047102	0.037790	0.030378	0.024465
26	0.083905	0.066314	0.052521	0.041683	0.033149	0.26415	0.021091
27	0.076278	0.059742	0.046894	0.036888	0.029078	0.022970	0.018182
28	0.069343	0.053822	0.041869	0.032644	0.025507	0.019974	0.015674
29	0.063039	0.048488	0.037383	0.028889	0.022375	0.017369	0.013512
30	0.057309	0.043683	0.033378	0.025565	0.019627	0.015103	0.011648
31	0.052099	0.039354	0.029802	0.022624	0.017217	0.013133	0.010042
32	0.047362	0.035454	0.026609	0.020021	0.015102	0.011420	0.008657
33	0.043057	0.031940	0.023758	0.017718	0.013248	0.009931	0.007463
34	0.039143	0.028775	0.021212	0.015680	0.011621	0.008635	0.006433
35	0.035584	0.025924	0.018940	0.013876	0.010194	0.007509	0.005546
36	0.032349	0.023355	0.016910	0.012279	0.008942	0.006529	0.004781
37	0.029408	0.021040	0.015098	0.010867	0.007844	0.005678	0.004121
38	0.026735	0.018955	0.013481	0.009617	0.006880	0.004937	0.003553
39	0.024304	0.017077	0.012036	0.008510	0.006035	0.004293	0.003063
40	0.022095	0.015384	0.010747	0.007531	0.005294	0.003733	0.002640
41	0.020086	0.013860	0.009595	0.006665	0.004644	0.003246	0.002276
42	0.018260	0.012486	0.008567	0.005898	0.004074	0.002823	0.001962
43	0.016600	0.011249	0.007649	0.005219	0.003573	0.002455	0.001692
44	0.015091	0.010134	0.006830	0.004619	0.003135	0.002134	0.001458
45	0.013719	0.009130	0.006098	0.004088	0.002750	0.001856	0.001257
46	0.012472	0.008225	0.005445	0.003617	0.002412	0.001614	0.001084
47	0.011338	0.007410	0.004861	0.003201	0.002116	0.001403	0.000934
48	0.010307	0.006676	0.004340	0.002833	0.001856	0.001220	0.000805
49	0.009370	0.006014	0.003875	0.002507	0.001628	0.001061	0.000694
50	0.008519	0.005418	0.003460	0.002219	0.001428	0.000923	0.000599

TABLE 6 Amount of an annuity $s_{\overline{n}|i} = \dfrac{(1 + i)^n - 1}{i}$

n	½%	¾%	1%	1¼%	1½%	1¾%	2%
1	1.000000	1.000000	1.000000	1.000000	1.000000	1.000000	1.000000
2	2.005000	2.007500	2.010000	2.012500	2.015000	2.017500	2.020000
3	3.015025	3.022556	3.030100	3.037656	3.045225	3.052806	0.060400
4	4.030100	4.045225	4.060401	4.075627	4.090903	4.106230	4.121608
5	5.050251	5.075565	5.101005	5.126572	5.152267	5.178089	5.204040
6	6.075502	6.113631	6.152015	6.190654	6.229551	6.268706	6.308121
7	7.105879	7.159484	7.213535	7.268038	7.322994	7.378408	7.434283
8	8.141409	8.213180	8.285671	8.358888	8.432839	8.507530	8.582969
9	9.182116	9.274779	9.368527	9.463374	9.559332	9.656412	9.754628
10	10.228026	10.344339	10.462213	10.581666	10.702722	10.825399	10.949721
11	11.279167	11.421922	11.566835	11.713937	11.863262	12.014844	12.168715
12	12.335562	12.507586	12.682503	12.860361	13.041211	13.225104	13.412090
13	13.397240	13.601393	13.809328	14.021116	14.236830	14.456543	14.680332
14	14.464226	14.703404	14.947421	15.196380	15.450382	15.709533	15.973938
15	15.536548	15.813679	16.096896	16.386335	16.682138	16.984449	17.293417
16	16.614230	16.932282	17.257864	17.591164	17.932370	18.281677	18.639285
17	17.697301	18.059274	18.430443	18.811053	19.201355	19.601607	20.012071
18	18.785788	19.194718	19.614748	20.046192	20.489376	20.944635	21.412312
19	19.879717	20.338679	20.810895	21.296769	21.796716	22.311166	22.840559
20	20.979115	21.491219	22.019004	22.562979	23.123667	23.701611	24.297370
21	22.084011	22.652403	23.239194	23.845016	24.470522	25.116389	25.783317
22	23.194431	23.822296	24.471586	25.143078	25.837580	26.555926	27.298984
23	24.310403	25.000963	25.716302	26.457367	27.225144	28.020655	28.844963
24	25.431955	26.188471	26.973465	27.788084	28.633521	29.511016	30.421862
25	26.559115	27.384884	28.243200	29.135435	30.063024	31.027459	32.030300
26	27.691911	28.590271	29.525631	30.499628	31.513969	32.570440	33.670906
27	28.830370	29.804698	30.820888	31.880873	32.986678	34.140422	35.344324
28	29.974522	31.028233	32.129097	33.279384	34.481479	35.737880	37.051210
29	31.124395	32.260945	33.450388	34.695377	35.998701	37.363293	38.792235
30	32.280017	33.502902	34.784892	36.129069	37.538681	39.017150	40.568079
31	33.441417	34.754174	36.132740	37.580682	39.101762	40.699950	42.379441
32	34.608624	36.014830	37.494068	39.050441	40.688288	42.412200	44.227030
33	35.781667	37.284941	38.869009	40.538571	42.298612	44.154413	46.111570
34	36.960575	38.564578	40.257699	42.045303	43.933092	45.927115	48.033802
35	38.145378	39.853813	41.660276	43.570870	45.592088	47.730840	49.994478
36	39.336105	41.152716	43.076878	45.115505	47.275969	49.566129	51.994367
37	40.532785	42.461361	44.507647	46.679449	48.985109	51.433537	54.034255
38	41.735449	43.779822	45.952724	48.262942	50.719885	53.333624	56.114940
39	42.944127	45.108170	47.412251	49.866229	52.480684	55.266962	58.237238
40	44.158847	46.446482	48.886373	51.489557	54.267894	57.234134	60.401983
41	45.379642	47.794830	50.375237	53.133177	56.081912	59.235731	62.610023
42	46.606540	49.153291	51.878989	54.797341	57.923141	61.272357	64.862223
43	47.839572	50.521941	53.397779	56.482308	59.791988	63.344623	67.159468
44	49.078770	51.900856	54.931757	58.188337	61.688868	65.453154	69.502657
45	50.324164	53.290112	56.481075	59.915691	63.614201	67.598584	71.892710
46	51.575785	54.689788	58.045885	61.664637	65.568414	69.781559	74.330564
47	52.833664	56.099961	59.626344	63.435445	67.551940	72.002736	76.817176

continues

TABLE 6 Amount of an annuity $s_{\overline{n}|i} = \dfrac{(1 + i)^n - 1}{i}$ *(continued)*

n	½%	¾%	1%	1¼%	1½%	1¾%	2%
48	54.097832	57.520711	61.222608	65.228388	69.565219	74.262784	79.353519
49	55.368321	58.952116	62.834834	67.043743	71.608698	76.562383	81.940490
50	56.645163	60.394257	64.463182	68.881790	73.682828	78.902225	84.579401
51	57.928389	61.847214	66.107814	70.742812	75.788070	81.283014	87.270989
52	59.218031	63.311068	67.768892	72.627097	77.924892	83.705466	90.016409
53	60.514121	64.785901	69.446581	74.534936	80.093765	86.170312	92.816737
54	61.816692	66.271796	71.141047	76.466623	82.295171	88.678292	95.673072
55	63.125775	67.768834	72.852457	78.422456	84.529599	91.230163	98.586534
56	64.441404	69.277100	74.580982	80.402736	86.797543	93.826690	101.558264
57	65.763611	70.796679	76.326792	82.407771	89.099506	96.468658	104.589430
58	67.092429	72.327654	78.090060	84.437868	91.435999	99.156859	107.681218
59	68.427891	73.870111	79.870960	86.493341	93.807539	101.892104	110.834843
60	69.770031	75.424137	81.669670	88.574508	96.214652	104.675216	114.051539
61	71.118881	76.989818	83.486367	90.681689	98.657871	107.507032	117.332570
62	72.474475	78.567242	85.321280	92.815210	101.137740	110.388405	120.679222
63	73.836847	80.156496	87.174443	94.975400	103.654806	113.320202	124.092806
64	75.206032	81.757670	89.046187	97.162593	106.209628	116.303306	127.574662
65	76.582062	83.370852	90.936649	99.377125	108.802772	119.338614	131.126155
66	77.964972	84.996134	92.846015	101.619339	111.434814	122.427039	134.748679
67	79.354797	86.633605	94.774475	103.889581	114.106336	125.659513	138.443652
68	80.751571	88.283357	96.722220	106.188201	116.817931	128.766979	142.212525
69	82.155329	89.945482	98.689442	108.515553	119.570200	132.020401	146.056776
70	83.566105	91.620073	100.676337	110.871998	122.363753	135.330758	149.977911
71	84.983936	93.307223	102.683100	113.257898	125.199209	138.699047	153.977469
72	86.408856	95.007028	104.709931	115.673621	128.077197	142.126280	158.057019
73	87.840900	96.719580	106.757031	118.119542	130.998355	145.613490	162.218159
74	89.280104	98.444977	108.824601	120.596036	133.963331	149.161726	166.462522
75	90.726505	100.183314	110.912847	123.103486	136.972781	152.772056	170.791773
76	92.180138	101.934689	113.021975	125.642280	140.027372	156.445567	175.207608
77	93.641038	103.699199	115.152195	128.212809	143.127783	160.183364	179.711760
78	95.109243	105.476943	117.303717	130.815469	146.274700	163.986573	184.305996
79	95.584790	107.268021	119.476754	133.450662	149.468820	167.856338	188.992115
80	98.067714	109.072531	121.671522	136.118795	152.710852	171.793824	193.771958
81	99.558052	110.890575	123.888237	138.820280	156.001515	175.800216	198.647397
82	101.055842	112.722254	126.127119	141.555534	159.341538	179.876720	203.620345
83	102.561122	114.567671	128.388390	144.324978	162.731661	184.024563	208.692752
84	104.073927	116.426928	130.672274	147.129040	166.172636	188.244992	213.866607
85	105.594297	118.300130	132.978997	149.968153	169.665226	192.539280	219.143939
86	107.122268	120.187381	135.308787	152.842755	173.210204	196.908717	224.526818
87	108.657880	122.088787	137.661875	155.753289	176.808357	201.354620	230.017354
88	110.201169	124.004453	140.038494	158.700206	180.460482	205.878326	235.617701
89	111.752175	125.934486	142.438879	161.683958	184.167390	210.481196	241.330055
90	113.310936	127.878995	144.863267	164.705008	187.929900	215.164617	247.156656
91	114.877490	129.838087	147.311900	167.763820	191.748849	219.929998	253.099789
92	116.451878	131.811873	149.785019	170.860868	195.625082	224.778773	259.161785
93	118.034137	133.800462	152.282869	173.996629	199.559458	229.712401	265.345021
94	119.624308	135.803965	154.805698	177.171587	203.552850	234.732369	271.651921

continues

TABLE 6 Amount of an annuity $s_{\overline{n}|i} = \dfrac{(1 + i)^n - 1}{i}$ (continued)

n	½%	¾%	1%	1¼%	1½%	1¾%	2%
95	121.222430	137.822495	157.353755	180.386232	207.606142	239.840185	278.084960
96	122.828542	139.856164	159.927293	183.641059	211.720235	245.037388	284.646659
97	124.442684	141.905085	162.526565	186.936573	215.896038	250.325542	291.339592
98	126.064898	143.969373	165.151831	190.273280	220.134479	255.706239	298.166384
99	127.695222	146.049143	167.803349	193.651696	224.436496	261.181099	305.129712
100	129.333698	148.144512	170.481383	197.072342	228.803043	266.751768	312.232306

TABLE 6 Amount of an annuity $s_{\overline{n}|i} = \dfrac{(1 + i)^n - 1}{i}$

n	3%	4%	5%	6%	7%	8%	9%
1	1.000000	1.000000	1.000000	1.000000	1.000000	1.000000	1.000000
2	2.030000	2.040000	2.050000	2.060000	2.070000	2.080000	2.090000
3	3.090900	3.121600	3.152500	3.183600	3.214900	3.246400	3.278100
4	4.183627	4.246464	4.310125	4.374616	4.439943	4.506112	4.573129
5	5.309136	5.416323	5.525631	5.637093	5.750739	5.866601	5.984711
6	6.468410	6.632975	6.801913	6.975319	7.153291	7.335929	7.523335
7	7.662462	7.898294	8.142008	8.393838	8.654021	8.922803	9.200435
8	8.892336	9.214226	9.549109	9.897468	10.259803	10.636628	11.028474
9	10.159106	10.582795	11.026564	11.491316	11.977989	12.487558	13.021036
10	11.463879	12.006107	12.577893	13.180795	13.816448	14.486562	15.192930
11	12.807796	13.486351	14.206787	14.971643	15.783599	16.645487	17.560293
12	14.192030	15.025805	15.917127	16.869941	17.888451	18.977126	20.140720
13	15.617790	16.626838	17.712983	18.882138	20.140643	21.495297	22.953385
14	17.086324	18.291911	19.598632	21.015066	22.550488	24.214920	26.019189
15	18.598914	20.023588	21.578564	23.275970	25.129022	27.152114	29.360916
16	20.156881	21.824531	23.657492	25.672528	27.888054	30.324483	33.003399
17	21.761588	23.697512	25.840366	28.212880	30.840217	33.750226	36.973705
18	23.414435	25.645413	28.132385	30.905653	33.999033	37.450244	41.301338
19	25.116868	27.671229	30.539004	33.759992	37.378965	41.446263	46.018458
20	26.870374	29.778079	33.065954	36.785591	40.995492	45.761964	51.160120
21	28.676486	31.969202	35.719252	39.992727	44.865177	50.422921	56.764530
22	30.536780	34.247970	38.505214	43.392290	49.005739	55.456755	62.873338
23	32.452884	36.617889	41.430475	46.995828	53.436141	60.893296	69.531939
24	34.426470	39.082604	44.501999	50.815577	58.176671	66.764759	76.789813
25	36.459264	41.645908	47.727099	54.864512	63.249038	73.105940	84.700896
26	38.553042	44.311745	51.113454	59.156383	68.676470	79.954415	93.323977
27	40.709634	47.084214	54.669126	63.705766	74.483823	87.350768	102.723135
28	42.930923	49.967583	58.402583	68.528112	80.697691	95.338830	112.968217
29	45.218850	52.966286	62.322712	73.639798	87.346529	103.965936	124.135356
30	47.575416	56.084938	66.438848	79.058186	94.460786	113.283211	136.307539
31	50.002678	59.328335	70.760790	84.801677	102.073041	123.345868	149.575217
32	52.502759	62.701469	75.298829	80.889778	110.218154	134.213537	164.036987
33	55.077841	66.209527	80.063771	97.343165	118.933425	145.950620	179.800315
34	57.530177	69.857909	85.066959	104.183755	128.258765	158.626670	196.982344
35	60.462082	73.652225	90.320307	111.434780	138.236878	172.316804	215.710755

continues

TABLE 6 Amount of an annuity $s_{\overline{n}|i} = \dfrac{(1+i)^n - 1}{i}$ (continued)

n	3%	4%	5%	6%	7%	8%	9%
36	63.275944	77.598314	95.836323	119.120867	148.913460	187.102148	236.124723
37	66.174223	81.702246	101.628139	127.268119	160.337402	203.070320	258.375948
38	69.159449	85.970336	107.709546	135.904206	172.561020	220.315945	282.629783
39	72.234233	90.409150	114.095023	145.058458	185.640292	238.941221	309.066463
40	75.401260	95.025516	120.799774	154.761966	199.635112	259.056519	337.882445
41	78.663298	99.826536	127.839763	165.047684	214.609570	280.781040	369.291865
42	82.023196	104.819598	135.231751	175.950545	230.632240	304.243523	403.528133
43	85.483892	110.012382	142.993339	187.507577	247.776496	329.583005	440.845665
44	89.048409	115.412877	151.143006	199.758032	266.120851	356.949646	481.521775
45	92.719861	121.029392	159.700156	212.743514	285.749311	386.505617	525.858734
46	96.501457	126.870568	168.685164	226.508125	306.751763	418.426067	574.186021
47	100.396501	132.945390	178.119422	241.098612	329.224386	452.900152	626.862762
48	104.408396	139.263206	188.025393	256.564529	353.270093	490.132164	684.280411
49	108.540648	145.833734	198.426663	272.958401	378.999000	530.342737	746.865648
50	112.796867	152.667084	209.347996	290.335905	406.528929	573.770156	815.083556

TABLE 6 Amount of an annuity $s_{\overline{n}|i} = \dfrac{(1+i)^n - 1}{i}$

n	10%	11%	12%	13%	14%	15%
1	1.000000	1.000000	1.000000	1.000000	1.000000	1.000000
2	2.100000	2.110000	2.120000	2.130000	2.140000	2.150000
3	3.310000	3.342100	3.374400	3.406900	3.439600	3.472500
4	4.641000	4.709731	4.779328	4.849797	4.921144	4.993375
5	6.105100	6.227801	6.352847	6.480271	6.610104	6.742381
6	7.715610	7.912860	8.115189	8.322706	8.535519	8.753738
7	9.487171	9.732274	10.089012	10.404658	10.730491	11.066799
8	11.435888	11.859434	12.299693	12.757263	13.232760	13.726819
9	13.579477	14.163972	14.775656	15.415707	16.805347	16.785842
10	15.937425	16.722009	17.548735	18.419749	19.337295	20.303718
11	18.531167	19.561430	20.654583	21.814317	23.044516	24.349276
12	21.384284	22.713187	24.133133	25.650178	27.270749	29.001667
13	24.522712	26.211638	28.029109	29.984701	32.088654	34.351917
14	27.974983	30.094918	32.392602	34.882712	37.581065	40.504705
15	31.772482	34.405359	37.279715	40.417464	43.842414	47.580411
16	35.949730	39.189948	42.753280	46.671735	50.980352	55.717472
17	40.544703	44.500843	48.883674	53.739060	59.117601	65.075093
18	45.599173	50.395936	55.749715	61.725138	68.394066	75.836357
19	51.159090	56.939488	63.439681	70.749406	78.969235	88.211811
20	57.274999	64.202832	72.052442	80.946829	91.024928	102.443583
21	64.002499	72.265144	81.698736	92.469917	104.768418	118.810120
22	71.402749	81.214309	92.502584	105.491006	120.435996	137.631638
23	79.543024	91.147884	104.602894	120.204837	138.297035	159.276384
24	88.497327	102.174151	118.155241	136.831465	158.658620	184.167841
25	98.347059	114.413307	133.333870	155.619556	181.870827	212.793017

continues

TABLE 6   Amount of an annuity $s_{\overline{n}|i} = \dfrac{(1+i)^n - 1}{i}$ *(continued)*

n	10%	11%	12%	13%	14%	15%
26	109.181765	127.998771	150.333934	176.850098	208.332743	245.711970
27	121.099942	143.078636	169.374007	200.840611	238.499327	283.568766
28	134.209936	159.817286	190.698887	227.949890	272.889233	327.104080
29	148.630930	178.397187	214.582754	258.583376	312.093725	377.169693
30	164.494023	199.020878	241.332684	293.199215	356.786847	434.745146
31	181.943425	221.913174	271.292606	332.315113	407.737006	500.956918
32	201.137767	247.323624	304.847719	376.516078	465.820186	577.100456
33	222.251544	275.529222	342.429446	426.463168	532.035012	664.665524
34	245.476699	306.837437	384.520979	482.903380	607.519914	765.365353
35	271.024368	341.589555	431.663496	546.680819	693.572702	881.170156
36	299.126805	380.164406	484.463116	618.749325	791.672881	1014.345680
37	330.039486	422.982490	543.598690	700.186738	903.507084	1167.497532
38	364.043434	470.510564	609.830533	792.211014	1030.998076	1343.622161
39	401.447778	523.266726	684.010197	896.198445	1176.337806	1546.165485
40	442.592556	581.826066	767.091420	1013.704243	1342.025099	1779.090308
41	487.851811	646.826934	860.142391	1146.485795	1530.908613	2046.953854
42	537.636992	718.977896	964.359478	1296.528948	1746.235819	2354.996933
43	592.400692	799.065465	1081.082615	1466.077712	1991.708833	2709.246473
44	652.640761	887.962666	1211.812529	1657.667814	2271.548070	3116.633443
45	718.904837	986.638559	1358.230032	1874.164630	2590.564800	3585.128460
46	791.795321	1096.168801	1522.217636	2118.806032	2954.243872	4123.897729
47	871.974853	1217.747369	1705.883752	2395.250816	3368.838014	4743.482388
48	960.172338	1352.699580	1911.589803	2707.633422	3841.475336	5456.004746
49	1057.189572	1502.496533	2141.980579	3060.625767	4380.281883	6275.405458
50	1163.908529	1668.771152	2400.018249	3459.507117	4994.521346	7217.716277

TABLE 7   Present value of an annuity $a_{\overline{n}|i} = \dfrac{1 - (1+i)^{-n}}{i}$

n	½%	¾%	1%	1¼%	1½%	1¾%	2%
1	0.995025	0.992556	0.990099	0.987654	0.985222	0.982801	0.980392
2	1.985099	1.977723	1.970395	1.963115	1.955883	1.948699	1.941561
3	2.970248	2.955556	2.940985	2.926534	2.912200	2.897984	2.883883
4	3.950496	3.926110	3.901966	3.878058	3.854385	3.830943	3.807729
5	4.925866	4.889440	4.853431	4.817835	4.782645	4.747855	4.713460
6	5.896384	5.845598	5.795476	5.746010	5.697187	5.688998	5.601431
7	6.862074	6.794638	6.728195	6.662726	6.598214	6.534641	6.471991
8	7.822959	7.736613	7.651678	7.568124	7.485925	7.405053	7.325481
9	8.779064	8.671576	8.566018	8.462345	8.360517	8.260494	8.162237
10	9.730412	9.599580	9.471305	9.345526	9.222185	9.101223	8.982585
11	10.677027	10.520675	10.367628	10.217803	10.071118	9.927492	9.786848
12	11.618932	11.434913	11.255077	11.079312	10.907505	10.739550	10.575341
13	12.556151	12.342345	12.133740	11.930185	11.731532	11.537641	11.348374
14	13.488708	13.243022	13.003703	12.770553	12.543382	12.322006	12.106249
15	14.416625	14.136995	13.865053	13.600546	13.343233	13.092880	12.849264
16	15.339925	15.024313	14.717874	14.420292	14.131264	13.850497	13.577709

continues

TABLE 7 Present value of an annuity $a_{\overline{n}|i} = \dfrac{1 - (1 + i)^{-n}}{i}$ (continued)

n	½%	¾%	1%	1¼%	1½%	1¾%	2%
17	16.258632	15.905025	15.562251	15.229918	14.907649	14.595083	14.291872
18	17.172768	16.779181	16.398269	16.029549	15.672561	15.326863	14.992031
19	18.082356	17.646830	17.226008	16.819308	16.426168	16.046057	15.678462
20	18.987419	18.508020	18.045553	17.599316	17.168639	16.752881	16.351433
21	19.887979	19.362799	18.856983	18.369695	17.900137	17.447549	17.011209
22	20.784059	20.211215	19.660379	19.130563	18.620824	18.130269	17.658048
23	21.675681	21.053315	20.455821	19.882037	19.330861	18.801248	18.292204
24	22.562866	21.889146	21.243387	20.624235	20.030405	19.460686	18.913926
25	23.445638	22.718755	22.023156	21.357269	20.719611	20.108782	19.523456
26	24.324018	23.542189	22.795204	22.081253	21.398632	20.745732	20.121036
27	25.198028	24.359493	23.559608	22.796299	22.067617	21.371726	20.706898
28	26.067689	25.170713	24.316443	23.502518	22.726717	21.986955	21.281272
29	26.933024	25.975893	25.065785	24.200018	23.376076	22.591602	21.844385
30	27.794054	26.775080	25.807708	24.888906	24.015838	23.185849	22.396456
31	28.650800	27.568318	26.542285	25.569290	24.646146	23.769877	22.937702
32	29.503284	28.355650	27.269589	26.241274	25.267139	24.343859	23.468335
33	30.351526	29.137122	27.989693	26.904962	25.878954	24.907970	23.988564
34	31.195548	29.912776	28.702666	27.560456	26.481728	25.462378	24.498592
35	32.035371	30.682656	29.408580	28.207858	27.075595	26.007251	24.998619
36	32.871016	31.446805	30.107505	28.847267	27.660684	26.542753	25.488842
37	33.702504	32.205266	30.799510	29.478783	28.237127	27.069045	25.969453
38	34.529854	32.958080	31.484663	30.102501	28.805052	27.586285	26.440641
39	35.353089	33.705290	32.163033	30.718520	29.364583	28.094629	26.902589
40	36.172228	34.446938	32.834686	31.326933	29.915845	28.594230	27.355479
41	36.987291	35.183065	33.499689	31.927835	30.458961	29.085238	27.799489
42	37.798300	35.913713	34.158108	32.521319	30.994050	29.567801	28.234794
43	38.605274	36.638921	34.810008	33.017475	31.521232	30.042065	28.661562
44	39.408232	37.358730	35.455454	33.686395	32.040622	30.508172	29.079963
45	40.207196	38.073181	36.094508	34.258168	32.552337	30.966263	29.490160
46	41.002185	38.782314	36.727236	34.822882	33.056490	31.416474	29.892314
47	41.793219	39.486168	37.353699	35.380624	33.553192	31.858943	30.286582
48	42.580318	40.184782	37.973959	35.931481	34.042554	32.293801	30.673120
49	43.363500	40.878195	38.588079	36.475537	34.524683	32.721181	31.052078
50	44.142786	41.566447	39.196118	37.012876	34.999688	33.141209	31.423606
51	44.918195	42.249575	39.798136	37.543581	35.467673	33.554014	31.787849
52	45.689747	42.927618	40.394194	38.067734	35.928742	33.959719	32.144950
53	46.457459	43.600614	40.984351	38.585417	36.382997	34.358446	32.495049
54	47.221353	44.268599	41.568664	39.096708	36.830539	34.750316	32.838283
55	47.981445	44.931612	42.147192	39.601687	37.271467	35.135445	33.174788
56	48.737757	45.589689	42.719992	40.100431	37.705879	35.513951	33.504694
57	49.490305	46.242868	43.287121	40.593019	38.133871	35.885947	33.828131
58	50.239109	46.891184	43.848635	41.079524	38.555538	36.251545	34.145226
59	50.984189	47.534674	44.404589	41.560024	38.970973	36.610855	34.456104
60	51.725561	48.173374	44.955038	42.034592	39.380269	36.963986	34.760887
61	52.463245	48.807319	45.500038	42.503301	39.783516	37.311042	35.059693
62	53.197258	49.436545	46.039642	42.966223	40.180804	37.652130	35.352640
63	53.927620	50.061086	46.573903	43.423430	40.572221	37.987351	35.639843
64	54.654348	50.680979	47.102874	43.874992	40.957853	38.316807	35.921415

continues

TABLE 7   Present value of an annuity $a_{\overline{n}|i} = \dfrac{1 - (1 + i)^{-n}}{i}$ (continued)

n	½%	¾%	1%	1¼%	1½%	1¾%	2%
65	55.377461	51.296257	47.626608	44.320980	41.337786	38.640597	36.197466
66	56.096976	51.906955	48.145156	44.761462	41.712105	38.958817	36.468103
67	56.812912	52.513107	48.658571	45.196506	42.080891	39.271565	36.733435
68	57.525285	53.114746	49.166901	45.626178	42.444228	39.578934	36.993564
69	58.234115	53.711907	49.670199	46.050547	42.802195	39.881016	37.248592
70	58.939418	54.304622	50.168514	46.469676	43.154872	40.177903	37.498619
71	59.641212	54.892925	50.661895	46.883630	43.502337	40.469683	37.743744
72	60.339514	55.476849	51.150391	47.292474	43.844667	40.756445	37.984063
73	61.034342	56.056426	51.634051	47.696271	44.181938	41.038276	38.219670
74	61.725714	56.631688	52.112922	48.095082	44.514224	41.315259	38.450657
75	62.413645	57.202668	52.587051	48.488970	44.841600	41.587478	38.677114
76	63.098155	57.769397	53.056486	48.877995	45.164138	41.855015	38.899132
77	63.779258	58.331908	53.521274	49.262218	45.481910	42.117951	39.116796
78	64.456973	58.890231	53.981459	49.641696	45.794985	42.376364	39.330192
79	65.131317	59.444398	54.437088	50.016490	46.103433	42.630334	39.539404
80	65.802305	59.994440	54.888206	50.386657	46.407323	42.879935	39.744514
81	66.469956	60.540387	55.334858	50.752254	46.706723	43.125243	39.945602
82	67.134284	61.082270	55.777087	51.113337	47.001697	43.366332	40.142747
83	67.795308	61.620119	56.214937	51.469963	47.292313	43.603275	40.336026
84	68.453042	62.153965	56.648453	51.822185	47.578633	43.836142	40.525516
85	69.107505	62.683836	57.077676	52.170060	47.860722	44.065005	40.711290
86	69.758711	63.209763	57.502650	52.513639	48.138643	44.289931	40.893422
87	70.406678	63.731774	57.923415	52.852977	48.412456	44.510989	41.071982
88	71.051421	64.249900	58.340015	53.188125	48.682222	44.728244	41.247041
89	71.692956	64.764169	58.752490	53.519136	48.948002	44.941764	41.418668
90	72.331300	65.274609	59.160881	53.846060	49.209855	45.151610	41.586929
91	72.966467	65.781250	59.565229	54.168948	49.467837	45.357848	41.751891
92	73.598475	66.284119	59.965573	54.487850	49.722007	45.560539	41.913619
93	74.227338	66.783245	60.361954	54.802815	49.972421	45.759743	42.072175
94	74.853073	67.278655	60.754410	55.113892	50.219134	45.955521	42.227623
95	75.475694	67.770377	61.142980	55.421127	50.462201	46.147933	42.380023
96	76.095218	68.258439	61.527703	55.724570	50.701675	46.337035	42.529434
97	76.711660	68.742867	61.908617	56.024267	50.937611	46.522884	42.675916
98	77.325035	69.223689	62.285759	56.320264	51.170060	46.705537	42.819525
99	77.935358	69.700932	62.659168	56.612606	51.399074	46.885049	42.960319
100	78.542645	70.174623	63.028879	56.901339	51.624704	47.061473	43.098352

TABLE 7   Present value of an annuity $a_{\overline{n}|i} = \dfrac{1 - (1 + i)^{-n}}{i}$

n	3%	4%	5%	6%	7%	8%	9%
1	0.970874	0.961538	0.952381	0.943396	0.934579	0.925926	0.917431
2	1.913470	1.886095	1.859410	1.833393	1.808018	1.783265	1.759111
3	2.828611	2.775091	2.723248	2.673012	2.624316	2.577097	2.531295
4	3.717098	3.629895	3.545951	3.465106	3.387211	3.312127	3.239720

continues

TABLE 7 Present value of an annuity $a_{\overline{n}|i} = \dfrac{1 - (1 + i)^{-n}}{i}$ (continued)

n	3%	4%	5%	6%	7%	8%	9%
5	4.579707	4.451822	4.329477	4.212364	4.100197	3.992710	3.889651
6	5.417191	5.242137	5.075692	4.917324	4.766540	4.622880	4.485919
7	6.230283	6.002055	5.786373	5.582381	5.389289	5.206370	5.032953
8	7.019692	6.732745	6.463213	6.209794	5.971299	5.746639	5.534819
9	7.786109	7.435332	7.107822	6.801692	6.515232	6.246888	5.995247
10	8.530203	8.110896	7.721735	7.360087	7.023582	6.710081	6.417658
11	9.252624	8.760477	8.306414	7.886875	7.498674	7.138964	6.805191
12	9.954004	9.385074	8.863252	8.383844	7.942686	7.536078	7.160725
13	10.634955	9.985648	9.393573	8.852683	8.357651	7.903776	7.486904
14	11.296073	10.563123	9.898641	9.294984	8.745468	8.244237	7.786150
15	11.937935	11.118387	10.379658	9.712249	9.107914	8.559479	8.060688
16	12.561102	11.652296	10.837770	10.105895	9.446649	8.851369	8.312558
17	13.166118	12.165669	11.274066	10.477260	9.763223	9.121638	8.543631
18	13.753513	12.659297	11.689587	10.827603	10.059087	9.371887	8.755625
19	14.323799	13.133939	12.085321	11.158116	10.335595	9.603599	8.950115
20	14.877475	13.590326	12.462210	11.469921	10.594014	9.818147	9.128546
21	15.415024	14.029160	12.821153	11.764077	10.835527	10.016803	9.292244
22	15.936917	14.451115	13.163003	12.041582	11.061240	10.200744	9.442425
23	16.443608	14.856842	13.488574	12.303379	11.272187	10.371059	9.580207
24	16.935542	15.246963	13.798642	12.550358	11.469334	10.528758	9.706612
25	17.413148	15.622080	14.093945	12.783356	11.653583	10.674776	9.822580
26	17.876842	15.982769	14.375185	13.003166	11.825779	10.809978	9.928972
27	18.327031	16.329586	14.643034	13.210534	11.986709	10.935165	10.026580
28	18.764108	16.663063	14.898127	13.406164	12.137111	11.051078	10.116128
29	19.188455	16.983715	15.141074	13.590721	12.277674	11.158406	10.198283
30	19.600441	17.292033	15.372451	13.764831	12.409041	11.257783	10.273654
31	20.000428	17.588494	15.592811	13.929086	12.531814	11.349799	10.342802
32	20.388766	17.873551	15.802677	14.084043	12.646555	11.434999	10.406240
33	20.765792	18.147646	16.002549	14.230230	12.753790	11.513888	10.464441
34	21.131837	18.411198	16.192904	14.368141	12.854009	11.586934	10.517835
35	21.487220	18.664613	16.374194	14.498246	12.947672	11.654568	10.566821
36	21.832252	18.908282	16.546852	14.620987	13.035208	11.717193	10.611763
37	22.167235	19.142579	16.711287	14.736780	13.117017	11.775179	10.652993
38	22.492462	19.367864	16.867893	14.846019	13.193473	11.828869	10.690820
39	22.808215	19.584485	17.017041	14.949075	13.264928	11.878582	10.725523
40	23.114772	19.792774	17.159086	15.046297	13.331709	11.924613	10.757360
41	23.412400	19.993052	17.294368	15.138016	13.394120	11.967235	10.786569
42	23.701359	20.185627	17.423208	15.224543	13.452449	12.006699	10.813366
43	23.981902	20.370795	17.545912	15.306173	13.506962	12.043240	10.837950
44	24.254274	20.548841	17.662773	15.383182	13.557908	12.077074	10.860505
45	24.518713	20.720040	17.774070	15.455832	13.605522	12.108402	10.881197
46	24.775449	20.884654	17.880066	15.524370	13.650020	12.137409	10.900181
47	25.024708	21.042936	17.981016	15.589028	13.691608	12.164267	10.917597
48	25.266707	21.195131	18.077158	15.650027	13.730474	12.189136	10.933575
49	25.501657	21.341472	18.168722	15.707572	13.766799	12.212163	10.948234
50	25.729764	21.482185	18.255925	15.761861	13.800746	12.233485	10.961683
51	25.951227	21.617485	18.338977	15.813076	13.832473	12.253227	10.974021

continues

TABLE 7   Present value of an annuity $a_{\overline{n}|i} = \dfrac{1 - (1 + i)^{-n}}{i}$ *(continued)*

n	3%	4%	5%	6%	7%	8%	9%
52	26.166240	21.747582	18.418073	15.861393	13.862124	12.271506	10.985340
53	26.374990	21.872675	18.493403	15.906974	13.889836	12.288432	10.995725
54	26.577660	21.992957	18.565146	15.949976	13.915735	12.304103	11.005252
55	26.774428	22.108612	18.633472	15.990543	13.939939	12.318614	11.013993
56	26.965464	22.219819	18.698545	16.028814	13.962560	12.332050	11.022012
57	27.150936	22.326749	18.760519	16.064919	13.983701	12.344491	11.029369
58	27.331005	22.429567	18.819542	16.098980	14.003458	12.356010	11.036118
59	27.505831	22.528430	18.875754	16.131113	14.021924	12.366676	11.042310
60	27.675564	22.623490	18.929290	16.161428	14.039181	12.376552	11.047991
61	27.840353	22.714894	18.980276	16.190026	14.055309	12.385696	11.053203
62	28.000343	22.802783	19.028834	16.217006	14.070383	12.394163	11.057984
63	28.155673	22.887291	19.075080	16.242458	14.084470	12.402003	11.062371
64	28.306478	22.968549	19.119124	16.266470	14.097635	12.409262	11.066395
65	28.452892	23.046682	19.161070	16.289123	14.109940	12.415983	11.070087
66	28.595040	23.121810	19.201019	16.310493	14.121439	12.422207	11.073475
67	28.733049	23.194048	19.239066	16.330654	14.132186	12.427969	11.076582
68	28.867038	23.263507	19.275301	16.349673	14.142230	12.433305	11.079433
69	28.997124	23.330296	19.309810	16.367617	14.151617	12.438245	11.082049
70	29.123421	23.394515	19.342677	16.384544	14.160389	12.442820	11.084449
71	29.246040	23.456264	19.373978	16.400513	14.168588	12.447055	11.086650
72	29.365088	23.515639	19.403788	16.415578	14.176251	12.450977	11.088670
73	29.480667	23.572730	19.432179	16.429791	14.183412	12.454608	11.090523
74	29.592881	23.627625	19.459218	16.443199	14.190104	12.457971	11.092223
75	29.701826	23.680408	19.484970	16.455848	14.196359	12.461084	11.093782
76	19.807598	23.731162	19.509495	16.467781	14.202205	12.463967	11.095213
77	29.910290	23.779963	19.532853	16.479039	14.207668	12.466636	11.096526
78	30.009990	23.826888	19.555098	16.489659	14.212774	12.469107	11.097730
79	30.106786	23.872008	19.576284	16.499679	14.217546	12.471396	11.098835
80	30.200763	23.915392	19.596460	16.509131	14.222005	12.473514	11.099849
81	30.292003	23.957108	19.615677	16.518048	14.226173	12.475476	11.100778
82	30.380586	23.997219	19.633978	16.526460	14.230069	12.477293	11.101632
83	30.466588	24.035787	19.651407	16.534396	14.233709	12.478975	11.102414
84	30.550086	24.072872	19.668007	16.541883	14.237111	12.480532	11.103132
85	30.631151	24.108531	19.683816	16.548947	14.240291	12.481974	11.103791
86	30.709855	24.142818	19.698873	16.555610	14.243262	12.483310	11.104396
87	30.786267	24.175787	19.713212	16.561896	14.246040	12.484546	11.104950
88	30.860454	24.207487	19.726869	16.567827	14.248635	12.485691	11.105459
89	30.932479	24.237969	19.739875	16.573421	14.251061	12.486751	11.105926
90	31.002407	24.267278	19.752262	16.578699	14.253328	12.487732	11.106354
91	31.070298	24.295459	19.764059	16.583679	14.255447	12.488641	11.106746
92	31.136212	24.322557	19.775294	16.588376	14.257427	12.489482	11.107107
93	31.200206	24.348612	19.785994	16.592808	14.259277	12.490261	11.107437
94	31.262336	24.373666	19.796185	19.596988	14.261007	12.490983	11.107741
95	31.322656	23.397756	19.805891	16.600932	14.262623	12.491651	11.108019
96	31.381219	24.420919	19.815134	16.604653	14.264134	12.492269	11.108274
97	31.438077	24.443191	19.823937	16.608163	14.265546	12.492842	11.108509
98	31.493279	24.464607	19.832321	16.611475	14.266865	12.493372	11.108724
99	31.546872	24.485199	19.840306	16.614599	14.268098	12.493863	11.108921
100	31.598905	24.504999	19.847910	16.617546	14.269251	12.494318	11.109102

TABLE 7 Present value of an annuity $a_{\overline{n}|i} = \dfrac{1 - (1 + i)^{-n}}{i}$

n	10%	11%	12%	13%	14%	15%	16%
1	0.909091	0.900901	0.892857	0.884956	0.877193	0.869565	0.862069
2	1.735537	1.712523	1.690051	1.668102	1.646661	1.625709	1.605232
3	2.486852	2.443715	2.401831	2.361153	2.321632	2.283225	2.245890
4	3.169865	3.102446	3.037349	2.974471	2.913712	2.854978	2.798181
5	3.790787	3.695897	3.604776	3.517231	3.433081	3.352155	3.274294
6	4.355261	4.230538	4.111407	3.997550	3.888668	3.784483	3.684736
7	4.868419	4.712196	4.563757	4.422610	4.288305	4.160420	4.038565
8	5.334926	5.146123	4.967640	4.798770	4.638864	4.487322	4.343591
9	5.759024	5.537048	5.328250	5.131655	4.946372	4.771584	4.606544
10	6.144567	5.889232	5.650223	5.426243	5.216116	5.018769	4.833227
11	6.495061	6.206515	5.937699	5.686941	5.452733	5.233712	5.028644
12	6.813692	6.492356	6.194374	5.917647	5.660292	5.420619	5.197107
13	7.103356	6.749870	6.423548	6.121812	5.842362	5.583147	5.342334
14	7.366687	6.981865	6.628168	6.302488	6.002072	5.724476	5.467529
15	7.606080	7.190870	6.810864	6.462379	6.142168	5.847370	5.575456
16	7.823709	7.379162	6.973986	6.603875	6.265060	5.954235	5.668497
17	8.021553	7.548794	7.119630	6.729093	6.372859	6.047161	5.748704
18	8.201412	7.701617	7.249670	6.839905	6.467420	6.127966	5.817848
19	8.364920	7.839294	7.365777	6.937969	6.550369	6.198231	5.877455
20	8.513564	7.963328	7.469444	7.024752	6.623131	6.259331	5.928841
21	8.648694	8.075070	7.562003	7.101550	6.686957	6.312462	5.973139
22	8.771540	8.175739	7.644646	7.169513	6.742944	6.358663	6.011326
23	8.883218	8.266432	7.718434	7.229658	6.792056	6.398837	6.044147
24	8.984744	8.348137	7.784316	7.282883	6.835137	6.433771	6.072627
25	9.077040	8.421745	7.843139	7.329985	6.872927	6.464149	6.097092
26	9.160945	8.488058	7.895660	7.371668	6.906077	6.490564	6.118183
27	9.237223	8.547800	7.942554	7.408556	6.935155	6.513534	6.136364
28	9.306567	8.601622	7.984423	7.441200	6.960662	6.533508	6.152038
29	9.369606	8.650110	8.021806	7.470088	6.983037	6.550877	6.165550
30	9.426914	8.693793	8.055184	7.495653	7.002664	6.565980	6.177198
31	9.479013	8.733146	8.084986	7.518277	7.019881	6.579113	6.187240
32	9.526376	8.768600	8.111594	7.538299	7.034983	6.590533	6.195897
33	9.569432	8.800541	8.135352	7.556016	7.048231	6.600463	6.203359
34	9.608575	8.829316	8.156564	7.571696	7.059852	6.609099	6.209792
35	9.644159	8.855240	8.175504	7.585572	7.070045	6.616607	6.215338
36	9.676508	8.878594	8.192414	7.597851	7.078987	6.623137	6.220119
37	9.705917	8.899635	8.207513	7.608718	7.086831	6.628815	6.224241
38	9.732651	8.918590	8.220993	7.618334	7.093711	6.633752	6.227794
39	9.756956	8.935666	8.233030	7.626844	7.099747	6.638045	6.230857
40	9.779051	8.951051	8.243777	7.634376	7.105041	6.641778	6.233497
41	9.799137	8.964911	8.253372	7.641040	7.109685	6.645025	6.235773
42	9.817397	8.977397	8.261939	7.646938	7.113759	6.647848	6.237736
43	9.833998	8.988646	8.269589	7.652158	7.117332	6.650302	6.239427
44	9.849089	8.998780	8.276418	7.656777	7.120467	6.652437	6.240886
45	9.862808	9.007910	8.282516	7.660864	7.123217	6.654293	6.242143
46	9.875280	9.016135	8.287961	7.664482	7.125629	6.655907	6.243227
47	9.886618	9.023545	8.292822	7.667683	7.127744	6.657310	6.244161
48	9.896926	9.030221	8.297163	7.670516	7.129600	6.658531	6.244966
49	9.906296	9.036235	8.301038	7.673023	7.131228	6.659592	6.245661
50	9.914814	9.041653	8.304498	7.675242	7.132656	6.660515	6.246259

Answers to Selected Exercises

• CHAPTER R

SECTION R-1

1. True **3.** False **5.** True **7.** True **9.** True **11.** False
13. True **15.** True **17.** True **19.** False **21.** True
23. True **25.** True **27.** False
29. (number line, closed dots at −5 and −1) **31.** (number line, open dots at −4 and −2)
33. (number line, open dot at −3, closed at 2) **35.** (number line, closed dot at 5)
37. (number line, closed dot at −3) **39.** (number line, open dot at −2)
41. (number line, open dot at 2) **43.** (number line, open dot at 2)
45. Closed **47.** Open **49.** Closed
51. (number line, closed dots at 3 and 9) **53.** (number line, closed dot at −4)
55. (number line, closed dot at 6) **57.** (number line, open dot at 4, closed at 9)
59. 0 **61.** 1 **63.** 2 **65.** 15 **67.** 20 **69.** 4 **71.** 9
73. 6 **75.** 13 **77.** 6 (number line, $\leftarrow 6 \rightarrow$ from 5 to 11)

79. 5 (number line, $\leftarrow 5 \rightarrow$ from −9 to −4)

SECTION R-2

1. $x = 6$ **3.** $x = 9$ **5.** $x = 12$ **7.** $x = 8$ **9.** $y = 10$
11. $\left(-\infty, 5\frac{1}{2}\right]$ (number line, closed dot at $5\frac{1}{2}$)
13. $\left(-\infty, 7\frac{1}{2}\right)$ (number line, open dot at $7\frac{1}{2}$)
15. $\left(-\infty, 10\frac{1}{3}\right]$ (number line, closed dot at $10\frac{1}{3}$)

17. $(-\infty, 3]$ (number line, closed dot at 3)
19. $[11, \infty)$ (number line, closed dot at 11)

SECTION R-3

1. 9 **3.** 25 **5.** $4^6 = 4096$ **7.** $\frac{1}{16}$ **9.** 64

11. $5^7 = 78,125$ **13.** $\frac{9}{25}$ **15.** $\frac{1}{64}$ **17.** $\frac{1}{8}$ **19.** 4 **21.** 7
23. $8^5 = 32,768$ **25.** 343 **27.** 36 **29.** 1
31. $7^5 = 16,807$ **33.** 5^{-6} **35.** $(-5)^{-3}$ **37.** x^{-8}
39. $4^{9/2} = 2^9$ **41.** $2^{1/5}$ **43.** $9^{4/7}$ **45.** $5^{7/3}$ **47.** $5^{-3/2}$
49. $x^{-5/2}$ **51.** $x^{-2/3}$ **53.** $9x^2$ **55.** $125x^3y^3$
57. $2 \cdot 9 = 18$ **59.** $\frac{5^3}{6^3} = \frac{125}{216}$ **61.** $\frac{x^5}{3^5} = \frac{x^5}{243}$ **63.** $\frac{x^2}{25}$

65. $\frac{-8}{x^3}$ **67.** $2^{12} = 4096$ **69.** $\frac{1}{3}$ **71.** 4.96×10^2
73. 8×10^9 **75.** 8×10^{-7} **77.** 5.6×10^{-1}
79. 3.57×10^{-3}

SECTION R-4

1. $3x + 12$ **3.** $-2x - 12$ **5.** $9x + 27$
7. $-4x^2 + 12x - 28$ **9.** $5x^4 - 20x^3 + 20x^2 + 25x$
11. $3x^6y^3 - 15x^2y^5 + 18x^3y^4$ **13.** $5(x + 4)$ **15.** $3(x - 9)$
17. $6(x - 5)$ **19.** $3x(x - 9)$ **21.** $-6x(x - 8)$
23. $7x(x + 4)$ **25.** $3xy^2(xy^2 + 2)$ **27.** $-5x^3y^6(x - 4y)$
29. $3x^2y^3(y^3 + 3x^3 + 2xy)$ **31.** $P(1 + rt)$ **33.** $P(1 + i)$
35. $x(ax - b)$ **37.** $P(1 + i)^3$ **39.** $3x(2x - 3)$
41. $(x + 3)(2x - y)$ **43.** $x(x - 2)(5y + 8x)$

SECTION R-5

1. $x^2 + x - 6$ **3.** $x^2 + 6x + 5$ **5.** $x^2 - 15x + 56$
7. $3x^2 + 2x - 5$ **9.** $8x^2 - 2x - 21$ **11.** $21x^2 + x - 2$

13. $x^2 - 9$ **15.** $x^2 - 81$ **17.** $9x^2 - 4$ **19.** $x^2 - 4x + 4$
21. $x^2 + 10x + 25$ **23.** $4x^2 - 12x + 9$

SECTION R-6

1. $(x + 9)(x - 2)$ **3.** $(x + 5)(x - 3)$ **5.** $(x - 2)(x - 1)$
7. $(x - 5)(x - 8)$ **9.** $(x - 9)(x + 9)$ **11.** $(x - 7)(x + 7)$
13. $(x + 3)^2$ **15.** $(x - 5)^2$ **17.** $(x + 9)^2$
19. $(x - 9)(x + 3)$ **21.** $(x - 9)(x + 5)$ **23.** $(x + 6)(x + 1)$

SECTION R-7

1. $(2x + 7)(x - 4)$ **3.** $(5x - 2)(x + 4)$
5. $(2x - 5)(3x + 1)$ **7.** $9(x - 2)(x + 2)$ **9.** $(2x + 5)^2$
11. $(5x - 7)^2$

SECTION R-8

1. $2x - 14$ **3.** $-x - 7$ **5.** x **7.** $\dfrac{x - 3}{x - 5}$ **9.** $\dfrac{x + 4}{x + 1}$

11. $\dfrac{x + 3}{x + 2}$ **13.** $\dfrac{1}{x}$ **15.** $\dfrac{x + 3}{x - 2}$ **17.** $\dfrac{x + 3}{x + 2}$

19. $\dfrac{x + 6}{2} = \dfrac{x}{2} + 3$ **21.** $\dfrac{9}{x}$ **23.** $\dfrac{-3(x + 16)}{x(x + 6)}$ or

$\dfrac{-3x - 48}{x(x + 6)}$ **25.** $\dfrac{9x - 49}{x^2 - 36}$ **27.** $\dfrac{7x - 5}{x(x - 9)}$ **29.** $x + \dfrac{7}{x}$

31. $3x - 36$ **33.** $4x^2 - 8x + 6$ **35.** $4x^2 + 8x - 12$

37. $5x^3 - 5x^2 + 30x - 10$ **39.** $x^3\left(1 - \dfrac{4}{x} + \dfrac{7}{x^2} + \dfrac{5}{x^3}\right)$

41. $x^2\left(1 + \dfrac{7}{x} + \dfrac{9}{x^2}\right)$ **43.** $\dfrac{1 - (1 + i)^{-20}}{i}$

45. $\dfrac{1 + i - (1 + i)^{-37}}{i}$

• EXTRA DIVIDENDS

1. 25% **3.** $72 **5.** $428.57 **7.** $14,800 **9.** $16,050
11. 123.3% **13.** 139.3% **15.** −1.6% **17.** $18,148.82
19. $22,321.43

• EXTRA DIVIDENDS

1. 175 **3.** $8,214,286 **5.** (a) 100% (b) 17.6% **7.** 1.18
9. 1.35 **11.** 1.1 **13.** 1.32 **15.** $321.44 **17.** $405.19

• CHAPTER 1

SECTION 1-1

1. (a) −2 (b) 10 **3.** (a) 7 (b) 5 (c) −3 (d) 13
5. (a) $\dfrac{5}{7}$ (b) $\dfrac{5}{8}$ (c) 5 (d) $\dfrac{1}{3}$

7.

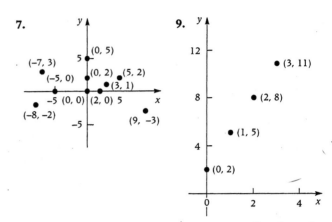

9.

11. All real x such that $x \neq 2$, $x \neq -7$ **13.** All real x such that $x \geq 2$ **15.** All real x such that $x \neq 3$ **17.** a, c, d
19. *Not* a function: $(4, 3)$ and $(4, -3)$ satisfy equation
21. (a) $f(x + h) = x^2 + 2xh + h^2 - 4x - 4h + 5$
(b) $f(x + h) - f(x) = 2xh + h^2 - 4h$

(c) $\dfrac{f(x + h) - f(x)}{h} = 2x + h - 4$

23. $\dfrac{f(x + h) - f(x)}{h} = 10x + 5h - 2$

25. $\dfrac{g(x + h) - g(x)}{h} = 3x^2 + 3xh + h^2 - 8x - 4h + 5$

27.

29. (a) $C(x) = \begin{cases} 5.00 & \text{if } 16 < x \leq 40 \\ 2.00 & \text{if } 8 \leq x \leq 16 \\ 1.25 & \text{if } 0 < x < 8 \end{cases}$

(b)

31. $P(x) = \begin{cases} 28 - x & \text{if } 0 \le x \le 35 \\ -7 & \text{if } x > 35 \end{cases}$

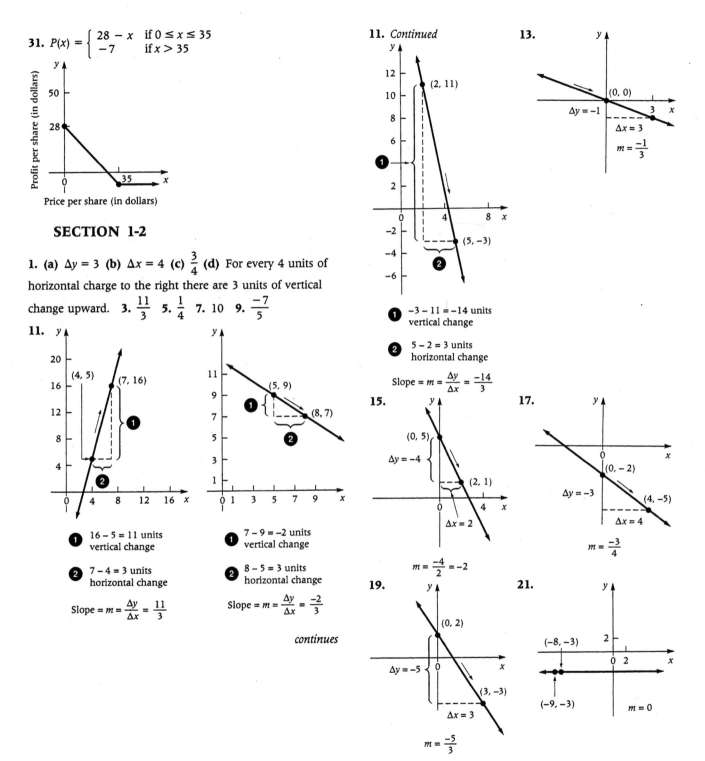

SECTION 1-2

1. (a) $\Delta y = 3$ **(b)** $\Delta x = 4$ **(c)** $\frac{3}{4}$ **(d)** For every 4 units of horizontal charge to the right there are 3 units of vertical change upward. **3.** $\frac{11}{3}$ **5.** $\frac{1}{4}$ **7.** 10 **9.** $\frac{-7}{5}$

11.

① $16 - 5 = 11$ units vertical change

② $7 - 4 = 3$ units horizontal change

Slope $= m = \dfrac{\Delta y}{\Delta x} = \dfrac{11}{3}$

① $7 - 9 = -2$ units vertical change

② $8 - 5 = 3$ units horizontal change

Slope $= m = \dfrac{\Delta y}{\Delta x} = \dfrac{-2}{3}$

continues

11. *Continued*

① $-3 - 11 = -14$ units vertical change

② $5 - 2 = 3$ units horizontal change

Slope $= m = \dfrac{\Delta y}{\Delta x} = \dfrac{-14}{3}$

13.

$\Delta y = -1$

$\Delta x = 3$

$m = \dfrac{-1}{3}$

15.

$\Delta y = -4$

$\Delta x = 2$

$m = \dfrac{-4}{2} = -2$

17.

$\Delta y = -3$

$\Delta x = 4$

$m = \dfrac{-3}{4}$

19.

$\Delta y = -5$

$\Delta x = 3$

$m = \dfrac{-5}{3}$

21.

$m = 0$

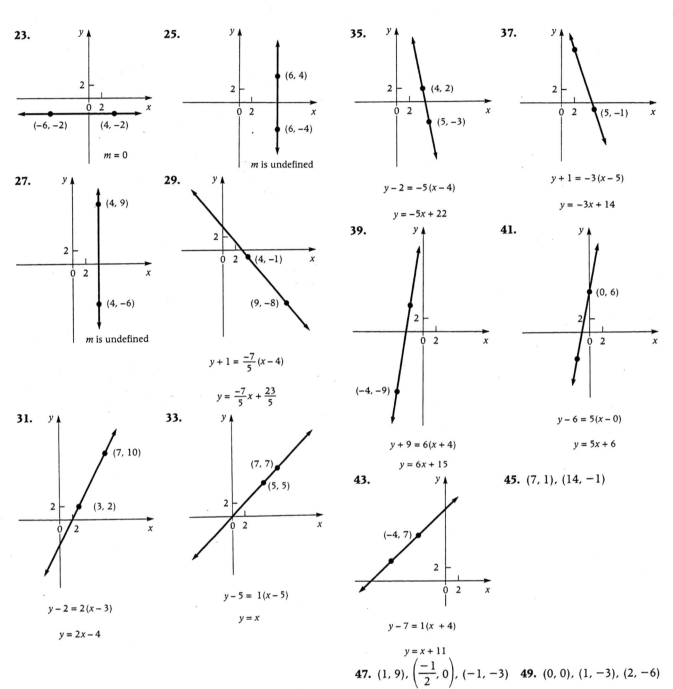

23. $m = 0$

25. m is undefined

27. m is undefined

29. $y + 1 = \dfrac{-7}{5}(x - 4)$

$y = \dfrac{-7}{5}x + \dfrac{23}{5}$

31. $y - 2 = 2(x - 3)$

$y = 2x - 4$

33. $y - 5 = 1(x - 5)$

$y = x$

35. $y - 2 = -5(x - 4)$

$y = -5x + 22$

37. $y + 1 = -3(x - 5)$

$y = -3x + 14$

39. $y + 9 = 6(x + 4)$

$y = 6x + 15$

41. $y - 6 = 5(x - 0)$

$y = 5x + 6$

43. $y - 7 = 1(x + 4)$

$y = x + 11$

45. $(7, 1)$, $(14, -1)$

47. $(1, 9)$, $\left(\dfrac{-1}{2}, 0\right)$, $(-1, -3)$ **49.** $(0, 0)$, $(1, -3)$, $(2, -6)$

51. **53.**

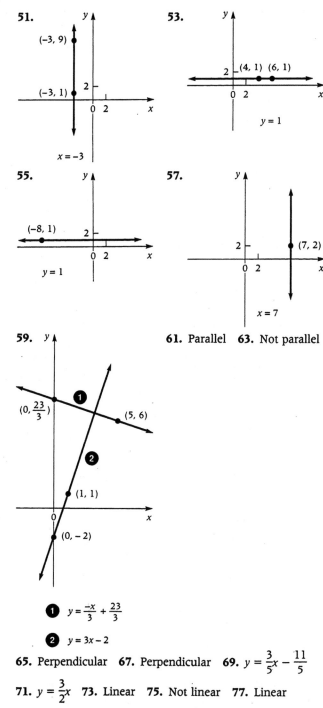

55. **57.**

59.

61. Parallel   **63.** Not parallel

① $y = \frac{-x}{3} + \frac{23}{3}$

② $y = 3x - 2$

65. Perpendicular   **67.** Perpendicular   **69.** $y = \frac{3}{5}x - \frac{11}{5}$

71. $y = \frac{3}{2}x$ **73.** Linear   **75.** Not linear   **77.** Linear

79. Not linear   **81. (a)** 132.825 **(b)** U.S. Overseas IOU's are increasing at the rate of 132.825 billion dollars per year during the indicated time interval.
(c) $y - 642 = 132.825(x - 1989)$
or
$y = 132.825x - 263,546.925$

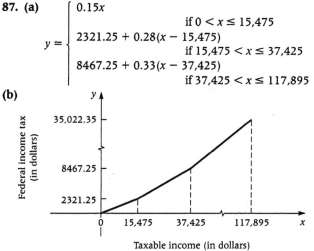

(d) $y = 132.825(1992) - 263,546.925$
   $= 1040.475$ billion dollars
83. (a) -52.1 **(b)** Defects per 100 vehicles decreased at the rate of 52.1 per year during the indicated time interval.
(c) $y - 149 = -52.1(x - 1989)$
or
$y = -52.1x + 103,775.9$
(d) $y = -52.1(1991) + 103,775.9$
   $= 44.8$
85. (a) 2500 **(b)** The value of the investment increased by $2500 per percentage point increase in inflation.
87. (a)
$$y = \begin{cases} 0.15x & \text{if } 0 < x \le 15,475 \\ 2321.25 + 0.28(x - 15,475) & \text{if } 15,475 < x \le 37,425 \\ 8467.25 + 0.33(x - 37,425) & \text{if } 37,425 < x \le 117,895 \end{cases}$$
(b)

SECTION 1-3

1. **3.** **5.** **7.**

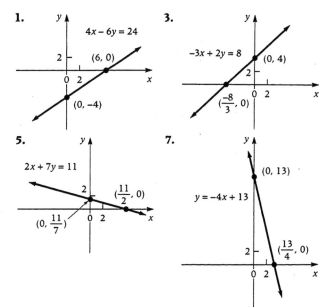

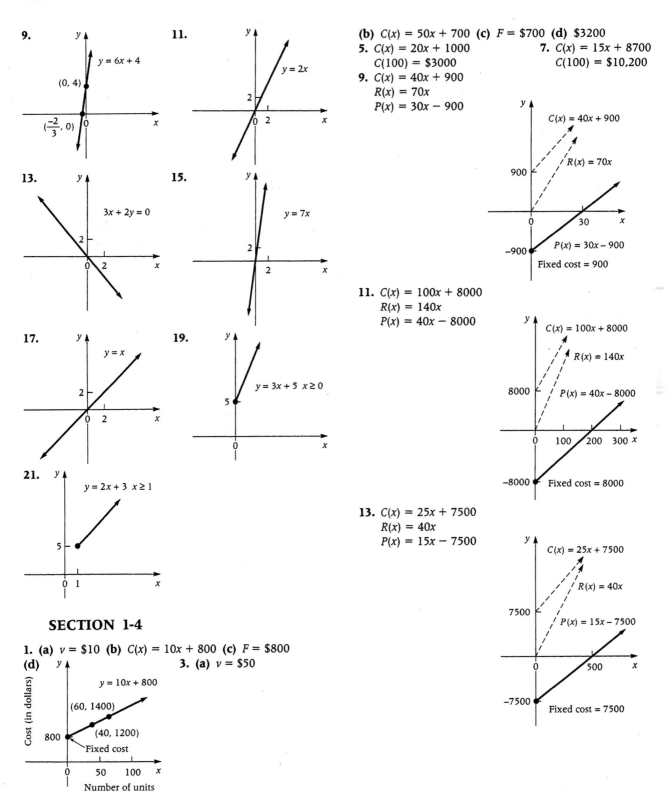

9.

$y = 6x + 4$

$(0, 4)$

$(\frac{-2}{3}, 0)$

11.

$y = 2x$

(b) $C(x) = 50x + 700$ **(c)** $F = \$700$ **(d)** $\$3200$
5. $C(x) = 20x + 1000$ **7.** $C(x) = 15x + 8700$
   $C(100) = \$3000$ $C(100) = \$10,200$
9. $C(x) = 40x + 900$
   $R(x) = 70x$
   $P(x) = 30x - 900$

$C(x) = 40x + 900$
$R(x) = 70x$
900
30
$P(x) = 30x - 900$
-900
Fixed cost = 900

13.

$3x + 2y = 0$

15.

$y = 7x$

11. $C(x) = 100x + 8000$
   $R(x) = 140x$
   $P(x) = 40x - 8000$

$C(x) = 100x + 8000$
$R(x) = 140x$
8000
$P(x) = 40x - 8000$
100 200 300
-8000 Fixed cost = 8000

17.

$y = x$

19.

$y = 3x + 5$ $x \geq 0$

13. $C(x) = 25x + 7500$
   $R(x) = 40x$
   $P(x) = 15x - 7500$

$C(x) = 25x + 7500$
$R(x) = 40x$
7500
$P(x) = 15x - 7500$
500
-7500 Fixed cost = 7500

21.

$y = 2x + 3$ $x \geq 1$

5

0 1

SECTION 1-4

1. (a) $v = \$10$ **(b)** $C(x) = 10x + 800$ **(c)** $F = \$800$
(d)   **3. (a)** $v = \$50$

$y = 10x + 800$
$(60, 1400)$
$(40, 1200)$
800
Fixed cost
0   50   100
Number of units
Cost (in dollars)

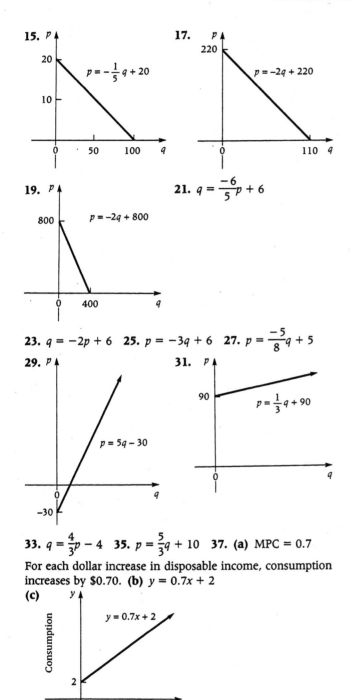

15. $p = -\frac{1}{5}q + 20$

17. $p = -2q + 220$

19. $p = -2q + 800$

21. $q = \frac{-6}{5}p + 6$

23. $q = -2p + 6$ **25.** $p = -3q + 6$ **27.** $p = \frac{-5}{8}q + 5$

29. $p = 5q - 30$

31. $p = \frac{1}{3}q + 90$

33. $q = \frac{4}{3}p - 4$ **35.** $p = \frac{5}{3}q + 10$ **37. (a)** MPC = 0.7
For each dollar increase in disposable income, consumption increases by $0.70. **(b)** $y = 0.7x + 2$
(c) $y = 0.7x + 2$

39. (a) MPC = 0.9 For each dollar increase in disposable income, consumption increases by $0.90. **(b)** $y = 0.9x + 7$

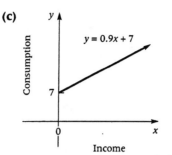
(c) $y = 0.9x + 7$

41. (a) MPC = 0.8 For each dollar increase in disposable income, consumption increases by $0.80. **(b)** MPS = 0.2 For each dollar increase in disposable income, personal savings increases by $0.20. **(c)** $y = 0.8x + 7$
(d) $75 billion **43.** $y = 90,000 - 20,000x$
45. $y = 45,000 - 15,000x$ **47. (a)** $y = 30,000 - 2900x$
(b)   **(c)** $12,600

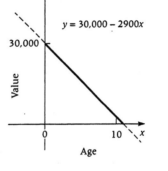
$y = 30,000 - 2900x$

SECTION 1-5

1. $C(x) = 5x + 1000$
$R(x) = 9x$
$P(x) = 4x - 1000$
$x = 250$

3. $C(x) = 20x + 100,000$
$R(x) = 120x$
$P(x) = 100x - 100,000$
$x = 1000$

5. $C(x) = 25x + 80,000$
$R(x) = 65x$
$P(x) = 40x - 80,000$
$x = 2000$

7. (a) $C(x) = 5x + 2000$ **(b)** $R(x) = 15x$
(c)   **(d)** 200

$C(x) = 5x + 2000$
$R(x) = 15x$
$P(x) = 10x - 2000$

c - - -
f ———

(e) $P(x) = 10x - 2000$ (f)

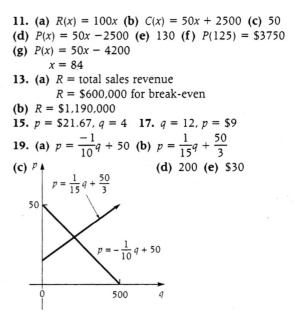

(g) $1000 (h) −$1000 (a loss) (i) 4200   9. (a) $1300
(b) $C(x) = 1300x + 260,000$ (c) $R(x) = 1800x$
(d)

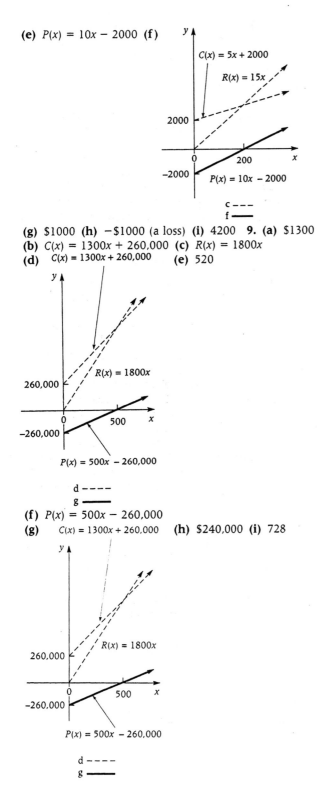

(e) 520

(f) $P(x) = 500x - 260,000$
(g) $C(x) = 1300x + 260,000$ (h) $240,000 (i) 728

11. (a) $R(x) = 100x$ (b) $C(x) = 50x + 2500$ (c) 50
(d) $P(x) = 50x - 2500$ (e) 130 (f) $P(125) = 3750
(g) $P(x) = 50x - 4200$
    $x = 84$
13. (a) R = total sales revenue
        $R = $600,000 for break-even
(b) $R = $1,190,000$
15. $p = $21.67, q = 4$ 17. $q = 12, p = 9
19. (a) $p = \dfrac{-1}{10}q + 50$ (b) $p = \dfrac{1}{15}q + \dfrac{50}{3}$
(c)   (d) 200 (e) $30

• EXTRA DIVIDENDS

Cost Accounting

1. (a) $y = x + 1500$ (b) $1500 (c) $1   3. (a) $0.80 per
machine hour (b) $20,000 per month (c) $240,000

Model Fitting

1. (a) For $y = 2x + 1$, $S = 41$
For $y = 3x - 2$, $S = 55$ (b) $y = 2x + 1$ is the better fit.
3. (a) For $y = 4x - 3$, $S = 42$
For $y = 3x + 2$, $S = 64$ (b) $y = 4x - 3$ is the better fit.
5. (a) For $y = 13x + 130$, $S = 3481.0598$
For $y = 20x + 70$, $S = 15,051.2198$ (b) $y = 13x + 130$ is
the better fit.   7. (a) For $y = 3x + 120$, $S = 27$
For $y = 4x + 115$, $S = 121$ (b) $y = 3x + 120$ is the better
fit.   9. (a) For $y = 2x + 170$, $S = 5462$
For $y = 3x + 100$, $S = 11,786$ (b) $y = 2x + 170$ is the
better fit.

• CHAPTER HIGHLIGHTS

1. *Function, domain, range.* A **function** is a rule that
associates a unique output value with each element in a set
of possible input values. The set of input values is called
the **domain** of the function. The set of output values is
called the **range** of the function.
Dependent variable, independent variable. If a function is
defined by an equation such as $y = 5x^2 - 6$, then the value
of y depends upon the value of x. Therefore, y is called the

dependent variable and x is called the **independent** variable.

Ordered pair, x-coordinate, y-coordinate. Each point in the rectangular coordinate system is denoted by an **ordered pair** (x, y) where x is called the **x-coordinate** and y is called the **y-coordinate**. The x- and y-coordinates indicate the location of the point relative to the axes.

x-axis, y-axis, origin, quadrant. The **x-axis** is the horizontal axis of a rectangular coordinate system, and the **y-axis** is the vertical axis. The point where the axes intersect is called the **origin**. The x- and y-axes partition the plane into four regions called **quadrants**.   **2.** Equation, relationship   **3.** *Vertical line test.* If a vertical line intersects a graph at more than one point, then that graph does not represent a function.   **4.**   **5.** Piecewise   **6.** d.

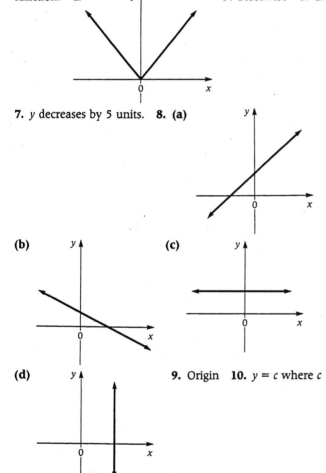

7. y decreases by 5 units.   **8. (a)**

(b)   **(c)**

(d)   **9.** Origin   **10.** $y = c$ where c

is a constant   **11.** $x = c$ where c is a constant
12. y-intercept, positive, negative   **13.** Tax rates
14. *x-intercept, y-intercept.* The point where a straight line crosses the x-axis is called the **x-intercept**; the point

where a straight line crosses the y-axis is called the **y-intercept.**   **15.** 0   **16.** 0   **17.** *Step 1:* Find the y-intercept by setting $x = 0$ and solving the resulting equation for y.

Step 2: Find the x-intercept by setting $y = 0$ and solving the resulting equation for x.

Step 3: Connect the intercepts with a straightedge.
18. Place a straightedge at the origin and set it so that the slope is m.   **19.** Cost; number of units produced.
20. Sales revenue; number of units produced.   **21.** Profit; number of units produced.   **22.** Variable cost per unit
23. *Fixed cost:* The cost of producing 0 units. These are costs that must be paid regardless of how few or how many units are produced.   **24.** Unit price, demand   **25.** Unit price, supply   **26.** Consumption, income   **27.** The MPC is the slope of a consumption function. The MPC indicates the portion spent of an additional dollar earned.

28. $y = C - \left(\dfrac{C - S}{n}\right)x$ where C = total cost of an asset
S = salvage value of the asset
n = number of years of asset life

The y-intercept, C, denotes the total cost of the asset. The slope, $(C - S)/n$, is the annual depreciation.
29. *Break-even point:* The point where total sales revenue = total cost.   **30.** Set $R(x) = C(x)$ and solve for x.
31. Break-even point   **32.** Set $P(x) = 0$ and solve for x.
33. Intersection point, demand   **34.** The first coordinate is called the **equilibrium quantity**; the second coordinate is called the **equilibrium price**. The equilibrium price is the unit price at which supply = demand for a given product; the corresponding supply or demand is the equilibrium quantity.

• REVIEW EXERCISES

1. $f(0) = -2$ **3.** $f(0) = -1$
 $f(1) = 2$ $f(1) = 2$
 $f(3) = 10$ $f(3) = 14$
5. 4   **7.** $2x + h - 4$ **9.** $x \geq 4$ **11.** All real x such that $x \neq 7, x \neq -5$ **13.** Not a function
15.

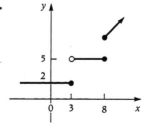

17. Let x = price per share of stock

$$P(x) = \begin{cases} -4 & \text{if } 0 \le x \le 20 \\ x - 24 & \text{if } x > 20 \end{cases}$$

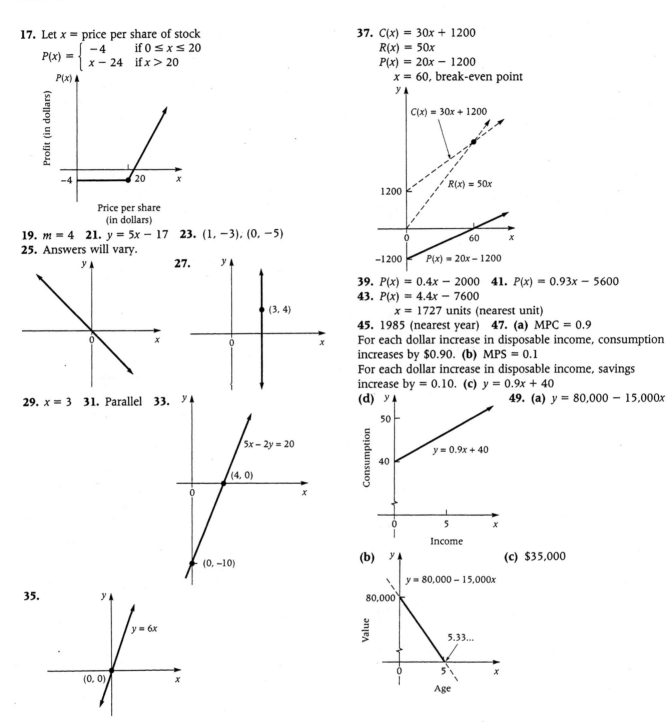

19. $m = 4$ **21.** $y = 5x - 17$ **23.** $(1, -3), (0, -5)$
25. Answers will vary.

27.

29. $x = 3$ **31.** Parallel **33.**

35.

37. $C(x) = 30x + 1200$
$R(x) = 50x$
$P(x) = 20x - 1200$
  $x = 60$, break-even point

39. $P(x) = 0.4x - 2000$ **41.** $P(x) = 0.93x - 5600$
43. $P(x) = 4.4x - 7600$
  $x = 1727$ units (nearest unit)
45. 1985 (nearest year) **47. (a)** MPC = 0.9
For each dollar increase in disposable income, consumption increases by $0.90. **(b)** MPS = 0.1
For each dollar increase in disposable income, savings increase by = 0.10. **(c)** $y = 0.9x + 40$
(d)   **49. (a)** $y = 80,000 - 15,000x$

(b)   **(c)** $35,000

• CHAPTER 2

SECTION 2-1

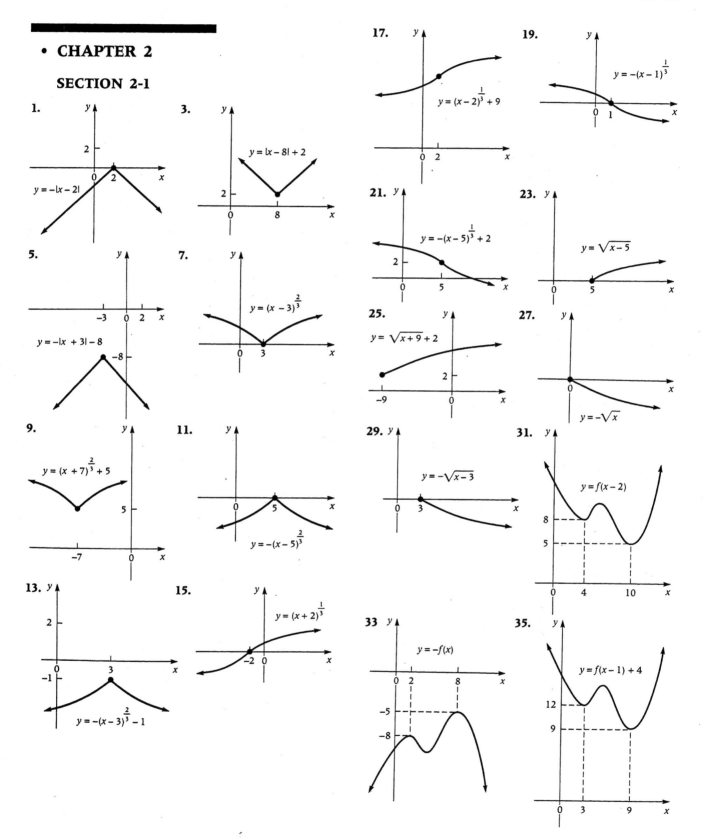

37 $y = -f(x-2) + 1$

39. $y = -f(x) - 6$

41. Odd **43.** Odd **45.** Odd

47. Odd

49. Shift upward 100 units **51.** $10

SECTION 2-2

1. $y = 5x^2$

3. $y = -\frac{1}{3}x^2$ $y = -x^2$ $y = -4x^2$

5. $y = x^2 + 7$

7. $y = x^2 - 9$

$y = x^3$

9. $y = 2x^2 - 8$

11. $y = (x-3)^2$

13. $y = 4(x-1)^2$

15. $f(x) = -2(x+5)^2$

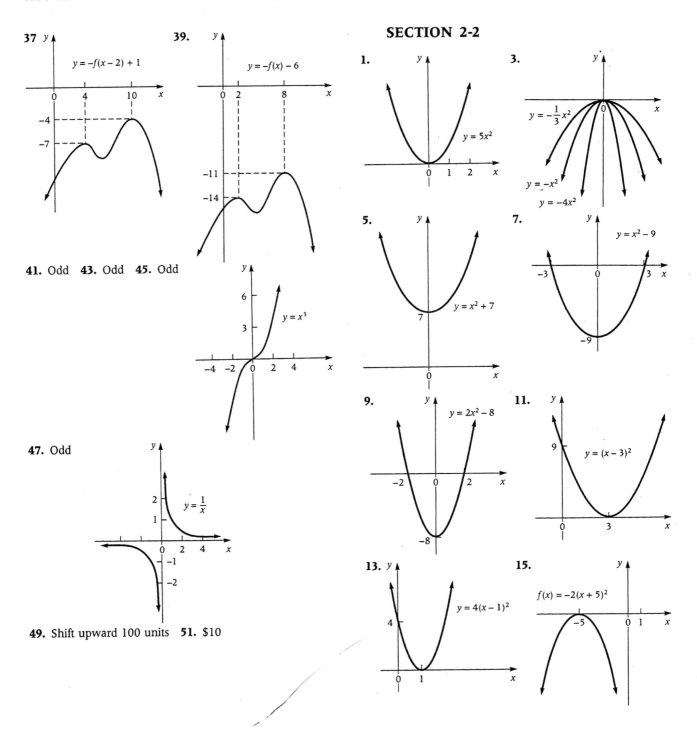

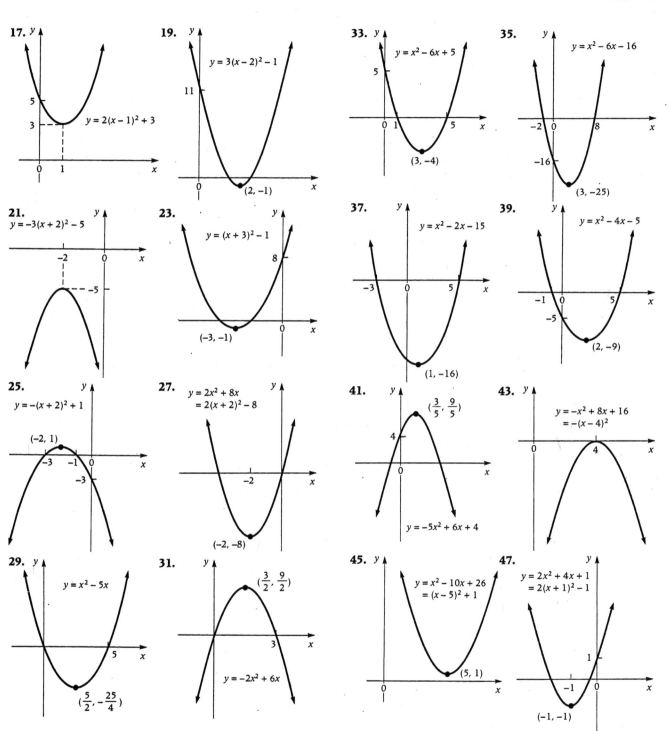

17. $y = 2(x - 1)^2 + 3$

19. $y = 3(x - 2)^2 - 1$; $(2, -1)$; 11

21. $y = -3(x + 2)^2 - 5$; -2 ; -5

23. $y = (x + 3)^2 - 1$; 8 ; $(-3, -1)$

25. $y = -(x + 2)^2 + 1$; $(-2, 1)$; -3 ; -1 ; -3

27. $y = 2x^2 + 8x = 2(x + 2)^2 - 8$; -2 ; $(-2, -8)$

29. $y = x^2 - 5x$; 5 ; $\left(\dfrac{5}{2}, -\dfrac{25}{4}\right)$

31. $y = -2x^2 + 6x$; $\left(\dfrac{3}{2}, \dfrac{9}{2}\right)$; 3

33. $y = x^2 - 6x + 5$; 5 ; 1 ; 5 ; $(3, -4)$

35. $y = x^2 - 6x - 16$; -2 ; 8 ; -16 ; $(3, -25)$

37. $y = x^2 - 2x - 15$; -3 ; 5 ; $(1, -16)$

39. $y = x^2 - 4x - 5$; -1 ; 5 ; -5 ; $(2, -9)$

41. $\left(\dfrac{3}{5}, \dfrac{9}{5}\right)$; 4 ; $y = -5x^2 + 6x + 4$

43. $y = -x^2 + 8x + 16 = -(x - 4)^2$; 4

45. $y = x^2 - 10x + 26 = (x - 5)^2 + 1$; $(5, 1)$

47. $y = 2x^2 + 4x + 1 = 2(x + 1)^2 - 1$; 1 ; -1 ; $(-1, -1)$

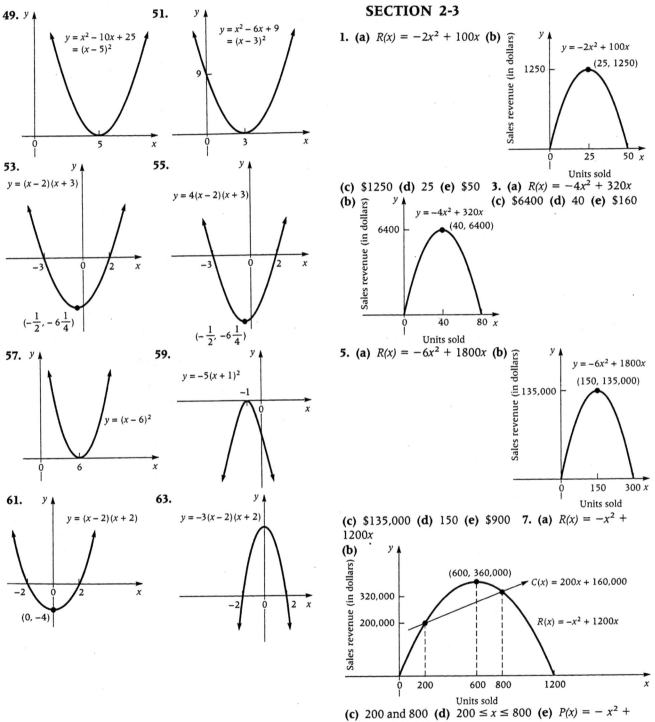

49. $y = x^2 - 10x + 25 = (x - 5)^2$

51. $y = x^2 - 6x + 9 = (x - 3)^2$

53. $y = (x - 2)(x + 3)$, $\left(-\frac{1}{2}, -6\frac{1}{4}\right)$

55. $y = 4(x - 2)(x + 3)$, $\left(-\frac{1}{2}, -6\frac{1}{4}\right)$

57. $y = (x - 6)^2$

59. $y = -5(x + 1)^2$

61. $y = (x - 2)(x + 2)$, $(0, -4)$

63. $y = -3(x - 2)(x + 2)$

SECTION 2-3

1. (a) $R(x) = -2x^2 + 100x$ **(b)** $y = -2x^2 + 100x$, (25, 1250), Units sold

(c) $1250 **(d)** 25 **(e)** $50

3. (a) $R(x) = -4x^2 + 320x$ **(c)** $6400 **(d)** 40 **(e)** $160 **(b)** $y = -4x^2 + 320x$, (40, 6400), Units sold

5. (a) $R(x) = -6x^2 + 1800x$ **(b)** $y = -6x^2 + 1800x$, (150, 135,000), Units sold

(c) $135,000 **(d)** 150 **(e)** $900

7. (a) $R(x) = -x^2 + 1200x$ **(b)** (600, 360,000), $C(x) = 200x + 160,000$, $R(x) = -x^2 + 1200x$, Units sold

(c) 200 and 800 **(d)** $200 \le x \le 800$ **(e)** $P(x) = -x^2 + 1000x - 160,000$

(f)

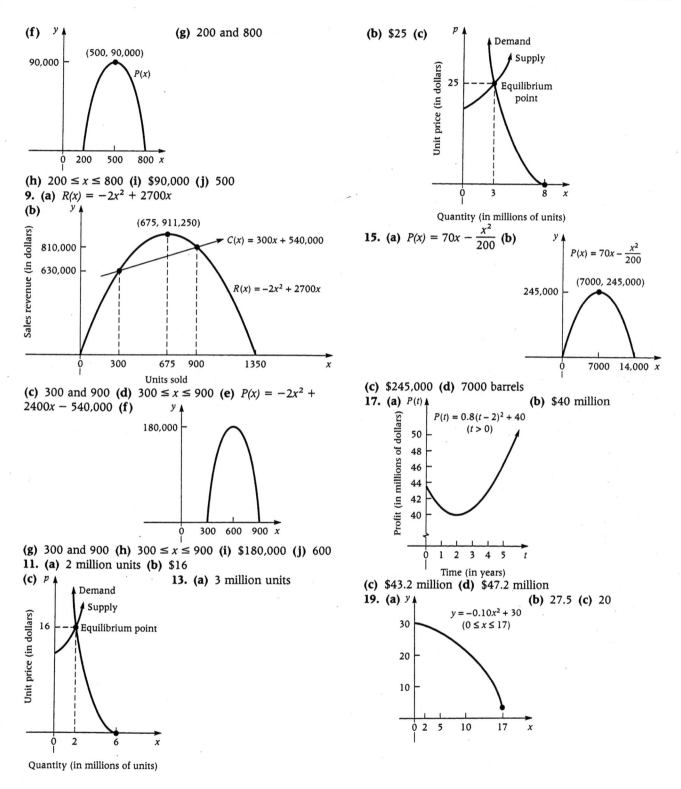

(g) 200 and 800

(h) $200 \le x \le 800$ **(i)** $90,000 **(j)** 500
9. (a) $R(x) = -2x^2 + 2700x$
(b)

(c) 300 and 900 **(d)** $300 \le x \le 900$ **(e)** $P(x) = -2x^2 + 2400x - 540,000$ **(f)**

(g) 300 and 900 **(h)** $300 \le x \le 900$ **(i)** $180,000 **(j)** 600
11. (a) 2 million units **(b)** $16
(c)

13. (a) 3 million units

(b) $25 **(c)**

15. (a) $P(x) = 70x - \dfrac{x^2}{200}$ **(b)**

(c) $245,000 **(d)** 7000 barrels
17. (a)

(b) $40 million

(c) $43.2 million **(d)** $47.2 million
19. (a)

(b) 27.5 **(c)** 20

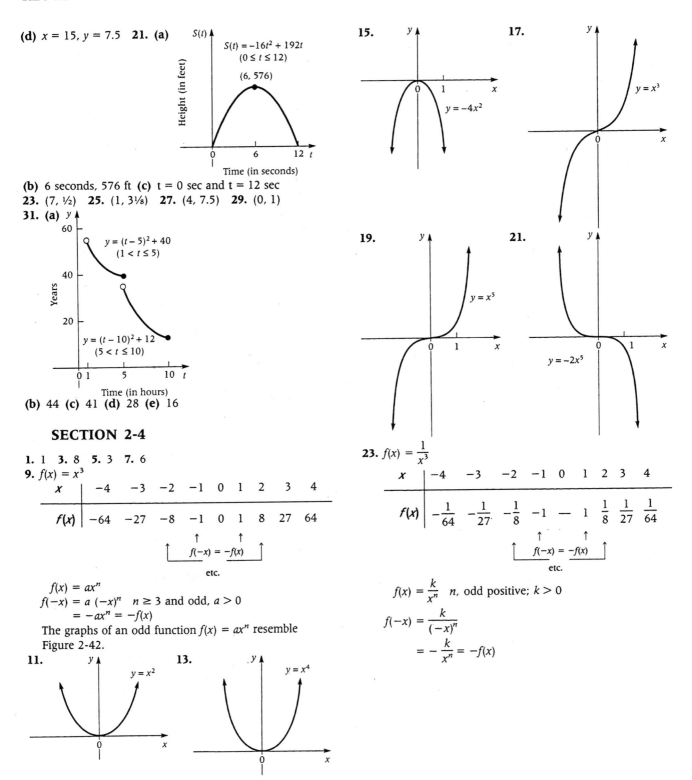

(d) $x = 15$, $y = 7.5$ **21. (a)**

$S(t) = -16t^2 + 192t$
$(0 \le t \le 12)$

$(6, 576)$

(b) 6 seconds, 576 ft **(c)** t = 0 sec and t = 12 sec
23. $(7, \frac{1}{2})$ **25.** $(1, 3\frac{1}{8})$ **27.** $(4, 7.5)$ **29.** $(0, 1)$
31. (a)

$y = (t - 5)^2 + 40$
$(1 < t \le 5)$

$y = (t - 10)^2 + 12$
$(5 < t \le 10)$

(b) 44 **(c)** 41 **(d)** 28 **(e)** 16

SECTION 2-4

1. 1 **3.** 8 **5.** 3 **7.** 6
9. $f(x) = x^3$

x	-4	-3	-2	-1	0	1	2	3	4
$f(x)$	-64	-27	-8	-1	0	1	8	27	64

$f(-x) = -f(x)$

etc.

$f(x) = ax^n$
$f(-x) = a(-x)^n$ $n \ge 3$ and odd, $a > 0$
  $= -ax^n = -f(x)$

The graphs of an odd function $f(x) = ax^n$ resemble Figure 2-42.

11. $y = x^2$
13. $y = x^4$

15. $y = -4x^2$
17. $y = x^3$
19. $y = x^5$
21. $y = -2x^5$

23. $f(x) = \dfrac{1}{x^3}$

x	-4	-3	-2	-1	0	1	2	3	4
$f(x)$	$-\frac{1}{64}$	$-\frac{1}{27}$	$-\frac{1}{8}$	-1	—	1	$\frac{1}{8}$	$\frac{1}{27}$	$\frac{1}{64}$

$f(-x) = -f(x)$

etc.

$f(x) = \dfrac{k}{x^n}$ n, odd positive; $k > 0$

$f(-x) = \dfrac{k}{(-x)^n}$

  $= -\dfrac{k}{x^n} = -f(x)$

The graphs of $f(x) = \dfrac{k}{x^n}$ (n, odd and positive) resemble Figure 2-47.

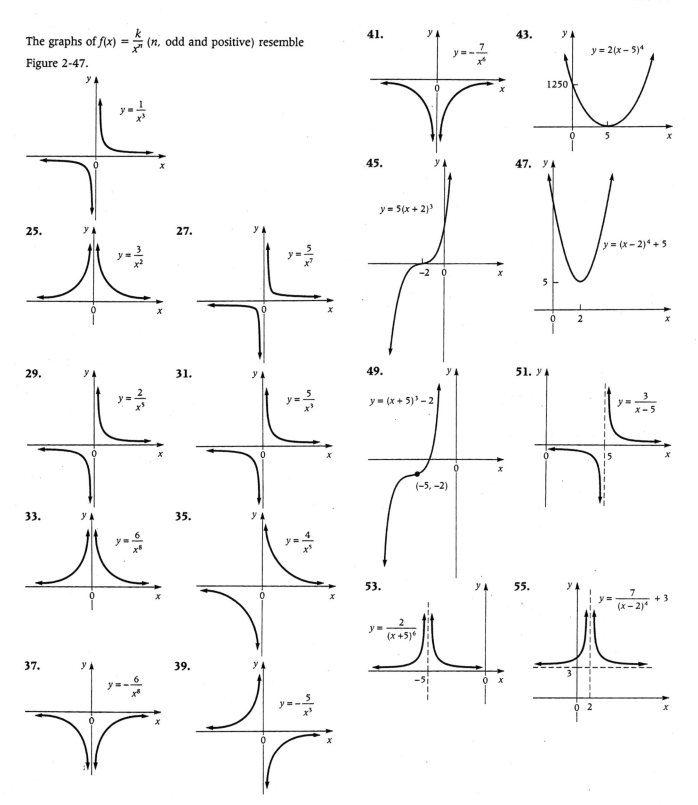

$y = \dfrac{1}{x^3}$

41. $y = -\dfrac{7}{x^6}$

43. $y = 2(x-5)^4$ 1250

25. $y = \dfrac{3}{x^2}$

27. $y = \dfrac{5}{x^7}$

45. $y = 5(x+2)^3$ -2

47. $y = (x-2)^4 + 5$ 5   2

29. $y = \dfrac{2}{x^5}$

31. $y = \dfrac{5}{x^3}$

49. $y = (x+5)^3 - 2$ $(-5, -2)$

51. $y = \dfrac{3}{x-5}$ 5

33. $y = \dfrac{6}{x^8}$

35. $y = \dfrac{4}{x^5}$

53. $y = \dfrac{2}{(x+5)^6}$ -5

55. $y = \dfrac{7}{(x-2)^4} + 3$ 3   2

37. $y = -\dfrac{6}{x^8}$

39. $y = -\dfrac{5}{x^3}$

57.

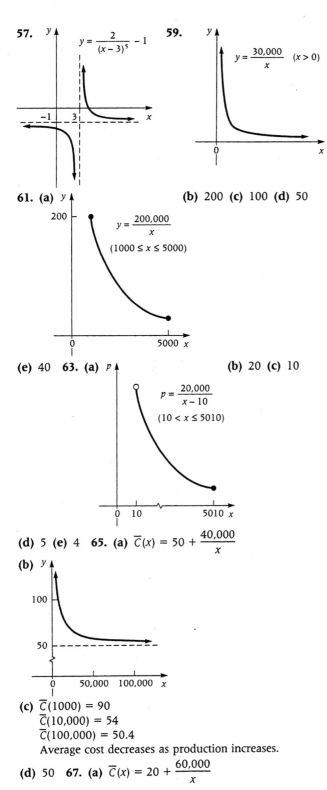

$y = \dfrac{2}{(x-3)^5} - 1$

59.

$y = \dfrac{30,000}{x}$ $(x > 0)$

(b)

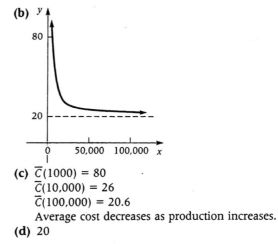

(b) 200 **(c)** 100 **(d)** 50

(c) $\overline{C}(1000) = 80$
$\overline{C}(10,000) = 26$
$\overline{C}(100,000) = 20.6$
Average cost decreases as production increases.
(d) 20

61. (a)

$y = \dfrac{200,000}{x}$

$(1000 \le x \le 5000)$

(e) 40   **63. (a)**

$p = \dfrac{20,000}{x-10}$

$(10 < x \le 5010)$

(b) 20 **(c)** 10

(d) 5 **(e)** 4   **65. (a)** $\overline{C}(x) = 50 + \dfrac{40,000}{x}$

(b)

(c) $\overline{C}(1000) = 90$
$\overline{C}(10,000) = 54$
$\overline{C}(100,000) = 50.4$
Average cost decreases as production increases.

(d) 50   **67. (a)** $\overline{C}(x) = 20 + \dfrac{60,000}{x}$

SECTION 2-5

1.

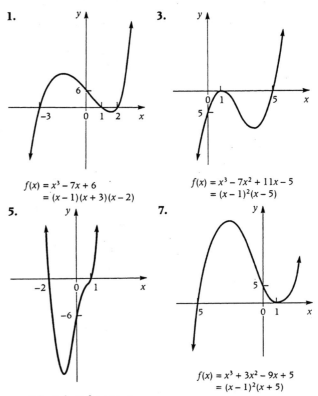

$f(x) = x^3 - 7x + 6$
$= (x-1)(x+3)(x-2)$

3.

$f(x) = x^3 - 7x^2 + 11x - 5$
$= (x-1)^2(x-5)$

5.

$y = 3x^4 - 3x^3 - 9x^2 + 15x - 6$
$= 3(x-1)^3(x+2)$

7.

$f(x) = x^3 + 3x^2 - 9x + 5$
$= (x-1)^2(x+5)$

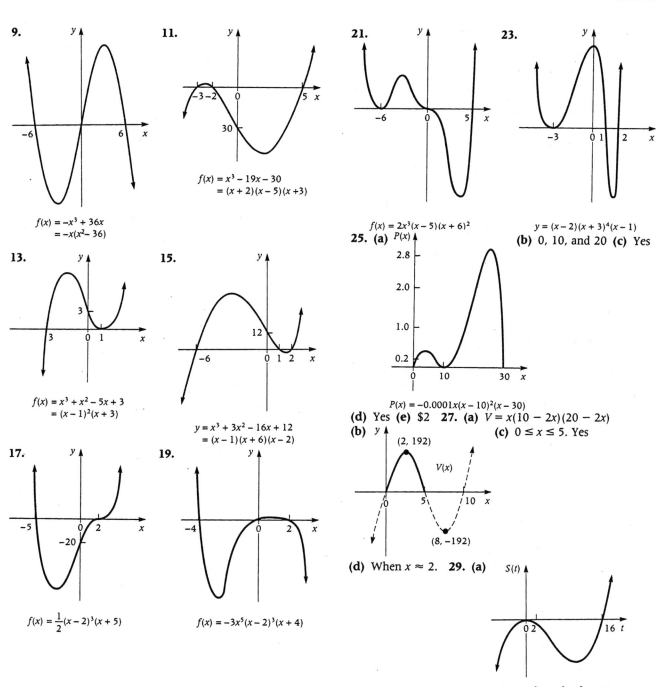

9.

$$f(x) = -x^3 + 36x$$
$$= -x(x^2 - 36)$$

11.

$$f(x) = x^3 - 19x - 30$$
$$= (x + 2)(x - 5)(x + 3)$$

21.

$$f(x) = 2x^3(x - 5)(x + 6)^2$$

23.

$$y = (x - 2)(x + 3)^4(x - 1)$$

13.

$$f(x) = x^3 + x^2 - 5x + 3$$
$$= (x - 1)^2(x + 3)$$

15.

$$y = x^3 + 3x^2 - 16x + 12$$
$$= (x - 1)(x + 6)(x - 2)$$

17.

$$f(x) = \frac{1}{2}(x - 2)^3(x + 5)$$

19.

$$f(x) = -3x^5(x - 2)^3(x + 4)$$

25. (a) $P(x)$

$$P(x) = -0.0001x(x - 10)^2(x - 30)$$

(b) 0, 10, and 20 **(c)** Yes **(d)** Yes **(e)** \$2   **27. (a)** $V = x(10 - 2x)(20 - 2x)$
(b) y **(c)** $0 \leq x \leq 5$. Yes

(2, 192)

$V(x)$

(8, −192)

(d) When $x \approx 2$.   **29. (a)** $S(t)$

$$S(t) = t^3 - 16t^2 = t^2(t - 16)$$

(b) 275 units to the left **(c)** 1600 units to the right
(d) $t = 0$ and $t = 16$ sec

SECTION 2-6

1.

$$y = \frac{(x-3)^2(x+8)}{(x-1)^2}$$

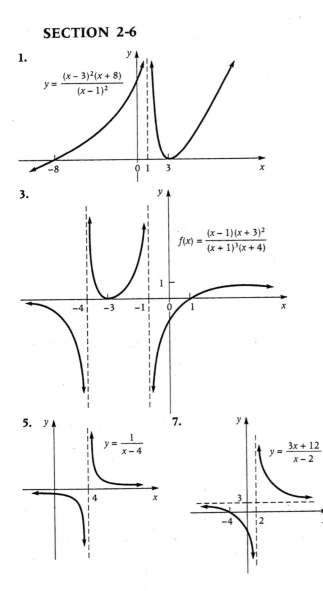

3.

$$f(x) = \frac{(x-1)(x+3)^2}{(x+1)^3(x+4)}$$

5.

$$y = \frac{1}{x-4}$$

7.

$$y = \frac{3x+12}{x-2}$$

9.

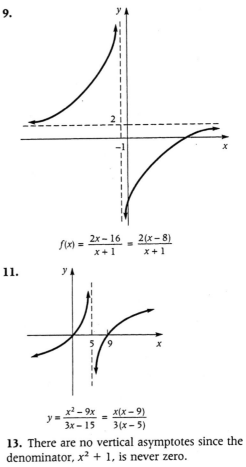

$$f(x) = \frac{2x-16}{x+1} = \frac{2(x-8)}{x+1}$$

11.

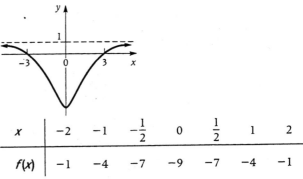

$$y = \frac{x^2-9x}{3x-15} = \frac{x(x-9)}{3(x-5)}$$

13. There are no vertical asymptotes since the denominator, $x^2 + 1$, is never zero.

x	-2	-1	$-\frac{1}{2}$	0	$\frac{1}{2}$	1	2
$f(x)$	-1	-4	-7	-9	-7	-4	-1

15. (a)

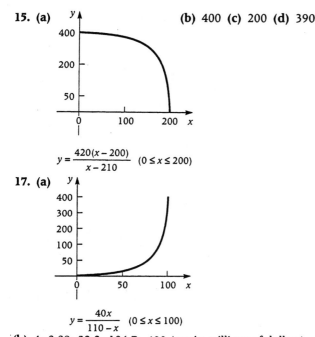

(b) 400 **(c)** 200 **(d)** 390

$$y = \frac{420(x - 200)}{x - 210} \quad (0 \le x \le 200)$$

17. (a)

$$y = \frac{40x}{110 - x} \quad (0 \le x \le 100)$$

(b) 4; 8.89; 33.3; 106.7; 400 (are in millions of dollars)

• EXTRA DIVIDENDS

1. For $y = 20x^2 + 10$, $S = 1600$
For $y = 100x - 90$, $S = 16{,}400$
$y = 20x^2 + 10$ is the better fit
3. $y = 48.4\,x + 768$

• CHAPTER HIGHLIGHTS

1. *Vertical shift.* Assume the graph of $y = f(x)$ is known. The graph of $y = f(x) + c$ is obtained by lifting the graph of $y = f(x)$ vertically by c units if $c > 0$ and lowering it by $|c|$ units if $c < 0$. **2.** *Horizontal shift.* Assume that the graph of $y = f(x)$ is known. The graph of $y = f(x - c)$ is obtained by shifting the graph of $y = f(x)$ horizontally to the right by c units if $c > 0$ and horizontally to the left by $|c|$ units if $c < 0$. **3.** *Reflection in the x-axis.* Assume the graph of $y = f(x)$ is known. The graph of $y = -f(x)$ is obtained by drawing the graph of $y = f(x)$ upside down. **4.** The graph of a function $f(x)$ is symmetric with respect to the vertical axis if $f(-x) = f(x)$. This means that if (x, y) is on the graph of $f(x)$, then $(-x, y)$ is also on the graph. Such a function is called an **even function.** **5.** If $f(-x) = -f(x)$, then $f(x)$ is an **odd function** and its graph is symmetric with respect to the origin. **6.** $y = ax^2 + bx + c$ with $a \ne 0$; x-coordinate of the vertex is $-b/2a$; y-intercept $= (0, c)$. **7.** If $a > 0$, the parabola opens up; if $a < 0$, the parabola opens down. **8.** Set $y = 0$ and solve for x or use the quadratic formula $x = (-b \pm \sqrt{b^2 - 4ac})/2a$. **9.** 2 **10.** Vertex

11. Sales revenue = (number of units sold)(unit price)
12. Profit = sales revenue − cost **13.** Set $P(x) = 0$ and solve for x. **14.** Set the supply equation equal to the demand equation and solve for x. **15.** Time series
16. $f(x) = a_n x^n + a_{n-1} x^{n-1} + \ldots + a_1 x + a_0$
17. $n - 1, n$ **18.**

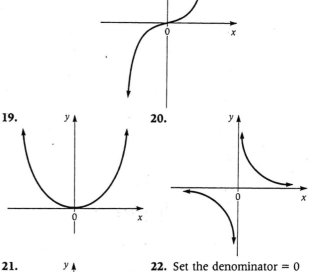

19.

20.

21.

22. Set the denominator = 0

and solve for x. Verify that the numerator does not equal 0 at the solution values of x. If the numerator equals 0 at a solution value of x, then the graph of the rational function does not have a vertical asymptote at that solution value of x. **23.** $\overline{C}(x) = C(x)/x$. **24.** If the factor yielding the x-intercept has an odd exponent, then the graph of the function crosses the x-axis at that x-intercept. If the factor yielding the x-intercept has an even exponent, then the graph of the function is tangent to and does not cross the x-axis at that x-intercept.
25. *Step 1:* Find the y-intercept by setting $x = 0$ and solving for y. *Step 2:* Find any x-intercept(s) by setting $y = 0$ and solving for x. Apply the x-intercept rule to determine tangency or crossing. Draw a sign chart (optional). *Step 3:* Determine the behavior of the function as x gets more and more positive and, also, as x gets more and more negative. Use the highest powered term for this analysis.
26. *Step 1:* Find the y-intercept by setting $x = 0$ and solving

for *y*. *Step 2:* Find any *x*-intercept(s) by setting $y = 0$ and solving for *x*. This results in setting the numerator $= 0$ and solving for *x*. Apply the *x*-intercept rule to determine tangency or crossing. *Step 3:* Find any vertical asymptotes by setting the denominator $= 0$ and solving for *x*. Then, verify that the numerator $\neq 0$ at the solution values of *x*. Apply the vertical asymptote rule. *Step 4:* Determine the behavior of the function as *x* gets more and more positive and, also, as *x* gets more and more negative. Use the quotient

$$\frac{\text{highest powered term of numerator}}{\text{highest powered term of denominator}}$$

for this analysis.   **27.** If the exponent of the factor yielding the vertical asymptote is even, the graph approaches the same end of the vertical asymptote from both sides. If the exponent of the factor yielding the vertical asymptote is odd, the graph approaches different ends of the vertical asymptote from both sides.

• REVIEW EXERCISES

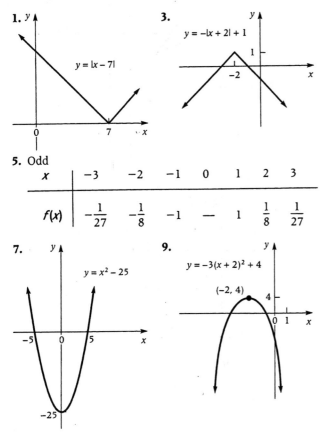

5. Odd

x	−3	−2	−1	0	1	2	3
$f(x)$	$-\dfrac{1}{27}$	$-\dfrac{1}{8}$	-1	—	1	$\dfrac{1}{8}$	$\dfrac{1}{27}$

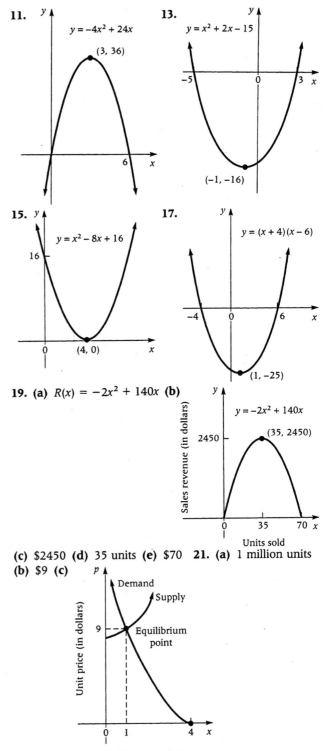

19. (a) $R(x) = -2x^2 + 140x$ **(b)**

(c) \$2450 **(d)** 35 units **(e)** \$70   **21. (a)** 1 million units **(b)** \$9 **(c)**

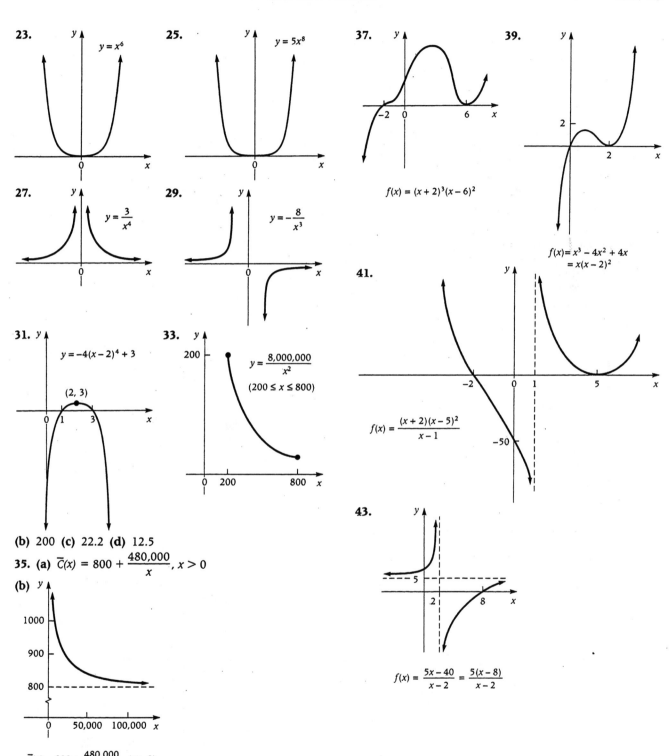

23. $y = x^6$

25. $y = 5x^8$

27. $y = \dfrac{3}{x^4}$

29. $y = -\dfrac{8}{x^3}$

31. $y = -4(x-2)^4 + 3$ (2, 3)

33. $y = \dfrac{8{,}000{,}000}{x^2}$ $(200 \le x \le 800)$

(b) 200 **(c)** 22.2 **(d)** 12.5

35. (a) $\overline{C}(x) = 800 + \dfrac{480{,}000}{x}$, $x > 0$

(b) $\overline{C}(x) = 800 + \dfrac{480{,}000}{x}$ $(x > 0)$

(c) \$1040; \$848; \$804.80 **(d)** \$800

37. $f(x) = (x+2)^3(x-6)^2$

39. $f(x) = x^3 - 4x^2 + 4x = x(x-2)^2$

41. $f(x) = \dfrac{(x+2)(x-5)^2}{x-1}$

43. $f(x) = \dfrac{5x-40}{x-2} = \dfrac{5(x-8)}{x-2}$

45.

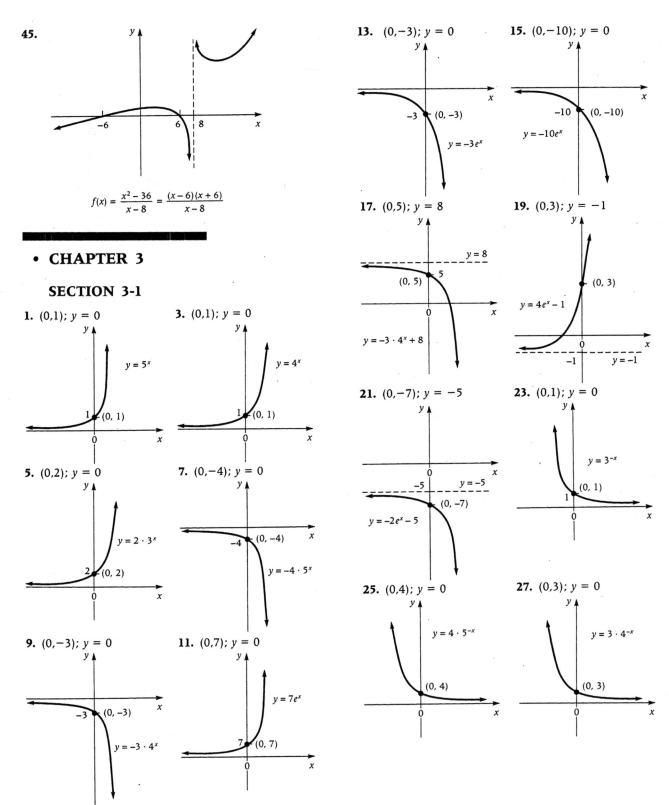

$$f(x) = \frac{x^2 - 36}{x - 8} = \frac{(x-6)(x+6)}{x-8}$$

• **CHAPTER 3**

SECTION 3-1

1. $(0,1)$; $y = 0$

$y = 5^x$
1 $(0, 1)$

3. $(0,1)$; $y = 0$

$y = 4^x$
1 $(0, 1)$

5. $(0,2)$; $y = 0$

$y = 2 \cdot 3^x$
2 $(0, 2)$

7. $(0,-4)$; $y = 0$

-4 $(0, -4)$
$y = -4 \cdot 5^x$

9. $(0,-3)$; $y = 0$

-3 $(0, -3)$
$y = -3 \cdot 4^x$

11. $(0,7)$; $y = 0$

$y = 7e^x$
7 $(0, 7)$

13. $(0,-3)$; $y = 0$

-3 $(0, -3)$
$y = -3e^x$

15. $(0,-10)$; $y = 0$

-10 $(0, -10)$
$y = -10e^x$

17. $(0,5)$; $y = 8$

$y = 8$
5
$(0, 5)$
$y = -3 \cdot 4^x + 8$

19. $(0,3)$; $y = -1$

$(0, 3)$
$y = 4e^x - 1$
-1 $y = -1$

21. $(0,-7)$; $y = -5$

-5 $y = -5$
$(0, -7)$
$y = -2e^x - 5$

23. $(0,1)$; $y = 0$

$y = 3^{-x}$
$(0, 1)$
1

25. $(0,4)$; $y = 0$

$y = 4 \cdot 5^{-x}$
$(0, 4)$

27. $(0,3)$; $y = 0$

$y = 3 \cdot 4^{-x}$
$(0, 3)$

29. $(0,-2); y = 0$

31. $(0,3); y = 0$

45. $(0,0); y = 10$

47. $(0,1); y = 0$

33. $(0,10); y = 0$

35. $(0,-7); y = 0$

49. $(0,1); y = 0$

51. $(0,6); y = 1$

37. $(0,7)\ y = 5$

39. $(0,5); y = 1$

53. $(0,4); y = 1$

55. $(0,-1); y = 1$

41. $(0,28); y = 30$

43. $(0,60); y = 30$

57. $(0,10); y = 0$

59. $(0,7); y = 0$

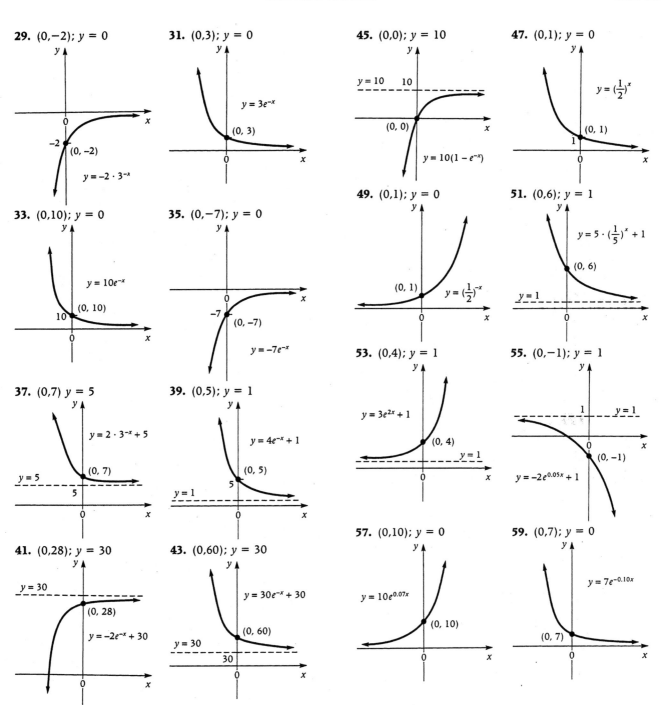

61. $(0,0)$; $y = 10$

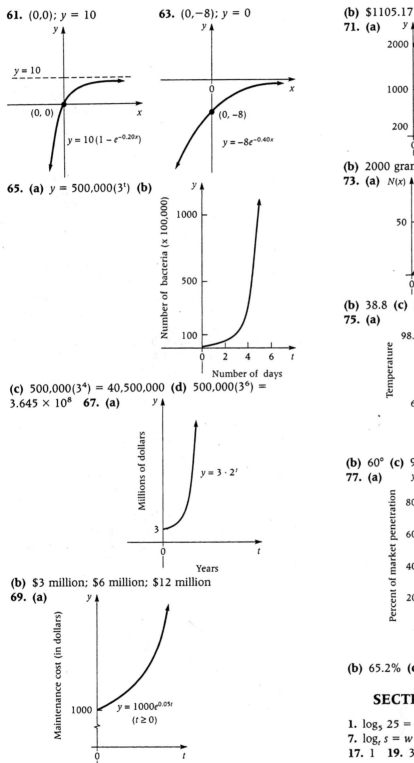

$y = 10$

$(0, 0)$

$y = 10(1 - e^{-0.20x})$

63. $(0,-8)$; $y = 0$

$(0, -8)$

$y = -8e^{-0.40x}$

65. (a) $y = 500,000(3^t)$ **(b)**

Number of bacteria (×100,000)

Number of days

(c) $500,000(3^4) = 40,500,000$ **(d)** $500,000(3^6) = 3.645 \times 10^8$ **67. (a)**

Millions of dollars

$y = 3 \cdot 2^t$

Years

(b) $3 million; $6 million; $12 million
69. (a)

Maintenance cost (in dollars)

$y = 1000e^{0.05t}$
$(t \geq 0)$

(b) $1105.17
71. (a)

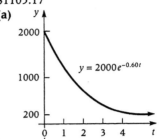

$y = 2000e^{-0.60t}$

(b) 2000 grams **(c)** 1481.6 grams **(d)** 330.6 grams
73. (a) $N(x)$

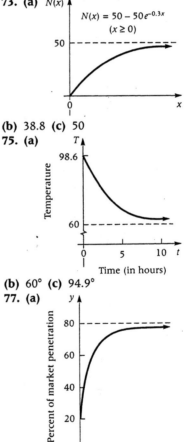

$N(x) = 50 - 50e^{-0.3x}$
$(x \geq 0)$

50

(b) 38.8 **(c)** 50
75. (a) T

Temperature

98.6

60

Time (in hours)

(b) 60° **(c)** 94.9°
77. (a) y

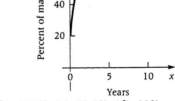

Percent of market penetration

Years

(b) 65.2% **(c)** 79.9% **(d)** 80%

SECTION 3-2

1. $\log_5 25 = 2$ **3.** $\log_2 64 = 6$ **5.** $\log_{10} 0.01 = -2$
7. $\log_t s = w$ **9.** $\log_b N = x + y$ **11.** 2 **13.** 0 **15.** 1
17. 1 **19.** 3 **21.** 5 **23.** 2 **25.** 5 **27.** 0 **29.** 0 **31.** 1

33. 3   **35.** 5   **37.** (1,0)

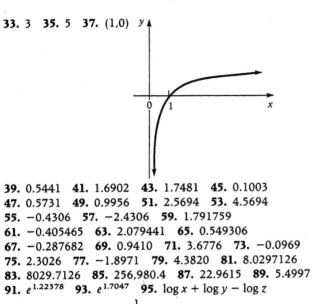

39. 0.5441   **41.** 1.6902   **43.** 1.7481   **45.** 0.1003
47. 0.5731   **49.** 0.9956   **51.** 2.5694   **53.** 4.5694
55. −0.4306   **57.** −2.4306   **59.** 1.791759
61. −0.405465   **63.** 2.079441   **65.** 0.549306
67. −0.287682   **69.** 0.9410   **71.** 3.6776   **73.** −0.0969
75. 2.3026   **77.** −1.8971   **79.** 4.3820   **81.** 8.0297126
83. 8029.7126   **85.** 256,980.4   **87.** 22.9615   **89.** 5.4997
91. $e^{1.22378}$ **93.** $e^{1.7047}$ **95.** $\log x + \log y - \log z$

97. $2 \log x + \log y$ **99.** $\frac{1}{2} (\log x + \log y)$

101. (a) $108,788.9 thousand
    $112,875.5 thousand
    $119,879.3 thousand
    $124,728.3 thousand
(b) $355.6 thousand; If the company increases its
advertising expenditures from 20 to 21 thousand dollars,
sales increase by $355.6 thousand. **(c)** $246.2 thousand
103. (a) $13.22 thousand; revenue from the sale of 1 unit.
    $16.13 thousand; revenue from the sale of 2
    units.
    $20.04 thousand; revenue from the sale of 5
    units.
    $23.03 thousand; revenue from the sale of 10
    units.
(b) $0.41 thousand; If the company increases its sales from
10 units to 11 units, revenue will increase by $0.41
thousand. **(c)** $0.21 thousand   **105. (a)** 2000 **(b)** 5.49
days **(c)** 6.93 days   **107. (a)** 13.9 years **(b)** 22.0 years
109. (a) $y = \dfrac{\ln p - 1}{0.3}$ **(b)** 4,341,950

SECTION 3-3

1. $a = 3.19$, $b = 1.37$ **3.** $a = 5.71$, $b = 1.52$ **5.** $a = 9.72$,
$b = 1.54$ **7. (a)** $y = 0.997(1.163)^x$ **(b)** 5.25
9. (a) $y = 2.965(1.157)^x$ **(b)** 9.52

• CHAPTER HIGHLIGHTS

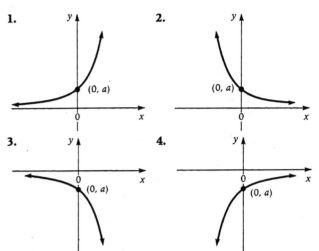

5. *Step 1:* Begin with the graph of $y = ab^x$ or $y = ab^{-x}$.
Step 2: Vertical Shift. If $c > 0$, lift the graph of Step 1
vertically by c units. If $c < 0$, lower the graph of Step 1
vertically by $|c|$ units.   **6.** $y = ae^{-kt} + c$ where y denotes the
temperature of the cooling object after t units of time and c
denotes the temperature of the medium surrounding the
cooling object. The letters a and k represent constants
associated with the cooling object.
7. *Modified exponential model:* $y = A - Be^{-mx}$

Logistic growth model: $y = \dfrac{A}{1 + Be^{-mx}}$

where y denotes the percentage of the market penetrated
by the product x years after it has been introduced; A and B
are constants.   **8.** Exponent   **9.** Natural (or Napierian)
10. Common   **11.** $\ln b$ **12.** 1   **13.** Let x, y, and b be
positive real numbers with $b = 1$. Let p be any real
number.
Property 1: $\log_b xy = \log_b x + \log_b y$
The logarithm of a product of two numbers equals the sum
of their logarithms. Example: $\log (5 \cdot 8) = \log 5 + \log 8$
Property 2: $\log_b(x/y) = \log_b x - \log_b y$
The logarithm of a quotient of two numbers equals the
difference of their logarithms. *Example:* $\log(7/9) = \log 7 -$
$\log 9$
Property 3: $\log_b x^p = p \cdot \log_b x$
The logarithm of the pth power of a number equals p times
the logarithm of the number. *Example:* $\log 5^3 = 3 \log 5$
Property 4: $\log_b b = 1$
The logarithm of its base equals 1. *Example:* $\log_5 5 = 1$
Property 5: $\log_b 1 = 0$.
The logarithm of 1 equals 0. *Example:* $\log_8 1 = 0$
14. $\log y = \log a + x \cdot \log b$ **15.** straight line

• **REVIEW EXERCISES**

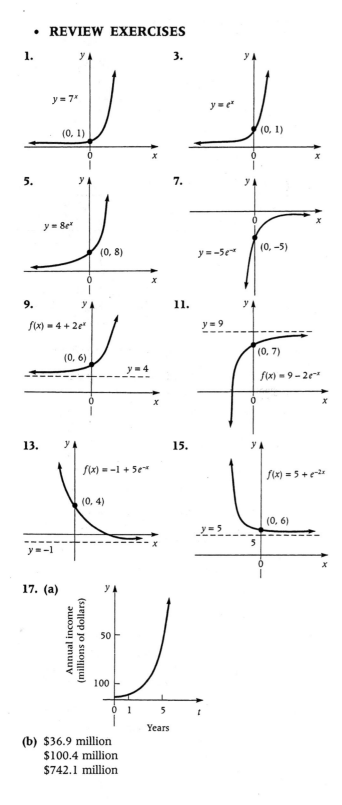

1. $y = 7^x$ (0, 1)

3. $y = e^x$ (0, 1)

5. $y = 8e^x$ (0, 8)

7. $y = -5e^{-x}$ (0, -5)

9. $f(x) = 4 + 2e^x$ (0, 6) $y = 4$

11. $y = 9$ (0, 7) $f(x) = 9 - 2e^{-x}$

13. $f(x) = -1 + 5e^{-x}$ (0, 4) $y = -1$

15. $f(x) = 5 + e^{-2x}$ (0, 6) $y = 5$

17. (a)

Annual income (millions of dollars)

(b) $36.9 million
$100.4 million
$742.1 million

19. (a)

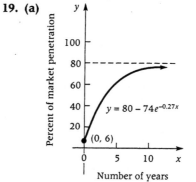

$y = 80 - 74e^{-0.27x}$ (0, 6)
Number of years
Percent of market penetration

(b) 47% **(c)** 75% **(d)** 80% **21.** $\log 10{,}000 = 4$
23. $\ln y = x$ **25.** 2 **27.** 0 **29.** 1 **31.** -0.0131
33. 7.7179 **35.** 36,307.8 **37.** $e^{1.5260563}$
39. $\log s + \log t - \log r$ **41.** $5(\log u + \log v)$
43. $\log u + \log v$ **45.**

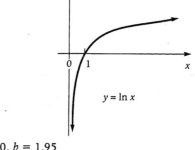

$y = \ln x$

47. $a = 2.10$, $b = 1.95$
$y = 2.10(1.95)^x$

• **CHAPTER 4**

SECTION 4-1

1. $210; $1210 **3.** $200; $5200 **5.** $60; $2060
7. (a) $S = 10{,}000 + 900t$ **(b)**

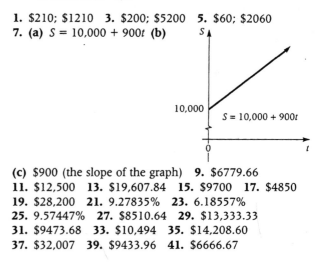

$10{,}000$ $S = 10{,}000 + 900t$

(c) $900 (the slope of the graph) **9.** $6779.66
11. $12,500 **13.** $19,607.84 **15.** $9700 **17.** $4850
19. $28,200 **21.** 9.27835% **23.** 6.18557%
25. 9.57447% **27.** $8510.64 **29.** $13,333.33
31. $9473.68 **33.** $10,494 **35.** $14,208.60
37. $32,007 **39.** $9433.96 **41.** $6666.67

43. (a) $2700 **(b)** $3300 **(c)** 16.3634%
45. (a) $5119.45 **(b)** 7.16736% **47.** $612
49. (a) $21,965 **(b)** $1035 **51.** $29,415

SECTION 4-2

1. $2208.04; $1208.04 **3.** $14,326.78; $6326.78
5. $6348.67; $1348.67 **7.** $4836.68; $1836.68
9. $5404.51 **11.** $2941.34 **13.** $1930.93 **15.** $5827.57
17. $4165.78 **19. (a)** $22,080.40 **(b)** $12,080.40
21. $1326.65 **23.** $24,405.82 **25.** $1879.82
27. $744.09 **29. (a)** $7013.80 **(b)** $8884.87
31. 6.09% **33.** 12.6825% **35.** 11.72 ≈ 12 years
37. 9.0065 ≈ 9 years **39.** 13.87 ≈ 14 years
41. 17.5 years **43.** 1.232926 ≈ 1.23
45. 1.489354 ≈ 1.49 **47.** 1.197031 ≈ 1.20
49. 1.309921 ≈ 1.31 **51.** 1.377079 ≈ 1.38
53. $14,917.59 **55.** $40,530.03 **57.** 8.08%
59. 5.92635% **61.** 8.5% compounded daily
63. 8.75% compounded monthly **65.** $7459.12
67. $8099.15 **69.** $4965.85 **71.** $3477.43
73. 7.25082% **75.** 9.41743%

SECTION 4-3

1. 312 **3.** 38,227 **5.** $75,401.26 **7.** 165,329.77
9. $45,632.79 **11.** $77,663.30 **13.** $173,596.26
15. $46,545.45 **17. (a)** $49,598.93 **(b)** $19,598.93
19. $6183.48 **21.** $6122.26 **23.** $16,770.91
25. 228.80304 **27.** 376.0953 **29.** $48,380.17
31. $48,783.34

SECTION 4-4

1. $56,741.78 **3.** $29,754.95 **5.** $109,161.26
7. $57,876.61 **9.** $30,647.60 **11.** $112,436.10
13. $24,924.42 **15.** 6540.57 **17.** $15,204.29
19. $19,327.03 **21.** $6671.38 **23.** 41.659417
25. 103.62462 **27.** $25,056.12 **29.** 25,202.28
31. $35,192.67

SECTION 4-5

1. $1440.49 **3.** $704.62 **5.** $3721.75 **7.** $699.78
9. $7712.77 **11.** $1836.62 **13.** $5886.54 **15.** $2201.25
17. $411.57 **19.** $352.31 **21.** $1956.11
23. (a) $12,928.25
    (b) $8287

(c) Sinking fund schedule

Payment number	Payment	Interest	Total
1	$12,928.25	$0	$12,928.25
2	12,928.25	1292.83	27,149.33
3	12,928.25	2714.93	42,792.51
4	12,928.25	4279.25	60,000.01

25. (a) $23,138.32
    (b) $25,691.60
    (c) Amortization schedule

Payment number	Payment	Interest	Principal reduction	Balance
0				$90,000.00
1	$23,138.32	$8100.00	$15,038.32	74,961.68
2	23,138.32	6746.55	16,391.77	58,569.91
3	23,138.32	5271.29	17,867.03	40,702.88
4	23,138.32	3663.26	19,475.06	21,227.82
5	23,138.32	1910.50	21,227.82	0.00
		25,691.60		

(d) $58,569.91
27. (a) $804.62 **(b)** $96,857.75 **29. (a)** $1080.15
(b) $194,427.00; $104,427.90 **(c)** $48,558.19

31. For a loan of L dollars: $R_L = \dfrac{L}{a_{\overline{n}|i}}$

For a loan of $2L$ dollars: $R_{2L} = \dfrac{2L}{a_{\overline{n}|i}} = 2R_L$ $\Bigg\} R_{2L} = 2R_L$

Let $A = R \cdot a_{\overline{n}|i}$, with fixed values of n and i. Then, $R = \dfrac{A}{a_{\overline{n}|i}} = cA$, where $c = \dfrac{1}{a_{\overline{n}|i}}$ is a constant. If $A = kL$, $R = c(kL) = k(cL)$. Hence, the periodic payment is proportional to the amount of the loan. **33.** For interest rate of 9.75% compounded monthly: $859.15; $209,294. For interest rate of 10.75% compounded monthly: $933.48; $236,052.80 **35.** $430,941.61 **37.** $1330.36 **39.** $3105.56

SECTION 4-6

1. $5127.98 **3.** $2191.05 **5.** $1914.80 **7.** $3656.26
9. $205.53 **11.** $2515.06 (years 1-2); $3772.59 (years 3-5) **13.** 7 quarters of deferment **15.** 17 monthly periods of deferment **17.** 21 quarterly periods of deferment **19.** $8797.85 **21.** $8417.48 **23.** $5120.61
25. $26,952.80; $14,836.16 **27.** $584,109.57; $287,343.90 **29.** $10,972.49 **31.** $17,274.71
33. $1109.41 **35.** $8142.58; $6427.83 **37.** $16,211.10; $6,847.74 **39.** $92.54 **41.** $1719.52

• EXTRA DIVIDENDS

1. $10,734.80 **3.** $36,663.67 **5.** $109,375 **7. (b)** Less than 10%, but more than 0% **9.** $80,640

• CHAPTER HIGHLIGHTS

1. $I = Prt$ where I is the amount of simple interest, P is the principal, r is the annual rate, and t is the time in years. **2.** Total amount, S, is the sum of principal and interest and is given by the formula $S = P + I$ or by the equivalent formula $S = P(1 + rt)$. **3.** Present value (or principal) is the amount of money needed now that will result in a specified future value at a given interest rate. Present value (assuming simple interest) is determined by the formula $P = S/(1 + rt)$. **4.** Simple interest is based on the principal whereas simple discount is based on the maturity value. **5.** $D = Sdt$ where D is the amount of simple discount, S is the maturity value, d is the discount rate, and t is the time in years. **6.** The amount of money received by a borrower using a discount note is called the **proceeds.** Proceeds, B, are determined by the formula $B = S - D$ or by the equivalent formula $B = S(1 - dt)$. **7.** Maturity value **8.** $S = P(1 + i)^n$ where S is the compound amount, i is the interest rate per period, and n is the total number of conversion periods.

$$\underset{P \longrightarrow\hspace{1.5cm} S = P(1 + i)^n}{\underline{|1_{\,|}2_{\,|}3_{\,|}\,\ldots\ldots\,_{\,|}n_{\,|}}}$$

9. The **interest rate per conversion period** is the annual rate divided by the number of conversion periods per year. It is given by the formula $i = r/m$ where r is the annual rate and m is the number of conversion periods per year.
10. The **total number of conversion periods,** n, is the number of conversion periods (or compoundings) throughout the duration of the investment. The formula for n is $n = mt$ where m is the number of conversion periods (or compoundings) per year and t is the duration (time) of the investment in years. **11.** $P = S(1 + i)^{-n}$ where P is the present value, S is the future value, i is the interest rate per conversion period, and n is the total number of conversion periods.

$$\underset{P = S(1 + i)^{-n} \longleftarrow\hspace{1.5cm} S}{\underline{|1_{\,|}2_{\,|}3_{\,|}\,\ldots\ldots\,_{\,|}n_{\,|}}}$$

12. If the compound amount of P dollars, invested for a given length of time at an annual rate r compounded m times a year equals the compound amount of P dollars invested for the same time period at an annual rate s compounded k times per year, then the rates are said to be *equivalent.* The following equation is used to find equivalent rates: $(1 + r/m)^m = (1 + s/k)^k$ where r, s, m, and k are defined in the preceding sentence. **13.** The **effective rate** is the rate s compounded annually that is equivalent to an annual rate r compounded m times per year. The effective rate is given by $s = (1 + r/m)^m - 1$. **14.** $S = Pe^{rt}$ where S is the future value, P is the present value (or principal), r is

the annual rate compounded continuously, and t is the duration (time) of the investment in years.

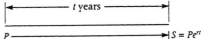

15. $P = Se^{-rt}$ where S is the future value, P is the present value (or principal), r is the annual rate compounded continuously, and t is the duration (time) of the investment in years.

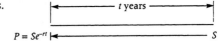

16. $s = e^r - 1$ **17.** An **annuity** is a series of equal payments made at equal intervals of time. **18.** If each payment of an annuity is made at the end of a payment period, the annuity is called an **ordinary annuity.** If each payment of an annuity is made at the beginning of a payment period, the annuity is called an **annuity due.**
19. The **total amount** (or future value) or an ordinary annuity is the sum of the compound amounts of the individual payments and is determined by the formula

$$S = R\left[\frac{(1 + i)^n - 1}{i}\right]$$
$$= R \cdot s_{\overline{n}|i}$$

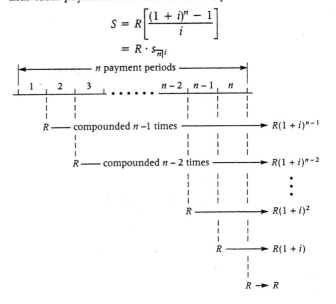

20.

$$S = R\left[\frac{(1 + i)^{n+1} - 1}{i} - 1\right]$$

Here, i is the interest rate per conversion period, n is the total number of conversion periods, and R is the periodic payment.

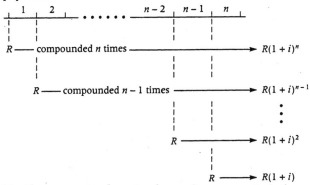

21. The **present value,** A, of an ordinary annuity is the sum of the present values of the individual payments and is determined by the formula

$$A = R\left[\frac{1 - (1 + i)^{-n}}{i}\right]$$
$$= R \cdot a_{\overline{n}|i}$$

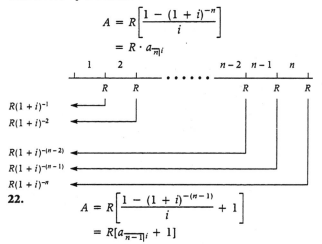

22.

$$A = R\left[\frac{1 - (1 + i)^{-(n-1)}}{i} + 1\right]$$
$$= R[a_{\overline{n-1}|i} + 1]$$

Here, i is the interest rate per conversion period, n is the total number of conversion periods, and R is the periodic payment.

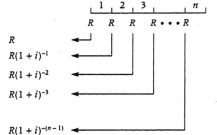

23. If a person desires to accumulate a sum of money by making periodic deposits into a fund so that, at the end of a specified time period, the deposits plus the interest earned equal the desired accumulated amount, the fund is called a **sinking fund.** The periodic payment is determined by the

formula $R = S/s_{\overline{n}|i}$ where S is the desired accumulated amount, i is the interest rate per conversion period, n is the total number of conversion periods, and $s_{\overline{n}|i} = [(1 + i)^n - 1]/i$. **24.** The interest for a given period is the product of i and the total value of the fund at the beginning of the period. **25.** To repay a loan by an annuity is to **amortize** the loan. The formula for determining the periodic payment is $R = A/a_{\overline{n}|i}$ where A is the amount of the loan, i is the interest rate per conversion period, n is the total number of conversion periods, and $a_{\overline{n}|i} = [1 - (1 + i)^{-n}]/i$. **26. (a)** The **interest** for each period is determined by multiplying i times the previous period's balance. **(b)** The **balance** is the difference between the previous period's balance and the principal reduction for the given period. **27.** Find the present value of the remaining annuity. **28.** *Step 1:* Compute the simple interest on the original loan amount (the principal) for the term of the loan. *Step 2:* Add the interest to the original loan amount. *Step 3:* Divide the resulting sum by the number of payments. This method results in a larger periodic payment than that determined by using the annuity formula. This is because the add-on-interest method entails computation of interest on the original loan amount for the entire term of the loan despite the fact that payments are made throughout the term of the loan. **29.** $(1 + i)^n$ where i is the interest rate per period and n is the number of periods that the payment is to be brought forward. **30.** $(1 + i)^{-n}$ where i is the interest rate per period and n is the number of periods that the payment is to be brought back. **31.** $s_{\overline{n}|i}$ where i is the interest rate per period and n is the number of payments in the annuity. **32.** $a_{\overline{n}|i}$ where i is the interest rate per period and n is the number of payments in the annuity. **33.** A **variable annuity** is an annuity where, at some point, later payments differ from earlier payments. **34.** A **deferred annuity** is an annuity whose payments begin later than at the end of the first period. **35.** A **complex annuity** is an annuity where the payment period does not coincide with the conversion (or interest) period. A **simple annuity** is an annuity where the payment period does coincide with the conversion (or interest) period. **36.** Interest rate

• REVIEW EXERCISES

1. (a) $540 **(b)** $1540 **3. (a)** $8000 **(b)** $18,000
5. (a) $8333.33 **(b)** $8250; $250 **7.** $23,699.19
9. $5,536.76 **11.** $30,777.84 **13.** $9577.74
15. 9.3807% **17.** 8.2195% **19.** $19,486.24
21. $14,552.57 **23.** $5950.99 **25.** $143.33
27. $6831.90 **29.** $331.11 **31.** $39,927.10
33. $5525.20 **35.** $2526.17 **37.** $122.44 **39.** $8926.48
41. $8094.06 **43.** $7630.85 **45.** $7681.19
47. $3537.08; $2380.35 **49.** $60,852.60; $38,179.68
51. $2133.77

• CHAPTER 5

SECTION 5-1

1. $(-3, -4)$ **3.** $\left(\frac{1}{2}, 6\right)$ **5.** $(5, 2)$ **7.** $\left(\frac{10}{7}, \frac{45}{7}\right)$ **9.** $(6, 4)$
11. $(2, 3)$ **13.** $(3, 15)$ **15.** $(7, 48)$ **17.** $(-1, 2)$
19. $(-1, 1)$

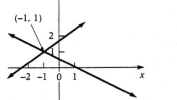

21. $\left(\frac{97}{28}, \frac{-19}{28}\right)$

23. $(4, 3)$

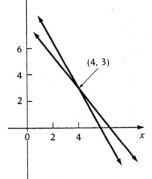

25. $(-5, 2)$ **27.** $(1, -5)$ **29.** $(1, -3)$ **31.** $(-1, -2)$
33. Eq. (1) $5x - 7y = 70 \rightarrow 10x - 14y = 140$
  Eq. (2) $-10x + 14y = 120$ $\underline{-10x + 14y = 120}$
                              $0 = 260$

Eq. (1) becomes $y = \frac{5}{7}x - 10$

Eq. (2) becomes $y = \frac{5}{7}x + \frac{60}{7}$

Lines of equal slope with different intercepts.

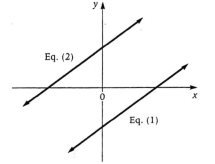

35. No solution   **37.** No solution   **39.** No solution
41. 2 lb meat, 1 lb spinach   **43.** 4000 wagons, 1000 cars
45. (400, 10,000); When 400 units are sold, the company's
sale revenue and cost are equal at $10,000.   **47.** $25,000
in corporate bonds, $75,000 in U.S. Treasury bonds
49. 5 lb cashews, 15 lb peanuts   **51. (a)** 100,000 units
(b) Machine I; $600,000 **(c)** Machine II; $880,000

SECTION 5-2

1. $\begin{bmatrix} 2 & 7 & | & 9 \\ -1 & 4 & | & 15 \end{bmatrix}$ **3.** $\begin{bmatrix} 3 & 0 & | & -1 \\ 4 & 3 & | & 7 \end{bmatrix}$

5. $\begin{bmatrix} 1 & 2 & 5 & | & 6 \\ 2 & -3 & -8 & | & 4 \\ -1 & 4 & 5 & | & 9 \end{bmatrix}$

7. $\begin{bmatrix} 5 & -7 & 0 & | & 4 \\ 0 & 3 & 0 & | & 9 \\ 1 & 0 & 1 & | & 15 \end{bmatrix}$

9. $\begin{aligned} 4x_1 + 8x_2 &= 5 \\ -2x_1 + 6x_2 &= 0 \end{aligned}$ **11.** $\begin{aligned} -x_1 + x_2 + 2x_3 &= 3 \\ 4x_1 \quad\quad - x_3 &= 5 \\ 2x_1 + x_2 \quad - x_3 &= 6 \end{aligned}$

13. $\begin{aligned} x_1 \quad + x_3 &= 2 \\ x_2 \quad &= 3 \\ x_3 &= 5 \end{aligned}$ **15.** Not a final tableau

17. Final tableau; $x_1 = 8, x_2 = 3$ **19.** Final tableau; $x_1 = 2$,
$x_2 = -4, x_3 = 5$ **21.** Not a final tableau
23. Let $x_1 =$ no. of conservative sweaters
   $x_2 =$ no. of sporty sweaters
   $x_3 =$ no. of practical sweaters
   $5x_1 + 2x_2 + 3x_3 = 660$ (cutting)
   $3x_1 + 2x_2 + 4x_3 = 480$ (sewing)
   $x_1 + 2x_2 + x_3 = 220$ (inspection)
25. $\begin{aligned} x_1 + x_2 \quad\quad &= 300 \\ x_3 + x_4 &= 200 \\ x_1 \quad + x_3 \quad &= 150 \\ x_2 \quad\quad + x_4 &= 350 \end{aligned}$ $\left.\vphantom{\begin{aligned} x \\ x \end{aligned}}\right\}$ production capacities $\left.\vphantom{\begin{aligned} x \\ x \end{aligned}}\right\}$ demands
27. Let $x_1 =$ investment in real estate
   $x_2 =$ investment in stocks
   $x_3 =$ investment in bonds

$$x_1 + \quad x_2 + \quad x_3 = 2{,}000{,}000 \text{ (funds)}$$
$$0.12x_1 + 0.09x_2 + 0.08x_3 = 0.11(2{,}000{,}000) \text{ (return)}$$
$$4x_1 + \quad 6x_2 + \quad 3x_3 = 5(2{,}000{,}000) \text{ (risk)}$$

SECTION 5-3

1. $\begin{bmatrix} 1 & 2 & | & 4 \\ 0 & 7 & | & 3 \end{bmatrix}$ **3.** $\begin{bmatrix} 1 & 2 & 8 & | & 5 \\ 0 & 1 & 8 & | & 9 \\ 3 & 1 & 2 & | & 4 \end{bmatrix}$

5. $\begin{bmatrix} 1 & 0 & 3 & | & 2 \\ 0 & -1 & -4 & | & 0 \\ 0 & 1 & 8 & | & 11 \end{bmatrix}$

7. $\begin{bmatrix} 1 & 0 & 0 & | & 8 \\ 0 & 1 & 0 & | & -14 \\ 0 & 0 & 1 & | & 3 \end{bmatrix}$ **9.** $(-3, -4)$ **11.** $(2, -4, 1)$

13. $\left(\dfrac{1}{2}, 1, 3\right)$ **15.** $(4, 3)$ **17.** $(-2, 1, 4)$ **19.** $(-1, 1, 3)$

21. $\left(\dfrac{-5}{2}, 1, \dfrac{19}{2}\right)$ **23.** $(-2, 3, -1)$ **25.** $(1, 2, 3, -1)$

27. No solution **29.** Infinitely many solutions; $\left(\dfrac{5}{4} + \dfrac{1}{4}t, t\right)$

31. No solution **33.** No solution **35.** Infinitely many

solutions; $\left(\dfrac{8}{3} - 3t, \dfrac{2}{3} + t, t\right)$ **37.** Infinitely many solutions;

$\left(-11 + \dfrac{5}{2}t, 6 - \dfrac{3}{2}t, 3 + \dfrac{1}{2}t, t\right)$ **39.** No solution

41. Infinitely many solutions; $(9 + 7s + t, -2 -3s, s, t)$
43. $(3, -2)$ **45.** Infinitely many solutions $(4 - 3t, t)$

47. $\left(\dfrac{1}{2}, 1, 3\right)$ **49.** $(40, 100, 80)$

51. $x = 100$, $y = 50$, $z = 20$, where
x = no. of conservative sweaters
y = no. of sporty sweaters
z = no of practical sweaters
53. Infinitely many solutions; $x_1 = -50 + t$, $x_2 = 350 - t$,
$x_3 = 200 - t$, $x_4 = t$ Since $x_i \geq 0$, $50 \leq t \leq 200$
55. $\begin{array}{l} x_1 + x_2 \qquad\qquad = 500 \\ \qquad\quad x_3 + x_4 = 300 \end{array}$ } production capacities
$\begin{array}{l} x_1 \qquad + x_3 \qquad = 600 \\ \quad x_2 \qquad + x_4 = 200 \end{array}$ } demands
Infinitely many solutions; $x_1 = 300 + t$, $x_2 = 200 - t$,
$x_3 = 300 - t$, $x_4 = t$
Since $x_i \geq 0$, $0 \leq t \leq 200$
57. Let x = gallons of A, y = gallons of B, z = gallons of C
$x + y + z = 100{,}000$ total gallons
$2x + 4y + 8z = 600{,}000$ cost
$-5.5x \qquad + z = 0 \qquad z = 5.5x$
10,000 gallons of A, 35,000 gallons of B, 55,000
gallons of C; solution is unique
59. 10 oz of food A, 20 oz of food B, 30 oz of food C

SECTION 5-4

1. 2×3 **3.** 3×3 **5.** 1×3 **7.** 4×1 **9.** Row matrix
11. Column matrix **13.** Not square **15.** Square matrix
17. True **19.** False **21.** $x = 4$, $y = -1$ **23.** $x = 1$,
$y = -4$, $z = 5$, $w = -7$ **25.** $\begin{bmatrix} 3 & -3 & 1 \\ -3 & 10 & -5 \end{bmatrix}$

27. $\begin{bmatrix} 7 & 4 & 2 \\ -3 & 10 & -3 \end{bmatrix}$ **29.** $\begin{bmatrix} 1 & 2 & -2 \\ -1 & 0 & 1 \end{bmatrix}$

31. $\begin{bmatrix} -4 & 1 & 1 \\ 4 & -10 & 4 \end{bmatrix}$ **33.** $\begin{bmatrix} 7 & 8 & 3 \\ -1 & 5 & 0 \end{bmatrix}$

35. $\begin{bmatrix} 7 & 0 & 1 \\ -5 & 15 & -6 \end{bmatrix}$ **37.** $\begin{bmatrix} 0 & 12 & 3 \\ 6 & -15 & 9 \end{bmatrix}$

39. $\begin{bmatrix} -9 & -3 & -6 \\ 3 & -15 & 6 \end{bmatrix}$ **41.** $\begin{bmatrix} -8 & -6 & 0 \\ 4 & -10 & 2 \end{bmatrix}$

43. $\begin{bmatrix} 3 & -11 & -1 \\ -7 & 20 & -11 \end{bmatrix}$ **45.** $\begin{bmatrix} -9 & 1 & -5 \\ 5 & -20 & 9 \end{bmatrix}$

47. $\begin{bmatrix} -5 & -1 & 3 \\ 5 & -10 & 3 \end{bmatrix}$ **49.** $[1 \quad -4 \quad 4]$

51. $[9 \quad -12 \quad 3]$ **53.** $[-1 \quad -4 \quad 7]$

55. $[-7 \quad 12 \quad -6]$ **57.** $\begin{bmatrix} 1 \\ 3 \end{bmatrix}$ **59.** $\begin{bmatrix} -15 \\ -1 \end{bmatrix}$

61. $\begin{bmatrix} 21 \\ -3 \end{bmatrix}$ **63.** $\begin{bmatrix} 33 \\ 11 \end{bmatrix}$ **65.** $\begin{bmatrix} -13 \\ 5 \end{bmatrix}$

67. $\begin{bmatrix} -1 & -5 \\ 5 & 9 \end{bmatrix}$ **69.** $\begin{bmatrix} -5 & 5 \\ 3 & -5 \\ 2 & -7 \end{bmatrix}$ **71.** $\begin{bmatrix} 1 & 8 \\ -7 & 22 \end{bmatrix}$

73. $\begin{bmatrix} 23 & 16 \\ 1 & -4 \end{bmatrix}$ **75.** $X = \begin{bmatrix} 3 \\ 4 \\ 6 \end{bmatrix}$

77. (a) $X = \begin{bmatrix} a & b \\ c & d \end{bmatrix}$, $X - X = \begin{bmatrix} a-a & b-b \\ c-c & d-d \end{bmatrix} =$
$\begin{bmatrix} 0 & 0 \\ 0 & 0 \end{bmatrix} = Z$ **(b)** $X + Z = \begin{bmatrix} a & b \\ c & d \end{bmatrix} + \begin{bmatrix} 0 & 0 \\ 0 & 0 \end{bmatrix} =$
$\begin{bmatrix} a & b \\ c & d \end{bmatrix} = X$

79. $J + A = \begin{bmatrix} 300 & 80 & 80 & 150 \\ 370 & 450 & 210 & 80 \end{bmatrix}$

81. $\begin{array}{ccc} A & B & C \end{array}$
$\begin{bmatrix} 30 & 40 & 60 \\ 25 & 40 & 50 \end{bmatrix}$ scarves mittens

83.

Person	Before	After
1	350	345
2	249	200
3	260	220
4	195	140
5	275	200
6	295	230

SECTION 5-5

1. 9 **3.** -2 **5.** 0.37 (rounded) **7.** 3×5 **9.** 4×4
11. Cannot be computed **13.** 2×2 **15.** 4×5

17. 2×2 **19.** $\begin{bmatrix} 11 & -2 \\ 3 & 0 \end{bmatrix}$ **21.** $[-6 \quad 9]$

23. $\begin{bmatrix} -17 \\ -28 \end{bmatrix}$ **25.** $\begin{bmatrix} 22 \\ -10 \\ 4 \end{bmatrix}$ **27.** $\begin{bmatrix} 11 & -13 \\ -8 & 17 \\ 13 & -9 \end{bmatrix}$

29. $\begin{bmatrix} 16 & 36 \\ 0 & 2 \\ 8 & 24 \end{bmatrix}$ **31.** $\begin{bmatrix} 2 & -7 & 9 \\ -8 & 2 & 7 \\ -1 & 5 & 6 \end{bmatrix}$

33. $\begin{bmatrix} -14 & 16 \\ -11 & 18 \end{bmatrix}$ **35.** No; $AB \neq BA$

37. BA cannot be computed **39.** CB cannot be computed

41. $\begin{bmatrix} 15 & 1 \\ -7 & 10 \end{bmatrix}$ **43.** AD cannot be computed

45. $\begin{bmatrix} -118 & 199 & 120 & -154 \\ -10 & 138 & 114 & 160 \\ 30 & 76 & 78 & 220 \end{bmatrix}$

47. $(AB)C = A(BC)$ by inspection **49.** $AB = \begin{bmatrix} 22 & 8 \\ 56 & -8 \end{bmatrix}$,

$BA = \begin{bmatrix} 20 & 21 \\ 24 & -6 \end{bmatrix}$ $AB \neq BA$ **51. (a)** $A^3 = \begin{bmatrix} -16 & 75 \\ -25 & 34 \end{bmatrix}$

(b) $A^3 = \begin{bmatrix} -512 & 0 \\ 52 & 8 \end{bmatrix}$ **(c)** $A^3 = \begin{bmatrix} 17 & 22 & 17 \\ 44 & -9 & 8 \\ 34 & 8 & 18 \end{bmatrix}$

(d) $A^3 = \begin{bmatrix} -117 & 86 & 51 \\ 113 & -94 & -23 \\ 136 & -112 & -56 \end{bmatrix}$

53. $A^n = \underbrace{A \cdot A \cdot A \cdots A}_{n \text{ times}}$, n is a positive integer

(A must be a square matrix)

55. $\begin{bmatrix} 1 & 5 \\ 4 & 8 \end{bmatrix}\begin{bmatrix} x_1 \\ x_2 \end{bmatrix} = \begin{bmatrix} 6 \\ 11 \end{bmatrix}$ **57.** $\begin{bmatrix} 2 & 3 & 1 \\ 1 & 0 & 2 \\ 0 & 4 & 5 \end{bmatrix}\begin{bmatrix} x \\ y \\ z \end{bmatrix} = \begin{bmatrix} 11 \\ 9 \\ 17 \end{bmatrix}$

59. $\begin{bmatrix} 2 & -1 \\ 3 & 2 \end{bmatrix}\begin{bmatrix} x_1 \\ x_2 \end{bmatrix} = \begin{bmatrix} 6 \\ 9 \end{bmatrix}$

61. $\begin{bmatrix} -1 & 1 & -2 \\ 6 & 0 & 2 \\ 0 & 1 & -1 \end{bmatrix}\begin{bmatrix} x_1 \\ x_2 \\ x_3 \end{bmatrix} = \begin{bmatrix} 10 \\ 5 \\ 9 \end{bmatrix}$

63. $\begin{aligned} x_1 - 3x_2 &= 3 \\ 2x_1 + 4x_2 &= -7 \end{aligned}$ **65.** $\begin{aligned} 4x_1 + x_2 - x_3 &= -4 \\ 5x_1 \quad\;\; + 2x_3 &= 1 \\ -2x_1 + x_2 - 2x_3 &= -1 \end{aligned}$

67. $\begin{aligned} x_1 + 4x_2 - x_3 &= 2 \\ 2x_1 + x_2 \quad\;\; &= 1 \\ 4x_1 + x_2 - 5x_3 &= 5 \end{aligned}$

69. $AI = \begin{bmatrix} 4 & 3 & 6 \\ 8 & 2 & 7 \\ -1 & 1 & 4 \end{bmatrix} = A$

$IA = \begin{bmatrix} 4 & 3 & 6 \\ 8 & 2 & 7 \\ -1 & 1 & 4 \end{bmatrix} = A$

71. $BI = \begin{bmatrix} 2 & 3 \\ 7 & 4 \\ 5 & 7 \end{bmatrix} = B$ **73.** $\begin{bmatrix} 31,000 \\ 46,000 \\ 79,000 \end{bmatrix}$ April May June

75. Votes $\begin{bmatrix} 105,000 \\ 171,900 \\ 43,100 \end{bmatrix}$ Republican Democrat; Democrat Independent

SECTION 5-6

1. Yes **3.** Yes **5.** Yes **7.** No **9. (a)** $\begin{bmatrix} 11 & -5 \\ -2 & 1 \end{bmatrix}$

(b) $AA^{-1} = \begin{bmatrix} 1 & 0 \\ 0 & 1 \end{bmatrix} = A^{-1}A = I$

11. $\frac{1}{32}\begin{bmatrix} 7 & 1 \\ 3 & 5 \end{bmatrix} = \begin{bmatrix} 7/32 & 1/32 \\ 3/32 & 5/32 \end{bmatrix}$ **13.** $\begin{bmatrix} -1 & 1 \\ 1 & 0 \end{bmatrix}$

15. $\frac{1}{57}\begin{bmatrix} 1 & 10 & 7 \\ 16 & -11 & -2 \\ 22 & -8 & -17 \end{bmatrix} =$

$\begin{bmatrix} 1/57 & 10/57 & 7/57 \\ 16/57 & -11/57 & -2/57 \\ 22/57 & -8/57 & -17/57 \end{bmatrix}$

17. $\frac{1}{29}\begin{bmatrix} 7 & 4 \\ 2 & -3 \end{bmatrix} = \begin{bmatrix} 7/29 & 4/29 \\ 2/29 & -3/29 \end{bmatrix}$

19. $\frac{1}{14}\begin{bmatrix} 1 & 3 \\ 4 & -2 \end{bmatrix} = \begin{bmatrix} 1/14 & 3/14 \\ 2/7 & -1/7 \end{bmatrix}$

21. $\frac{1}{7}\begin{bmatrix} -1 & 2 & 1 \\ 4 & -1 & -4 \\ 0 & 0 & 7 \end{bmatrix} = \begin{bmatrix} -1/7 & 2/7 & 1/7 \\ 4/7 & -1/7 & -4/7 \\ 0 & 0 & 1 \end{bmatrix}$

23. K^{-1} does not exist

25. $\dfrac{1}{6}\begin{bmatrix} -2 & 0 & 0 & 1 \\ 2 & 0 & 2 & -1 \\ 2 & 0 & -2 & 2 \\ 0 & 3 & 0 & 0 \end{bmatrix}=$
$\begin{bmatrix} -1/3 & 0 & 0 & 1/6 \\ 1/3 & 0 & 1/3 & -1/6 \\ 1/3 & 0 & -1/3 & 1/3 \\ 0 & 1/2 & 0 & 0 \end{bmatrix}$

SECTION 5-7

1. $x_1 = 12, x_2 = 1$ **3.** $x_1 = 18, x_2 = 1$

5. $\begin{bmatrix} 1 & 2 \\ -1 & 3 \end{bmatrix}\begin{bmatrix} x_1 \\ x_2 \end{bmatrix}=\begin{bmatrix} 9 \\ 1 \end{bmatrix}; A^{-1}=\dfrac{1}{5}\begin{bmatrix} 3 & -2 \\ 1 & 1 \end{bmatrix}; \begin{bmatrix} x_1 \\ x_2 \end{bmatrix}=\begin{bmatrix} 5 \\ 2 \end{bmatrix}$

7. $\begin{bmatrix} 1 & 0 & 1 \\ 0 & 1 & 4 \\ 2 & 3 & 1 \end{bmatrix}\begin{bmatrix} x_1 \\ x_2 \\ x_3 \end{bmatrix}=\begin{bmatrix} 11 \\ 39 \\ 22 \end{bmatrix};$
$A^{-1}=\dfrac{1}{13}\begin{bmatrix} 11 & -3 & 1 \\ -8 & 1 & 4 \\ 2 & 3 & -1 \end{bmatrix}; \begin{bmatrix} x_1 \\ x_2 \\ x_3 \end{bmatrix}=\begin{bmatrix} 2 \\ 3 \\ 9 \end{bmatrix}$

9. $\begin{bmatrix} 1 & 1 & 1 \\ 1 & 2 & 3 \\ 0 & 1 & 4 \end{bmatrix}\begin{bmatrix} x_1 \\ x_2 \\ x_3 \end{bmatrix}=\begin{bmatrix} 3 \\ 10 \\ 17 \end{bmatrix};$
$A^{-1}=\dfrac{1}{2}\begin{bmatrix} 5 & -3 & 1 \\ -4 & 4 & -2 \\ 1 & -1 & 1 \end{bmatrix}; \begin{bmatrix} x_1 \\ x_2 \\ x_3 \end{bmatrix}=\begin{bmatrix} 1 \\ -3 \\ 5 \end{bmatrix}$

11. $\begin{bmatrix} 1 & 1 & 0 \\ 0 & 1 & 3 \\ 4 & 6 & 7 \end{bmatrix}\begin{bmatrix} x_1 \\ x_2 \\ x_3 \end{bmatrix}=\begin{bmatrix} 3 \\ -7 \\ -5 \end{bmatrix};$
$A^{-1}=\begin{bmatrix} -11 & -7 & 3 \\ 12 & 7 & -3 \\ -4 & -2 & 1 \end{bmatrix}; \begin{bmatrix} x_1 \\ x_2 \\ x_3 \end{bmatrix}=\begin{bmatrix} 1 \\ 2 \\ -3 \end{bmatrix}$

13. $\begin{bmatrix} 2 & -3 \\ 1 & -7 \end{bmatrix}\begin{bmatrix} x \\ y \end{bmatrix}=\begin{bmatrix} 6 \\ 25 \end{bmatrix}; A^{-1}=\dfrac{-1}{11}\begin{bmatrix} -7 & 3 \\ -1 & 2 \end{bmatrix};$
$\begin{bmatrix} x \\ y \end{bmatrix}=\begin{bmatrix} -3 \\ -4 \end{bmatrix}$

15. $\begin{bmatrix} 2 & 3 & -5 \\ 1 & 2 & 3 \\ 3 & -4 & -7 \end{bmatrix}\begin{bmatrix} x \\ y \\ z \end{bmatrix}=\begin{bmatrix} -13 \\ -7 \\ 15 \end{bmatrix};$
$A^{-1}=\dfrac{1}{94}\begin{bmatrix} -2 & 41 & 19 \\ 16 & 1 & -11 \\ -10 & 17 & 1 \end{bmatrix}; \begin{bmatrix} x \\ y \\ z \end{bmatrix}=\begin{bmatrix} 12/47 \\ -190/47 \\ 13/47 \end{bmatrix}$

17. $\begin{bmatrix} 5 & 7 & 1 \\ 3 & 2 & 3 \\ 2 & 3 & 5 \end{bmatrix}\begin{bmatrix} x_1 \\ x_2 \\ x_3 \end{bmatrix}=\begin{bmatrix} 1 \\ 8 \\ 19 \end{bmatrix};$
$A^{-1}=\dfrac{1}{53}\begin{bmatrix} -1 & 32 & -19 \\ 9 & -23 & 12 \\ -5 & 1 & 11 \end{bmatrix}; \begin{bmatrix} x_1 \\ x_2 \\ x_3 \end{bmatrix}=\begin{bmatrix} -2 \\ 1 \\ 4 \end{bmatrix}$

19. $\begin{bmatrix} 4 & 1 \\ 6 & -2 \end{bmatrix}\begin{bmatrix} x_1 \\ x_2 \end{bmatrix}=\begin{bmatrix} 8 \\ -9 \end{bmatrix}; A^{-1}=\dfrac{1}{14}\begin{bmatrix} 2 & 1 \\ 6 & -4 \end{bmatrix};$
$\begin{bmatrix} x_1 \\ x_2 \end{bmatrix}=\begin{bmatrix} 1/2 \\ 6 \end{bmatrix}$

21. $\begin{bmatrix} 2 & 1 & 3 \\ 4 & 3 & -2 \\ 6 & 5 & -4 \end{bmatrix}\begin{bmatrix} x \\ y \\ z \end{bmatrix}=\begin{bmatrix} 11 \\ -1 \\ -4 \end{bmatrix};$
$A^{-1}=\dfrac{1}{6}\begin{bmatrix} -2 & 19 & -11 \\ 4 & -26 & 16 \\ 2 & -4 & 2 \end{bmatrix}; \begin{bmatrix} x \\ y \\ z \end{bmatrix}=\begin{bmatrix} 1/2 \\ 1 \\ 3 \end{bmatrix}$

23. $\begin{bmatrix} 1 & 0 & 1 & -1 \\ 0 & 1 & -1 & 2 \\ 4 & 0 & 5 & -3 \\ 0 & 0 & 2 & 3 \end{bmatrix}\begin{bmatrix} x_1 \\ x_2 \\ x_3 \\ x_4 \end{bmatrix}=\begin{bmatrix} -2 \\ 12 \\ 2 \\ 27 \end{bmatrix};$
$A^{-1}=\begin{bmatrix} 21 & 0 & -5 & 2 \\ -28 & 1 & 7 & -3 \\ -12 & 0 & 3 & -1 \\ 8 & 0 & -2 & 1 \end{bmatrix}; \begin{bmatrix} x_1 \\ x_2 \\ x_3 \\ x_4 \end{bmatrix}=\begin{bmatrix} 2 \\ 1 \\ 3 \\ 7 \end{bmatrix}$

25. (a)
$A=\begin{bmatrix} 500 & 200 \\ 100 & 800 \end{bmatrix}$ Meat Spinach; protein, iron

(b) $B=\begin{bmatrix} 1200 \\ 1000 \end{bmatrix}$ protein, iron

(c) $\begin{bmatrix} 500 & 200 \\ 100 & 800 \end{bmatrix}\begin{bmatrix} x \\ y \end{bmatrix}=\begin{bmatrix} 1200 \\ 1000 \end{bmatrix}$

(d) $\begin{bmatrix} x \\ y \end{bmatrix}=\begin{bmatrix} 2 \\ 1 \end{bmatrix}$; Hence $x = 2$ lb meat, $y = 1$ lb spinach

(e) $\begin{bmatrix} x \\ y \end{bmatrix}=\begin{bmatrix} 3 \\ 4 \end{bmatrix}$

27. Let x = # units of XB17, y = # units of XB18
(a) $0.01x + 0.03y = 220$
$0.02x + 0.005y = 330$
(b) $\begin{bmatrix} 0.01 & 0.03 \\ 0.02 & 0.005 \end{bmatrix}\begin{bmatrix} x \\ y \end{bmatrix}=\begin{bmatrix} 220 \\ 330 \end{bmatrix}$
(c) $A^{-1}=\begin{bmatrix} -100/11 & 600/11 \\ 400/11 & -200/11 \end{bmatrix}$
(d) $\begin{bmatrix} x \\ y \end{bmatrix}=\begin{bmatrix} -100/11 & 600/11 \\ 400/11 & -200/11 \end{bmatrix}\begin{bmatrix} 220 \\ 330 \end{bmatrix}=\begin{bmatrix} 16,000 \\ 2000 \end{bmatrix}$

(e) $\begin{bmatrix} x \\ y \end{bmatrix} = \begin{bmatrix} -100/11 & 600/11 \\ 400/11 & -200/11 \end{bmatrix} \begin{bmatrix} 440 \\ 110 \end{bmatrix} = \begin{bmatrix} 2000 \\ 14{,}000 \end{bmatrix}$

29. (a) $x + y = 100{,}000$ available funds
$0.07x + 0.09y = 8500$ yield

(b) $\begin{bmatrix} 1 & 1 \\ 0.07 & 0.09 \end{bmatrix} \begin{bmatrix} x \\ y \end{bmatrix} = \begin{bmatrix} 100{,}000 \\ 8500 \end{bmatrix}$

(c) $A^{-1} = \begin{bmatrix} 4.5 & -50 \\ -3.5 & 50 \end{bmatrix}$

(d) $x = \$25{,}000$ invested at 7%
$y = \$75{,}000$ invested at 9%

(e) $x = \$150{,}000$; $y = \$50{,}000$

SECTION 5-8

1. (a) $A = \begin{bmatrix} 0 & 1/4 \\ 1/2 & 0 \end{bmatrix}$ oil
   coal

(b) $\begin{bmatrix} 380 \\ 680 \end{bmatrix}$

3. $\begin{bmatrix} 41\frac{1}{3} \\ 36 \end{bmatrix}$ **5.** $\begin{bmatrix} 120.8 \\ 75.2 \\ 135.2 \end{bmatrix}$ **7.** $\Delta x = \begin{bmatrix} 2 \\ 3.2 \end{bmatrix}$ **9.** $\Delta x = \begin{bmatrix} 7.7 \\ 2.4 \end{bmatrix}$

• EXTRA DIVIDENDS

1.

	Well in Saudi Arabia	Well in Kuwait	Well in Egypt	Demand
Regular	0.2	0.3	0.4	19
Unleaded	0.1	0.2	0.1	10
Kerosene	0.3	0.1	0.4	20

3. $\begin{bmatrix} 0.2 & 0.3 & 0.4 \\ 0.1 & 0.2 & 0.1 \\ 0.3 & 0.1 & 0.4 \end{bmatrix} \begin{bmatrix} x \\ y \\ z \end{bmatrix} = \begin{bmatrix} 19 \\ 10 \\ 20 \end{bmatrix}$

5. $\begin{bmatrix} x \\ y \\ z \end{bmatrix} = \begin{bmatrix} 50/3 \\ 100/3 \\ 50/3 \end{bmatrix}$ Saudi Arabia
   Kuwait
   Egypt

• CHAPTER HIGHLIGHTS

1. Straight line   **2.** Intersection point   **3.** Parallel
4. Coincide   **5.** Method of elimination; method of substitution
6. *Step 1:* Identify the unknowns *Step 2:* Organize the information and write the linear system *Step 3:* Solve the linear system

7. (a) $\begin{bmatrix} 1 & 0 & | & c_1 \\ 0 & 1 & | & c_2 \end{bmatrix}$ **(b)** $\begin{bmatrix} 1 & 0 & 0 & | & c_1 \\ 0 & 1 & 0 & | & c_2 \\ 0 & 0 & 1 & | & c_3 \end{bmatrix}$

8. (a) $a_1x_1 + a_2x_2 = b$ **(b)** $a_1x_1 + a_2x_2 + a_3x_3 = b$
(c) $a_1x_1 + a_2x_2 + \ldots + a_nx_n = b$

10. $\begin{bmatrix} 1 & 0 & 0 & 0 & | & c_1 \\ 0 & 1 & 0 & 0 & | & c_2 \\ & & \vdots & & | & \vdots \\ 0 & 0 & 0 & 1 & | & c_n \end{bmatrix}$

no solutions or infinitely many solutions

11. $\begin{bmatrix} 1 & 4 & | & 7 \\ 0 & 0 & | & 5 \end{bmatrix}$

12. Variables than equations; basic variables in terms of the nonbasic variables   **13.** Rectangular   **14.** Same dimension and corresponding entries must be equal   **15.** Same dimension   **16.** Multiply each matrix entry by the number.
17. $m \times r$ **18.** The number of columns of the left matrix must equal the number of rows of the right matrix.

19. $\begin{bmatrix} 1 & 0 & 0 \\ 0 & 1 & 0 \\ 0 & 0 & 1 \end{bmatrix}$ $\begin{bmatrix} 1 & 0 & 0 & 0 \\ 0 & 1 & 0 & 0 \\ 0 & 0 & 1 & 0 \\ 0 & 0 & 0 & 1 \end{bmatrix}$

$\begin{bmatrix} 1 & 0 & 0 & 0 & 0 \\ 0 & 1 & 0 & 0 & 0 \\ 0 & 0 & 1 & 0 & 0 \\ 0 & 0 & 0 & 1 & 0 \\ 0 & 0 & 0 & 0 & 1 \end{bmatrix}$

20. Given a square matrix A, its inverse (if it exists) is that square matrix A^{-1} that satisfies both conditions $AA^{-1} = I$ and $A^{-1}A = I$.   **21.** No   **22.** Yes   **23.** Multiplicative inverse; A^{-1} **24.** $A^{-1}B$; A^{-1} **25.** Internal demand; final (or external) demand   **26. (a)** Production or total output matrix **(b)** Internal demand matrix **(c)** Final or external demand matrix   **27.** X; $X = (I - A)^{-1}D$; $(I - A)^{-1}$

• REVIEW EXERCISES

1. $(4, -1)$ **3.** No solution   **5.** $(4, 15)$ **7.** $(6, 30)$
9. (a) (1) $15x - 6y = 60$
   (2) $\underline{-15x + 6y = -60}$
                  $0 = 0 \Rightarrow$ infinitely many solutions

Let $x = t$, $y = \frac{5}{2}t - 10$

(b) Eq. (1) becomes $y = \frac{5}{2}x - 10$

Eq. (2) becomes $y = \frac{5}{2}x - 10$

Equations are the same.

(c) Let $t = 0, 1, 2$.

Solutions are $(0, -10)$, $\left(1, \dfrac{-15}{2}\right)$, $(2, -5)$

$(\bar{x}, \bar{y})$ is the solution.

11.

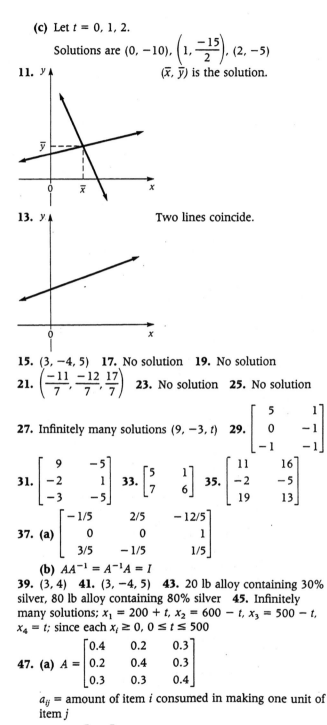

13. Two lines coincide.

15. $(3, -4, 5)$ **17.** No solution   **19.** No solution

21. $\left(\dfrac{-11}{7}, \dfrac{-12}{7}, \dfrac{17}{7}\right)$ **23.** No solution   **25.** No solution

27. Infinitely many solutions $(9, -3, t)$ **29.** $\begin{bmatrix} 5 & 1 \\ 0 & -1 \\ -1 & -1 \end{bmatrix}$

31. $\begin{bmatrix} 9 & -5 \\ -2 & 1 \\ -3 & -5 \end{bmatrix}$ **33.** $\begin{bmatrix} 5 & 1 \\ 7 & 6 \end{bmatrix}$ **35.** $\begin{bmatrix} 11 & 16 \\ -2 & -5 \\ 19 & 13 \end{bmatrix}$

37. (a) $\begin{bmatrix} -1/5 & 2/5 & -12/5 \\ 0 & 0 & 1 \\ 3/5 & -1/5 & 1/5 \end{bmatrix}$

(b) $AA^{-1} = A^{-1}A = I$

39. $(3, 4)$ **41.** $(3, -4, 5)$ **43.** 20 lb alloy containing 30% silver, 80 lb alloy containing 80% silver   **45.** Infinitely many solutions; $x_1 = 200 + t$, $x_2 = 600 - t$, $x_3 = 500 - t$, $x_4 = t$; since each $x_i \geq 0$, $0 \leq t \leq 500$

47. (a) $A = \begin{bmatrix} 0.4 & 0.2 & 0.3 \\ 0.2 & 0.4 & 0.3 \\ 0.3 & 0.3 & 0.4 \end{bmatrix}$

a_{ij} = amount of item i consumed in making one unit of item j

(b) $D = \begin{bmatrix} 200 \\ 500 \\ 400 \end{bmatrix}$

d_i = units of item i for external demand

(c) $X = \begin{bmatrix} 5312\frac{1}{2} \\ 5687\frac{1}{2} \\ 6166\frac{2}{3} \end{bmatrix}$

x_i = total output of item i

• CHAPTER 6

SECTION 6-1

The solutions to problems 1–24 are graphs, shown in the accompanying figures. Shaded areas include points that do *not* satisfy the given inequalities.

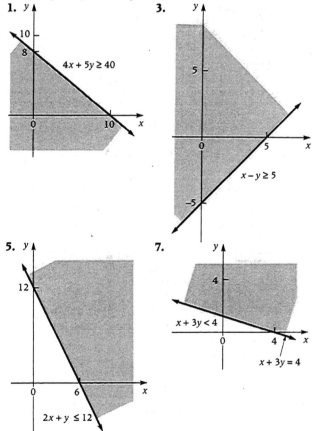

9.

11.

13.

15.

17.

19.

21.

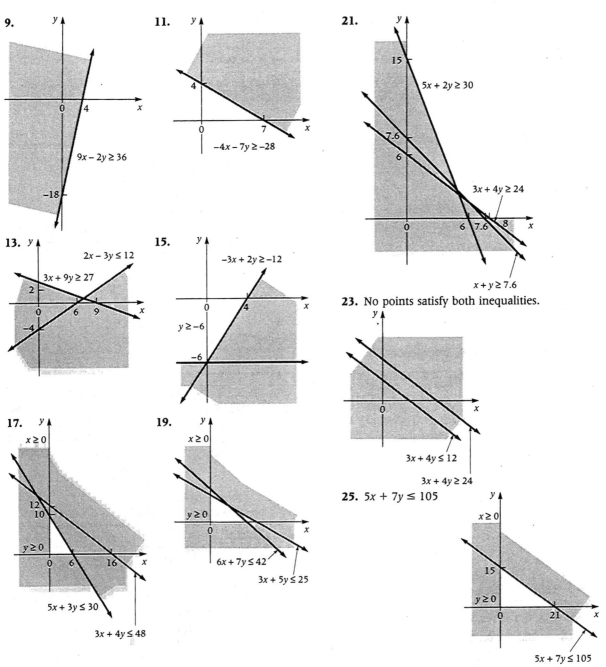

23. No points satisfy both inequalities.

25. $5x + 7y \leq 105$

27. Let g and w represent the gadgets and widgets, respectively. $4g + 5w \leq 80$

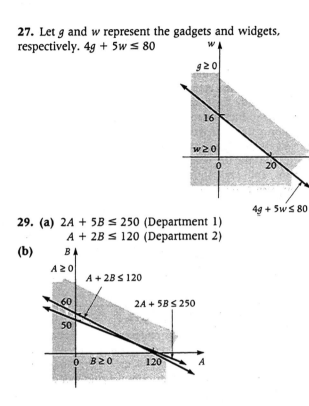

29. (a) $2A + 5B \leq 250$ (Department 1)
$A + 2B \leq 120$ (Department 2)

(b)

(c) Vertex points are $(0, 0)$, $(0, 50)$, $(100, 10)$ and $(120, 0)$

31. Let x = number of families in city 1
y = number of families in city 2
(a) $30x + 40y \leq 12,000$ (cost)
$x \geq 100$
$y \geq 120$

(b)

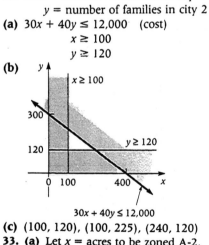

(c) $(100, 120)$, $(100, 225)$, $(240, 120)$

33. (a) Let x = acres to be zoned A-2,
y = acres to be zoned A-3
$x + y \leq 1,000,000$ (acres)
$\dfrac{x}{2} + \dfrac{y}{3} \geq 480,000$ (lots)
$x \geq 200,000$
$y \geq 60,000$

(b)

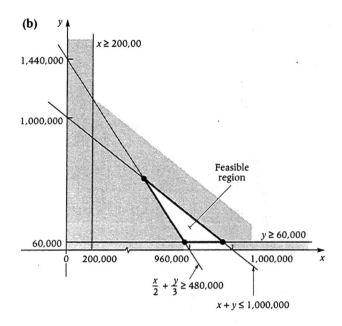

(c) $(880,000, 120,000)$, $(920,000, 60,000)$, $(940,000, 60,000)$

SECTION 6-2

1. Maximum $Z = 73$ at $(6, 7)$ **3.** Minimum $Z = 4.6$ at $(2, 8)$ **5.** Maximum $Z = 12.8$ at $(10, 16)$ **7.** Maximum $P = 36.8$ at $(6.4, 1.2)$ **9.** Minimum $C = 48$ at $(12, 0)$ **11.** Maximum $Z = 165$ at $(0, 5.5)$ **13.** Minimum $Z = 240$ at $(12, 0)$ **15.** Maximum $Z = 122$ at $(4, 22)$

17. Maximum $Z = 344\frac{4}{9}$ at $\left(\dfrac{140}{9}, \dfrac{10}{9}\right)$

19. (a) x = number of casual jackets
y = number of formal jackets
Maximize $P = 30x + 50y$

	Casual	Formal	
Unit profits	30	50	At most
Cutting dept.	2 person-hrs/ jacket	3 person-hrs/ jacket	960 hrs
Sewing	1 person-hrs/ jacket	1 person-hrs/ jacket	400 hrs

At least 150 casual jackets must be produced.
At least 50 formal jackets must be produced.
Constraints:
Cutting dept.: $2x + 3y \leq 960$
Sewing dept.: $x + y \leq 400$
Demand $x \geq 150$
$y \geq 50$

Maximum P = \$15,500 at (150, 220).
Cutting dept.: slack = 0
Sewing dept.: slack = 3.
Constraint: $x \geq 150$, surplus = 0
$\quad\quad\quad\quad y \geq 50$, surplus = 170
(b) 960 **(c)** 370
21. Maximize $R = 0.18x + 0.22y$
$\quad\quad$ Maximum R = 3760 at (16,000, 4000)
$\quad\quad$ *Constraint 1:* Total amount invested = 20,000
$\quad\quad\quad\quad\quad$ slack = 0
$\quad\quad$ *Constraint 2:* Average risk level for the optimal
$\quad\quad\quad\quad\quad$ solution = 3
$\quad\quad\quad\quad\quad$ slack = 0
23. (a) 1500 radio ads and no TV ads **(b)** \$1,800,000
(c) *Constraint 1:* surplus = 300 ads
$\quad\quad$ *Constraint 2:* surplus = 0 families
(d) 1,500,000 families **(e)** 1500 ads
25. Minimum cost of \$7.50 at 2 lb meat and 1 lb spinach.
Constraint 1: surplus = 0
Constraint 2: surplus = 0
27. (a) 70 acres of A and 30 acres of B **(b)** \$43,000
(c) *Constraint 1:* slack = 0 acres
$\quad\quad$ *Constraint 2:* slack = 0 person-hours
(d) 100 **(e)** 6600 **29. (a)** 1960 gallons of F10,
1840 gallons of F20 **(b)** \$4964
(c) *Constraint 1:* surplus = 0
$\quad\quad$ *Constraint 2:* surplus = 11.2 lbs ash
$\quad\quad$ *Constraint 3:* 0
(d) 3800 **(e)** 131.2 **(f)** 136 **31. (a)** All points on the
line connecting (170, 80) and (185, 50) are equally
profitable. **(b)** \$840 **(c)** At (170, 80), *Constraint 1:*
slack = 0; *Constraint 2:* slack = 0; *Constraint 3:* slack = 20;
Constraint 4: surplus = 120; *Constraint 5:* surplus = 30
(d) 420 **(e)** 500 **(f)** 580 **33. (a)** 2400 units to
wholesale outlets, 3200 units to retail outlets **(b)** \$600,000
(c) *Constraint 1:* slack = 0, *Constraint 2:* slack = 0 **(d)** 5600
(e) 17,280 **35. (a)** 4480 units to wholesale outlets, 1120
units to retail outlets **(b)** \$537,600 **(c)** *Constraint 1:*
slack = 2496 hrs, *Constraint 2:* slack = 0, *Constraint 3:*
slack = 0 **(d)** 5600 **(e)** 14,784

SECTION 6-3

1. (2, 9) **3.** (9, 0) **5.** Along the boundary from (0, 8)
to (7, 5) **7.** (2, 4) **9.** (9, 4) **11.** (9, 4) **13.** (1, 2.5)
15. No feasible region since $x + y$ cannot be both ≤ 5
and ≥ 7. **17.** Minimum z = 48 at (4, 0)
19. Unbounded solution: an optimal solution does not
exist because there is always a better solution.

• CHAPTER HIGHLIGHTS

1. $ax + by \leq c$ or $ax + by \geq c$ **2.** First graph the
corresponding straight line and then determine whether the

points (x, y) satisfying the inequality lie above or below the
straight line. **3.** Graph each inequality on the same set of
axes. For each inequality, shade the region to be discarded.
The remaining region, the unshaded (white) region, if it
exists, constitutes the region associated with the system.
4. *Step 1:* Identify the quantity to be either maximized or
minimized and the related unknowns. *Step 2:* Organize the
given information and write the inequalities that express
any relationships existing among the unknowns.
Step 3: Determine the values of x and y that satisfy the
constraints and, also, optimize the value of the objective
function. *Step 4:* Investigate the implications of the optimal
solution. **5.** *Step 1:* Graph the feasible region (if it exists).
Step 2: Identify the vertex points. *Step 3:* Substitute the
coordinates of each vertex point into the objective function
to determine the optimal solution (if it exists).
6. For a ($\leq$) constraint, Slack = RHS − LHS. Slack
represents any unused capacity for a ($\leq$) constraint.
7. ($\leq$) **8.** *Binding constraint:* This means that all of the
available capacity or resource of the constraint is being
utilized by the optimal solution. **9.** For a ($\geq$) constraint,
Surplus = LHS − RHS. Surplus represents the amount by
which the minimal constraint requirement is exceeded.
10. ($\geq$) **11.** *Binding constraint:* This means that the
minimal requirement of the constraint is being met exactly.
12. An optimal solution, if one exists, to a linear
programming problem will occur at one or more of the
vertex points or on the boundary of the feasible region.
13. Yes **14.** There may or may not be an optimal solution.
15. There is more than one optimal solution.
16. An unbounded feasible region that results in there not
being an optimal solution because there is always a better
solution. **17.** There is no optimal solution.

• REVIEW EXERCISES

The solutions of Exercises 1–8 are graphs, shown in the
accompanying figures. *Shaded areas* include points that do
not satisfy the given inequalities.

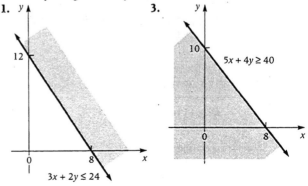

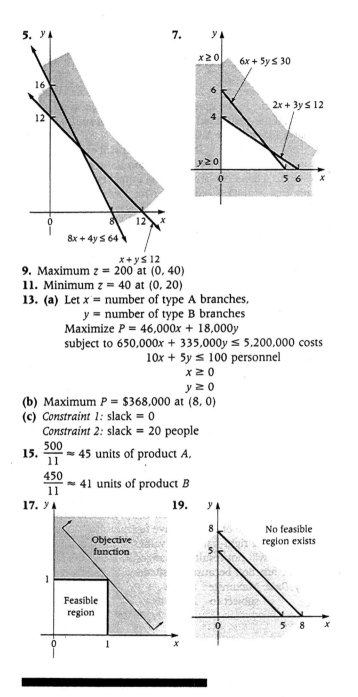

5. $8x + 4y \le 64$

$x + y \le 12$

7. $x \ge 0$ $6x + 5y \le 30$ $2x + 3y \le 12$ $y \ge 0$

9. Maximum $z = 200$ at $(0, 40)$

11. Minimum $z = 40$ at $(0, 20)$

13. (a) Let x = number of type A branches,

   y = number of type B branches

   Maximize $P = 46{,}000x + 18{,}000y$

   subject to $650{,}000x + 335{,}000y \le 5{,}200{,}000$ costs

   $10x + 5y \le 100$ personnel

   $x \ge 0$

   $y \ge 0$

(b) Maximum $P = \$368{,}000$ at $(8, 0)$

(c) *Constraint 1:* slack = 0

   Constraint 2: slack = 20 people

15. $\dfrac{500}{11} \approx 45$ units of product A,

   $\dfrac{450}{11} \approx 41$ units of product B

17. Objective function

Feasible region

19. No feasible region exists